Rahim Penangwala

COMPUTER ARCHITECTURE

A Designer's Text Based on a Generic RISC

McGraw-Hill Series in Computer Science

Senior Consulting Editor

***C. L. Liu**, University of Illinois at Urbana-Champaign*

Consulting Editor

***Allen B. Tucker**, Bowdoin College*

Fundamentals of Computing and Programming
Computer Organization and Architecture
Systems and Languages
Theoretical Foundations
Software Engineering and Database
Artificial Intelligence
Networks, Parallel and Distributed Computing
Graphics and Visualization
The MIT Electrical Engineering and Computer Science Series

Computer Organization and Architecture

Bartee: *Computer Architecture and Logic Design*
Bell and Newell: *Computer Structures, Readings and Examples*
Cavanagh: *Digital Computer Arithmetic, Design and Implementation*
Feldman and Retter: *Computer Architecture: A Designer's Text Based on a Generic RISC*
Hamacher, Vranesic, and Zaky: *Computer Organization*
Hayes: *Computer Architecture and Organization*
Hwang: *Advanced Computer Architecture: Parallelism, Scalability, Programmability*
Kogge: *The Architecture of Symbolic Computing*
Scragg: *Computer Organization: A Top-Down Approach*
Siewiorek, Bell, and Newell: *Computer Structures: Principles and Examples*
* **Ward and Halstead:** *Computation Structures*

** Co-published by The MIT Press and McGraw-Hill, Inc.*

McGraw-Hill Series in Electrical and Computer Engineering

Senior Consulting Editor

Stephen W. Director, *Carnegie Mellon University*

Circuits and Systems
Communications and Signal Processing
Computer Engineering
Control Theory
Electromagnetics
Electronics and VLSI Circuits
Introductory
Power and Energy
Radar and Antennas

Previous Consulting Editors

Ronald N. Bracewell, Colin Cherry, James F. Gibbons, Willis W. Harman, Hubert Heffner, Edward W. Herold, John G. Linvill, Simon Ramo, Ronald A. Rohrer, Anthony E. Siegman, Charles Susskind, Frederick E. Terman, John G. Truxal, Ernst Weber, *and* ***John R. Whinnery***

Computer Engineering

Senior Consulting Editors

Stephen W. Director, *Carnegie Mellon University*
C. L. Liu, *University of Illinois at Urbana-Champaign*

Bartee: *Computer Architecture and Logic Design*
Bell and Newell: *Computer Structures: Readings and Examples*
Feldman and Retter: *Computer Architecture: A Designer's Text Based on a Generic RISC*
Garland: *Introduction to Microprocessor System Design*
Hamacher, Vranesic, and Zaky: *Computer Organization*
Hayes: *Computer Architecture and Organization*
Horvath: *Introduction to Microprocessors Using the MC 6809 or the MC 68000*
Hwang: *Advanced Computer Architecture: Parallelism, Scalability, Programmability*
Kohavi: *Switching and Finite Automata Theory*
Lawrence-Mauch: *Real-Time Microcomputer System Design: An Introduction*
Levine: *Vision in Man and Machine*
Navabi: *VHDL: Analysis and Modeling of Digital Systems*
Peatman: *Design of Digital Systems*
Peatman: *Design with Microcontrollers*
Peatman: *Digital Hardware Design*
Ritterman: *Computer Circuit Concepts*
Rosen: *Discrete Mathematics and Its Applications*
Sandige: *Modern Digital Design*
Sze: *VLSI Technology*
Taub: *Digital Cicuits and Microprocessors*
Wear, Pinkert, Wear, and Lane: *Computers: An Introduction to Hardware and Software Design*
Wiatrowski and House: *Logic Circuits and Microcomputer Systems*

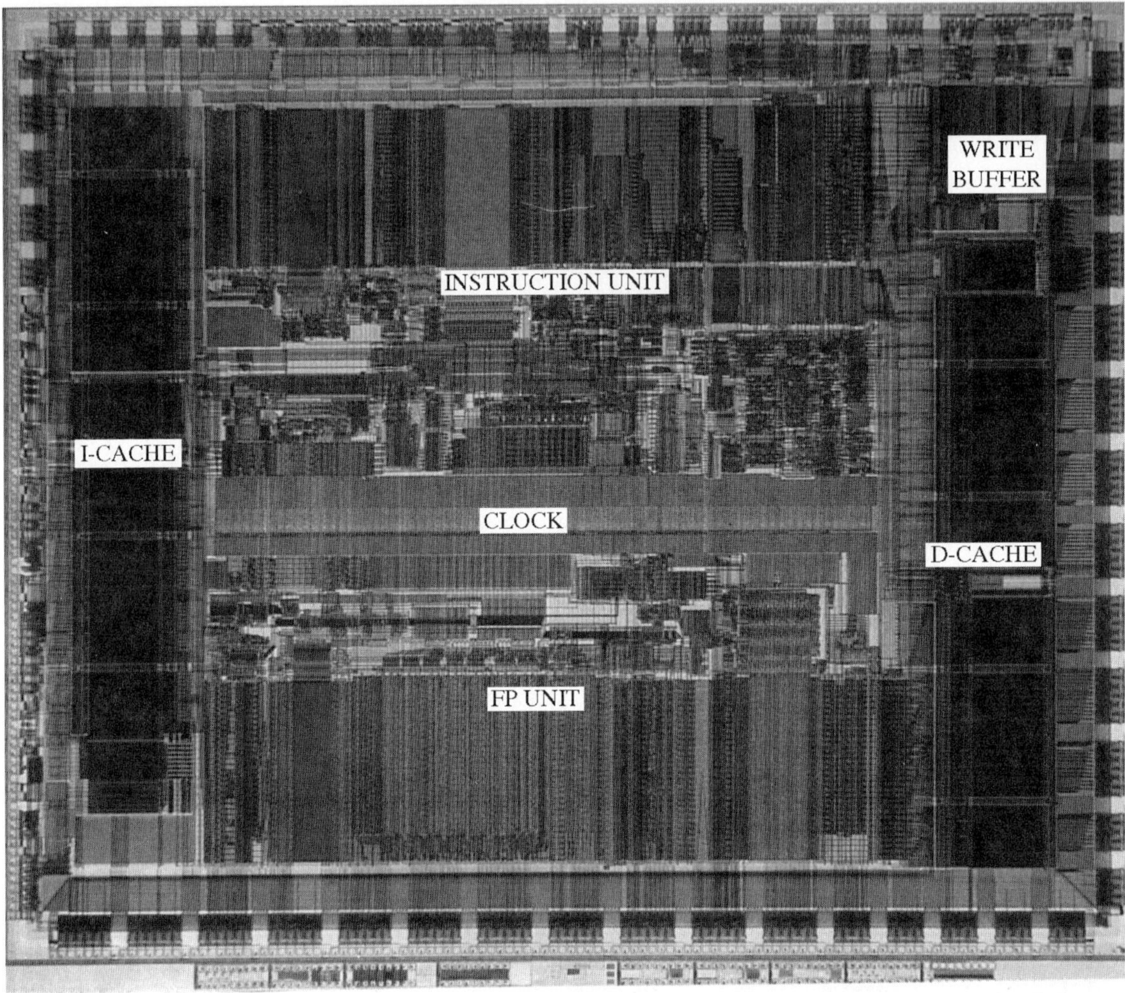

Photomicrograph of Digital Equipment's first-generation Alpha CPU chip, the 21064. This photo appears in color on the cover. The chip contains 1.7 million transistors and includes onboard I-cache, D-cache, integer CPU, and FPU. The chip is fabricated in 0.75-μm CMOS on a die of 16.8 mm × 13.9 mm. Operating at 200 MHz and at 3.3 V and dissipating 30 W, the processor can achieve peak throughputs of 400 MIPS and 200 MFLOPS. The sections which are outlined on the figure are central themes in this text. Photograph reproduced with the permission of the Digital Equipment Corporation.

COMPUTER ARCHITECTURE

A Designer's Text Based on a Generic RISC

James M. Feldman

Northeastern University

Charles T. Retter

U. S. Army Research Laboratory

McGraw-Hill, Inc.

New York St. Louis San Francisco Auckland Bogotá
Caracas Lisbon London Madrid Mexico City Milan
Montreal New Delhi San Juan Singapore Sydney Tokyo Toronto

This book was set in Times Roman by American Composition & Graphics, Inc.
The editor was Eric M. Munson;
the production supervisor was Kathryn Porzio.
The cover was designed by Rafael Hernandez.
Project supervision was done by The Total Book.
R. R. Donnelley & Sons Company was printer and binder.

COMPUTER ARCHITECTURE
A Designer's Text Based on a Generic RISC

This book is printed on recycled, acid-free paper containing a minimum of 50% total recycled fiber with 10% postconsumer de-inked fiber.

2 3 4 5 6 7 8 9 0 DOH DOH 9 0 9 8 7 6 5 4

ISBN 0-07-020453-5

Library of Congress Cataloging-in-Publication Data

Feldman, James M.
Computer architecture: a designer's text based on a generic RISC / James M. Feldman and Charles T. Retter.
p. cm.
Includes index.
ISBN 0-07-020453-5
1. Computer architecture. 2. Reduced instruction set computers.
I. Retter, Charles T. II. Title.
QA76.9.A73F35 1994
004.2'56—dc20 93-34111

ABOUT THE AUTHORS

James M. Feldman is Professor of Electrical and Computer Engineering at Northeastern University in Boston. He received his Ph.D. in Electrical Engineering in 1960 from Carnegie Mellon University. He has served on the faculties of Carnegie Mellon, the Technion, and Tel Aviv University. He spent a year as Visiting Consulting Engineer at Digital Equipment Corporation. He is the author of *The Physics and Circuit Properties of Transistors*, John Wiley & Sons, 1972, and has been a contributor, with Professor Retter, to *The Encyclopedia of Microcomputers*, Vol. 3, 1988, Marcel Decker, and *The Electrical Engineering Handbook*, CRC Press, 1993. He is a Senior Member of the IEEE and a member of the American Physical Society, the American Society for the Advancement of Science, the Association for Computing Machinery and Sigma Xi. Professor Feldman is Associate Editor of the *IEEE Transactions on Education*.

Charles T. Retter received his Ph.D. in Electrical Engineering from Johns Hopkins University. From 1978 to 1985 he worked for Data General Corporation in central-processor development, the department described in Tracy Kidder's *Soul of a New Machine*. During the period covered by that book, Dr. Retter was in the next lab debugging his own new machine, the Nova 4/C. He later led the team that designed the Eclipse S/280 and worked on several other central processors. Prior to joining Data General, he worked as an engineer at Raytheon Corporation, NASA/Goddard Space Flight Center, and Gaertner Research, Inc. In addition to the computers he designed for these companies, Dr. Retter has designed and built four computers for his own use, starting with a core-memory machine in 1969. From 1985 to 1992, he was an Associate Professor in the Department of Electrical and Computer Engineering at Northeastern University, where he taught computer architecture and error-correcting codes. He is currently an SCEEE Senior Research Associate at the Army Research Laboratory at Aberdeen Proving Ground. His research has been primarily in the area of Reed-Solomon codes. He is the author of many technical papers about error-correcting codes and holds three patents involving computer design. He is a member of IEEE, ACM, the International Association for Cryptologic Research, and Sigma Xi.

To Dorothy A. Feldman and Charles W. Retter, Jr.,
for instilling love of knowledge
and the written word
in their children.

CONTENTS

Appendices

PREFACE

This book explores principles and design tradeoffs in all of the key components of a modern computer. The two interconnected threads running through the book are the design of processing units and the design of input/output structures from cache to disk. In both cases, after plausible alternatives are considered, substantial portions of a system are carried through to specific hardware. Hardware that receives detailed design includes the CPU, MMU, D-cache, FPU, and backplane bus. The book provides a thorough grounding in the interactions of the hardware with the operating system, including such items as the file system, processes and context switches, memory management, and virtual memory support. Our objective has been to create a single text which introduces a reasonably computer-literate student to how the system's several components function and interact to produce the behavior that we call a *computer*. Our readers probably are generally familiar with the basic functions of the components—CPU, backplane, memory, operating system, coprocessor, cache, and disk drives—but they will have little sense of the details or the engineering compromises that go into constructing an engine that does what they know it should do. We have tried to put in one place some sense of the engineering issues that must be addressed for each of the principal components to achieve good performance of the whole system.

We assume that readers have used computers both as platforms for doing work and as engines to program in one or more high-level languages (HLLs). We expect as well that readers have had typical undergraduate exposure to logic design and assembly language programming. With that background, however attained, readers are ready to ask how to take this knowledge and use it to design a whole system.

Our approach begins with a user's objective—running application programs written in a HLL such as C—and moves out from the demands of such programs to the design of the principal blocks of a moderately powerful, single-processor computer. In the nine chapters of this book and five appendices, we develop the following themes:

- Code analysis, a processor design philosophy, and an effective instruction set. (Chapters 1 and 2 and Appendix I)
- Operating systems, memory management, and the creation, execution, and termination of a process. The principal example is UNIX. (Chapters 3 and 4 and Appendix IV)
- Cache design including the design of most of the finite-state machine which operates the data cache and memory management unit in our machine. (Chapter 5)
- CPU design including an on-board instruction cache. A hardwired engine is developed. Focus is on hardware design to execute one instruction per clock. The simplicity of the RISC instruction set permits a tight design within the confines of a single chapter. (Chapter 6)
- I/O, considered first in the context of the operating system (Chapter 3), is an important subject in its own right. Chapter 7 takes a look at file systems and raises the question of *what limits the speed of I/O*. The answer is both a file-system issue and a hardware issue. In Chapter 8 and Appendices II and III, the subject of I/O hardware is covered in unusual detail with speed the central theme. Bus speed is considered for the Futurebus and VMEbus. Peripheral busses such as SCSI are explored. Finally, both data security and transfer speed are considered for shadowing, striping, and RAID configurations.
- The idea of a coprocessor, initiated in Chapter 2, is carried down to the hardware level for a floating-point processor. The IEEE standard is used for the target and the chip is developed, for pedagogical reasons, as a microcoded engine. (Chapter 9)
- Having pursued RISC architecture throughout the book, Appendix V considers two interesting alternatives, VLIW and stack machines.

While we have tried to include a reasonable menu of choices at each juncture, to keep the book modest in length, we have made no attempt to be encyclopedic in current technology or to relate the many turns of technology and innovation which have led us to the remarkable products and techniques the computer engineer can call upon today. That tale of invention is a most fascinating one, but we have left it to another book and other authors to relate. In a field in which it seems that you can invite obsolescence by going out for a quick lunch, we have tried to pick out essential and enduring elements of computer architecture and to show how different choices in their design lead to constraints on the one hand and benefits on the other.

There are numerous places in the text and in the problem sets where some simulation and numerical analysis have been employed. While time-consuming, these are central aspects of real design and tend to make believable and palpable the concepts introduced in the course of the chapters. To assist in such efforts, software tools are available with the text. Among these are a cross-assembler, a cross-linker, and an emulator for the processor.

We have used the text for a one-quarter course at the first-year graduate level. The text is marginally long for a quarter but about right for a semester. We believe that the material would work equally well for well-prepared undergraduates at the senior level.

Once one aims beyond a *first course*, student preparation is always somewhat mixed. In our own teaching of this material as well as in the comments that we have received from our reviewers, great gaps and differences in student preparation emerge. Some have had a course in operating systems; others have not. Some are comfortable with electronics, wave propagation, and circuits; others are deft and comfortable with data structures, data bases, and transaction processing. Some have done considerable software design; others have designed ASICs using VLSI tools; still others come to this material for tools to do signal processing. To accommodate this variety of backgrounds and interests while keeping the body of the text brief enough to cover within the span of a semester, we have presented in extensive appendices material of considerable importance to understanding computer behavior or to simulating that behavior.

Many people have contributed to this text and its "peripherals." We wish to thank the students who beta tested the text, making important suggestions and finding many bugs. Three students made unique contributions. Robert Dunn wrote the *Linker* and *Emulator/Debugger* which work with the *Assembler*. Hussain Al-Asaad did a most conscientious and careful transformation of chapters written in an older word processor into the document processing language *Framemaker*. Many glitches disappeared under his detailed and knowledgeable reading. Mounir Nouri did a detailed analysis of the CPU in VHDL, the IEEE's hardware description language. Colleagues both on and off campus have aided the design of the machine and the design of the text. Professors Edward Czeck and Man-Kwan Vai at Northeastern University made many suggestions and contributed to the VHDL analysis. Henry Feldman of ORSI-America and David Feldman variously at Apple and at Specular (and probably immortalized as the *quack* on the Macintosh) read and critiqued numerous sections of the manuscript to the definite benefit of the book. Dr. David Thompson of IBM made many valuable suggestions for the material on disk drives. Finally, we thank our reviewers, Professors Gary L. Craig, Syracuse University; Wen-mei Hwu, University of Illinois; Rayno D. Niemi, Rochester Institute of Technology; and Krithi Ramamritham, University of Massachusetts, Amherst, whose detailed suggestions and most careful review of the text both encouraged us and guided us in this project. All of these people contributed to the successful parts of this text; the errors and weak spots are of our own manufacture.

James M. Feldman

Charles T. Retter

CHAPTER 1

IN WHICH WE SPECIFY THE INSTRUCTION SET

PHILOSOPHY FIRST AND THEN THE CRITICAL STEP

1.1 BEGINNINGS

This is a long book—one is reminded of Blaise Pascal's marvelous comment "I have made this letter longer than usual, only because I have not had the time to make it shorter" [Pascal, 57]. We too have had an objective which conflicted with time. Our purpose in writing this book was to put in one place a solid introduction to all of the elements which go into designing a complete computing machine. The conflict with time is compelling. Even as we write, the subject changes. As a result, while we have covered much, we have not covered all; while we have focused on recent methods and recent hardware, the design that we pursue is not and cannot be at the cutting edge. The reader who continues in machine design and computer architecture will forever find more to learn, but we think that the foundation that he or she obtains from this text will provide both an overview of the whole process and substantial insight into the tradeoffs which comprise computer design.

With the dual objectives of *overview* and *design*, this text is noticeably different from its many predecessors. We assume that our readers are computer-literate, that they can write working programs in a high-level language, and that they have at least a modest understanding of what a computer looks like to an assembly language programmer. Building on this background, we present a sequence of chapters, supported by several appendices, which should allow the reader to understand both the objectives and the constraints that are placed on each of the blocks which make up a computer. Four of the nine chapters are concerned with hardware design. The other five provide the background needed for the design. In many cases, we are rather parochial. We focus on solving our design problems rather than on being generalists. That means that we leave some things out. It also means that we have a coherent design. Tradeoffs.

In this chapter we begin the design. The very first thing to do is to specify our objectives. These are to build a machine that executes code from several common *high-level languages* (HLLs) with great speed and moderate cost. These objectives may sound almost universal, but they are more restrictive than you might expect. We will look at studies of the code derived from HLL source programs and see what they seem to need. In particular, we will consider programs that come through our example HLL, C and occasionally Pascal. Once we can define what is needed, we can pick one of several ways of meeting the requirements we have set for ourselves.

As a small aside before beginning, it is not immediately obvious that one could not build the machine to read and perform Pascal or C statements directly. Languages have been constructed with that in mind and machines built to operate on such source code. While natural computers (e.g., students) seem to prefer their input in wordy form, the machines that mankind has constructed seem to have very different needs. The machines and languages that attempted a direct linkage between HLLs and electronic computation have been relatively unsuccessful, principally because they are slower and not as "universal" as their designers had hoped. This may not continue indefinitely. Research in *artificial intelligence* has made great strides in reducing the inherent differences between biological and electronic computation, but at this time, it makes sense in a beginning course to focus on machines of more traditional lines. Even within the tradition, there are many quite different paths to follow in design.

No matter which route we take, certain items will be there in our design. These must include a variety of memories, one or more processors, and connections or *interfaces* between the components. These components are found in every computer, be it a single chip or a huge crate full of circuit boards. What we are about to do is specify the operations that our central processor can perform. Before starting on that effort, we should lay out the principal parts of the machine that we are starting to design. Figure 1.1 presents a rather complete generic computer.

The first thing in the figure that should strike you is the dominance of the stripe down the middle—the *bus*. This is the central connective highway through which all parts of the computer can communicate with other parts. Its centrality in the picture is no accident of illustration. Busses and the need to communicate over them dominate much of the thinking in design. While in one sense a bus is nothing but a "bunch of wires," it proves to be a potential bottleneck that can severely limit a computer's performance. The specifics of bus performance are the central theme of Chapter 8.

To the right, we have a variety of generic input/output (I/O) devices. Included are such devices as secondary storage media (tapes and all forms of disks), printers, terminals (keyboards and monitors), digital communication ports (the serial port), and ways to measure and create analog signals (A/D and D/A). The following strange statement is true: Most computers have, as their total input/output set, only some number of the three one-line, unboxed I/O devices in the figure. The reason why this is true is that *most* computers spend their lives making machines and other devices run well. The biggest single customer for microprocessors is reported to be General Motors. They put

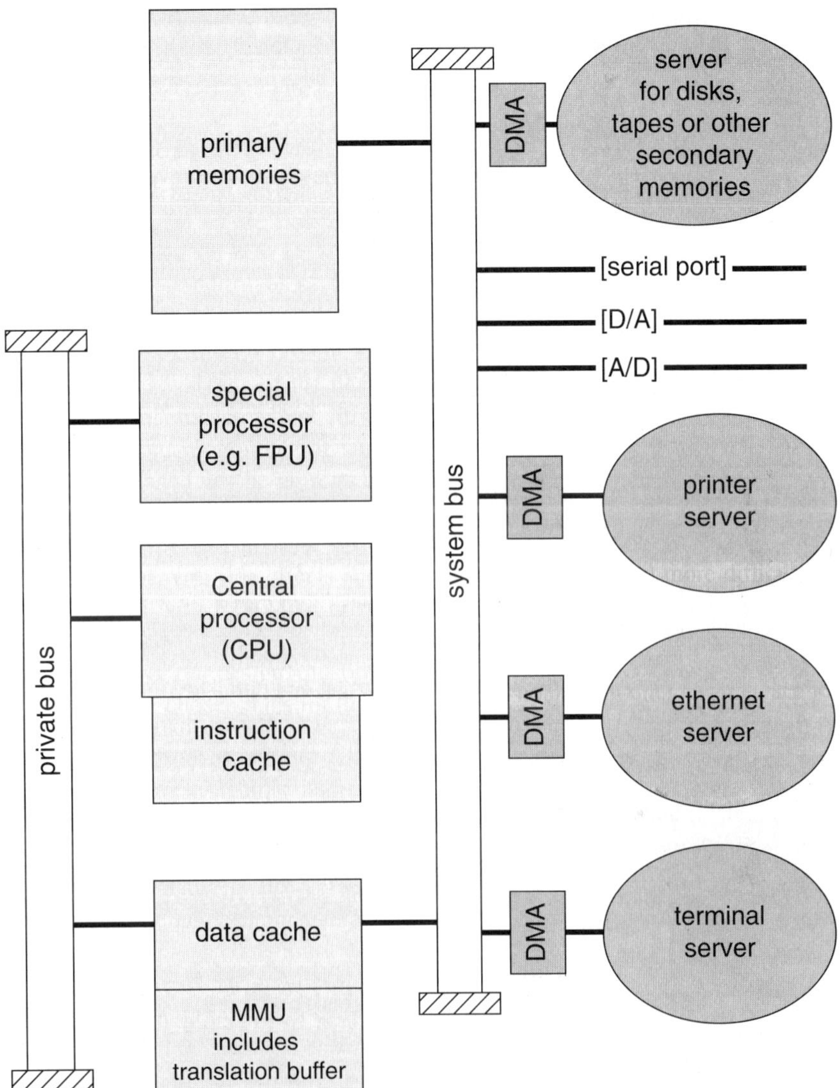

FIGURE 1.1 Some major components of a reasonably complete computer.

one to three or more in every car that they sell. These processors are full-fledged computers, but they never see a keyboard or a disk drive.

The computer we have drawn in Figure 1.1, however, represents what you might have on your desk or share in the university. Bigger computers will have more or bigger or faster versions of what is in the illustration, but the layout of principal parts is virtually universal.

Notice that there are two classes of things on the right: One class is labeled *servers*; the other is not. The server class has connectors called DMAs or "direct memory access" controllers. In many cases, both the DMA and the server are special-purpose computer systems designed to take on the task of efficiently moving data and programs between the primary memories and the mass-storage or secondary memories. The non-server class is shown as directly connected to the bus, indicating that the computer system's central processor must tend to their needs. Servers could be added there too or deleted from the other devices. They help to unload a surprisingly large burden from the central processors, so where performance dominates, servers are common.

Figure 1.1 can also be looked at as a diagram of the book. It is appropriate and reasonable in developing insight into system details that many of the structures in this figure appear in several chapters and that the discussion of the structures be both reentrant and recursive. There are basically two interwoven threads in this book:

- *processor design*, comprising Chapters 1, 2, 6, and 9
- *memory design*, comprising Chapters 3, 4, 5, 7, and 8

Processor design includes both the *central processing unit* (CPU), which does most computational tasks, and the *floating-point unit* (FPU), which handles all floating-point calculations. Chapters 1 and 2 focus on *instruction-set design*; 6 and 9 are concerned with the hardware to realize the instruction set. Memory comprises all of the layers of Figure 1.1 in which data can reside: cache, primary memory, and secondary memory (disk and tape). Memory management is both a hardware and a software affair and spans such topics as data security, data availability, transmission and reception of digital data, traffic management, and cost. The topic begins with the functions and obligations of the operating system (Chapter 3), memory management (Chapter 4), and the design of the *memory management unit* (MMU) and *data cache* (Chapter 5), and it concludes with a hard look at what limits the speed of I/O (Chapters 7 and 8).

These are the parts. Now to our design path.

1.2 DESIGNING FOR SPEED AND COST

There is little argument with the statement that computers should be small, cheap, and fast. The problems begin when you try to choose the proportions. The range is rather breathtaking. Motorola and Intel (and many others) produce single-chip systems with enough of the components above to function independently of any components other than power supply. The price is of the order of a dollar. At the other end are supercomputers such as those produced by Cray. These come through the door at several million dollars each. It is interesting to note that the processing speed goes up less rapidly than the price, leading many companies and universities into research on how to use lots of inexpensive processors to match supercomputer speed at much lower price.

At the moment, the major part of the general-purpose computer market is shared by what used to be called the micro- and minicomputer systems. These terms were coined when a microcomputer had a single chip as its processor while a minicomputer had a moderately large number of chips in its processor. Price differences were of the order of 20 to 50/1. With advances in large-scale integration of semiconductor circuits, one may now put everything that is on the left-hand side of Figure 1.1, except for a large memory, into two or even one remarkably complex chip. Such a chip would have more than one million transistors on it and typically sell for several hundred dollars. Finished systems using these chips come at prices one to two orders of magnitude above the price of the chip itself, putting truly enormous computing power in the public's hands as a commodity—something one buys for normal service such as a car or furniture in an open, competitive market. There is now no clear line between minis and micros. There is simply a continuum of machines and performance ranging from about \$1000 to 100 times that amount. Beyond the \$100,000 range, you find rather large steps leading to superminis, mainframes, and supercomputers. Even at the uppermost end, the lines are very blurred. The "little guys" often provide a better price/performance ratio, and the decision on which box to buy is often dictated more by issues such as service, software, and the ability to ease the transition from whatever system is now doing the task.

When someone buys such a machine, his or her expectation is that it will do whatever computing task is asked of it. These tasks can be quite varied, may not have been specifically envisaged by the computer's designer, and will probably change over the life of the particular machine. What faces the typical system architect is the design of a computer system satisfactory to the customer when the architect can neither identify the customer with any great specificity nor know exactly what that customer will want to do with the computer system upon buying it or some years later. Marketing is much harder than many of us suppose. We can certainly guess the customer will want the beast to be fast. Let us begin with the issue of speed.

1.2.1 Designing for Speed

Let us state at the outset a pair of basic premises:

1. Computer speed is to be measured in delivering to customers the computing service that they desire. As such, speed measures both software and hardware performance.
2. Computer cost includes both hardware and software acquisition, training, and maintenance costs.

While these seem "self-evident" to us, it can be hard to measure either of them, and there are few good measurements of real cost or real speed on competitive designs. Our reason for stating these principles is to motivate a moderately careful inspection of the hardware and software consequences of some of the decisions we are about to make.

Speed may be obtained from both hardware and software by:

1. Employing the fastest technology available. A gallium arsenide gate is about four times faster than a silicon gate; unsaturated logic is faster than saturated logic; well-engineered optimizers on compilers can produce code that runs two to four times faster than simpler compilers. All of these steps increase costs in one or more ways.
2. Reducing the number of layers which must be traversed in doing a particular task. In both hardware and software, this involves maximizing the amount of work done in

parallel. A second, less self-evident approach is to streamline the processing by putting maximum performance at the bottlenecks. This involves both study of where bottlenecks are occurring in current designs and judgment on how emerging technology will affect each bottleneck. Reducing jams at bottlenecks frequently involves compromises between competing objectives.

3. Optimization of the performance of the processor in hardware by putting the effort into each operation according to its frequency of use and in software by making the compiler strive to use the algorithms best suited to the processor in question. This last step requires that the compiler "understand" the hardware. In fact, maximum flexibility and effectiveness may be achieved by making the compiler responsible for arranging the precise order in which the hardware handles the instructions.

The first item is somewhat of a "throw money at it" solution, but if extremely high speed is necessary, it may be the only way to proceed. For example, one use for the extremely fast and extremely costly Cray machines is to try to put weather prediction on a real-time basis. Predicting yesterday's weather does not need a computer. Predicting tomorrow's requires that you start when today's data are available and finish computing before the weather happens tomorrow. That complex fluid-dynamics problem is still beyond or just at the edge of current capability. If one would break through that computational barrier, the option of "fastest possible technology" cannot be ignored. We, however, will limit ourselves to "next-best" in doing speed estimates. That technology at this time is CMOS with propagation times of the order of 1 nanosecond per gate. (For an excellent and thorough discussion of the TTL, CML, and CMOS logic families, see Chapter 2 of [Wakerly, 90].)

Method 2 is used by everyone. Maximum parallelism is evident in the servers of Figure 1.1. The idea is to have the central processor doing computation relating to programs while the servers do computation related to I/O. Do not get the idea that the I/O processor is a weak cousin to the central processor. The really big Cray, IBM, and DEC computers all use one or more full-fledged big machines to do I/O. I/O rates depend strongly on the operating system, so they are a proper subject for several later chapters, but even at this stage, it should be obvious that instructions and data must be brought into memory before they can be used. Results are useful only when they have been delivered. Doing lots of computation implies that lots of data are moved into central memory and that somewhat less must be moved out to secondary memory. Waiting for disk operations may be acceptable in typical single-user environments, but very high performance machines more often find application as servants to many users at one time. Getting good value from the processor's high computation rate requires that the I/O tasks proceed in parallel with what the user perceives as computation. While user A awaits a disk operation, user B's process proceeds apace.

Other parallelism is hidden in the same figure. The processor needs a new instruction in each cycle and new data in many cycles. Since both must come from primary memory in the figure (other organizations are certainly possible) and travel down the same central bus, a traffic jam is in the making. One route around that jam is to have a local copy of the currently operating portion of the program and possibly even its data. Those copies are in the caches at the bottom of the figure. Since many instructions and even lots of data get used several times in a program's operation, the caches reduce the processor's need for access to primary memory. The reason for the *two* caches is to lessen conflicts between the processor's need for data and its need for instructions. The operation of these caches are the central subject of Chapter 5 and an important topic in Chapter 6.

One "layering" issue of central importance to the design that we will pursue is the "level" at which we program our machine. Anyone taking this course has certainly compiled an HLL program. The output of the compilation (and linking) of the HLL program is usually called *machine language*. The alternative to compilation is to use an interpreter that controls the machine in response to HLL statements. The language Basic is often run in that mode. Interposing that interpretive software layer generally results in a conspicuous reduction in apparent performance. Compilation to machine language removes that layer and speeds up the effective processor speed.

The last sentence implies that machine language directly controls the computer, but in many computers, this is not the case. Buried inside the processor itself is an interpreter, a little computing engine that uses each "machine language" instruction as a call to one or more subroutines in *microcode*. Microcode is simply one more layer between what you write and what really controls the machine. Layers add delay. They may contribute some benefit, such as versatility, binary compatibility, code brevity, or adaptability, but they add delay. If you want your program to run as fast as possible, then bring the real machine right out to the program. Such a step does not mean writing your program in conventional microcode; it means designing a machine which directly serves—in hardware—the output of the compiler. As soon as you do that, the logic of letting the compiler be completely aware of and responsible for the hardware becomes more compelling.

We will expand on this issue several times as we proceed through this and subsequent chapters, but a small illustration is called for here to be sure that the basic issue is clear. An integer operation in a HLL might be

```
A = B + C;
```

Nothing could be much simpler in the HLL, but the compiler might find itself with a pretty elaborate job of getting to the three variables. They might be buried deep in the middle of complex structures. What the compiler does is generate a series of instructions of whatever depth is necessary to accomplish the four steps of:

1. getting pointers to the three variables (addressing)
2. bringing the two source variables into the processor (loading)
3. doing the addition to produce the result within the processor
4. returning the result to its final storage location (storing)

Obviously, any computer that is going to do these things must have the primitive operations to accomplish them. Those primitives are all hardware operations, where electrical signals are applied to the inputs of gates and results received from the outputs of the gate arrays. One very visible difference between the *streamlined* or RISC[1] computers of the '80s and '90s and the CISC[2] computers with origins in the 1960s is in the number of sequential hardware steps that may be evoked by a single instruction. In a "true" RISC, one instruction invokes one hardware step; in a CISC, a single instruction can call forth hundreds or even thousands of sequential operations. For example, the VAX instruction to accomplish the add operation above can do all four steps in a single instruction ranging in length from 3 to 20 bytes. In one of its most elaborate forms, that one VAX instruction could require the processor to fetch five different numbers from memory, do three address calculations, each involving sums of three numbers, and, finally, write one number back to memory.

Exactly the same combinations are available in the RISC, only not in what is called "a single instruction." What the CISC appears to give you is the possibility of more compact encoding of machine instructions at the cost of more processor complexity. A CISC advocate—and there are many—would say that a CISC trades processor complexity for programming simplicity. Obviously, both machines get the job done, but to answer the question of which is better, you must start from one of our central hypotheses: Programs are written in HLLs and reduced to machine code by compilers. This eliminates any need to make the machine code appealing to human programmers. It also leads to the question: "How do you make compiled code run very fast?"

The answer, as you must suspect by now for all of the fuss we are making, is not obvious. Those who designed machines in the '60s and '70s thought that they were creating instruction sets which provided precisely those tools that a compiler needed. Their insight came from the widespread use of "human" compilers—assembly language programmers. They were constrained by the technology of the time, which was changing with such rapidity that it is sometimes difficult to put ourselves in their shoes to determine whether a particular design was "good." Those who were taking data at the time, particularly in the '70s, were asking both what compilers did and what programs did. Lots of data taken from the outputs of a wide variety of good compilers say that good compilers tend to use a rather limited array of instructions and addressing modes. This was not for want of compiler brain power, but because the fastest storage elements were and still are the central processing unit's (CPU's) registers. Keeping the most active parameters and variables in register tends to make the program run faster. Doing operations which involve multiple memory cycles might lead to very compact code but it did not lead to very fast code. This realization was one of the motivations behind the swing to instruction sets which had a limited but very well chosen set of tools.

While some designers approached the *reduced instruction set* paradigm with an enthusiasm that bordered on religion, much of the revolution evolved from measurements

---

[1] The term *streamlining* was first applied to computer architectures by Professor John Hennessy of Stanford. The more common term, RISC, for *reduced instruction set computer*, was coined by Professors David Patterson and Carlo Séquin of Berkeley.

[2] CISC, for *complex instruction set computer*, is generally used as the converse of RISC, though in truth the term has no really exact definition.

showing that improvements could be obtained by such designs. One of the most telling results was a serendipity that came out of an experiment at IBM Research Labs. (See [Cocke, 90].) John Cocke and his colleagues were simulating in a rather curious way what we now would call a RISC. They constructed a subset of the language PL/I, which they dubbed PL/.8, and wrote a new compiler which did an excellent job of code optimizing for their (at that time) hypothetical machine, the 801. The simulation was running on an IBM 370, model 168. The compiler would generate the 801 code and then translate it into the appropriate sequence of 370 instructions. In comparing the performance, Cocke was struck by the fact that the most commonly issued 801 instructions had 370 equivalents, but that the 801 would get them done in one cycle while the 370 would do several microcoded instructions to achieve the same results. That insight—that the microcoded machine was doing more work for the instructions that were most frequently issued—was perhaps the critical philosophical leap that leads not only to RISC computers but even to much faster versions of CISC computers. The issue is not so much how many instructions but how quickly the CPU steps through the instructions it does most often. Lots of other issues are important, but this is the central idea of streamlining.

To get some idea of Cocke's accomplishment with his new compiler, which was generating the 370 equivalent of his still hypothetical 801 processor, it generated code which ran two to three times faster than did code from the regular PL/I compilers for the 370. In other words, without changing the architecture, he more than doubled the speed by *refraining from using some of the CISC instructions* and by doing better optimization of register usage. Later-model 370s reduced this advantage through much more complex pipelining and greater caching, but if ever there was an indication of the power of streamlining, doubling the speed by not using the draggy part of the machine has got to be it.

We will define a successfully streamlined machine to be one that is fast enough to handle all of its common instructions as rapidly as the local (cache) memory can deliver them. One tick of the computer's clock, one common instruction done. This definition has nothing to do with RISC versus CISC. The most excruciatingly CISC chip on the market—the Intel 80x86—has achieved this goal in the 80486 model, with an attendant factor of 4 increase in speed over the 80386. Notice that this definition can make the "best" design a strong function of the character and position of the bottlenecks and of what the computer does most often. Bottlenecks are functions both of technology and of design. As they change, so must the design. Similarly, the streamlining must take into account the target use. If the application changes, so may the instruction frequency. To meet our criterion, the instructions must be sized to fit what can get through the processor in that one clock pulse. One clock pulse, one unit of work delivered. One might object to this criterion as arbitrary and not necessarily optimal. However, it goes without saying that the CPU can hardly do *more* than it can do in one clock pulse. By making those bite-sized pieces of work the tools of the instruction set, we allow the compiler the opportunity to manipulate both the instructions and the data distribution—in register, cache, and memory—to optimize the throughput of this particular machine. Streamlining does not lead to a unique design. Instead, it tends to shape the products of teams that pursue it.

How much streamlining is beneficial depends on what problem one is trying to solve. It is doubtful that a streamlined turtle would gain much benefit from a "better" shape. It is designed to minimize edibility. It is up to us to show that the streamlined design that we propose below will serve a class of problems well. We will do this to the extent that the level of this course permits.

The last point, which really describes how we will select the instruction set, says *put into hardware only those features which will be used frequently.* More carefully specified, what we wish to do is to take the product of frequency of use and delay in doing each operation in a particular way (a dimensionless quantity) and then minimize the sum of the products over the most important applications for this machine. To do the minimization, we must be able to specify how much the introduction of operation B will influence the time for operation A. We would probably want to include cost in the calculation as well. There can be problems in doing this calculation where the design is really new. One would not have working examples of use to consider. All that one has to depend on are data from similar applications on other architectures.

Some very interesting results derive from such studies for already extant but still developing architectures. The need to reduce the complexity of the VAX architecture in order to squeeze the big VAX onto a single chip obliged Digital Equipment to do a very careful study of instruction frequency for a whole variety of commercially valuable applications on the VAX line. (A whole issue of the *Digital Technical Journal* is devoted to this design effort. See [Dobberpuhl, 86].) Dobberpuhl et al. found that moving many rarely used instructions and data types from hardware to software had almost no impact on performance—even in those programs that used the complicated instructions. The special instructions were moved into software in what is called a "trap" operation. All the old programs still run; the "left out" instructions simply call short software subroutines where they once got hardware support. At worst, programs ran more slowly by a couple of percent. In most cases, no impact was observed. The result was a reduction of several orders of magnitude in the cost of the central processor. The projected transistor count for the full VAX instruction set had been cut from 1.2 million (impossible to accomplish at that date) to the quite doable 100,000. In the process, the 304 instructions had been reduced to 175 and the 14 data types to 6. That chip and its successors power the first generation of DEC workstations. Without the streamlining, the product would have priced itself out of the marketplace.

Should everyone be switching to streamlined designs as they rush to move their products onto ever fewer chips? The answer depends on time scale and starting point. Digital started massive integration with the VAX already a commercial success; Intel was in the same position with its 8080 family. They were hardly going to drop lines that were so successful and that had such a huge customer base. But what would they do if they really started a no-strings, brand-new design? In fact, both developed or acquired RISC processors.

What we will do is take data for data-type and instruction-usage frequencies that have been gathered over the years on a variety of machines. We will select what we believe is essential, adding whatever seems good to have up to the point that we can still support a streamlined design. The result should be a spare but functional design. Anything that we cannot fit into the hardware set will be moved to the software domain. We must be careful not to create software absurdities in doing that, but keep in mind that if an operation occurs only 0.01 percent of the time, making it take 1000 times as long as a hardware operation that occurs 10 percent of the time gives equal weight to each in the customer's program.

The next thing that we turn to, as a preface to the actual design, is cost. It is here that we ask the question: "Would our streamlined machine please the user?" The answer to which is: "That depends."

1.2.2 Maximizing Value ≠ Minimizing Processor Cost

From the customer's point of view, the computer includes the machine itself and the software which makes it do useful work. Whether he or she writes sophisticated software or buys the products of others, good performance equates to ease of use. Within the domain of ease of use at this time in computer development, we include:

1. a "user-friendly" interface
2. fast response
3. multitasking, including sophisticated displays and output

The first can lead to all sorts of arguments, since it depends so much on the user's expectation. Our approach is to start by presuming that even sophisticated programmers will deal with our machine only through HLLs. Other users will use packages created by those sophisticated programmers. Nobody is expected to write in assembly language. Human generation of assembly code has been shown to be inefficient and costly in almost all circumstances. If programmers are going to use only HLLs, then no benefit derives from making the machine language itself fit for human consumption. The choices on the instruction set should be made only to optimize machine performance for HLL written code.

If assembly code for the Intel iAPX86 family is weird (it is!), so what? If our assembly code is a bit tedious to write (it is!), no problem. The only people who should ever see these issues are the compiler writers (and students of computer architecture). The only thing that we (or Intel) should have to worry about is whether the set of instructions provided can make HLL programs run fast. We have promised to address that point.

Multitasking and displays and I/O are subjects for later chapters. Given that they can be solved, we come to the other question that most customers ask: What will it cost? This is a complex and interesting question. The customer buys a whole system. He or she is generally not interested in buying a machine on the basis of some performance figures and then sitting down and reading a book on how to write a good data base manager. The question of what software is available and at what cost in dollars and learning time is critical.

Learning time is not just the issue of reading the manual. It can involve arcane translations of data bases between incompatible forms and between machines that do not "speak to each other." Picture a not untypical situation where a moderate-sized firm has an inventory and a payroll program running on an old and weary machine. No one now at the firm had anything to do with creating this software, but the day-to-day operation of the firm depends on it. The old machine has limited capability and unsatisfactory reliability. Here you have an ideal sales opportunity for someone who can provide a smooth transition to a new machine. "Smoothness" does not include a catastrophic four-week halt to the company's operations.

Some computer companies have made upward compatibility a product standard. For Intel, this policy has propagated some of the odd architectural features of the 8-bit 8008 (the very first 8-bit microprocessor) right through its remarkably sophisticated 32-bit 80486 chip. Digital Equipment went so far as to drop its DEC-10/20 series to standardize on the VAX family to achieve a situation where all DEC software ran on all DEC machines. No one can argue with the commercial success of that decision. DEC's newest machines, based on the *Alpha* architecture, have a RISC native code that is decidedly different from VAX code. Before management would approve this new architecture, they required demonstration of direct porting of VAX applications to Alpha. Alpha's designers responded with two quite distinct translation methodologies, one based on recompilation and one based on a mix of direct machine code translation and VAX emulation. There are tradeoffs for each, but the essential feature of both methods is that old VAX code "works" on the new machine. Their customers can migrate to Alpha and bring all of their old and beloved baggage with them. If you own machine X and have a whole set of valuable applications running thereon, changing everything and everybody over to a new system is an awesome task. On the other hand, if the salesperson says: "4X better performance for all of your current applications at Y dollars and only 1 weekend's downtime," the buyer can seriously entertain the proposal.

The reason for including the last paragraph is to place firmly in front of us the reasons for the persistence of the old successful computer architectures—the big IBMs, the VAXs, the Intel 80x86 family, and the Motorola MC68000 series. The CISCs still hold the edge in the general computing market because they run the software that the general users own. We are going to present and defend what is the current trend in new designs—a class of streamlined computers or *RISC*s. It is generally conceded that RISCs have taken over the workstation market for two very good reasons: they are faster, and they are cheaper.

Why cheap? The central reason is well expressed in the name John Redford gave to an embedded 16-bit streamlined processor that he designed for some DEC I/O chips. He dubbed it the QUIP— *quickly integrated processor*. It is small enough to be a "chip component"—that is, it fits on one corner of a variety of chips and runs programs stored on board to make the chips seem smart to the outside world. It was designed, tested, and verified rapidly by a small team. It is fast. Simple and fast and quick to market translate to inexpensive and successful.

A similar experience was reported by Acorn Corporation of England, which brought its 32-bit streamlined processor (ARM) onto the market in 1985. The ARM has about the same number of transistors in it as Intel's old 8080 (25K), yet it is a fast, powerful general-purpose processor. Acorn reported that with CAD/CAM tools current at the time, it was able to verify the design to the extent that the very first units to be manufactured worked in all respects. This effort is to be compared with other 32-bit single-chip processors that carry on the older architectures. Their chips bear almost two orders of magnitude more transistors, tend to be a little slower, and have to be more expensive to cover the higher engineering costs and lower production yields that the size difference entails. It costs more to have more complex designs.

Which is better? Software availability is foremost in most customers' minds, and the cost of the processor is only about 10 percent of the cost of the delivered computer. RISCs moved into the workstation market because workstations almost all ran the same (UNIX) operating system, used a standard user interface (X-windows), and used software that was readily ported to different UNIX platforms. Also, it was a new market without a huge installed base dependent on proprietary support systems. Many other, more established markets will be harder to penetrate. When you ask which is better, you come back to our first answer: "That depends." Marketing is principally the art of selecting those products which you can sell at a profit. It is a discipline that can be ignored in the real world only with great hazard. Here in an academic course aimed at developing effective design skills and an appreciation of the inner workings of computers, we can afford to pick our design target only to try to make our readers more marketable. To that end, we have chosen a streamlined computer architecture. It is both the current vogue—though a vogue driven by good economic and engineering arguments—and simple enough for us to cover many of its details in a single text.

We are now ready to look at what an HLL expects from the underlying processor.

1.3 COMPILER EXPECTATIONS

An HLL program has declaration parts where data and program relationships are defined and program parts where the action expected is defined. While a good HLL has a rich vocabulary and great flexibility, there really are not many classes of statement that can be created. Using broad classifications, we find that a statement comprises one or more instances of only two types of instruction:

1. Data management
2. Program control

While there are truly enormous ranges of possible statements if you count all of the minutiae possible, the idea that there are only two general classes of operation suggests that a compiler does not need a huge bag of machine instructions to do what it is asked to do in any HLL program. While you may accept that statement at face value, be prepared to be startled by the results of analyzing large numbers of compiled programs. Even very sophisticated compilers use a very limited range of instructions and data types, and of those that they do use, only a small subset is used with any great frequency. Since this result obtains in all studies and with a wide variety of very sophisticated and successful compilers, let us begin by simply accepting it as a natural truth and not argue whether it *should* be so or not. Compilers are that way. A little later, we will seek out some reasons why, but let us first establish this "truth" with some specific data. Let us begin with a small but interesting result.

In 1978, Gideon Yuval [Yuval, 78], then of Hebrew University, did a quick static analysis (instruction count from a program listing) of two word-processing tools that run under UNIX on a PDP-11: ED and ROFF. The first came from a C compiler, the second from hand assembly. His results are shown in Table 1.1. If you have never looked at instruction-frequency data, you will be stunned by the huge fraction of code devoted to moving things back and forth to memory (MOV and MOVB) and to branching. Between them, they comprise between one-third and one-half of the two programs. The PDP-11 has the full capability of doing its operations on data starting and finishing in memory. Instead, things are consistently brought into register, then used and then put back—this in spite of the fact that the PDP-11 had only six general-purpose registers. Note also that even in a language-oriented program, byte operations (MOVB) are rare. Another thing that is evident is that subroutine calls (JSR) are frequent. [The curious absence of a subroutine return (RTS) on the left results from the use of a JMP to a return routine instead.] The order of the day for these programs is: data moves, comparisons, branches on results, subroutine calls, and also-rans. While some also-rans are nice to have, we are already beginning to focus on where the action is. How about some other data?

Well, we are talking about compilers. What about compilers? Anyone who has watched what goes on in a university computer center knows that university computers spend a substantial fraction of their time doing compilation. Cheryl Wiecek [Wiecek, 82] did a thorough job pursuing six of the most commonly used VAX compilers—Basic, Bliss, Cobol, Fortran, Pascal, and PL/I (C is very much a "second cousin" in many VAX-VMS environments). Her numbers come from dynamic measurements of instruction frequency. That is, they were taken while the program in question was actually running. Thus, if the program loops through five instructions in a single loop 100 times, each of those instructions appears 100 times in the data. The data below

TABLE 1.1 Instruction frequency in two character-handling programs

ED			ROFF		
MOV	438	26%	branches	412	18%
branches	371	22%	MOV	378	16%
JSR	224	13%	JSR	278	12%
CMP	135	8%	CMP	210	9%
TST	99	6%	RTS	145	6%
JMP	83	5%	ADD	120	5%
CLR	66	4%	JMP	88	4%
MOVB	63	4%	CLR	84	4%
ADD	59	4%	TST	78	3%
INC	18	1%	MOVB	61	3%
others	112	17%	others	468	20%
total	1668	100%	total	2322	100%

TABLE 1.2 **Compiler instruction usage on the VAX**

Instruction	Frequency	
MOV (all types)	22.0	
conditional BR	11.8	
CMP (all types)	10.1	used with the conditional BRs
MOVAB	4.4	generates a pointer
unconditional BR	4.3	
CALLS	2.4	
RET	2.4	
ADDL2	1.7	
INC	1.4	shorter, special version of ADDL2
total(%)	60.5	

represent averages over the compilers, so they are not indicative of any particular language—just what compilers in general demand. For instruction usage she found the results of Table 1.2. Note that the only intentional arithmetic that is done in any large amount is associated with the looping and branching operations. That is, CMP, where two numbers are compared and then a conditional branch is taken on the basis of the result without the result itself being returned to register or memory. Even the stalwart of integer arithmetic—ADD—appears only at the 1.4 percent level. If you include INC, which is really just ADDL2 with 1 as one argument, you still get only to 3.1 percent. In other words, when doing compilation, you call a procedure almost as often as you add a number.

How about the use of the VAX's vast addressing vocabulary? The VAX admits 13 different modes of address that one can use to reference an operand. How much do the sundry compilers use that vocabulary? Wiecek found the frequency of use (in percent) shown in Table 1.3. Since the three displacement modes are there only to save space

TABLE 1.3 **Frequency of address mode usage in three VAX compilers**

MODE (mode number)	Bliss	Fortran	Pascal	
register (5)	38.1	41.0	45.1	
displacement (10,12,14)	25.2	20.6	26.1	
literal (0-3)	18.5	18.2	15.5	in VAX, literals=0...63
indirect (6)	8.6	9.1	2.0	
autoincrement (8)	3.3	4.1	2.6	includes "immediates"
index (4)	3.0	5.6	7.6	
totals(%)	96.7	98.6	98.9	

(the modes differ in the number of bytes for the displacement operand), two addressing formats account for over 60 percent of the addressing used and four formats cover over 90 percent! Once again, we see that some of the hardware could be removed with little if any programming awkwardness. The issue can be stated in this way: If all that the fancier modes do for you is a calculation that you could do in software and do not much care to do anyway, and if you could get a faster machine or a cheaper one by stripping out the hardware, why would you not want to do just that?

Now if you happen to be an addicted assembly language programmer and want to answer that question with "Because they make my life easier!" recall our premise. We stated that it is almost inevitably better practice to let the compiler generate your machine code for you. Compilers can be designed to work superbly with only a very limited addressing vocabulary. If that is the case, then do not burden the machine with unnecessary hardware. To do so would be poor engineering.

Finally, let us consider a set of instruction weights put together by Intel to compare its 80286 computer with competitors. Intel based these weights on a wide range of studies, none of which contradict the basic rules we have seen already: data movement, comparisons, and branching dominate the code, followed by procedure calls, and then, somewhere down in the dust, the operations that we all think of as the "essence of computation," the arithmetic and logical operations. This Intel list is shown in the data in Table 1.4. These data are for "general" computing tasks, but a comparison between these numbers and the previous two tables shows no special differences. Perhaps the arithmetic operations are a little more prevalent, but in the previous two examples,

TABLE 1.4 Intel's expected relative frequency for the iAPX286†

Instruction	Frequency
LOAD	21.3
STORE	13.7
BRANCH (all conditions)	9.5
MOV (register to register)	6.0
MOV (immediate to register)	5.8
ALU (register, register)	4.5
JUMP	3.1
ALU (register to memory)	3.1
ALU (immediate to memory)	3.1
CALL	2.9
SHIFT	2.9
ALU (immediate to register)	2.9
RET	2.8
total(%)	81.6

† We have combined the several forms of LOAD and STORE. ALU operations are integer arithmetic and logic steps. Immediates are constants stored with the instructions.

much of the arithmetic could be ascribed to the counting and comparisons that are part of loop execution. If those steps were singled out in the Intel data, other arithmetic would probably fall off the bottom of the list.

Three different machines, three different tasks, but always the same story. There are hundreds of such studies. At first [Knuth, 71] they conflicted with everyone's intuitive ideas. But as study after study confirmed the results, the intuitive ideas changed. Now we are ready. Let us specify a lean, streamlined machine that will provide very high performance on the limited range of operations which compilers seem to use. While we focus on instructions in this chapter, that is only one aspect of the streamlining. Other parts will come later.

"Wait!" you say, in one last attempt to prevent us from charging off on a terrible mistake. "What about floating-point operations in numerically oriented programs?" The examples above really didn't focus on those special types of programs: fluid dynamics, signal processing, power-system stability, contingency estimates, and certainly chemistry and physics model building. Will our new machine be able to do them well? The answer is: Yes, if we want it to!

The people who do such calculations used to be a *very* small part of the computer market. True, they had money, and it would have been a shame not to take some of it, but most computing made only limited use of floating-point operations. In recent years, this has begun to change. No, your typical user has not become suddenly interested in astrophysics. What has happened is best described as the workstation. The computational engine on many desks must now present itself in graphics. Programs executed in many fields from sciences to engineering to art and presentation are done in elaborate color and in moving displays that may well be classical three-dimensional drawings. When you see those dazzling displays of titles and symbols on TV, they have been done on a workstation. Moving those images around and rotating them in front of you requires an enormous amount of trigonometry and matrix operations—floating point. While TV or movie frame generation may be a most esoteric market, similar displays have become very common tools in a wide variety of fields. At the moment, workstations represent one of the hottest areas of computer sales, and workstations are expected to do floating-point operations with speed.

Since floating point can be important, we should not ignore it, but as we show a bit further on in this chapter, even in an intensive floating-point routine, the floating-point operations tend to be embedded in a slew of integer operations concerned with subscripts and loop control. Thus, both integer and floating-point operations are going on concurrently. One very suitable approach is to put the floating-point processes into what has come to be known as a coprocessor. Machines ranging from the biggest to almost the smallest provide high floating-point speed through a parallel, highly specialized processor. Sometimes these are separate, as shown in Figure 1.1, and sometimes they are integrated into the CPU. In a VAX it is called a *floating-point accelerator*; in most of the microprocessor-based families, the Intel name of *coprocessor* has been adopted for the separate chip, and in many of the largest IBM designs, it is simply a processor that comes with the machine and parallels the integer processor. In effect, rather than trying to make a bell out of a whistle, we simply supply both bells and whistles as well as a way to play them in a coordinated fashion. The position of the coprocessor is shown in Figure 1.1. It need not even do floating point. Any special function that requires some specialized hardware service to provide quick response is a candidate for a coprocessor. For example, some elaborate display management can be relegated to a coprocessor. If someone does not need both forms of processor, he or she can get an occasional floating-point calculation or an elaborate screen update done in software. It will be 100 times slower, but if it comes up only infrequently, doing it in software is the best solution.

1.3.1 Instruction Counts and Code Evaluation

There are five large elements that must be matched and assembled to create a salable general-purpose computer. These comprise:

- an instruction set
- an engine that can execute the instructions
- the several layers of I/O to support the engine
- the operating system, under which applications run
- optimizing compilers and linkers to permit applications written in HLLs to become effective programs that a user may call

No element is very useful without the others and a failure of any of them to work effectively will prevent the system as a whole from performing well. Most users, including programmers who use only a HLL to express their thoughts, see only the applications and whatever parts of the operating system are needed to invoke and support the applications. Assembly language programmers see a bit of the engine and certainly the instruction set, but the whole interacting configuration is visible only to the designers. IBM appropriated the word *architecture* to define the perspective of the machine that would be seen by the assembly language programmer. It was a good usage of the word, since that view could remain constant while the engine underlying the outer prospect could change with advancing technology. However, the architect as the designer of the structure must be aware of all the layers, visible and hidden, and must ensure that all these elements work effectively together. In this usage, computer architecture includes all the parts.

To be an effective architect, one must be able to make harmonious decisions across the span of very different technologies listed above. This rather lengthy section is going to consider the issue of evaluating the instruction set, but that cannot be done effectively without considering how the instruction set will be implemented and how it will interact with the other parts of the machine. We can bring in some of those elements here, but others must await developments in later chapters. Let us begin with the issue of dynamic and static counts and then see what the compiler can do and cannot do in terms of optimizing our program's performance. We will look here at a classical floating-point–intensive routine to see how different it is from the more ordinary sorts of computation that we have considered to this point.

Consider the following piece of C code which will perform the inner product of two matrices. Remember that to have an inner product the matrices must match on their *inner* dimension. In other words, if we have two matrices, **A** and **B**, with dimension $m \times n$ and $n \times j$ respectively, then we can form a third matrix, **C** = **A•B**, which will have dimensions $m \times j$. You cannot, however, do the commuted inner product, **B•A**, because in that direction the inner dimensions do not match. A good way to view the operation is that you are *dotting* the row vectors of **A** with the column vectors of **B**. To have the two vectors be the same length the number of columns in **A** must be the same as the number of rows in **B**.

```
typedef
    double matrix [20][20];

Inner (aRows, Com, bCols, a, b, c)
      int aRows, Com, bCols;
      matrix a, b, c;
          /*Com is common to the two arrays; c will have aRows*bCols
          In Matrix multiplication order is important; A·B ≠ B·A*/
{     int   i, j, k;
      for (i = 0; i<aRows; i++)
          for (j = 0; j< bCols; j++)
          {
              c[i][j] = 0;
                 for (k = 0; k<Com; k++) c[i][j] = c[i][j] + a[i][k] * b[k][j];
          }
}
```

The **typedef** statement defines the storage dimension of MATRIX to be 20*20, or an array of 400 double-precision elements to be thought of as 20 rows of 20 elements (or in Fortran, which was invented by IBM, 20 columns of 20 elements). These dimensions do not specify the matrices themselves but rather how they will be stored. What is passed to the procedure itself are the actual dimensions of the matrices (anything less than or equal to 20) and pointers to the arrays. Consider the array as 400 elements in a row (800 longwords). If **A** were 5×4, then elements 0:3 will contain the first row, 20:23 will house the second row, and so on to 80:83, which will contain the fifth row. The filling of the cells in placing the 5×4 matrix into the 400 allocated storage places is shown in Figure 1.2. All of this discussion of where the goods are stored is relevant to what the compiler must do to access the data. [The diagram, which begins in the upper-right-hand corner, is appropriate to a machine in which the least significant part of a number is at the lowest address—so-called *little endian* machines. For one that puts the largest part of a number in the lowest address—a *big endian* machine—the appropriate arrangement would be that of a normal page, with the (0,0) cell and the first entry on the upper left.]

We will compare the compiled version of this little program on two machines using two compilers, both of which purport to read and understand C and write well-

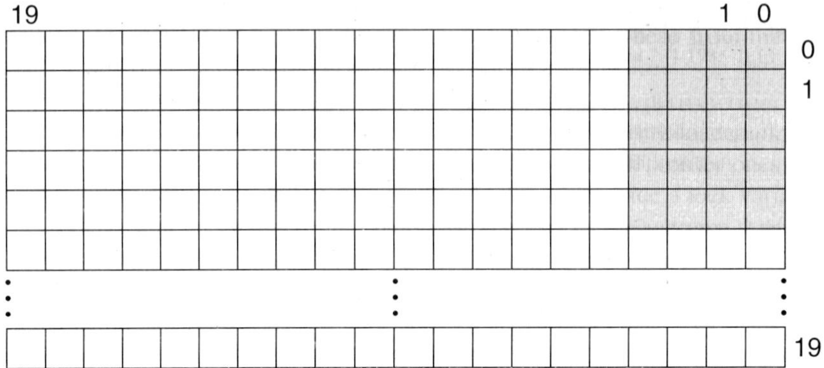

FIGURE 1.2 Storage of the elements of a 5 x 4 matrix in the storage block set aside for a matrix up to 20 x 20. Storage is shown in *little endian* format with the lowest-numbered cell in the upper right.

optimized, machine-specific code to accomplish the C program. Our two machines will be the VAX (running under VMS), which is a CISC, and a Solbourne SPARC (running under UNIX), which is one of the most prevalent RISC architectures. Our objectives are three:

- to learn how to evaluate blocks of code
- to critique what the compiler is doing to optimize the code
- to have a first look at the *architectures* of two very successful commercial machines of rather different vintage and style

We fed the C program to its appropriate compiler, requesting the assembly code and maximum optimization in both cases. What emerged depended, of course, both on the object machine and the compiler. For the VAX, the machine has complex, variable-length instructions. Arithmetic instructions can have either two or three arguments. If two, the second is both a source and the destination. The VAX has a variety of ways of referencing data in memory. And it has 16 registers, 4 of which are already spoken for in hardware as argument pointer, frame pointer, stack pointer, and program counter (R12:R15). [The notation (R12:R15) means "register 12 to register 15, inclusive."] With that brief introduction, what emerges from the compiler is shown in the listing below. The code bytes are read from right to left and the assembly code from left to right.

```
                           byte
      machine code         count                assembly code
               OFFC        0000      Inner::    .word ^m<r2,r3,r4,r5,r6,r7,r8,r9,r10,r11>
         5E    08    C2    0002                 subl2 #8,sp
;for (i = 0; i<aRows; i++)
               5B    D4    0005                 clrl r11
   6E    04    AC    DE    0007                 moval 4(ap),(sp)
```

```
        00   BE    5B   D1   000B          cmpl r11,@0(sp)
                   64   18   000F          bgeq 60$
                   50   D5   0011          tstl r0
                        01   0013          nop
    ;for (j = 0; j< bCols; j++){
                   58   D4   0014    10$:  clrl r8
             0C    AC   D5   0016          tstl 12(ap)
                   52   15   0019          bleq 50$
        5A   5B    14   C5   001B          mull3 #20,r11,r10
        59   0018  CC   D0   001F          movl 24(ap),r9
    ;c[i][j] = 0;
        52   5A    58   C1   0024    20$:  addl3 r8,r10,r2
             69    42   7C   0028          clrq (r9)[r2]
    ;for (k = 0; k< Com; k++) c[i][j] = c[i][j] + a[i][k] * b[k][j];
                   53   D4   002B          clrl r3
             08    AC   D5   002D          tstl 8(ap)
                   33   15   0030          bleq 40$
        57   5B    14   C5   0032          mull3 #20,r11,r7
        52   57    58   C1   0036          addl3 r8,r7,r2
        54   18    AC   D0   003A          movl 24(ap),r4
        56   0010  CC   D0   003E          movl 16(ap),r6
        55   0014  CC   D0   0043          movl 20(ap),r5
                             0048    30$:
        51   57    53   C1   0048          addl3 r3,r7,r1
        50   53    14   C5   004C          mull3 #20,r3,r0
             50    58   C0   0050          addl2 r8,r0
50  65  40   66    41   65   0053          muld3 (r6)[r1],(r5)[r0],r0
        64   42    50   60   0059          addd2 r0,(r4)[r2]
                   53   D6   005D          incl r3
        08   AC    53   D1   005F          cmpl r3,8(ap)
                   E3   19   0063          blss 30$
    ;   }
                   58   D6   0065    40$:  incl r8
        0C   AC    58   D1   0067          cmpl r8,12(ap)
                   B7   19   006B          blss 20$
                             006D    50$:
                   5B   D6   006D          incl r11
        00   BE    5B   D1   006F          cmpl r11,@0(sp)
                   9F   19   0073          blss 10$
    ; }
                        04   0075    60$:  ret
```

There are a few instructions that would not be obvious to the uninitiated. The top line is a mask that is used first by the CALL instruction to push to the stack the registers listed and then by the RET instruction at the bottom to pop them back off again. The instruction MOVAL calculates the address of the first item and puts it—the address—in the destination. The sizes of operands used include *longwords* (4 bytes), *quadwords* (2 longwords), and *doubles* (same size as a quadword but organized as a double-precision floating-point number). When a quadword or double is referenced in register, as in the MULD3 instruction, the 8 bytes include not only the register named but its successor register as well. The RET instruction not only restores registers but AP, FP, SP, and PC as well, putting the program back at the proper place in the calling program with nothing left to clean up.

Since the assembly code expresses the C code rather directly, we have assumed that you can follow it even if you are not a VAX jock. The machine code on the left is useful for determining the size of each instruction as well as occasionally making sense of what gets written on the right. We will make no other use of it here. Our next task is to analyze this code to see what the compiler has accomplished and to get some metrics by which we can judge the effectiveness of the architecture itself. The spreadsheet, Table 1.5, shows the static and dynamic analysis of this code sample.

We begin by assigning the code to one of four instruction classifications:

- move
- integer arithmetic
- floating-point arithmetic
- branch, jump, or call

These classifications are somewhat broader than those of Tables 1.1 to 1.4, but given the results of those tables, they should serve well. To get the static analysis, we simply assign each and every instruction to one of these classes. To that end, sometimes we have to decide what the computer is really doing. For example, the instruction **clrl r1** puts a 0 into r1. It could just as easily accomplish that task by performing **r1** $\Leftarrow$ **r1 - r1** as by doing **r1** $\Leftarrow$ **0**, and from the outside, you cannot tell which was done. We have guessed that the instruction effectively moves a zero into the target. This decision has some impact on our statistics since the *only* explicit MOV instructions are the one above the label 20$, the three in the middle above 30$, and the MOVAL. However, in the overall scheme of things, this decision, while interesting, is not critical. A somewhat more contentious assignment is weighting the MULL instruction as 16 integer instructions rather than 1. As always, multiplication is accomplished by multiple addition. We have assumed a 2-bit Booth's algorithm multiplier, which yields the 16 cycles, while at the same time, we have assumed that the floating-point processor can do its multiplication roughly in the time of an integer operation. This initially curious division of resources is typical of modern computers.

Having assigned all the instructions, we can calculate the percentage of each type. Note that this static analysis does not take into account how many times a given instruction is actually called, only its frequency in the listing. The static analysis figures are found at the bottom of the chart. The static analysis does not do too bad a job for itself, though one must be struck by how many arithmetic operations there are compared with Tables 1.1, 1.2, and 1.4. That is not too surprising for a routine so obviously

TABLE 1.5 Static and dynamic analysis of the code generated by the VAX/VMS C compiler from the small subroutine Inner

		Static						Dynamic				
		mov	int	flt	br	mem	wgt	mov	int	flt	br	mem
inner::	.word ^m<r2,r3,r4,r5,r6,r7,r8,r9,r10,r11>	10	10			10.5	1	10	10			10.5
	subl2 #8,sp		1			0.75	1		1			0.75
	clrl r11	1				0.5	1	1				0.5
	moval 4(ap),(sp)	1				3	1	1				3
	cmpl r11,@0(sp)		1			3	1		1			3
	bgeq 60$				1	0.5	1				1	0.5
	tstl r0		1			0.5	1		1			0.5
	nop					0.25	1					0.25
10$:												
	clrl r8	1				0.5	17	17				8.5
	tstl 12(ap)		1			1.5	17		17			25.5
	bleq 50$				1	0.5	17				17	8.5
	mull3 #20,r11,r10		16			1	17		272			17
	movl 24(ap),r9	1				2	17	17				34
20$:												
	addl3 r8,r10,r2		1			1	204		204			204
	clrq (r9)[r2]	2				2.75	204	408				561
	clrl r3	1				0.5	204	204				102
	tstl 8(ap)		1			1.5	204		204			306
	bleq 40$				1	0.5	204				204	102
	mull3 #20,r11,r7		16			1	204		3264			204
	addl3 r8,r7,r2		1			1	204		204			204
	movl 24(ap),r4	1				2	204	204				408
	movl 16(ap),r6	1				2	204	204				408
	movl 20(ap),r5	1				2	204	204				408

TABLE 1.5 *(cont.)* **Static and dynamic analysis of the code generated by the VAX/VMS C compiler from the small subroutine Inner**

		Static						Dynamic				
		mov	int	flt	br	mem	wgt	mov	int	flt	br	mem
30$:												
	addl3 r3,r7,r1		1			1	4080		4080			4080
	mull3 #20,r3,r0		16			1	4080		65280			4080
	addl2 r8,r0		1			0.75	4080		4080			3060
	muld3 (r6)[r1],(r5)[r0],r0			1		5.5	4080			4080		22440
	addd2 r0,(r4)[r2]			1		5	4080			4080		20400
	incl r3		1			0.5	4080		4080			2040
	cmpl r3,8(ap)		1			2	4080		4080			8160
	blss 30$				1	0.5	4080				4080	2040
40$:												
	incl r8		1			0.5	204		204			102
	cmpl r8,12(ap)		1			2	204		204			408
	blss 20$				1	0.5	204				204	102
50$:												
	incl r11		1			0.5	17		17			8.5
	cmpl r11,@0(sp)		1			2	17		17			34
	blss 10$				1	0.5	17				17	8.5
60$:												
	ret	16	10			16.3	1	16	10			16.25
		36	83	2	6	77.3		1286	86230	8160	4523	69999
		28%	65%	2%	5%			1%	86%	8%	5%	

arithmetically oriented. However, given that we are doing the inner product of two double-precision matrices, one might well expect that a lot of the work would be floating-point instructions. On a static basis, the percentage of floating-point operations is minuscule. The arithmetic is dominated by indices and addresses.

The last column in the static calculations is the number of longwords that each instruction requires from memory. This count includes the length of the instruction itself and all the addresses or operands that must be fetched from memory. The entry mask and RET are complex instructions involving many references to the stack. Accordingly, they are memory hogs. Interestingly enough, so are the two floating-point instructions, though only because the operands are long and reside in memory.

This column makes little sense by itself. The impact of a given instruction on memory traffic depends too heavily on how often it is called to make a static analysis of much use. However, we need the column to generate the dynamic count so it is included in the static set.

The dynamic analysis should be done by running the whole range of "typical" application programs and recording the frequency with which each instruction occurs. As an indication of the result of such an analysis, we have selected a reasonably large pair of matrices: 17×20 and 20×12. These choices determine the number of times each loop will run. With that data, the dynamic analysis can be done. The results are revealing and informative.

The most critical portion of the routine will be the innermost loop. Those instructions will be run the most often and therefore deserve the greatest effort at optimization. If we may assume that each instruction and each memory reference takes roughly the same time, then we can see how well this C compiler has accomplished its task. The answer is: Not so well! The first thing that must strike your eye is the enormous number of cycles devoted to integer multiplication in the inner loop. As we have accounted for the cycles, 65 percent of the whole program is devoted to integer multiplication in the inner loop! This overstates the case, possibly by 10 percent or so because of undercounting time on the floating-point operations, but there is no doubt that a huge proportion of the code cycles are focused on that one instruction. Could it be avoided? Indeed, and by methods which are visible to at least some compilers, one of which we will consider in a moment.

What else has the compiler done for us or to us? Consider the memory cycles for a moment. Note that the intermediate sum is kept in memory (ADDD2).[3] This means that the double must be brought in and put out each time for 16,320 extra memory cycles, or 23 percent of the total. Look a little further down and note that the index test at the bottom of the loop compares the index with a constant (COM), which has been left on the argument list in memory. That adds another 4080 memory references, or 6 percent. The cautious reader should ask if the compiler could do what we ask, that is, if there is room enough to store the variable and the argument in register. To answer

[3] This poor choice is really ours, not the compiler's. While we know that *c*, *b*, and *a* are all different, the compiler cannot be sure that this will always be true. The compiler is obliged to put the result back in memory in case the programmer expects the results to be there. To avoid this choice, the *programmer*, rather than the compiler, should use a local variable for the sum within the inner loop. *c* would then be set equal to the local variable in the appropriate outer loop. Not all mediocre translations should be attributed to the programmer, but without the insight into the compiler's rules of behavior, most programmers would be tempted to do it the way we have presented.

that question, determine all the register references inside the inner loop. They comprise eight (r0:r7). Since the VAX provides 12 quite general registers and since we would need two for the partial sum and one for COM, there are indeed enough registers. What there is not, at least in this compiler, is a global register allocation scheme that would assign three more registers to the innermost loop.

There is a critically important lesson to be learned from this first exercise in code analysis. The performance of a VAX in executing this C program would be noticeably degraded by the compiler. If you were to run one of the classical benchmark programs for scientific computation, Linpack, which does just the sort of operations that INNER performs, the computer would appear to be slower than it really is. There is no accurate way to compare disparate machines—machines with different architectures—simply by running some standard program against a clock. It is rather like asking whether Shakespeare sounds better in French or in Russian. Who knows? The result is too dependent on the skill of the translator. You can get performance measurements including the compiler, but even then, one always has to ask whether the benchmark used for the test accurately represents a particular buyer's applications. Still, it is both fun and profitable in our present context to look at several quite different architectures as well as to see what different compilers accomplish. To that end, we next consider the output of the C compiler running on a RISC, in this case a Solbourne SPARC processor. The SPARC has 32 integer registers divided into four groups of eight: INS, LOCALS, OUTS, and GLOBALS. The eight INS are also the calling program's OUTS, so parameter passing may be achieved in register. The code and the register set are shown in Table 1.6. The boldfaced entries in the registers represent the contents just after the first instruction (SAVE). The elements on the left are the parameters passed by the calling routine; the right-justified entries are what the function INNER puts there. The data in the middle are standard items such as the frame pointer (fp) and the stack pointer (sp).

The SPARC derives directly from the Berkeley RISC. It finishes one instruction per clock, but to achieve that speed, it limits its instructions to a length of one word (32 bits), and it must avoid the complicated sorts of transactions of which the VAX is so replete. Its instructions either do a load or store of data (LD or ST), process data in registers (ADD or SUB), or do branches or jumps (BGE or JUMPL). Instructions such as ADD or SUB do not change condition codes unless CC is appended, as in SUBCC. Other instructions do not change condition codes. Floating-point operations are executed in a coprocessor that has 32 floating-point registers (f0:f31), each capable of holding an IEEE single-precision number (32 bits). They may be paired (even:odd as f0:f1) to do double-precision operations by referencing the even register with an appropriate instruction (FADDD).

The instruction pair SAVE/RESTORE "rotate" the register set to expose either a new set of 16 or the previous set of 16. There are no memory operations involved in these instructions. We will discuss this Rolodex register system later in this chapter. Finally, global register 0 as a source is a hard-wired zero and as a destination is a wastebasket. For example, the instruction

```
subcc %i5,%i1,%g0
```

TABLE 1.6 The SPARC version of INNER

```
        .global          _Inner
_Inner:
        save sp,-64,sp    ! expose 16 new registers. After
                          ! instruction, fp is r30, sp = fp-64 is r14
                          ! and return address is in r31.
        !for (i = 0; i<aRows;i++)
        add r0,0,r17      ! r0 is a hardwired 0
        add r0,r24,r16
        subcc r17,r16,r0
        add r0,r27,r18
        add r0,r29,r19
        bge LY1
        st r24,[fp+68]    ! this instruction is done
                          ! before branch
LY2:    !for (j = 0; j<bCols; j++){
        add r0,0,r21
        subcc r21,r26,r0
        add r0,0,r22
        add r0,r18,r20
        bge L16
        add r22,r19,r23
LY3:    !c[i][j] = 0;
        sethi %hi(L2000000),r11
        lddf [r11+%lo(L2000000)],f0
```

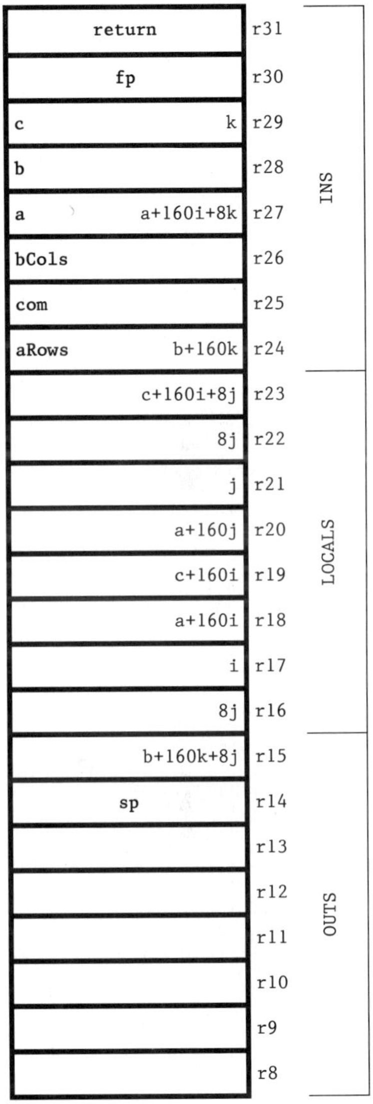

Register	Contents	Group
r31	return	INS
r30	fp	INS
r29	c k	INS
r28	b	INS
r27	a a+160i+8k	INS
r26	bCols	INS
r25	com	INS
r24	aRows b+160k	INS
r23	c+160i+8j	LOCALS
r22	8j	LOCALS
r21	j	LOCALS
r20	a+160j	LOCALS
r19	c+160i	LOCALS
r18	a+160i	LOCALS
r17	i	LOCALS
r16	8j	LOCALS
r15	b+160k+8j	OUTS
r14	sp	OUTS
r13		OUTS
r12		OUTS
r11		OUTS
r10		OUTS
r9		OUTS
r8		OUTS

TABLE 1.6 *(cont.)* **The SPARC version of INNER**

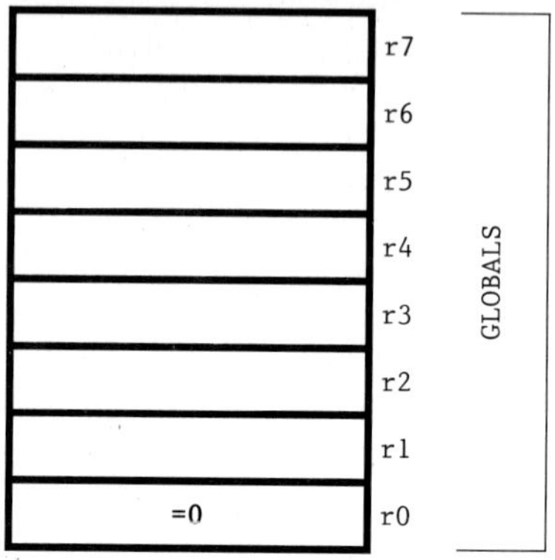

```
        st f0,[r23]
        st f1,[r23+4]
!       for (k = 0;k<Com;k++) c[i][j] = c[i][j] + a[i][k] * b[k][j];
        add r0,0,r29
        subcc r29,r25,r0
        add r0,r28,r24
        bge L20
        add r0,r20,r27
LY4:
        ldf [r27],f4
        ldf [r27+4],f5
        ldf [r23],f8
        ldf [r23+4],f9
        add r24,r22,r15
        ldf [r15+4],f3
        ldf [r15],f2
        fmuld f4,f2,f6
        add r29,1,r29
        subcc r29,r25,r0
        add r27,8,r27
        add r24,160,r24
        faddd f8,f6,f10
        stf f10,[r23]
        bl LY4
        stf f11,[r23+4]
L20:
        add r21,1,r21
        subcc r21,r26,r0
        add r22,8,r22
        bl LY3
        add r23,8,r23
```

r7
r6
r5
r4
r3
r2
r1
r0 =0
GLOBALS

TABLE 1.6 *(cont.)* **The SPARC version of INNER**

```
L16:
      add r17,1,r17
      subcc r17,r16,r0
      add r18,160,r18
      bl LY2
      add r19,160,r19
LY1:
      jumpl r31,r0       ! return to calling program
      restore r0,0,r8
      .seg "data"
      .align 8
L2000000:
      .word 0
      .word 0
```

sets the condition codes according to the result of (i5-i1), but the result itself goes nowhere. It is quite equivalent to the VAX instruction CMPL R4, R5.

SETHI is a little strange on first meeting. Because each instruction must fit in 32 bits, a single instruction cannot carry a full 32-bit address to put into a register. Instead, SETHI puts the high 22 bits of an address into a specified register, and then one uses a 10-bit offset on that register in a subsequent instruction to specify the full address. The instruction pair

```
sethi %hi(L2000000),%o3
ldd   [%o3+%lo(L2000000)],%f0
```

is an example of that construction. Note that L2000000 is a label pointing to a couple of words in the data section. It can be found at the bottom of the program.

Well, all right, this is the new wave of computer hardware. How well does its compiler do in generating "optimum" code? The first thing you must notice is that the RISC version of INNER is much longer than the VAX version. One of the design objectives in the VAX was to make the program itself short. Obviously, the designers succeeded, but we must question the value of what they accomplished. Let us get some numbers to work with. Just as with the VAX/VMS program, we put the assembly language program into a spreadsheet and determine the static and dynamic counts for instruction types and memory references. This is shown in Table 1.7. For the SPARC, we need not include the register/address part of the instruction because all instructions are precisely one word—four bytes—in length and any associated memory references

TABLE 1.7 The static and dynamic analysis of the code generated by the Solbourne SPARC C compiler for the short subroutine INNER

		Static						Dynamic				
		mov	int	flt	br	mem	wgt	mov	int	flt	br	mem
_Inner:												
	save		1			1	1		1			1
	add		1			1	1		1			1
	add		1			1	1		1			1
	subcc		1			1	1		1			1
	add		1			1	1		1			1
	add		1			1	1		1			1
	bge				1	1	1				1	1
	st	1				2	1	1				2
LY2:												
	add		1			1	17		17			17
	subcc		1			1	17		17			17
	add		1			1	17		17			17
	add		1			1	17		17			17
	bge				1	1	17				17	17
	add		1			1	17		17			17
LY3:												
	sethi		1			1	204		204			204
	lddf	1				3	204	204				612
	st	1				1	204	204				204
	st	1				1	204	204				204
	add		1			1	204		204			204
	subcc		1			1	204		204			204
	add		1			1	204		204			204
	bge				1	1	204				204	204
	add		1			1	204		204			204
LY4:												
	ldf	1				2	4080	4080				8160
	ldf	1				2	4080	4080				8160
	ldf	1				2	4080	4080				8160

TABLE 1.7 *(cont.)* **The static and dynamic analysis of the code generated by the Solbourne SPARC C compiler for the short subroutine INNER**

		Static						Dynamic				
		mov	int	flt	br	mem	wgt	mov	int	flt	br	mem
	ldf	1				2	4080	4080				8160
	add		1			1	4080		4080			4080
	ldf	1				2	4080	4080				8160
	ldf	1				2	4080	4080				8160
	fmuld			1		1	4080			4080		4080
	add		1			1	4080		4080			4080
	subcc		1			1	4080		4080			4080
	add		1			1	4080		4080			4080
	add		1			1	4080		4080			4080
	faddd			1		1	4080			4080		4080
	stf	1				2	4080	4080				8160
	bl				1	1	4080				4080	4080
	stf	1				2	4080	4080				8160
L20:												
	add	1				1	204	204				204
	subcc	1				1	204	204				204
	add	1				1	204	204				204
	bl	1				1	204	204				204
	add	1				1	204	204				204
L16:												
	add	1				1	17	17				17
	subcc	1				1	17	17				17
	add	1				1	17	17				17
	bl				1		17				17	
	add	1				1	17	17				17
LY1:												
	jumpl				1	1	1				1	1
	restore	1				1	1	1				1
		22	21	2	6	61		34342	21511	8160	4320	101365
		43%	41%	4%	12%			50%	31%	12%	6%	

are determined by the opcode. A quick glance along the tabulation rows shows two very distinct differences between the VAX and the SPARC. The SPARC seems to have a much higher percentage of loads and stores, and it seems to make a great many more references to memory. The first effect is an artifact of the coding paradigm; the second is most definitely real but not important. These two observations need some comment.

The reason why the SPARC appears to have so many loads and stores is simply that they are distinct. Whenever data must be moved, the code says so explicitly. For the VAX, most of the loads and stores are folded into the addressing format. That leads to more compact coding, but it does not in itself reduce the number of data that must be fetched or returned or shorten the time necessary to do it. In a loop, the benefits of shorter code length are multiplied by the repetition number. The VAX's more compact code notation leads directly to the apparent savings seen in the memory operation column. The ratio is 1.45/1. Since that is impressive, the reader must wonder why we say it is not important. The answer is found way back in Figure 1.1. There we show a typical modern single-CPU configuration. The critical items there for this question are the two caches, particularly the instruction cache. The instruction cache is essentially inside the CPU. The instruction cache normally has a separate path to the instruction unit, and the whole arrangement fits together so snugly that there is no cost whatsoever for instructions coming in from the instruction cache. Effectively, every time that the instruction unit needs another instruction (or part thereof in the VAX), it is immediately at hand.

Once an instruction is fetched the first time, it can reside in this cache until its space is needed for another, more recent acquisition. The rate of replacement depends both on the cache and the code, but for almost any modern computer, which would include both SPARC and many VAXs, the innermost loop would dwell comfortably within the cache for the duration of that loop and possibly for the entire routine. Thus, if the loop fits in cache, longer code length is an almost no-cost option.

With the RISC code, where all the transactions tend to be exposed, this decidedly floating-point routine spends 50 percent of its effort moving data, 31 percent doing integer arithmetic for indices and addresses, and only 12 percent doing floating-point operations. The low fraction of time devoted to floating-point operations is a direct result of putting in a floating-point coprocessor. While a floating-point unit assists a routine like this, it might seem far less useful to other, more ordinary computational tasks. Why are they now included in the high-end PCs? Among other arguments, windows and other graphical tasks involve trigonometric operations that are inherently floating-point, and speed there has a very direct impact on the user. Another widely used application that gets substantial acceleration from a floating-point coprocessor is the spreadsheet.

Let us finish this lengthy section with an evaluation of the Solbourne compiler's success in generating admirable code. The Solbourne does not do one of the VAX compiler's gross translations. Instead of simply multiplying out the expression for the address of each element of the matrices, as in

```
&a[i][k] == &a[0][0] + i*160 + k*8 /* each double takes 8 bytes */
```

the Solbourne takes advantage of the regularity of the expression and calculates the product by adding 160 to the row address every time that i increments and then adding that to a product of k*8 formed in the same additive fashion. This neatly removes the most egregious and costly piece of clumsiness in the VAX code. A second nice item in the Solbourne code is the separation of the two floating-point operations by several other integer operations. This separation allows the coprocessor to complete its operation in parallel with useful work in the integer unit. It is much easier to do this in a machine where the individual operations are all laid out in separate instructions. One of the motivations in simplifying the instruction set is to let the compiler do just this kind of optimization. (Another school of thought argues that one should go entirely in the other direction and pack many operations into one very long instruction word. The idea there is to allow the machine itself to do the scheduling in real time, responding correctly to dynamic, data-dependent path changes that no compiler can foresee. The argument is both current and unresolved, but one way or another, optimization of parallel processing units is beneficial.) These good words notwithstanding, perfection does not come through the Solbourne compiler either. Note that the SPARC code, just like the VAX code, puts back the partial sum every time rather than storing it in register. (Refer back to footnote 3 on page 25.) Then there is the arcane and wasteful way that the partial sum is initiated. Not only does it load that 0 from memory into the coprocessor and then run it back out to memory, but it also recreates its address each time! A single FSUBD f2,f2,f2 clears out two f registers, f2 and f3. It is not unfair to ask: "If I know that, why doesn't the compiler know that?" The general observation is that if the loop length is short enough, human intervention often improves the code. In fact, one classical benchmark for number crunching—*Linpack*—was so important for establishing which machine to buy that programmers would routinely hand-code the critical loops in that benchmark, sometimes achieving as much as a factor of 2 performance enhancement [Weicker, 90]. Since the purpose of the test for the consumer was to see how the machine and its compiler would do his or her task, hand-coding bordered on deceptive practice. By common agreement, only the Fortran-compiled results were reported. The basic lesson here is that a machine and its compiler are an inseparable organism. While evolution and improvements are the norm for both, you cannot speak of processor speed in the abstract. The user sees only the speed with which the program performs, not the individual parts. With these two examples of design and some concern about making the compiler designer's life easy, let us proceed to designing an instruction set.

1.4 DESIGNING THE INSTRUCTION SET

We have lots of loose pieces above. Let us begin by summing up what is there.

1. For general-purpose computing, the compiler-generated instructions most important by frequency of occurrence either fetch data from memory or put it back. The next most important class are the operations required for looping and branching. These include comparisons, incrementing and decrementing, and the branches themselves. Then come procedure calls. And finally general arithmetic and logic.

2. Fewer layers of logic mean faster response from the logic. However, in the final analysis, hardware does it all. If there is not enough hardware of sufficient versatility to respond simply, directly, and swiftly to the most common programming needs, programs will run slowly.
3. Less complex logic means substantially lower engineering and production costs and generally a much shorter time from concept to market. However, pushing more requirements onto software can make software engineering costs and time-to-market as much of a problem as the hardware, or more so.
4. Compilers seem to use only simple addressing modes, generate their best code when they have lots of registers to work with, and cannot be counted on—at least yet—to squeeze the last full measure of swiftness out of small, tight loops.

These points are not now much in dispute, but what response should they engender? The answers have been and will always be driven by a combination of technology and marketing savoir faire. One designer in particular has always pursued the lean-and-mean designs responsive to these observations even before they were commonly held. This is Seymour Cray. The breakthrough that has made it possible for "the rest of us" to pursue the same goals even in as underfunded an environment as a university is VLSI. Substantial integration began in the '70s and reached a level of maturity in the '80s, so it is not surprising that the fruit of these new designs is first seen in the '80s. To put Cray in proper perspective, he has been designing machines that can properly be labeled RISCs since the early '60s.

In the mid '70s, new architectures developed that attempted to take full advantage of these insights into what compiler-generated programs needed from the hardware. These first efforts were neither in small, unconstrained start-up companies nor in universities, but right in the money-making stodgy heart of the industry itself. Nor were these designs "little machines." Apart from Seymour Cray's work, the very first such design to reach production [Allison, 86] was the National Cash Register (NCR) 8500, a mainframe machine with almost all of the basic characteristics that have come to the fore in streamlined designs. As we have cited before [Cocke, 90], John Cocke and his group at IBM did some elegant research in the late '70s in the development of their 801 streamlined machine, a prototype that showed remarkable promise but whose elegant concepts reached the user market in fits and snatches. The only early version delivered to customers was the PC RT, in some sense a "toy," with only 16 registers and a 16-bit bus. However, hidden inside one of IBM's great mainframe machines—the 3090—was an 801 doing I/O processing and tearing along at 40 MHz.

Others were not sitting still. By the time the PC RT reached the market, there were three fully developed university designs and seven commercial products out or announced,[4] all of which embodied in a much fuller sense the innovations and style

---

[4] RISC I, RISC II, and SOAR from UC at Berkeley and MIPS from Stanford, plus processor chips and/or complete systems from Ridge, Pyramid, Novix, Acorn, Fairchild, and MIPS (named after the design commercialized from the Stanford design).

that derived from the 801. (The terms "RISC" and "streamlined" were applied first to the university designs, but they have become popular and are now used for the general class of such architectures whether or not they are entirely "true" to the objectives of the architects who first coined them. We will use "RISC" and "streamlined" in that sense and not with specific reference to RISC I and II of Berkeley or MIPS of Stanford.) By the time IBM finally concluded that the workstation market was worthy of its interest and delivered a powerful, second-generation RISC (the RS/6000 series) in 1990, Sun and Hewlett-Packard had both produced very competitive RISC products (SPARC and HP's Precision Architecture) and DEC was delivering workstations based on the MIPS 5000 RISC chip set. All of these machines deliver very high computation speeds, and they do it at remarkably low cost.

What are the common properties of such designs? One of the first items that strikes many observers is the large number of general registers in the designs. The numbers range from 16 (roughly the same as the VAX) to 138 in RISC II. The advantage of lots of registers is that you can reduce the number of LOADs and STOREs. John Cocke uses the graphic term "spilling registers" for what happens when there are too few registers. Defining "plenty" is one of the areas of contention, but there is no question that lots of registers can speed up programs for any processor style. Modern compilers try to pick out the best "register variables" by code analysis. What is best is a dynamic that requires an overview of large segments of a program, something that most compilers find difficulty achieving. Having plenty of registers makes the allocation easier and enables the compiler to make a real impact on processing speed. A plenitude of registers can also help speed up the frequent procedure calls, but they do present a burden in a "context switch" or change of task. We take up this subject in several later chapters.

As a consequence of all four items above, a streamlined design will have fewer and simpler instruction types and addressing formats than the complex-instruction machines of the previous era. If you enjoy somewhat silly but spectacular examples, recall the VAX's complicated ADD instruction cited above. In tallying all the possible combinations of that instruction, we find that the VAX can recognize 29,547 versions of ADD for two binary numbers.[5] Our machine will have two. That is certainly a noteworthy reduction, but we urge a little caution to the religious enthusiasm that seems to have come upon the counters of instructions. Smaller is not inherently better. A Boeing 747—aptly named the "jumbo"—has as good a glide ratio (a measure of aerodynamic efficiency) as the typical two-passenger training glider: 20/1. The 747 is certainly streamlined; small it isn't, successful it is.

The overall task of the computer designer is to generate a machine that, when it reaches the market, will be highly competitive. To be competitive, the new product must be more cost-effective than the current machines. Effectiveness involves both price and performance.

---

[5] A realistic comparison would start by separating out the LOAD and STORE parts of the VAX ADD instruction since these are present as separate instructions in the RISC design. Once that is done, the VAX seems to have "only" 42 distinguishable forms of binary integer ADD.

Instead of the complex analysis of hardware and software interaction that a real optimization of the design would entail, we adopt here a reasonably robust set of rules that will not get us into much trouble but that we do not suggest are best by any measure. If we follow them, our design will be fast and well streamlined. That someone else can do better with greater effort we have no doubt. Here are our rules:

1. Essentially all instructions should execute in a single clock cycle and that clock cycle should be very short—of the order of time that it takes to add two integers, or about 5 to 100 ns. Notice that, to the extent that we succeed in following this rule, all instructions will have equal "costs."
2. Instructions should not have "side effects." While it is early to make this statement, what it means is that an instruction should either execute completely, doing everything that is expected of it, or it should do nothing at all to the registers or flags. (It may seem peculiar at this stage to consider an instruction "failing to complete," but this is a reasonably common occurrence in sophisticated computers. We will discuss examples particularly in the sections on memory management. A hint of the potential problem is given in the next rule.)
3. Instructions shall all be of the same length. Our main objective here is to simplify the interpretive logic and to make the pipeline starkly simple. Another important reason is that we must always be able to fetch a whole instruction in a single clock cycle. In a VAX, an instruction's length can vary from 1 to 54 bytes. Variable-length instructions lead to complex, many-layered interpretive logic. Furthermore, with automatic memory management (virtual memory), variable lengths mean that it is possible to get started fetching, interpreting, and executing an instruction and only then find that its end is not in primary memory. One could still have full-size and half-size instructions and always fetch a full-sized unit from memory, but our desire for streamlined, simple interpretive logic says: Make it all one size.
4. Use simple addressing formats. Addressing modes should support words (a length yet to be defined) and bytes and should permit reaching any address in the address space from any starting position. In other words, we want little or no inherent segmentation of memory.

These are enough. Now let us consider the implications.

1.4.1 Choosing the Word Size

If byte data types are supported, the word size should be an integer number of bytes. Two other factors enter when trying to set a word size. These are the range of addresses one wants to have available and the size of word necessary to store common data types. Both of these depend on what one expects to do with the machine in question. Let us consider a few examples of usage.

What constitutes an "adequate" address range is not at all self-evident. It is only vaguely related to program size, the amount of physical memory that will be installed, or even the type of computation. In the 1940s, when modern computers were first being designed, 1000 words was considered enough; in the early '70s, when the PDP-11 was designed, 64 KB was thought to be enough; by the late '70s, the same company planned its VAX series to have 4 GB; that now seems limiting for certain applications. At Intel, the designers of the 80386 leaped beyond the competition by having an address range of 64 TB (46-bit addresses). Is this finally enough? All that one can really conclude from this brief history is that however big you declare your memory address space, wheel that number once around the block and you will find yourself with users complaining of inadequate space for some application you had not even considered at design time.

In today's applications, a range >4 GB is considered "reasonable" if not capacious. If we have a 32-bit address and use it to point to words rather than bytes, we will have 4 GW of address range. This is a first cut at the word size, since we know that we want an address to fit in a single word. Let us see how that word size would fit the "store common data types" criterion.

If you were using this machine in a bank, you would want to be able to do integer arithmetic on sums ranging up to possibly a trillion dollars or so (10^{12}). Bank ledgers are kept to an accuracy of at least $0.001—a tenth of a cent. This means that to do arithmetic at the bank the computer must handle 14 decimal digits. That demands a 41-bit word size (to include both positive and negative numbers). If we choose our word size to be an integral number of bytes, that would push us up to 48 bits. Well, why not? Why not indeed! Word width costs money or time. If you handle the whole word at one time, your data paths must be very wide and that makes the hardware very expensive. Alternatively, if you pick up your word in pieces, each transaction is going to take more calls to memory. What should we do?

Hark back to our discussion of what programs do most of the time. They fetch and store, test and branch, and only occasionally do end-use arithmetic. Since our rule is to put into hardware only those things which make a significant impact on the program's running speed, the occasional demand for multiple-precision arithmetic should not inspire us to spend lots of money on hardware. If we stick with 32 bits, then to do a big bank's ledger in integer arithmetic, we will have to use a multiple-precision routine—roughly 10 instructions rather than 4. Do recognize that this slowdown of 2.5 times must be scaled by the relative frequency with which the operation is invoked. If you do it only 1 percent of the time, then it is 2.5 percent slowdown, not a 250 percent slowdown.

How about other data types? Well, text processing is initially taken care of by our decision to have a word be an integer number of bytes. That leaves floating-point (FP) operations as our other obvious primitive. The most common FP convention today (counting the number of machines which support it, not the number of numbers processed) is the IEEE standard that defines two formats and extensions: a single-precision number (*float* in C) occupying 4 bytes and a double-precision number (*double* in C) occupying 8 bytes. Here we are staring at a choice between 32 and 64 bits of width. The usual solution, where economy is an important driving force, is to select some integral submultiple of 64 bits as the word size and then arrange a FP processor to work at the maximum width needed. In that way, one does not slow down the FP operations by being too stingy, but at the same time the machine can be used with the standard 32-bit busses.

Notice where this leaves us: 32 bits is our minimum for addresses. Our rule that we want to haul a full instruction or datum from memory in one cycle says that we need a 32-bit word there, and 32 bits also seems to be a good compromise for integer and FP arithmetic. Not too surprisingly, we arrive at the very popular size of 32 bits for a word. At the same time, you can see that a drive for super speed or vast memory address space could demand longer words. Word sizes in relatively modern designs have ranged from 8 bits (small, relatively slow, and very inexpensive processors) to 72 bits (large, extremely fast, expensive, scientific data processors). Digital's Alpha processor, a very powerful RISC first implemented in 1992, uses 64-bit integers and doubles. It seems very likely that the next five years will see many 64-bit processors and 64-bit busses.

1.4.2 The Register Set Size Problem

The register set is the programmer's working space. All of our data operations, apart from LOAD and STORE, deal exclusively with the register set. A very large fraction of the operations which involve addresses—LOADs, STOREs, JUMPs, and CALLs—will use addresses located in registers. Registers are just very local, very fast, and very expensive memory locations. Having many of them means that the program can keep a lot of local data on hand; having only a few means that the program must devote much more time to fetching data from and returning data to the main memory. What may not be obvious at first is that unless special use is made of the register set, a very large fraction of the traffic between memory and the register file is a consequence of procedure calls. Just look at the top and bottom of INNER in the VAX version to see this traffic. Apart from such data-hungry routines as INNER, the register preservation overhead often dominates the data flow in a subroutine. Look at Problem 1.2 for another example.

Although the urge would seem to be to generate a huge set of registers—as SPARC indeed has done—there is as usual a piper to be paid. The issue is a conflict between minimizing both the time and memory traffic in a procedure call and the same objectives in a context switch. A context is a whole task, such as running a program; a procedure call takes place within a context. Switching between concurrent contexts or passing down and up through the layers of a single process involves sharing the resources of the machine while not trampling upon the other users thereof. The most precious resource is the register file, and any switch or CALL usually requires making copies of registers that may be overwritten and then later recopying these saved values back into registers.

The principal difference between a context switch and a CALL is that since different contexts have no relationship either in time or behavior to each other, all of the registers must be copied in a context switch, while in a CALL, where conventions of common usage obtain, only those registers which will be overwritten need be saved. A context switch will occur:

1. whenever the current context needs a "slow" resource (e.g., something that is out on disk or input from a keyboard),
2. whenever the program does something evil (e.g., tries to overwrite the operating system), or

3. whenever a process completes its current time allocation (in a multiprocessing system with multiple jobs sharing a processor in a sequential fashion)

All of these events are essentially random within the context and completely random between contexts. To achieve high resource utilization, the operating system frequently finds itself assigned to copying the current task back out in the job queue (in memory) and copying in the next in line. Since the whole context is preserved, much memory traffic ensues.

A CALL within a context is much less expensive but much more frequent. Normally, a CALL involves passing a few parameters to a subroutine, having the subroutine run, and then returning a result. When the subroutine runs, it usually requires some local variable space. The number of local variables is defined at compile time, so there is a chance to plan ahead. The usual need is for a few words. These will fit nicely and efficiently within the register set, but the calling routine may well be using these same registers and can reasonably insist that they be unmodified upon return. This places an obligation on the subroutine to save and restore the contents in the registers it uses. Once again, more memory traffic is involved. In most machines, this saving and restoring is done by writing to a local storage space on the stack,[6] though if you recall our example INNER above, coded for the SPARC, there is an alternative, the Rolodex file system. To quantify the steps involved when "spilling registers to the stack," Figure 1.3 shows a procedure call of single depth in the RISC that we are designing.

The compiler knows that it will use r9..r12 in procedure B, so it puts code into routine B to make some space on the stack (SP <— SP-4) and then saves those registers' contents in this stack area. Then, before returning to A, B restores those four registers by reloading them from the stack. Then it puts the stack pointer back to its original place and finally JUMPs back to A. This figure deals only with preservation issues, but even there we have been obliged to do five STOREs [including A's saving of the return address in RA (r28)] and five LOADs. B might not do any other LOADs or only a few more. With respect to all of those LOADs and STOREs in the tables for "normal" programs above, it would appear that between a fourth and half of them are associated with calls within a program. Reducing that burden should be an important objective in computer/compiler design. Neither the problem nor its solution has much to do with CISC versus RISC, though it has been a major issue in recent RISC designs.

There are two quite distinct and noninterfering approaches to reducing the save-and-restore burden. Groups at IBM and Stanford have pressed software solutions; Berkeley and several of the companies designing machines in the '80s have explored hardware solutions.

[6] The stack is usually just the top part of unassigned memory. A register is assigned as the stack pointer (SP) and set to the highest value in the stack area. From then on, as each layer needs local space, it is added (downward) on the stack. When a lower layer finishes and returns, the pointer is moved back one layer's worth. In this way, each routine controls its own local space and a program can go to great depth without ever having one routine intrude on another's variable space.

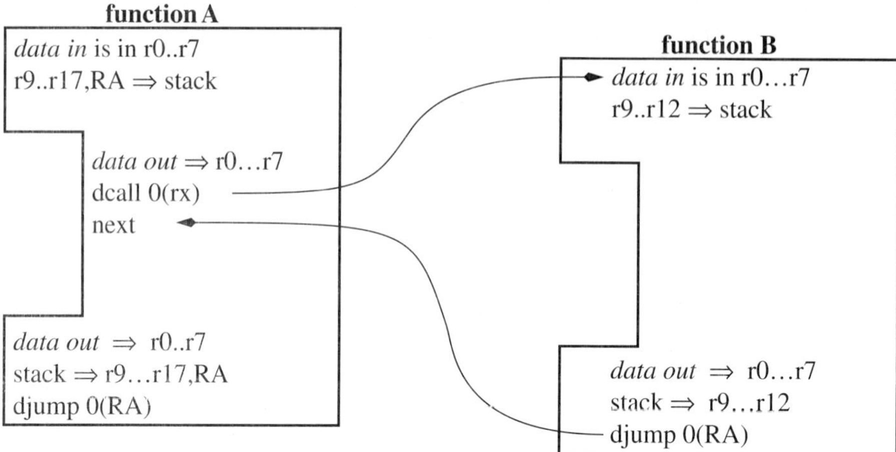
function A
data in is in r0..r7
r9..r17,RA ⇒ stack
data out ⇒ r0…r7
dcall 0(rx)
next
data out ⇒ r0..r7
stack ⇒ r9…r17,RA
djump 0(RA)
function B
data in is in r0…r7
r9..r12 ⇒ stack
data out ⇒ r0…r7
stack ⇒ r9…r12
djump 0(RA)

FIGURE 1.3 Illustration of the save-and-restore steps in a subroutine call within our RISC machine. Each stacking operation is a STORE operation; each unstacking operation is a LOAD. CALL puts the PC of A into RA (r28) and the starting address of B into PC. DJUMP 0(RA) takes the value in RA and puts it into the PC.

There are two parts of that burden. One is preservation. The other is communication between caller and callee. The former one is really making room in the register set for the next routine. The latter one is passing parameters. Both must be provided for. One can, of course, use registers for either of these obligations. But how many registers would be needed? If we want to pass parameters through registers, then we must ask: How many parameters are likely to be passed? Furthermore, we need to know: What would suffice for an allocation of local variables within each context? Tanenbaum answered both of these rather decisively, finding that room for passing five parameters would cover better than 98 percent of all CALLs and that room for seven local variables would cover better than 98 percent of local variable needs [Tanenbaum, 78]. A little caution on these numbers. Obviously, the next subroutine to be invoked has exactly n parameters and m local variables. A mechanism that always allocates 5 and 7, respectively, will waste space on many CALLs and not be adequate on a few. On the other hand, a fixed-size hardware mechanism may be very fast. This choice between a fixed-size hardware register-set switch and a dynamic software approach has led to the two very different schools of design cited above.

The first came from the particularly software-oriented group under John Cocke at IBM. They asked:

> If a good compiler that truly optimized register usage could have as many registers as it wanted, how many would it really want?

In a sense, Cocke's group designed a compiler algorithm that was assigning registers with such care that the resulting programs had to save and restore them relatively infrequently. This optimization means fewer save/restore operations at both the CALL and context-switch levels.

The second response came from a particularly hardware-oriented group at Berkeley under Séquin and Patterson, who were designing the RISC I and II. They asked:

> If we had *multiple overlapping register sets* (MORS) that could be switched by simply changing a single hardware pointer, then how many register sets do we need to substantially reduce the LOAD and STORE burden involved in subroutine calls?

The multiple overlapping register set idea—the Rolodex—was briefly introduced above by its use in the SPARC version of INNER. In that machine, 128 registers are available on the Rolodex, but the program at any point sees only 24 of the 128. The Rolodex is of length 128 and the window 24. Upon issuing a SAVE instruction, the hardware rolls the register pointer 16 slots, thus exposing 16 new registers and leaving 8 registers common to the caller and callee. On RESTORE, the window is rolled back 16. Again, parameters can be returned and the old context restored with no copying to and from memory. Obviously, this method runs out when your program comes to the end of the Rolodex. At that point, the hardware must arrange to clear a new space. It does this by causing an exception (interrupt). The exception handler opens up a window by copying the highest level of window into the stack and tagging the window to indicate that it has spilled into the stack. When the program gets back to the upper end of the shade, the tagged registers are restored from the stack. If one includes the copied-out windows in memory as virtual register sets, the MORS can have any depth whatsoever. Obviously, once you start spilling registers, the MORS is ineffective. However, a design that is good for a certain class of programs will not have to do this copying very often. The observation is that programs often reach a quasi-steady state in depth and if the MORS has sufficient depth, it settles down for long periods with little copying at all. Figure 1.4 illustrates the operation of MORS. Notice that the illustration ends with the level in the middle. We could program two calls or one return from that point with no copying at all.

There is, as usual, a piper to be paid. When the system does a context switch, all of the active registers must be copied out to the process data block and the next process's registers must be copied in. The average burden is probably somewhat less than half the total number of registers so with 8 globals and 128 in the MORS, the average burden is about 70 registers. (There will also be some "hidden" registers to be saved.) Since the typical RISC without a MORS has 32 registers plus some hidden ones, the burden of extra saves and restores on the context switch is about a factor of 2.

MORS do cut down memory traffic, though at a considerable hardware cost. They have been implemented commercially in the Pyramid computer (derived from the Berkeley RISC_II) and in the SPARC. Their 136 registers are 4.25 times the register investment that was made in the IBM 801, RS/6000, and MIPS 5000 processors. Since all are second-generation commercial RISCs, the "better" choice is not obvious at all. The choices are neither opposites nor do they have anything to do with CISC versus RISC. A study of applying MORS to the VAX and taking them away from RISC_II has shown that MORS generally reduce memory traffic substantially, though it is not difficult to construct a deliberate counterexample [Hitchcock, 85]. However, if the chip size

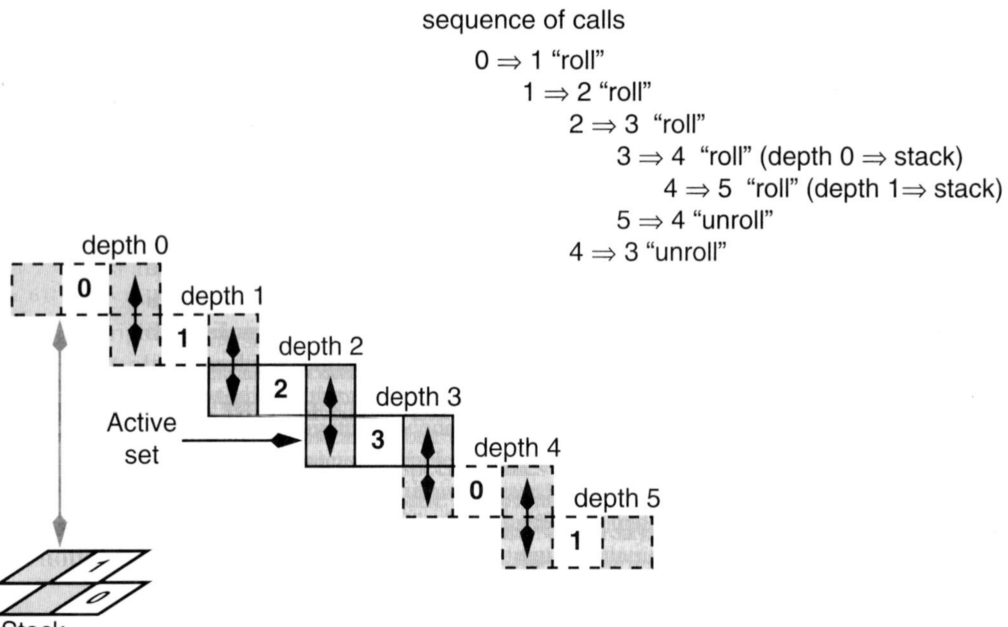

FIGURE 1.4 Illustration of the operation of a MORS system with four overlapping register sets. Four CALLs may be handled simply by moving the pointer to the next register set. On the fifth call, the data from depth 0 must first be copied to the stack. Then data from depth 4 go into set 0. On the sixth call, data from depth 1 are copied to the stack and depth 5 then goes into 1. After the two returns (which involve only a pointer shift) there are two empty register sets for subsequent CALLs from depth 3, and two register sets reside on the stack. This is the situation shown in the figure. As long as calls from depth 3 do not invoke a depth of more than 2, no further copies are necessary. When a return is executed from depth 2, depth 1 must be restored from the stack to set 1. Note that parameters are transferred from the out group to or from the in group of the subsequent block by the simple mechanism of replacing only two-thirds of each block. In the SPARC architecture, one of the parameters passed automatically is the stack pointer. The recipient treats it as a frame pointer (beginning of the stack) and uses the proper register in the out group as the new stack pointer.

represents a fixed parameter, investing in a MORS arrangement means giving up some other features. Let us consider an alternative.

The alternative approach is the IBM/Stanford optimized compiler design, which finds a minimum-traffic solution to the allocation of a fixed register set. This has been shown to be equivalent to the classical map-coloring problem. The idea is to allocate all registers with a global perspective, never saving and restoring a register when a different allocation could have avoided it. While it is anything but obvious that such an optimum solution can be found, the problem has been solved for essentially all real computer problems [Chatin, 81] [Chow, 84]. Several examples of the method are explored in the problems at the end of the chapter. IBM has used the technique in both its PL/.8 and its derivative ROMP compiler for the PC RT [Hopkins, 86]; the MIPS group has developed the same sort of algorithm within their highly optimizing compiler for the MIPS machine [Chow, 86]. Figure 1.5 illustrates the concept for a very simple problem.

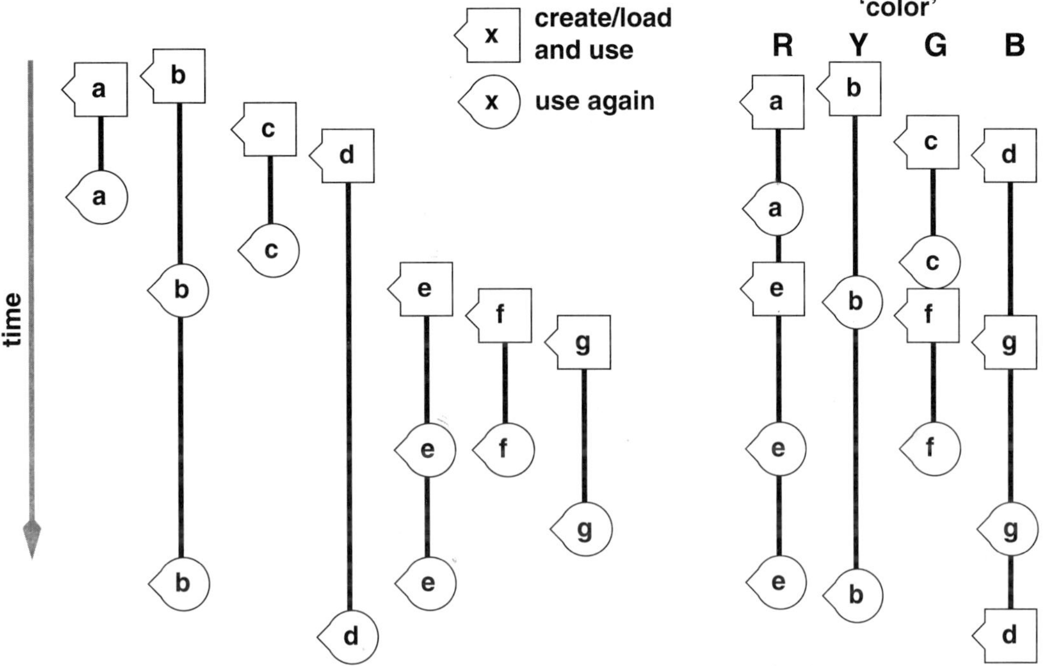

FIGURE 1.5 Optimum assignment of seven variables with different lifetimes into a set of four registers. No two variables may have the same "color" at the same time. A variable must be in register when it is used. Exchanging **f** and **g** will not produce as good a solution if the graph continues, because the green register would not be free as soon. Observe the unavoidable save and restore on variable **d**. This is the minimum-memory traffic this problem admits. For a more interesting puzzle, try using only three registers.

Now we must choose. We are going to adopt the IBM approach because we wish to use our "extra" register space for speeding up interrupt handling and system calls. This will be discussed in Chapters 2 and 6.

We are still left with the question of how many registers to put into our fixed set. The choices are really 16 or 32, given the binary encoding format. Work at IBM showed that at least one good compiler lost its appetite for more registers when the number reached the mid twenties. That measures the "grain size" of programs in the sense that a section of program will have only so many pointers and so many active intermediate results to hold in register for immediate recall. The compiler's preferences are only one factor, of course. Others include cost, what current technology can reasonably deliver, and even reliability.

What we are doing here is spending money. Registers are relatively expensive in two ways. They require approximately 10 transistors per bit (so that is 320 per 32-bit register) and they require decoders of a size that is proportional to the number of registers. Programming efficiency pushes the number up; cost pushes it down. Cost, by the way, can translate to area on the chip for a single-chip processor or number of chips on a board-scale processor. If you make the register set too big, you push something else off (or you make your chip more expensive to design and produce). Notice that IBM used 32 registers in the experimental 801 but felt that 16 would do for the commercialization of those ideas into the PC RT. With a look at the success of the competition, this seems to have been an example of thinking too small.

If we take 32 registers as an upper bound on our needs, we end up needing 5 bits to specify the register number whenever we select a register. A good question to ask at this point is: How well does a 5-bit register address fit into our instruction? To answer that, the designer must decide how many instructions there will be (i.e., how many bits it will take to specify which operation the machine must execute) and how many registers can be referenced in a single instruction. We find that we can do quite nicely with 32 instruction slots, so we need only 5 bits for the operation code. In specifying that we want a whole operation to complete every single clock pulse, we must provide two input paths from the register set to the arithmetic and logic unit (ALU) and one output path from ALU to the register set. Three paths says that we should provide for three register specifications within our instruction. That is 15 bits of register specification and 5 for operation (or opcode). These 20 bits fit most comfortably into our 32-bit instruction width, leaving us 12 more bits if we choose to use them for something.

Notice that we are being quite unruffled by the possibility of wasted space in our instruction stream. This luxury is a consequence of the recent development of "cheap" memory. In the '70s, memory was still precious; now it is a cheap commodity. While it is not free, it is inexpensive enough not to be an important constraint. Consider instead what one might do if memory was very dear indeed. A designer would worry a lot about packing the instruction stream. Such a concern leads directly to the idea of variable-length instructions, a common element in almost all computers designed in the '70s. What this does is to require considerably more complexity in the instruction-interpretation logic, but in the '70s the cost of that complexity was offset by being able to use smaller memories. Furthermore, speed was limited principally by memory performance, so the added layers of logic in the processor did not interfere with system performance. Today, the availability of cheap, fast memory has changed the design rules. Not surprisingly, the new designs that result are not simply extensions of previous designs.

So what do we now have? A 32-bit word size, 32 registers, and 16 GB (4 GW) of address space. We are now ready to specify the details of the instruction set itself. Let us get on with that task.

1.5 THE INSTRUCTION SET

As we commented above, most of the time what programs do is fetch and store, test and branch, and now and then do end-use arithmetic. We must provide these elements. For fetching and storing we will have:

LOAD STORE

Within our processor itself, we will provide the following arithmetic and logic operations. They will be used most often in testing and looping; next most often in address calculations; and least frequently in doing end-use arithmetic. However, whatever the objective, an ADD is an ADD is an ADD. The same set will do for all integer arithmetic and all logical operations. These instructions include:

ADD	AND
SUB	OR
MUL	XOR
DIV	SHIFT

That is a pretty small list—in fact, it is smaller than it looks. MUL and DIV are not what you think. They are the primitives of their parent operations, not unlike what you do when you are forced (by battery failure or other uncivilized happenstance) to do long division or long multiplication by hand.

SHIFT could be in either column, depending on whether you think of it as moving bits or multiplying by a power of 2. It is on the right mostly because there were already four on the left.

Have we met our goal of putting in only what is essential? While this depends on what you want to do with the machine, we think that we have a spare but versatile set of operations. SHIFT, MUL, and DIV require a shifter; MUL, DIV, and all the others run on a simple ALU (arithmetic and logic unit). Most important for our one-tick–one-instruction design rule, all these operations are relatively easily accommodated in a single cycle of the clock.

You might wonder if we haven't cheated our customers by putting in only the primitives for MUL and DIV. After all, couldn't we do them much faster in hardware? Well, yes, we could. It has been done on almost every larger machine, with one curious early exception. Seymour Cray didn't find it necessary to put integer division into hardware, and nobody suggests he builds slow machines. The truth is, integer division hardly ever occurs. All that we have provided in DIV is an efficient organization of subtract and shift. In fact, the decision to put DIV in followed the decision to put in a MUL primitive. The same hardware works for both. Well, all right, did we need MUL? It does come up in the problem of accessing components of structured variables, but as you saw in INNER, for regular access into a multidimensional array (in contrast to randomly selecting a single element of such an array), addition is all you need. Many of the RISC designs have MUL and DIV in this primitive form (including such commercial ones as the HP Spectrum and Sun's SPARC); some do not. As we have said, this is a good set. It is not the definitive set.

Half of program control is arithmetic; the other half is conditional (or unconditional) branching—go yet one more time around the loop or don't go one more time around the loop. For program control, we will have four instructions:

JUMP	CALL
TRAP	RFI (return from interrupt)

CALL is an unconditional jump which stores the current program position so that the subroutine can do something and then return (with a JUMP). TRAP is something like CALL but generates a "vectored interrupt" instead. Interrupts are one way of calling for some system service. Requests for such service can come from a program (using TRAP) or from hardware either within or outside the processor. To get back where the program was previously operating, one uses RFI. That instruction is used only by system procedures called by an interrupt or TRAP. The mechanism used to service interrupts is discussed from various aspects in Chapters 2, 3, and 6.

JUMP is a simple, conditional branch in the program. Saying that JUMP is one instruction might seem to be overstating the simplicity of our instruction set. The JUMP instruction includes which test to use to determine if the jump is to happen or not. Since we specify 19 such conditions, you might think of JUMP as representing a whole family of instructions, but from the logical point of view, it is but one instruction. The field which determines which condition to test is treated just like a field which determines which register to use.

We are up to 14 distinct instructions. Is that all? Almost but not quite. We need some method for interacting with coprocessors and some method for testing and setting a bit directly in memory as an atomic operation. Just as all branches get folded into a single JUMP, all instructions for all possible coprocessors get folded into a single instruction, CP. There are two reasons why we can get away with so simple a mechanism even though there could be hundreds of different coprocessor instructions. (We will specify 28 for the floating-point coprocessor alone.) The principal "trick" is identical with JUMP: The five leading bits specify CP. The remaining 27 bits then specify which coprocessor and which instruction in that coprocessor's panoply of instructions. The second reason is less visible but quite consistent with RISC design: Addresses are generated by the integer unit. Accordingly, a load instruction for the coprocessor will be followed by one or more address-generating CPU instructions. Since we never have to put an address in a CP instruction, those 27 bits are plenty to specify any transaction that we want.

The test-and-set instruction, LODSET, is a response to a system necessity. There has to be some way for the several independent processors in the system to keep out of each other's hair. In particular, the problem of queuing and unqueuing messages demands that only one processor access a queue at one time. We will deal with this problem at some length in Chapter 3, but essentially what the computer needs is a way for one processor to tell all others: "Buzz off, this queue is temporarily busy." To that end, a semaphore is used in which potential users read the (prior) status of the semaphore in the same atomic (indivisible) operation that sets the semaphore. If the semaphore was already set, no change takes place; alternatively, if the semaphore that was read was reset, then the reader knows that it can proceed and that the semaphore is now set. The semaphore can be reset simply by storing a 0 there.

Now we have 16 instructions. Is that enough? We have certainly covered the principal needs according to the studies of frequency of instruction occurrence and we have accounted for instructions to make other parts of the machine work. It is up to us both as authors and as designers to establish over the remainder of this text that we have not left out anything critical. However, if we have, we will still have 2 slots remaining in our 32 to form a patch. You might wonder why we have only 2 slots left if we have only 16 instructions. That is easy. Some of these instructions come in several flavors. Loads, stores, jumps, and calls all use addresses. Since these are all important instruction types, it behooves us to make them efficient. There are several different paradigms for address generation. To accommodate at least a reasonable measure, we will have three different versions of each of these instructions as well as a version of load and store suitable for bytes and halfwords.

Another very common need, as indicated in Table 1.3, is the loading, addition, or subtraction of a constant to a register. To that end, we provide all our arithmetic and logical operations with two forms: one operates on the contents of a pair of registers; the other includes one register and a single constant carried in the instruction itself. With that, we have specified all that we are going to specify for operation codes. We will have 32 slots with 30 of them filled with meaningful opcodes. This leaves us only the specification of addressing modes to finish our overview. (The next chapter will go into the instructions in detail.)

1.5.1 Addressing Modes

How will our computer determine which word to bring into a register or where to store one that is already there? The lowest level of answer is "by address" but that begs the issue. We have already decided that "an address" is a 32-bit unsigned number. The question we are asking here is how that number gets formed.

Consider your favorite HLL for a moment. What different modes of reference do you use therein? There are elemental forms such as constants or simple variables, and then there is a variety of structured variables, the richness of the variety being dependent on the language you chose. All numerically oriented HLLs provide subscripted variables such as vectors or strings as well as matrices. Good ones, such as C and Pascal, will also provide you with *records* or *structs*, a structure that can contain any mix of different data types and that you can mold to your own needs. You can combine these to form both useful and bizarre arrangements of variables whose pieces you wish to extract without undue labor.

For example, you might have, as the elements of a record, a set of strings and numbers. The record may contain a student's name, address, class, social security number, age, and sex. A section might contain some number of these records, and a course might comprise an array of sections. A typical data base problem is to scan through the ensemble of data and form a sectionlike grouping of all of the students with some common parameter, say being from New York State. This sort of operation is a not uncommon use for a computer. From the point of view of the user, it may look as if the "work" is testing a particular field for being equal to NY, but if you think about doing the same task yourself using index cards, you would see that the principal task is shuffling cards.

Consider that task for a moment. If each such record contained 75 words (300 bytes), going on to the next card translates to adding 75 to the current base address. We already have ADD above, so that is no problem, but where will the base address be, how will the computer find 75, how will the computer utilize the resulting address, and how will we make it easy for the computer to access the characters to compare with N and Y within the record? These are the questions we must answer here.

Let us begin by proposing that we allow some room for a constant in the instruction itself. The name for such a constant is a *literal* because you use those bits literally for a number. The instruction to add 75 to the base then becomes:

ADD constant {to} source register {and put it in} destination register

The other "kind" of ADD in our machine will be a three-register affair:

ADD source 1 {to} source 2 {and put it in} destination

How will the assembler know which one we mean? We will use LADD when we want a literal and ADD when we do not. How will the computer know which operation to do? The two operations will have different opcodes.

Now consider two closely related ways to "use the resulting address." In one, we take the contents of a register and add to it a literal in the instruction itself, using the resulting sum as the address desired. The number in the register is called the *base*, and the constant in the instruction is called the *displacement*. We can use this format for stepping a known distance into a structure. For example, if our base pointed at the current record and the record structure was such that the home state was found in the 56th word, we could get that word by doing:

LOAD {the value at} displacement+base_register {into} destination

This works only if we know ahead of time how far into the structure we wish to go. Often, we must compute how far we want to step in. We can do that calculation in a single register and then use the base-displacement format with a displacement of 0. However, it is quite often nice to be able to maintain values in two registers and add them at will to obtain the address without modifying either number. The processor is indifferent to where it gets the numbers it adds, but we must tell it. Accordingly, just as we can specify two source registers for the ADD, we allow two source registers for the address. To differentiate it in human parlance from the base-displacement format, we call this one (quite arbitrarily) *base-index*. You can think of this as being:

LOAD {the value at} base_register+index_register {into} destination

It is not obvious at this point that we need both of these—in fact, we really do not *need* them—but as we show later on, there is an efficiency in having both. However, if we were pushed for instruction space, we could drop the base-index form and make do quite nicely without it. Base-displacement, on the other hand, we would be most loath to give up.

We are almost done. Two more convenience items are all that is left before we home in on the little details. The first of these concerns the ability to specify an address completely within the instruction itself. Such an address is called *absolute*, and the instruction format is essentially:

LOAD {the value at} this_address {into} destination

Notice that we have only 22 bits to specify the address in such absolute addressing. This is the same problem that the designers of the SPARC faced when they came up with SETHI. We solve this problem in a different way. We will have a one-instruction method for loading an address from memory (and for getting a static address loaded there). Accordingly, we will live with the range that the 22 bits provide. The 22 bits get us to 4 MW in our address space, a mere drop in the bucket[7] in our 4-GW address space. This is a definite limitation, but one we choose to live with in our desire to keep to a fixed instruction size. In Chapter 2, we will show that the restriction to 4 MW has implications but is not really confining.

The second convenience item concerns loading and storing bytes and halfwords. To work with individual bytes without special instructions to help requires that the processor spend an inordinate amount of time unpacking and packing words. The question is: How often do we really want to do byte or halfword operations? Gideon Yuval's data in Table 1.1 above suggest that byte operations are not as valuable as one might think, even in word processing. We do not disagree with the finding, but some caution is needed in interpreting the data. Notice that it represents a static analysis. Where do byte operations occur? Generally, byte operations are in the middle of a loop that scans down an array of bytes. One instruction is found in a static analysis, but that same instruction shows up multiple times in dynamic analyses (which show what is being used). Furthermore, the byte operations may be the "work" of the loop, but as we have already seen, the actions needed for looping and program control frequently dominate the work instructions. Thus, the Yuval data may not correctly indicate how useful byte operations really are.

Cheryl Wiecek's dynamic data on what compilers do (which we have compacted in Table 1.2) put MOVZBL[8] in seventh place among all of the instructions used. Along with that is the MOVB (move byte) instruction, which is ranked 16th. Given that compilers are doing more than word processing, we find these rankings to mean that the ability to fetch and store individual bytes is important. Certainly, one can do it in software, but at considerable expense. One of our objectives is to provide the hardware that will make our processor fast in the customer's eyes. It seems that byte addressing will help. Halfwords are less frequently used, but the new universal ASCII code, which will cover even Chinese, will use 16-bit characters. It would be a shame not to be able to accommodate the change that we know is coming. Besides, once we have done it for bytes, adding halfword operations is almost a trivial extension. How then to access bytes and halfwords?

Since bytes are almost inevitably parts of strings, the load-store pair should be suitable for indexing into structured data. The most general form of structured addressing is BASE-INDEX, so that is what we will use. The memory address will still specify a word, but two bits will be used to extract and right-justify the byte desired. This completes the naming of instructions. Structural details and assembler notation will be provided in Chapter 2, so let us sum up the work so far with a table.

---

[7] Believe it or not, *drop in the bucket* is from Isaiah 40:15.

[8] This instruction moves a byte from memory to register, left-filling the register with 0's. In effect, it puts the byte on the right with the rest of the register's 32 bits set to 0.

1.5.2 Summary of the Instruction Set

Table 1.8 includes three data for each instruction: opcode, name or mnemonic, and address format. The table could be said to define 32 different instructions (two of which are unused). Alternatively, you could just as well say that the table defines 16 operations, 3+ data types,[9] and 5 ways to specify the location of operands. The latter is the form in which instruction counts are tallied for most machines.

For a VAX, the same form of counting gives 304 distinguishable operations, 21 addressing modes, and 14 data types. You can easily see why the name RISC seemed so appropriate and became so popular. However, there is no special inherent advantage to having a small vocabulary. Keep in mind that the reasoning behind this deliberate weight-loss diet we have indulged in is that we can deliver more performance for less

[9] The three are BYTES, HALFWORDS, and WORDS. The "+" implies that new data types could be defined for CP operations. For example, the floating-point coprocessor will define two new types corresponding to the IEEE's single- and double-precision formats.

TABLE 1.8 The 30 processor operations and the associated opcodes. S/U stands for signed/unsigned in the SHIFT operation. C/X stands for change condition codes/don't change condition codes on the arithmetic and logical instructions. TRAP and RFI are different operations, but they share the same opcode. These details will be described in full measure as we explore the instruction set and its implications in the next chapter.

Code	Name	Address format	Code	Name	Address format
00000	JUMP	Absolute	10000	IJUMP	Base-Index
00001	CALL	Absolute	10001	ICALL	Base-Index
00010	LOAD	Absolute	10010	ILOAD	Base-Index
00011	STORE	Absolute	10011	ISTORE	Base-Index
00100	DJUMP	Base-Displacement	10100	CP (coprocessor)	
00101	DCALL	Base-Displacement	10101	LOADH/B	Base-Index
00110	DLOAD	Base-Displacement	10110	STOREH/B	Base-Index
00111	DSTORE	Base-Displacement	10111	LODSET	Base-Index
01000	SHIFTyz	Literal (y= s/u)	11000	unused	
01001	LADDz	Literal	11001	ADDz	Register
01010	LSUBz	Literal (z= c/x)	11010	SUBz	Register
01011	LANDz	Literal	11101	ANDz	Register
01100	LORz	Literal	11100	ORz	Register
01101	LXORz	Literal	11101	XORz	Register
01110	TRAP/RFI	Absolute	11110	MUL	Register
01111	unused		11111	DIV	Register

money in less time by very carefully selecting our vocabulary. It is more bang for the buck that has motivated us, not a mystical preference for a smaller instruction set.

We next must look at the details of the instruction formats. This will include both how we want to write them (assembly language format) and how they will be presented to the machine (machine language format). These details and their implications for hardware and software on this streamlined computing machine form the heart of the next chapter.

PROBLEMS

1.1. The most popular memory chips available at the time of the writing of this book have a storage capacity of 1 Mb (2^{20} bits). If you think of memory as one long column of words, with the *n*th bit of each word lining up with those above and below to form a subcolumn, then the following calculation should give you some idea of the physical scale of our processor's potential memory span.

If we need 38 bits per word (32 for data and 6 to provide for the detection and correction of memory errors), then:

(a) How many memory chips will it take to build a 16-MW memory board? If each chip requires a board area of 1 x 3 cm^2, how much area will this board require just for the memory chips? (Memories of 16 to 64 MB are common among current multiuser computers.)

(b) Now, if someone overburdened with money really wanted to expand the memory to its full capacity, how many memory chips would be required? How much total board area will this memory demand?

(c) If each chip dissipated 100 mW, how much power must be removed for each of the two memories above?

(d) The biggest memory chips now in process are 16 Mb with a 4x4-Mb configuration being one popular format. They dissipate roughly twice what the 1-Mb chips do. The area is 2 x 2 cm. While these chips are currently noticeably more expensive, space and dissipation are also expensive quantities, both on a first-cost and a lifetime basis. Recompute ***(a)***, ***(b)***, and ***(c)*** with these chips. Also determine what the minimum 32-bit-wide memory module would be. Include the parity bits.

1.2. Let us consider a floating-point routine of a much different variety from INNER. This one should be novel and inspire a little thinking about what your calculator does when you press the function buttons. In general, it does *not* start doing a Taylor series expansion. However, culture aside, our purpose here is to get an instruction analysis such as the ones done for INNER. Questions are asked below.

The objective of the code is to compute the sine of an angle, Y, given in radians. One reasonably quick computational method is to rotate the angle into the first quadrant, remember the sign of the result, and then compute the sine to approximately 10 places of accuracy using a sum of Chebyshev polynomials to the fifth order to obtain a *minimax* fit. A functional example that is good to at least nine decimal places is shown in the subroutine SINE embedded in the complete test program. The questions concern that subroutine, although running the whole program should provide some quick confirmation that the method works.

```
#define order 5
#include <math.h>
```

```
#include <stdio.h>
#include <stdlib.h>

double pi2 = 3.14159265358979323/2;
double a[] = {+1.0,-0.1666666664,+0.0083333315,-0.0001984090,
              +0.0000027526,-0.0000000239};


double SINE(double x){
    double y,y2,final;
    long n,quadrant,sign;
            /* rotate into the first quadrant */
     y = x/pi2;
     n = y; /*truncation conversion */
     quadrant = abs(n) % 4;
     if (x<0){
          quadrant = 3-quadrant;
          y += (-n+1);
          }
     else y -= n;
     switch (quadrant){
          case 0: sign = 0;
                  break;
          case 1: sign = 0;
                  y = 1-y;
                  break;
          case 2: sign = 1;
                  break;
          case 3: sign = 1;
                  y = 1-y;
        }
     y *= pi2;
     y2 = y*y;
     final = 0;
     for (n=order; n>=0; n--) final = final*y2+a[n];
     final *= y;
     if (sign) return -final;
     else return final;
     }

main(){
     int n;
     double x, result, dif;

     for (n=0;n<41;n++){
```

```
        x = -pi2*n/10.0;
        result = SINE(x);
        dif = result - sin(x);
        printf("SINE(%12.9f) = %12.9f; difference = %12.9f\n",x,result,dif);
        }
}
```

(a) Compile this on the machine available to you and obtain the unoptimized object code. On a VAX/VMS system, that calls for cc/noopt/machine_code/list {name of C code file}. Now do a static count of the instructions in the SINE function. Do the same with a dynamic counting. Normalize them to the fraction of the total instructions in each count, and compare your results. In doing the count, group them according to the following classes:

- MOV (all kinds including small changes in the operand)
- integer arithmetic including compare and clear
- floating-point operations including conversions
- branches

(To make the counting rules uniform, put NOPs in only if they are executed; where an instruction, such as INDEX, does multiple operations, put multiple entries in. INDEX, for example, does four integer operations, including two subtractions, one multiplication, and one addition. Ignore address calculation unless the result is stored.)

(b) Determine the number of memory references in the dynamic count. Count both the instruction fetches and the data loads and stores. Normalize so that a transfer of 4 bytes is 1 memory reference.

(c) Now turn optimization on (CC/opt/machine_code/list), and determine how much better the code is in terms of total references to memory. If any incompetent coding occurs, point it out and say how to do it better.

1.3. Figure 1.3 invited you to do an optimum fit in the assignment of seven variables with the lifetimes and use patterns shown to three registers. How few overflows (LOAD/SAVE pairs) can you get away with?

REFERENCES

[Allison, 86] Allison, Andrew, *RISCs Challenge Mini, Micro Suppliers*, **Mini–Micro Systems,** 127 (Nov, 1986).

[Chatin, 81] Chatin et al, **Computer Languages 6**, 47 (1981).

[Chow, 84] Chow, Frederick, and John Hennessy, **ACM SIGPLAN Notices, 6**, 222 (1984).

[Chow, 86] Chow et al, **IEEE COMPCON Proceedings**, 132 (1986).

[Cocke, 90] Cocke, John, and V. Markstein, *The evolution of RISC technology at IBM*, **IBM Journal of Research and Technology 34**(1), 4–11 (1990).

[Dobberpuhl, 86] Dobberpuhl, John, Robert Supnik, and Richard Witek, *The MicroVAX 78032 Chip, a 32–bit Microprocessor*, **Digital Technical Journal, 1**(2),12–23 (1986).

[Hitchcock, 85] Hitchcock, C.Y. , and H.M.B. Sprunt, **IEEE Proceedings of the 12th International Symposium on Computer Architecture,** 55 (1985).

[Hopkins, 86] Hopkins, M.E., **IBM Publication SA23–1057**, (1986).

[Knuth, 71] Knuth, D.E., An Empirical Study of Fortran Programs, **Software, Programs and Experience 1**, 105 (1971).

[Pascal, 57]	Pascal, Blaise, **Lettres Pronvinciales** (1657).
[Tanenbaum, 78]	Tanenbaum, A.S., **Communications of the ACM 21**, 237 (1978).
[Wakerly, 90]	Wakerly, John F., **Digital Design Principles and Practices**, Prentice Hall (1990).
[Weicker, 90]	Weicker, Reinhold, *An Overview of Benchmarks*, **Computer 23**(12), 65–75 (1990).
[Wiecek, 82]	Wiecek, C., *A Case Study of VAX–11 Instruction Usage for Compiler Execution*, **Symposium on Architectural Support for Programming Languages, ACM,**177 (1982).
[Yuval, 78]	Yuval, G., **Software—Practice and Experience 8**, 495 (1978).

CHAPTER 2

DETAILS OF THE INSTRUCTION SET

FORMATS AND HARDWARE AND SOFTWARE: THE IMPLICATIONS OF EACH INSTRUCTION

2.1 OBJECTIVE

Chapter 1 presented the RISC or streamlined philosophy of processor design. This philosophy proposes that the "best designs" in the sense of maximum performance per dollar of hardware are to be obtained by a very lean instruction set, one that contains all of the critical pieces but avoids adding conveniences or special-purpose instructions which are rarely called.

While we subscribe to this approach, we cautioned that one must proceed with much care to avoid overdoing the pare-down. It is all too easy to find yourself with a machine that is so lean and spare that you are obliged to reinstall missing hardware in the form of relatively slow and inefficient software. The list of instructions presented at the end of the last chapter can be seen at a glance to be lean. The question that you cannot answer by looking at such a list is whether it "does the job." To do that, we must first understand, in complete detail, how the instructions will work. That detail must include hardware considerations as well as such practical matters as the assembler notation, what the instructions do, and how they can be used to accomplish what a program needs. From these details will emerge an understanding both of what we have in the list of Table 1.8 on page 50 as well as what restrictions or program structure this choice of instructions will force upon us.

It is the objective of this chapter to bring out these details, along with usage examples to get you started in understanding this machine's inner workings. While

Chapter 6 will develop complete hardware structures to execute the instructions, here we have but one hardware interest: to view the hardware from the user or program perspective, seeing the data and instructions flowing through the machine to accomplish the purpose of the program. Along the way, we will see that our streamlining has some "implications" on how programs and data will interact. We leave to Chapter 6 the confirmation that we have achieved our very central purpose of being able to complete one instruction in each clock cycle.

Let us begin.

2.2 INSTRUCTION FORMATS

In the next several sections, we expand the instructions of Table 1.8 to show what these instructions would look like in assembly code and machine code. Here we get down to the very fine details of how the instructions are written and precisely how they will act. Some overview items to bear in mind while you look at the minutiae are:

1. For instructions in this machine, one size fits all—a word. While some fit tightly, others waste space.
2. The operation and the way in which the operands are obtained are completely specified by the leftmost 5 bits of the instruction (the *opcode*).
3. Every instruction will allow the CPU to complete one instruction in each pulse of the clock. Even for CP, which launches an action in a coprocessor, the central processor finishes one task in one clock cycle. CP passes on to the coprocessor what is being asked of it. If the coprocessor is busy for more clock cycles to do its last assigned tasks and the CPU has another CP to deliver, the CPU might have to wait, but that really does not interfere with the perception that the central processor completes one instruction per clock.

These three items are at the heart of streamlined design. The simplicity implied by (1) and (2) means that the interpretive logic for our processor will be vastly less complex than the typical CISC. (3) is impressive in itself, but if this machine is to perform at high speed in the customer's eyes, the set of instructions that we have chosen to implement must fit well with the needs of the compilers that our customers will use. In other words, the step that is done in one clock should be a whole step in the customer's eyes. Most but not all of our instructions will meet that requirement. Now to the details.

What we will do is present each instruction type in assembler notation and in the machine code format. A brief discussion is included as necessary as well as an example translation worked out in complete detail. We begin with the arithmetic/logical operations, since they are the most obvious.

2.2.1 Arithmetic and Logic Operations

In reading the terse examples below, you need to know that the following rules have been used:

Register Format, Normal Operations

assembly notation

machine format

31 27	26 22	21 17	16 12	11	10 0
OP	dest Reg C	source Reg B	source Reg A	c / x	unused

ADD $\frac{c}{x}$ RA, RB, RC

example:

assembly	binary machine code	hex code
`SUBc r3, r7, r21`	11010 10101 00111 00011 1 0→	D54E 3800

where: C = A OP B and OP can be an arithmetic or logical operator in the set:

ARITHMETIC		LOGICAL	
ADD	C = A+B	AND	C = A∩B
SUB	C = A-B	OR	C = A∪B
		XOR	C = A⊕B

If bit <11> is set, the status or condition flags are set according to the results of the operation. If bit <11> is clear, the flags do not change.

FIGURE 2.1 Description of the REGISTER format.

- Wherever a register is mentioned, any of the 32 possible registers may be used. The assembler will be indifferent to case, so R5 and r5 refer to the same register. In general, a space or a comma may be used as a separator. Extra spaces are ignored (e.g., space-comma-space is equivalent to either one space or one comma). However, extra commas would be an error. Other punctuation, such as parentheses, should be used precisely as shown.
- Bits are counted from the least significant to the most significant, starting with 0. An inclusive range of bits is indicated by an expression such as <31:27>. The notation is inclusive in that the end points and any bits in between are part of the set indicated.
- The default radix for the assembly language is decimal.
- Only arithmetic and logic operations change the condition codes (flags), and they change the codes only if the program so specifies. In other words, every such instruction can be issued in one of two forms: one form will change the flags which record what happened on the last operation (such as the result being 0 or negative); the other form will inhibit flag changes, although the operation result will be the same. MUL and DIV are exceptions since they always store a bit in C or N respectively.

Let us now look at the two forms of arithmetic and logic operations: *register* format and *literal* format. The *register* format, shown in Figure 2.1, is both general and simple. With a format of

Literal Format, Normal Operations

assembly notation

machine format

LADD$\frac{c}{x}$ lit, RB, RC

31 27	26 22	21 17	16	15 0
OP	dest Reg C	source Reg B	c / x	Signed literal A

example:

assembly	binary machine code	hex code
`LADDx -127, r7, r21`	01001 10101 00111 0 1111111110000001	4D4E FF81

where: C = literal OP B and OP can be an arithmetic or logical operator in the set:

ARITHMETIC		LOGICAL	
LADD	C = lit+B	LAND	C = lit∩B
LSUB	C = lit-B	LOR	C = lit∪B
		LXOR	C = lit⊕B

An important issue here is that the signed literal is "sign-extended" to make a 32-bit integer. That is, its leftmost bit <15> is replicated in bits <31:16> of the resulting operand.

If bit <16> is set, the status or condition flags are set according to the results of the operation. If bit <16> is clear, the flags do not change.

FIGURE 2.2 Description of the LITERAL format.

```
Op rA, rB, rC
```

one expresses the HLL construct

```
rC = rA Op rB
```

Any register is acceptable in any field. All three may be different or two or all three may be the same. The result of `SUB r5, r5, r5` is to clear r5. This fact should begin to reveal the power and the simplicity of the instruction set. A VAX has a special instruction to clear a register, `CLRL r5`. It also can do `SUBL3 r5, r5, r5` or `SUBL2 r5, r5` to do the same job, but CLRL is a shorter instruction than the other two. When memory was a slow, precious commodity, choosing processor complexity to obtain compact code was logical; in our current world of cheap, fast memory, it is less compelling.

The *literal* format, shown in Figure 2.2, replaces the register operand A with a signed 16-bit integer. Thus, the A operand is contained in the instruction itself. We are limited to 16 bits so $-32{,}769 < A < 32{,}768$. While that is a real limitation which we will have to deal with, most compiler uses for this instruction format are for incrementing addresses or simple counting (as in a FOR loop) and the 64K range is usually more than adequate. In fact, the VAX provides a literal range of only 0 to 63. In Wiecek's study (Table 1.3), this mode (0-3) was used 16 percent of the time—the third most common address mode.

One important issue that is hidden in the literal example is the solution to the problem of getting both (lit - B) and (B - lit). The solution is simple enough. We already have (lit - B), and, since (B - lit) = [(-lit) + B], we could use the LADD with a negative literal. To do that, the assembler or the programmer must change the sign. Given that doing arithmetic has almost died out in the human species, it makes sense to let the computer do the sign change. Thus, if you write `LSUBx r3, 7, r5`, the assembler will actually produce `LADDx -7, r3, r5`. On the other hand, if you want `LSUBx 7, r3, r5`, you will get precisely what you asked for: $r5 = 7 - r3$.

Note that the programmer chooses whether to set the status flags or not. This permits one to separate arithmetic operations which set the flags from the JUMP statements which test the flags. The optimizing section of the compiler runs better when it has as much freedom as possible in instruction order. Both in this chapter and in Chapter 6, you will see that the ability to effect this separation between setting and testing the flags is a distinct advantage. Another option is at the opposite spectrum, making the test and branch one instruction. A number of RISC designs have adopted that format, arguing among other things that the elimination of flags reduces the burden in recovering from exceptions and interrupts. Since our MUL and DIV instructions require flags and since coprocessors frequently employ flags, we have adopted the flag-with-setting-freedom option. As the coding example in Chapter 1 showed, SPARC uses the same method.

This rather brief discussion has covered all but two of the arithmetic and logical operations in our machine. Those left out comprise MUL and DIV. As primitives of their namesakes, MUL and DIV are really quite different and much more complex instructions (at least for the reader) than ADD or OR. Accordingly, we postpone them until the latter half of the chapter.

2.2.2 Instruction Formats—CALL, LOAD, and STORE

The four instructions—JUMP, CALL, LOAD, and STORE—all specify one address. The last three also specify one register, while JUMP uses that same field for specifying which condition to test to see whether to perform the jump. The machine code is quite regular:

```
OP / source or destination register or test / address specification
```

The assembly formats, on the other hand, have quite a bit of variability to permit the assembly code to fit more nearly what the writer is thinking. Thus, we would write

```
LOAD / source address specification / destination register
```

or

```
STORE /source register / destination address specification
```

As you work with the assembler and linker, you will see that an address specification can be pretty far removed from machine code. In fact, it can simply be a name that is known to the linker. However, here we deal only with explicit address specifications. There are three ways to form an address. They are:

Absolute. In absolute addressing, the unsigned, 22-bit number in the instruction itself is *0-extended* to form the 32-bit address. The format is indicated by the absence of a leading letter (no I or D). An absolute address may not be signed. The format is simply

26737 example: `LOAD 26737, r15`

Note that this does NOT load 26,737 into R15; it puts the contents of memory location 26737 into R15. In most instances, the address will be specified as a label, with the number being substituted by the linker. The absolute format is illustrated in Figure 2.3.

Base-index. Add the base register to the index register. To be sure that you mean what you write (which helps to make the notation robust in the sense that single errors are likely to be detected), you indicate that you mean *base-index* by adding an *I* to the instruction name and also by writing the address format as

(Rb, Ri) example: `ILOAD (r9, r11), r26`

FIGURE 2.3 Description of the ABSOLUTE format and the LOAD operation.

Absolute Format, LOAD Operation

assembly notation

machine format

`LOAD source, RC`

31 27	26 22	21 0
OP	dest Reg C	absolute address

example:

assembly	binary machine code	hex code
`LOAD 1023, R14`	00010 01110 0000000000001111111111	1380 03FF

The contents of the memory location specified by source are loaded into the destination register. The contents of the memory location are unchanged. The address is formed by appending a 10-bit zero field to the left of the 22-bit address field in the instruction.

Both the parentheses and an internal separator (space or comma) are required. Since both registers are 32 bits wide and since carry-outs or overflows are not observed in forming the address, it makes no difference whether you think of these numbers as signed or not. If you go "over the top," you roll around to the bottom and start up again. Thus, whether you think of index FFFF FFFF as the largest integer available or -1, when you add it to the base, you get the location 1 before the base. (Note that base-index for byte/halfword addressing is different and is discussed below.) The base-index format is illustrated in Figure 2.4.

Base-displacement. Add the sign-extended displacement (from the instruction) to the base register. The *base-displacement* address format is indicated both by the addition of the *D* to the instruction name and also by writing the address format as

signed_displacement(Rb)   example: `DLOAD -26(r9), r26`

Note that the displacement gets *sign-extended*—bit 16 gets replicated to fill the 32-bit word. Once the addition takes place, overflows or carry-outs are ignored just as in base-index addressing. This format is illustrated in Figure 2.5.

The first and last formats have limitations imposed on their range that come directly from our decision that all instructions shall be precisely one word wide. The opcode field and each register (or test) field are 5 bits wide. Thus, for displacement format, with an opcode and two registers to specify, there are only 17 bits left; for the absolute format, with an opcode and one register, there are 22 bits left. This gives a displacement range of

FIGURE 2.4 Description of the BASE-INDEX format and the CALL operation.

Base-index Format, CALL Operation

assembly notation

`ICALL RC, (RB,RI)`

machine format

31–27	26–22	21–17	16–12	11–0
I_OP	return Reg C	base Reg B	index Ri	unused

example:

assembly	binary machine code	hex code
`ICALL r25, (R6,R5)`	10001 11001 00110 00101 0—>	8E4C 5000

The contents of the program counter (PC or R31) are loaded into RC and the address specified by the destination address is loaded into the PC. For this mode, the contents of the index register are added to the contents of the base register to form the destination address. The contents of neither RB nor Ri are modified.

Base-displacement Format, STORE Operation

assembly notation

machine format

assembly notation	31–27	26–22	21–17	16–0
`DSTORE RC, number(RB)`	D_OP	source Reg C	base Reg B	signed displacement

example:

assembly	binary machine code	hex code
`DSTORE r24,126(R5)`	00111 11000 00101 00000000001111110	3E0A 007E

The contents of the source register are loaded into the memory location specified by the destination address. For this mode, the leftmost bit of the signed displacement <16> is copied into bits <31:17> and the resulting number is added to the contents of the base register to form the destination address. Neither the contents of RB nor of RC are modified.

FIGURE 2.5 Description of the BASE-DISPLACEMENT format and the STORE operation.

$$-65{,}536 \le \text{displacement} \le 65{,}535$$

and an absolute addressing range of

$$0 \le \text{absolute address} < 4{,}194{,}304$$

Since the displacement gets added to a 32-bit base, the base-displacement format can reach any address in the entire range. The same is not true for absolute addressing. It is really limited to the first 4 MW of memory space. While not much of a problem, this limit on absolute addressing will have some impact on how we will partition memory for program and variables.The last thing that we must cover in this section are the actions of the instructions themselves. We will use LOAD, STORE, and CALL to illustrate the three modes of address as well as to specify the action that is taken by the processor. We begin with LOAD in absolute format in Figure 2.3.

While both CALL and JUMP are structurally related to LOAD and STORE, their functions are so separate from data movement instructions that they deserve and receive their own sections. A complete discussion of the use of the CALL instruction is given in Section 2.3, where the issues of making a procedure call are developed; JUMP introduces the idea of "test and branch" and is found in Section 2.2.3.

LOAD and STORE may appear to be symmetric operations. Programmatically they are, but there is a very important asymmetry between the two. The issue derives from the fact that there are delays in delivery of the data; the difference between the two instructions is a direct result of "who" is in charge of seeing that a subsequent request for the transferred data is always satisfied by *fresh* data. In the case of LOAD, the programmer (or his or her agent, the compiler) must not attempt to use the datum until it is in the designated register. Many machines provide hardware interlocks which delay the request until the datum is there, but that inevitably leads to a slower machine. In our machine, where our objective is to obtain one instruction per clock, we provide the programmer the opportunity to do something else useful while the datum is in transit. Delivery takes one extra clock, so you will always need an instruction after the LOAD before your program uses that new datum. Most of the time, you will find a useful instruction to put in there, but when you don't, you must insert a NOP (discussed below).

Why doesn't the same problem arise with STORE? Well, to begin with, it would be rather quixotic programming to ask immediately for the data you had just stored. The issue should not come up in normal programming, but if you were to write such code, the D-cache (Figure 1.1) is strictly obligated to handle requests in the order in which it receives them. Where it is unable to comply immediately, either because the memory has not delivered the requested data or because it has not finished the last operation it had begun, the D-cache will simply stall the CPU until the data become available.

This *delayed* LOAD issue is replicated in the JUMP and CALL instructions. All of these apparent delays derive from the fact that we will be running an assembly line or *pipeline*. Each instruction will be active in some sense for a total of three clock cycles. To get the *one-instruction-per-clock* performance that we are pursuing, we will overlap the steps in such a way that three instructions can be being processed free of interference with each other. Almost any powerful processor chip today does this *pipelining*. What is unique about the RISC approach is the willingness to burden the programmer or compiler with the task of handling the delays. The objective in passing this burden on is the opportunity for better performance optimization by having *each* program make optimal use of the inherent delays as instructions pass through the pipeline.

2.2.2.1 LOADB AND STOREB AND LOADH AND STOREH. These four instructions, which are in reality two instructions (i.e., two opcodes), work only with the base-index addressing format. The reason for this limitation is that we have chosen to address words, not bytes or halfwords, in all other instructions. If you think of this pair of instructions as continuing that choice—words, not bytes or halfwords—then the index should be thought of as having two parts: a 30- or 31-bit index to be added to the base and a 2- or 1-bit selector for choosing the byte or halfword within the word. This, in fact, is roughly how the hardware views the address. The byte address is constructed by the CPU as shown in Figure 2.6. The resulting standard 32-bit word address is treated just as any other word address. The extra 2 bits, which specify which byte is to be extracted, are passed by the CPU to the D-cache as *control bits*, not as part of the address. The halfword construct is identical except that the index is shifted only 1 bit right.

We have the choice of treating the index as signed or unsigned. If signed, the base would have to point to the middle of a byte array to get the full range. If unsigned, the base could point to the initial word and still give the full range. It is not obvious that either would lead to any problem, but the idea of treating an array of bytes as a structure whose base points to its first element is much more appealing than having it point somewhere in the middle. Accordingly, we have chosen the unsigned option.

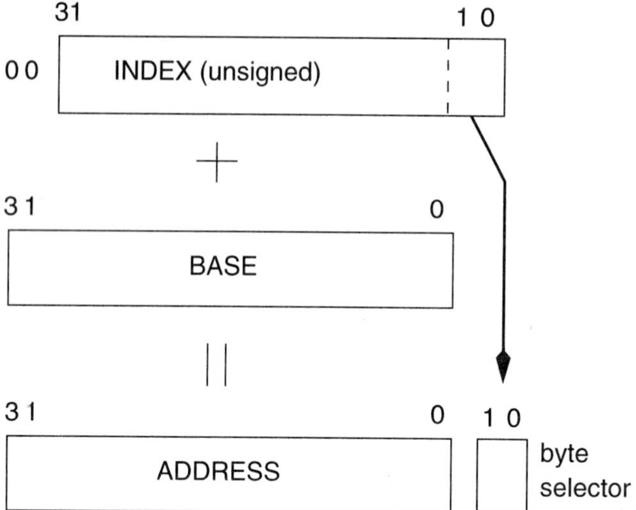

FIGURE 2.6 The formation of the address for the two byte operations. Note that the index is used as an unsigned number. For halfword operations, the shift is only 1 bit and the bit shifted out is the halfword selector.

The use of word-only addresses has both advantages and liabilities. By adopting word addresses, we have extended our address range by a factor of 4. That is a clear advantage. On the other hand, by making byte and halfword addressing work as we have shown, a given base can serve as a reference to only one-fourth or one-half of the memory. Given that that one-fourth is as large as the whole VAX address space, we can conclude that it is not much of a restriction at all. The only impact that it would have is on the ability of the program to use PC-relative addressing for the byte or halfword data. PC-relative addressing is a powerful tool for making code relocatable. However, it is fully functional only in machines which permit full addresses (32 bits in this machine) to be part of an instruction. Since this machine, like many RISCs, adheres strictly to the rule that every instruction must fit within a word, PC-relative addressing is not a powerful construct. In fact, it is used only for local branching. We will develop an equivalent construct for accessing any static element of data or program a little later in this chapter.

Note that the construction we have chosen—word addressing with a local selection of subset of the word—avoids one common exception in byte-addressed machines: the *odd-address fault*. In machines such as the PDP-11, MC68000, and even the SPARC, there are requirements that certain addresses be even. Some CISCs, notably the VAX, overcome the problem by allowing the microcode to fetch two or more longwords and to store fractions of a longword when the object asked for spans a longword boundary. However, by addressing at the normal unit of transmission—the word—and having an address mode which can access only aligned subunits of this normal unit, a hardware data alignment problem cannot occur. The principal problem not solved by our choice is what to do about storing subunit data. In other words, if someone stores a byte, what does the D-cache of Figure 1.1 do about it? A variety of choices could be

Base-index Format, STOREH/B

assembly notation

machine format

31 27	26 22	21 17	16 12	11	10 0
I_OP	Reg C	base Reg B	index Ri	h / b	unused

`STOREH/B RC, (RB,RI)`

example:

assembly	binary machine code	hex code
`STOREH r23, (R6,R5)`	10110 10111 00110 00101 100000000000	B5CC 5800

With the 1 in position 11, the contents of the index register are divided by 2 (shifted right 1 place) and added to the contents of the base register to form the destination address. The bit shifted out is retained. The contents of RC is stored in the left half of the destination word if the retained bit is 1 and in the right half if it is zero.

FIGURE 2.7 The BASE-INDEX format for the STOREH/B instruction. The assembler recognizes the two mnemonics and places the 1 or 0 in bit <11> to specify the object size.

made. One method, supported by almost all general busses, is to provide a way to transfer individual subunits. In that case, you can store a byte just as you would a word. On each memory transaction, the D-cache would signal to memory precisely which byte(s) were to be transferred. While common, byte or halfword transfers are an inefficient use of the bus. There is a *pay-as-you-enter* piece of overhead in acquiring the bus from other users and in addressing memory. To get good service out of the bus, one must transfer a relatively big block of data for each expenditure of that overhead. Sending a byte is awful. The modern trend is to send 16 to 32 bytes on every transaction. Accordingly, all of our byte transactions are handled in the D-cache. That this works well we leave to Chapter 5 where we design our D-cache. This decision to put byte and halfword handling in the D-cache has a small hook which we should mention here. Many standard peripheral interface chips operate only in halfwords or bytes. While it is usually possible to "glue anything to anything" with enough silicon, we are really choosing here to use only those peripheral chips which operate in words. These are really bus issues. From the programmer's perspective, the program reads or writes bytes, halfwords, or words. How they get there and how they get back is not the programmer's concern.

When a byte is brought in by a LOADB, the byte selected always goes into the low-order position (<7:0>) and it is always sign-extended to the full width. Similarly, when halfword is brought in, it is right-justified and sign-extended. When a byte is written out by a STOREB, the lowest 8 bits of the register are placed in the memory word specified by the address and in the position specified by the byte selector. The rest of the bytes in that word are undisturbed by this operation. The halfword store takes the lower half of the register into a halfword in memory. The layout of the instruction is shown in Figure 2.7.

Programs and programmers are not obliged to use explicit byte operations to do text manipulation. One can unpack and pack bytes in registers using the shift or logical operations. However, as we show in the problem set, this is a little clumsier than you might at first suspect. The need for halfwords arises first from the natural desire to copy extant software at minimal expense. If that software expects to use 16-bit objects, and if you can accommodate that need with minimal cost, then it pays to do it. A more pressing need is arising from the recent agreement to extend the ASCII code to a more general code which will encompass "all languages," both alphabetic and logographic. That extension is to use 16-bit character codes. As it comes into more general use, the ability to manipulate 16-bit symbols will become quite important. Since the hardware extension to handle halfwords is small, we have elected to do it.

The inclusion of byte and halfword objects has little impact on the CPU. It adds a truly tiny amount of logic to the instruction decoder, adds the delay of the sign-extension MUX in the data path (it is there anyway for address formation), and requires a few control lines between the D-cache and the CPU to signal the object size and position. The downside of having byte and halfword objects is that it makes our D-cache more complicated. It must be able to deal in bytes as well as halfwords. That is plainly and simply an extra piece of hardware that we will have to add if we want this ability in our machine. Tests of the tradeoff, in the sense of simulation of running with and without the ability to fetch and store bytes, do not show a major difference in performance. Our reasons for including it here are to show how it could be done as well as a base prejudice in favor of having byte operations.

2.2.3 JUMP and the Status Flags

JUMP has the form:

If (Boolean expression) then go to (address) else continue.

There are two ways of approaching such an operation. One is to allow a processor (or coprocessor) operation to set latches or *flags* to indicate any of a variety of results and then, at some later moment, test the setting of those flags and branch based on a test of those flags; the other is to combine the test and branch into a single, atomic instruction.

With flags, a zero result would set the zero flag (*Z*) while a non-zero result would reset it. Following that operation and up until another arithmetic or logical operation changes Z, it can be tested at will. Thus, a *jump if zero* (JUMPZ) instruction executed after a zero result would cause a jump while a *jump if NOT zero* (JUMP_Z) would allow the program to *fall through* (proceed in order).[1] The equivalent test-and-branch instruction would perform a subtraction, discard the result itself, and branch immediately if the result were zero.

[1] Notice that, in the assembly language for this CPU, to negate a condition, you place an underscore before the condition specifier.

The advantages of the flag method are that rather sophisticated tests may be performed by testing several flags at the same time and the result tested can be the output of any operation. For example, to tell if A is less than or equal to B, do $A - B$. Then do the Boolean test:

If
(overflow AND NOT negative) OR (NOT overflow AND negative) OR (zero)
then JUMP

Notice that three flags have been tested in several combinations. While a large fraction of such tests may be coverable by a well-designed test-and-branch suite of instructions, flag-based tests normally provide more variety.

The disadvantage of the flag method is that it leaves some loose baggage lying around in the processor. Not infrequently, the processor gets interrupted by events external to your program, so if your process is to continue at a later time, the current state of the flags must be preserved during the interruption. The flags are normally set aside on the stack for short interruptions or written back into the application's memory space for longer interruptions. Pushing onto and poping off of the stack require memory operations with side effects and they, in turn, may make it more difficult to handle the interrupts with RISC-like crispness. When we get to the instructions TRAP and RFI, you will see that we have a very rapid way of getting out to and back from an interrupt, so for our design, this objection has been eliminated.

We have chosen flags for three reasons:

1. We want a wide range of test options. It is difficult to test easily for conditions such as overflow, particularly if the overflow is not the result of a subtraction. Overflow is a direct way to test that the *integer* range in a HLL has not been exceeded in an arithmetic operation such as an arithmetic shift. We have no room in the instruction set for specifying a variety of tests with every instruction. The counterargument to this lack-of-variety objection is that tests show that almost all jumps follow (or can be made to follow) subtraction tests, which we do not dispute. However, while jumps based on coprocessor results are not all that common, they are used, they are part of the IEEE standard on floating point and it has been one of our goals to make a design that does not make normal operations too clumsy. Since it is difficult to predict all possible coprocessor flag meanings, limiting our machine to tests on subtraction appears too restrictive.
2. The use of multiplication and division primitives (i.e., doing long division and long multiplication by repeating the same sort of steps that you would do on paper) requires that information be passed from step to step. This requires either that you have a mechanism for preserving the state (e.g., flags that get saved) or that you prevent interrupts until the repetitive use of the primitive completes—that is, until you have completed your entire multiplication or division. If we adopted the *hold-interrupts* method, an interrupt could occasionally be put off for as much as 3.2 μs. That may or may not be a problem for whatever is requesting the interrupt, but we have decided to permit interrupts after every instruction. Since this meant that we must save flags for

the MUL and DIV primitives, we saw no extra burden in saving them for any and all operations that can usefully communicate through flags.

3. All of our instructions do at most one arithmetic operation. Since subtraction and address formation are both arithmetic operations, and since we wish to provide all normal addressing modes to JUMPs, we would either have to provide parallel paths in the processor or separate the test from the branch. In choosing this separation, we are going down the same path as SPARC.

All right, flags we will have, but which ones? The set we chose are those concerned with integer arithmetic and logic operations, comprising V (overflow), N (negative), Z (zero), C (carry), and HV (halfword overflow). The 5 CPU flags are defined in Table 2.1, along with the 10 floating-point coprocessor flags and their relationship to the CPU flags on transfer. In the general case, the CP flags might number more or less than 10, but they are to be tested 5 at a time.

When coprocessor flags are to be tested, they are transferred to the CPU flags, five at a time, by one of the CP instructions. Once transferred they may be tested, with meaning appropriate to that coprocessor.

Once we have a set of flags, we wish to define a set of jumps which test the flags. Some tests will test a single flag. For example, testing if the last result was 0, you will want the processor to examine its Z flag. On the other hand, if you wanted to know if A > B where the two numbers are to be treated as unsigned (a 32-bit positive number), then if you subtracted B from A, you would need to test C and Z. If C=1 and Z=0, then the test is true. (We do not think that is obvious, but if you try it, you will see that it works.)

One question at this point is: How do we wish to write the command for such a test? This is quite a different question from asking what the machine code will be. Here we are selecting the notation that we regard as reasonably friendly. The assembler will translate our notation to whatever the machine needs. Our choice is to append some letters on the end of the JUMP instruction to indicate which test we want the machine to make. For example, the test to see if the last result was zero is either JUMPZ or JUMP_Z, depending on whether we want the jump to take place if there was a 0 or if there was *not* a 0.

That choice of name may not suit everyone, so we also include a pair of synonyms which reflect an arithmetic perspective. These are JUMPEQ and JUMPNE for *jump if equal* and *jump if NOT equal.* The assembler produces the same code for JUMPZ and JUMPEQ. Table 2.2 presents the whole set of jumps that have been defined. You will see on examining the table that an even number in the TEST field implies that the jump is to be taken if the test is TRUE; the odd field numbers correspond to a jump taken if the test is FALSE. Here is a first look at the design of the interpretive logic. The even/odd test is a single bit. The Boolean result of the test itself is XORed with that bit in the instruction TEST field. The jump is taken if the output of the XOR is true.

Notice that the very first entry is JUMP (always). The converse of *always* is *never*, and a JUMP (never) instruction is a perfect NOP (just a space in the instruction stream). Programs and programmers seem to need a NOP for a variety of reasons. One common old-fashioned usage is to provide for a time delay between events. For

TABLE 2.1 Flag names and conditions which set the flags. The five flags form part of the processor status word. Flags from the coprocessors must be transferred to the CPU before they can be tested (see discussion of CP instruction). As a quite separate issue, the setting of a flag such as *FP unordered* can cause an interrupt without being transferred or tested. The FP flags are discussed in Chapter 9.

Label	Name	Condition which sets the flag
V	overflow	TRUE if carry-out from bit <30> != carry-out from bit <31> in the last operation
N	negative	TRUE if bit <31> == 1 in last operation
Z	zero	TRUE if all the bits <31:0> were zero in the last operation
C	carry	TRUE if there was a carry-out of bit <31> in the last operation. Also used for multiply and divide primitives but with different meaning.
HV	halfword overflow	TRUE if carry-out from bit <14> != carry-out from bit <15> in the last operation.
		Set #0: Flags resulting from the compare operation (essentially A – B):*
V	FP unordered	TRUE if one of the operands in the comparison was a NaN (discussion following Table 9.2 on page 475).
N	FP less than	TRUE if A < B.
Z	FP equal	TRUE if A == B.
C	FP greater than	TRUE if A > B.
HV	invalid operation	TRUE if any operation performed since the last reset of this flag in the coprocessor was not defined. (e.g., $\infty \times 0$).
		Set #1: Flags resulting from any operation
V	FP overflow	TRUE if any operation produces an overflow.
N	FP inexact	TRUE if any operation produces an inexact result.
Z	FP Div 0	TRUE if an attempt has been made to divide by zero.
C	FP underflow	TRUE if any operation produces an underflow.
HV	FP NAN	TRUE if any operation attempts to use a NaN (not a number).

* Apply with an IEEE compliant floating-point coprocessor.

example, if some external hardware needed some time between two inquiries from the central processor, the programmer could pad his timing loop by putting NOPs inside the loop and outside the loop. Each NOP would consume one clock pulse each time it was executed. Our principal use will be related to this "time delay" function, but the hardware in question is the processor pipeline. While we say that we do one instruction per clock, that is not quite the same thing as saying that an instruction takes one clock to execute. In fact, each instruction takes precisely three clocks from start to finish. In a

TABLE 2.2 A list of jump conditions. The assembler will accept equivalent names when two or more are given for the same test. The flag name references a particular CPU flag. The alternative name is based on the assumption that the test follows a subtraction operation which tests A's relationship to B. Signed comparisons would treat -4 as less than 3 while an unsigned comparison (such as a comparison of addresses) would get the opposite result. The coprocessor names reference the flag assignments made in Table 2.1. Which test one would get depends on which set of CP flags had been loaded with FPFLAGS. As new coprocessors are added, additional names would be added to the assembler to keep the assembly code current.

JUMP names and tests			
Test field	**Jump name**	**Flags**	**Alternate name(s) from A-B, A is xx to B**
No-flag jumps			
0	JUMP	(always)	
1	NOP	(literally JUMP never)	
One-flag jumps			
2	JUMPZ	Z = 1	JUMPEQ (also jumpFPEQ & FPDZ)
3	JUMP_Z	Z = 0	JUMPNE (also jumpFPNE & FP_DZ)
4	JUMPN	N = 1	(also jumpFPLT & FPINX)
5	JUMP_N	N = 0	(also jumpFPGTE & FPXAC)
6	JUMPC	C = 1	(also jumpFPGT & FPUV)
7	JUMP_C	C = 0	(also jumpFPLTE & FP_UV)
8	JUMPV	V = 1	(also jumpFPUN & FPOV)
9	JUMP_V	V = 0	(also jumpFP_UN & FP_OV)
A	JUMPHV	HV = 1	(also jumpFPINV & FPNAN)
B	JUMP_HV	HV = 0	(also jumpFPVAL & FPNUM)
Multiple-flag jumps			
C		(V = 0,N = 0) or (V = 1,N = 1)	JUMPGTE
D		(V = 1,N = 0) or (V = 0,N = 1)	JUMPLT
E		(V = 0,N = 0,Z = 0) or (V = 1,N = 1,Z = 0)	JUMPGT
F		(V = 1,N = 0) or (V = 0,N = 1) or (Z = 1)	JUMPLTE
10		(C = 1) or (Z = 1)	JUMPGTEU
11		(C = 0,Z = 0)	JUMPLTU
12		(C = 1,Z = 0)	JUMPGTU
13		(C = 0) or (Z = 1)	JUMPLTEU

Note: All coprocessor tests require transfer of the coprocessor flags to the CPU. This is a separate instruction (see CP). The flags may then be tested with normal jumps, but the meaning depends on what the coprocessor flags mean.

JUMP, you must calculate the jump address before you use it. That address will be available only at the end of the second stage in the pipeline. The instruction immediately following the instruction will have already entered stage one and will get executed regardless of whether the jump is taken or not. From the programmatic point of view, one must wait one instruction before a branch (CALL or JUMP) is executed. When we cannot find a useful instruction to insert into that *bubble* in the pipeline, we must insert a NOP. As an example, consider the very common paradigm where you do an operation, update the count, test the count, and repeat if you have not reached the end point. This is shown in three forms in Table 2.3.

If you go back to Figures 2.1 and 2.2, you will see that the flags get set only when an arithmetic or logical operation permits them to change (or if the instruction to move them from a coprocessor is executed). In this way, one may separate the instruction which sets or resets the flags from the instruction which tests the flags. In Chapter 6, when we design the pipeline for this machine, you will see how useful such a choice is. At this point, it is simply one more function that the programmer/compiler controls.

An example of the JUMP instruction is given in Figure 2.8. Note that for this instruction, the name of the instruction gets decoded into two fields—the OP field and the TEST field.

2.2.4 Special Registers and Register Conventions

In the discussion of why we were using flags, we noted that most test-and-branch operations involve first a subtraction and then a conditional jump based on the result of that subtraction. The result of the subtraction itself often is not wanted. The data in the flags are all that is desired. The VAX deals with this case by having the instruction CMP (compare), which performs the subtraction, sets the flags, and then throws the result

TABLE 2.3 **The issue of delayed branching in a specific example.** The left column has operations in the order that you would regard as logical, but with the one-cycle delay in JUMP execution, the program would execute the last ADD instruction every time that it went around the loop. Proper coding is shown in the middle and right columns. The middle uses a NOP to properly space the instructions; the right uses reordering to fill the bubble.

Incorrect but logical order	**Correct but wasted cycle**	**Correct and efficient coding**
repeat:	repeat:	repeat:
ADDx r4,r5,r4	ADDx r4,r5,r4	SUBc r8,r12,r6
SUBc r8,r12,r6	SUBc r8,r12,r6	DJUMPNE repeat
DJUMPNE repeat	DJUMPNE repeat	ADDx r4,r5,r4
ADDx r4,r7,r19	NOP	‹*JUMP executed*
‹*JUMP executed*	‹*JUMP executed*	ADDx r4,r7,r19
	ADDx r4,r7,r19	

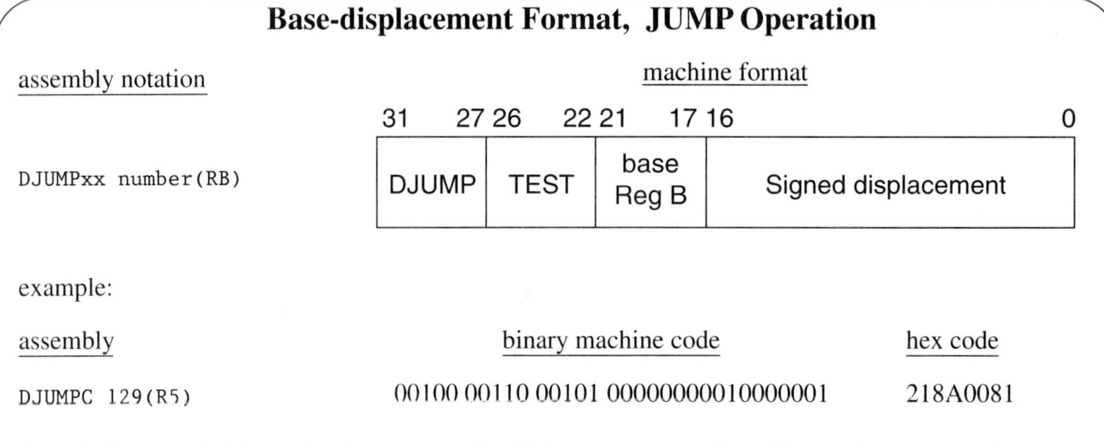

FIGURE 2.8 Description of the JUMP operation, using base-displacement format.

itself into the wastebasket. We have the SUB instruction; what we want here is the *wastebasket*.

Another need is for a "dedicated zero," that is, a register name which always brings in 0. Why would we want that? Well, let us say that you want to put a constant into a register. For example, you want to count down from 12 in doing a loop. We have no way so far defined to load a constant (other than to have the constant already in memory). What we are looking for is a "zero" to use in the instruction LADD, which would be used as

```
LADDx 12, "zero", r9     ;put 12 into register 9, don't set flags
```

We can satisfy our needs both for 0 and for a wastebasket by observing what the program counter (PC or r31) really does in life. It points to the next instruction to be executed. It does nothing else. Since we have provided a full set of PC-modifying instructions (CALL and JUMP), there is no reason to accomplish identical actions by having any other instructions deposit a result in the PC. Thus, there is no reason to have the PC be the target register of any instruction. Given that, why not have the PC-as-target be our wastebasket? Accordingly, we write

```
ADDc r12, r19, PC        ;add r12 to r19, throw the result away, set flags
```

We will have set the flags according to the sum but the sum itself has not been deposited anywhere.

Now one might well object that this is obscure coding at best and downright confusing at worst. We agree, regardless of the merits of having a wastebasket. The problem is not with the logic but with the name. Instead, let us employ NUL for this usage. NUL, PC, and R31 all get translated by the assembler to the same numeric value (1F), but it makes for much clearer notation to put down what you mean. Thus, the line above will be written as

```
ADDc r12, r19, NUL        ;add r12 to r19, throw the result away, set flags
```

The NUL reference also seems natural to satisfy our need for a dedicated 0. Thus, you could write

```
LADDx 27, NUL, r9         ;load 27 into r9, do not set flags
```

Notice that we cannot use the literal field for the dedicated zero. We have only one literal field in the instruction and that must contain the value we wish to load.

While the need for a dedicated zero/wastebasket is compelling enough to have led us to invent the concept for ourselves shortly after we began this project, it is equally compelling to other designers. In SPARC, MIPS, MC88000, and i860 register 0 is set aside for this function. We have no history of this invention, but most of us have reinvented the wheel. Only the hubcap—using the PC as NUL—appears to be novel to this design.

The next section, which provides the details on the versatile SHIFT operation, provides yet one more application for NUL.

There is one important class of instructions in which PC is a legitimate reference to the current value of the program counter. This is *any* use of the PC as a base register in address formation. For example, JUMP -22(PC) will cause the program to jump back 22 instructions (including the JUMP itself). A particularly important but possibly obscure form is where one jumps or calls to an address that is visible in the current module. The form would be either DJUMP *label* or DCALL *label*, RA. The value of *label* is replaced by the correct displacement off the PC. To see this actually transpire, we commend you to the assembler available with this text.

One other register has a "hardware" definition. This is the register that holds the multiplier in MUL or the quotient in DIV, so it bears the name MQ. It is R28. What makes this register special is that it can shift left or right and bring in bits that depend on the outcome of the last ALU operation. Other than that, it works just like the other registers as a storage location for operands.

No regular register other than the PC and MQ has a hardware definition. They are all available for any use whatsoever to the programmer. However, if programs are to be constructed in segments that will be *linked* together to form an executable module, if the module is to run under the oversight and control of an operating system, and if more than one module can be resident in the memory at one time, the whole system must

TABLE 2.4 **Symbolic register definitions**

Symbol	Register	Name
PC, NUL	r31	program counter
SP	r30	stack pointer
RA	r29	return address
MQ	r28	multiplier/quotient

employ some conventions—common definitions—which allow the different pieces to coexist and to communicate with each other.

To this end, we define RA, *return address*, and SP, *stack pointer*. They have no hardware significance, but they are known to the assembler and will be translated appropriately. The four special names are shown in Table 2.4.

Function calls require a convention for passing parameters and returning results. Normally there is also a convention which says that some fraction of the registers get preserved across the call. We will discuss the reasons for our choices in Section 2.3, but to keep all of the definitions in one place, we state here our conventions. These are: R0...R7 and F0...F2 are scratch registers. All other registers are preserved across a call. Integer parameters may be passed in R0...R7 (leftmost in R0). Floating-point parameters may be passed in F0...F2. Integer returns are in R0. Floating returns are in F0.

2.2.4.1 SIGNED AND UNSIGNED SHIFTS. In a mechanical sense, shift operations move the number right or left in the window provided by our 32-bit word. The shift can be viewed in a variety of ways, particularly as simply moving a bit pattern or as multiplication or division by the base (2 in this case). Our shift operation will permit shifts of 0 to 31 places in either direction. As usual, the operation takes one clock cycle.

Continuing with the mechanical sense, think of the bits going out as passing through the C (carry) flag. This preserves the last bit to be shifted out. The rest of the bits shifted out are lost. (That is, they are not in the result, but they do remain in the source register, if that is not also the destination register.)

Clearly, we have a choice to make on the bits that come in. One unifying view of the choice is to consider the contents of the register being shifted as either a signed or an unsigned number and the shift operation as a multiplication or division by a power of 2. By convention, all numbers in the window are extended to the right by adding zeros. To the left, the extension is that of the "sign bit." However, with unsigned numbers, that sign bit is the nonextant bit-32 and it is always 0; for signed numbers, it is bit-31 and it is whatever it happens to be. When you instruct the computer to shift, you must tell it whether the shift is *signed* or *unsigned*.[2] The specification of signed or

[2] The more common names for these two shifts are arithmetic and logical, but we find that the signed/unsigned names are more quickly understood.

unsigned is no more than specifying where the shifter looks for bits that get shifted in from the left. Those that come in from the right are always 0.

Shifts are used for several quite unrelated objectives. Only some of these are explicitly recognized by HLLs. For example, extracting the second byte of a word could be done in Pascal by writing

```
x := (y DIV 256) MOD 256;
```

In assembly language, this would be most effectively accomplished by *left-shifting* by 16 bits (to clear the upper 2 bytes) and then *right-shifting* by 24 bits (to dump the low-order byte and right-justify the extracted byte). It is a clever compiler indeed that would recognize the two-shift expansion of the above expression.[3] Pascal provides you with no better expression for extracting a bit field from a number. C, being initially a language to write an operating system in, does allow explicit shifts. These find many uses outside numerical operations. Bit-field extraction such as the operation above is one. Another, which is assuming ever-increasing importance in our rapidly computerizing world, is in *window management* such as the Apple Macintosh's versatile display.

For window operation, where bit maps of the contents of each window must be offset by amounts determined only at run time, one would want a dynamic shift length (i.e., one which is determined at run time). Other shift operations, such as the byte-extraction example above, are static. They are known at compile time. To provide for both (both are acceptable in C), the shift length is determined as the sum of the least-significant 6 bits in rA and a 6-bit signed literal. In this sense, the SHIFT is like the base-displacement instructions. However, there are also source and destination registers, making SHIFT rather like a regular arithmetic operation. For purely static shifts, the shift register (A) should be NUL.[4]

Note that a "u" or an "s" is appended to the instruction to specify whether the source is to be taken as signed or unsigned. As usual, "c" and "x" specify whether or not the flags will be set by this operation.

Shifts of 0 to 31 places in either direction are supported with the rules given in Figure 2.9. Since the useful range possible includes 0 to 31, left or right, we need 6 bits to specify the length of shift. Accordingly, only the rightmost 6 bits are interpreted by the computer. If the programmer inserts a literal value outside the range of ±31, the assembler can and will tag it as an error. For the dynamic part of the shift—rA—no such check is performed; only the least significant 6 bits are used.

---

[3] The arithmetic expression above works only if $y \geq 0$. Pascal has no "unsigned" type. Strict typing can get in your way if you want to play with the bits yourself. However, if Pascal itself were extracting the byte from a recognized bit array or packed array in the register, it certainly would use an efficient method such as the two shifts.

[4] For those with enough prescience to realize that there is a potential problem with specifying two source registers plus a literal, note that both the literal and one source are 6-bit fields. They can fit together with room to spare on a single 32-bit bus, so there is no problem in getting all three items to the ALU at one time.

Modified Register Format, SHIFT Operation

assembly notation — machine format

31–27	26–22	21–17	16–12	11	10	9–6	5–0
L_OP	dest Reg C	source Reg B	shift Reg A	c/x	s/u	not used	signed literal

SHIFT$\frac{s\ c}{u\ x}$ `lit(RA),RB,RC`

example:

assembly	binary machine code	hex code
`SHIFTsc -3(r2),r9,r21`	01000 10101 01001 00010 1 1 0000 111101	4552 2C3D

In all cases, the shift length is the signed 6-bit number comprising the rightmost 6 bits of the sum of bits <5:0> of the instruction and the contents of rA. A positive shift is a left (multiplicative) shift.

1) the **unsigned shift**: s/u = 0. All 32 bits shift as a unit. The bits that come in are all 0's. (e.g., A shift of K places to the right moves the K bits on the right out of the register and brings in K 0's from the left.)

FLAGS: See below.

2) the **signed shift**: All 32 bits shift as a unit, but such an operation should preserve sign. For a right shift (division) this can always be done. The sign bit (bit <31>) must be reproduced. On negative numbers, 1's come in from the left; on positive numbers, 0's come in from the left. On a left-signed shift (multiplication by the base), 0's come in from the right. However, the sign bit may flip as bits are shifted through the 31st place.

FLAGS: Flags change if 'c' is set. If bit-31 ever changes value in the shift, the V bit is set. The last bit to be shifted out is stored in the C flag. N is identical to bit <31> of the result. Z is true if all the bits of the result are 0.

FIGURE 2.9 Description of the SHIFT format.

As a usage example, to divide a signed integer in r4 by 64 (2^6), change the flags, and put the results in r11, you would write

```
SHIFTsc -6(NUL), r4, r11
```

whereas to do the byte extraction shown in Pascal above, so that the second character moved, sign-extended, into the low-order position, you would write

```
SHIFTux 16(NUL), r4, r11
SHIFTsx -24(NUL), r11, r11
```

Note the use of NUL for the base where we want a fixed base of 0.

One final note on shifting signed numbers. When you do a signed right shift of a negative number, the number ceases to change when it reaches -1, not 0. From an arithmetic point of view, the result of dividing any odd negative number by 2 using SHIFT operations is not the same as the result you would expect from arithmetic.

2.2.5 MUL and DIV

MUL and DIV are developed at some length in Appendix I. Here we proceed as above and provide a terse description of the operation of the command. On a first reading, it would be normal to begin with the appendix. After that, this section should provide needed details.

MUL and DIV differ from all other instructions in three ways:

1. They make special use of r28 (MQ), with two consequences:
   a. Since the partial sum or remainder is both a source and destination register for the operation, only two *different* register fields are specified in the instruction itself.
   b. Two registers change value on a single instruction.
2. They are intended to be repeated 16 or 32 times respectively to produce a completed arithmetic operation, with the intermediate results being of little use.
3. There is an initial setup before the repetitive calls for either instruction, and after DIV, several steps may be required to render quotient and remainder results of the correct sign.

MUL uses a 2-bit Booth's algorithm to sum 2-bit partial-products of a pair of 32-bit signed numbers in two's-complement notation. The instruction is shown in Figure 2.10. To obtain the full product, the programmer must repeat the instruction 16 times. Prior to doing it the first time, the programmer must put the multiplier into any register, rB, put the multiplicand into MQ, and then set the register chosen to be the *partial-sum* register to 0 by doing

```
SUBc rPS, rPS, rPS
```

This clears not only rPS but the C (carry) bit as well. Following that, the programmer should immediately start with successive MULs. The reason for the immediacy is to be sure that the C bit is not set by any intervening operation. After 16 repetitions, the correctly signed product is found in the pair of registers PS:MQ.

DIV is also an instruction that is intended only for repetitive application. It is shown in Figure 2.11. The setup is similar to MUL with the additional obligation to make both divisor and dividend positive. The sign bit, N, is used rather than C. The program must determine whether to negate the quotient or remainder after completing division. One begins by loading a positive divisor into any register, rB, and a positive

Register Format, MUL Operation

assembly notation — machine format

31 27	26 22	21 17	16 12	11 0
OP	par_sum rPS	mltiplr rB	par_sum rPS	unused

```
MUL rPS, rB, rPS
```

example:

assembly	binary machine code	hex code
MUL r7, r9, r7	11110 00111 01001 00111 0—>	F1D2 7000

The MUL instruction is intended to be used repetitively (16 times) to produce a full product. The algorithm and the hardware to perform a 2-bit Booth's Algorithm multiplication are described in Appendix I. The instruction uses three registers—PS, MQ, and B—as well as the *carry* bit. MQ is by implication and does not appear explicitly; PS and B can be any other registers. Prior to using MUL, the multiplier must be placed in B, the multiplicand in MQ, and both PS and the carry bit must be cleared by doing SUBc rPS, rPS, rPS. When the full product of two 32-bit numbers is completed, the 64-bit product is found in PS:MQ. In the usual HLL application where the product must be limited to a single register, the PS must be simply the sign-extension of MQ. Otherwise, an overflow has occurred. The assembler checks to be sure that the first and third fields are identical.

FIGURE 2.10 Description of the MUL instruction.

dividend into MQ. Then one clears remainder register, any general register, rREM, with the instruction[5]

```
SUBc rREM, rREM, rREM
```

which leaves both rREM and the N bit 0. 32 repetitions of DIV determine the quotient and *apparent* remainder.

DIV uses a *nonrestoring* division algorithm. (See Appendix I.) One of the consequences of such an algorithm is that the apparent remainder (which is in register REM at the end) can be negative even though both divisor and dividend are positive. If that occurs, the program must add the divisor to the negative apparent remainder to get the

[5] With proper care, one may divide a double-precision dividend rREM:MQ by a single-precision divisor. Instead of clearing rREM, the upper word of the dividend goes there. N must be cleared by a separate operation. It is up to the program to be sure that rB > 2•rREM before beginning the operation of division. If rB fails this test, a division overflow has occurred.

Register Format, DIV Operation

assembly notation	machine format				
	31–27	26–22	21–17	16–12	11–0
`DIV rR, rB, rR`	OP	rmndr rREM	divisor rB	rmndr rREM	unused

example:

assembly	binary machine code	hex code
`DIV r7, r19, r7`	11110 00111 10011 00111 0—>	F9E6 7000

The DIV instruction is intended to be used repetitively (32 times) to produce a full quotient. The instruction requires a positive divisor and dividend. It uses a *nonrestoring* division algorithm described in detail in Appendix I. The instruction uses three registers—REM, MQ, and B—as well as the *sign* bit, N. MQ is by implication and does not appear explicitly; REM and B can be any other registers. Prior to using DIV, the divisor must be placed in B and the 64-bit dividend in REM:MQ. Overflow will occur if, prior to starting, 2 ¥ REM > B. The N bit must be cleared by doing either SUBc rREM, rREM, rREM or LADDC 0, rREM, rREM as appropriate. When the full division is complete, the correct quotient is found in MQ and the apparent remainder in rREM. If REM<0, the true remainder is rREM+rB, otherwise it is rREM. The assembler checks that the first and third register fields are identical. Appendix I provides a C routine for doing all of the setup and operand checking and for returning the correctly signed results of a signed division. The DIV instruction repeated 32 times would replace the loop in that routine.

FIGURE 2.11 Description of the DIV instruction.

true remainder. Finally, the sign of the quotient and of the remainder must be set by the program according to the signs of the original divisor and dividend.

Appendix I gives complete routines for executing both regular and extended division. The latter uses a 64-bit dividend, making it symmetric with the multiplication operation which yields a 64-bit product.

2.3 CALL AND THE USE OF REGISTERS AND THE STACK

When two or more completely independent processes share one processor, they stay out of each other's hair by having independent chunks of memory and by having the operating system save their entire register set when the OS switches from one process to another. When it is your process's turn to run, it gets the whole register set and its own section of the memory. If your process attempts to read or write outside of its assigned space, the *memory management* hardware interrupts your process and returns control to the operating system. (Chapter 5 discusses how this is done.)

Such complete isolation is not practical or even particularly desirable within the workings of a single program. Different parts of the same program must have ways to communicate and also ways to get some privacy. It would be wasteful to have to save and reload the entire register set every time that there is a call to a function or subroutine. In place of such complete isolation, modern HLLs achieve both communication and privacy through conventions in the use of the registers and memory. Older or more simplistic languages such as Fortran and Basic do not employ all of these conventions, and as a result, they have restrictions on what the programmer can do with subroutines. In particular, all modern HLLs provide a mechanism whereby, during the "life" of a subroutine, it gets space in memory for its local variables—space that will not be used by any other part of the program *until the subroutine finishes execution.*

There are four items needed to accomplish a well-isolated procedure or function call:

1. The calling procedure must be able to pass data and a return address to the called procedure.
2. The called procedure must be able to obtain a chunk of memory space in which to store its local variables during the time that it is active and there should be a mechanism for returning this space for reuse when this particular invocation of the subroutine is finished.
3. The called procedure must be able to return to the correct place in the calling program, returning any data that are expected.
4. The calling program must be able to resume its work with the assurance that it knows where all of its data, both new and old, are resident.

These objectives are achieved through conventions and the instruction CALL.

The CALL instruction is available in some form or another on almost any computer. For all machines, no matter what the instruction may be named, it must accomplish at least two things:

1. It must place in the PC a pointer to (i.e., the address of) the first instruction in the called subroutine.
2. It must pass to the called subroutine the previous value in the PC—that is, it must pass to the subroutine the return address.

In some machines, the CALL instruction does a great deal more, formalizing in microcode much of what we will do by convention below. In most studies of the use of more elaborate CALLs, it is found that this formalization at the hardware or microcode level precludes local optimization and thus slows down program execution. A surprisingly large fraction of the LOADs and STOREs in the studies cited in Chapter 1 are found to be associated with setting up calls to subroutines. Therefore, it is very important that the computer system be designed to make such calls as efficient as possible. Let us take a concrete example to make the problem clear at all levels.

TABLE 2.5 The FFT function in C and Pascal. Examples have been written to emphasize their equivalence and to make them easier to comprehend. Both reference a global variable (or constant), NTOTAL, which is the number of entries in the original array. On the initial call, index = 0 ; size = NTOTAL .

C	Pascal

`int fft(start,index,size)`
`COM_PAG * start;`
`int index,size;`
 	
`{int odd, even, new, step;`
 	
`    if (size==1) return(index);`
`    step = NTOTAL / size;`
`    even = fft(start,index,size/2);`
`    odd  = fft(start,index+step, size/2);`
`    new  = butterfly(start,even,odd,size);`
`    return(new);`
`}`
	`function fft(start:com_blk_ptr;`
	`index,size:integer):integer;`
	
	`var odd, even, new, step: integer;`
	
	`begin`
	`    if size=1 then fft:=index`
	`    else begin`
	`        step:= NTOTAL DIV size;`
	`        even:= fft(start,index, size DIV 2);`
	`        odd:= fft(start,index+step,size DIV 2);`
	`        fft:= butterfly(start,even,odd,size);`
	`    end;`
	`end;`

2.3.1 A Recursive Function Call

Let us choose as our example a short but intensely recursive piece of HLL. The idea is to introduce as many real problems as we can without making the code too long. In Table 2.5, we provide both a C and a Pascal version so that you may read the flavor of your choice. The item presented is a function[6] which is *recursive*—that is, it calls itself repeatedly until it reaches a terminal point. Then it returns through its multiple calls to deliver the final results to the original caller. Recursive coding is typically very compact but often achieves that compactness of code through longer running time. The reason is simple: All of those calls have a price.

The example program performs a *fast Fourier transform* (FFT) on a set of data, and although that fact is irrelevant to our interest in it, it is necessary to know what the data structure on which it operates looks like. The basic lump of input data is an array of NTOTAL complex numbers beginning at START. It is required (both by the algorithm and the program) that NTOTAL be an integer power of 2. What the program does is to repetitively divide the array of data into even- and odd-numbered subarrays until it gets down to arrays of only one element. Then it backs up through the ever-doubling

[6] C has only functions, though a function can return nothing. In Pascal, a function that returns nothing directly is formalized to a procedure.

arrays, cross-multiplying them and summing them in an arrangement called a *butterfly*, the name we have chosen for a procedure called by FFT.

Begin by reading the program in the language of your choice and then the following comments on it:

1. START points to the beginning of a subscripted array; INDEX is the subscript of a particular element of the array; each element is a complex number, so it is a RECORD in Pascal and a STRUCT in C.
2. The function returns an index into the data array. (Returning a pointer would be more normal in C.)
3. The function receives three parameters from the calling program. Since one of these (START) is a pointer, all of the subroutines can "see" and change data in the array. The other two parameters are "passed by value"—that is, a copy of the number itself is passed. Accordingly, while anything can be done to the copy, the original value cannot be changed by the called routine.
4. Each version of FFT that is called (referred to as an *activation*) requires room for four local variables.

The essential issue here is that this function calls itself. Notice that if NTOTAL=8, the first call to FFT, with SIZE=8, generates two more calls to FFT, each with SIZE=4. Each of these generates two calls with SIZE=2 and, finally, each of these generates two calls with SIZE=1. At greatest depth, in the example just cited, there would be four FFTs active at one time. Each of them has four local variables, using the same names but with different values, and each of them is passed three variables and returns one.

Not only do we have up to 4 concurrent calls to FFT at any one time, there will be a total of 15 calls to FFT and 7 calls to BUTTERFLY before the process ends. These and their associated structures have to "vanish" when they are done. Otherwise, our memory will fill up with heaps of useless garbage. A pair of constructs are used to provide both for easy generation of well-separated local space and for later garbage collection. These constructs are referred to as the *stack* and the *heap*. They were invented well after the origins of HLLs (which began with Fortran and Cobol in the mid-1950s) and marked a very important step in HLL development. They are intrinsic parts of both C and Pascal. They are not required parts of either Fortran or Cobol, so the recursive code above will not necessarily work in either of those now antique languages.

2.3.2 The Stack and the Heap

In modern computer usage, when a program has been compiled and linked, it exists as a couple of tightly packed blocks of code and data. For execution, these are normally loaded into the low end of memory space. This leaves the huge block of addresses above the static data and program free of any commitment. This room is used for creating structures that arise (and vanish) during the course of a program's run. Since these structures come and go during the program, they are called *dynamic*. The data structures and program that remain fixed throughout the program are called *static*.

Figure 2.12 shows what the memory space will look like in our computer. Most other machines will use similar arrangements.

Just as an aside, since we will not discuss virtual memory (VM) until Chapter 4, what Figure 2.12 represents is the VM or programmer's view of the entire address space. The address space vastly exceeds the normal complement of physical memory (PM). The OS brings into PM only those parts of a program that are currently active (the rest being out on disk) and keeps track of where things really are. The hardware takes care of translating the virtual addresses to physical addresses. Now back to stack and heap.

The dynamic space is defined by a top and a bottom. Since there is no way to know how much of each kind of dynamic space a program will require, it makes sense to define one dynamic structure which proceeds from bottom up and another from top down. As long as they do not crash into each other, this arrangement allows them to

FIGURE 2.12 Placement of programs and data in the address space. The bins refer to memory assignments according to usage. They figure prominently in the output of the assembler for this machine.

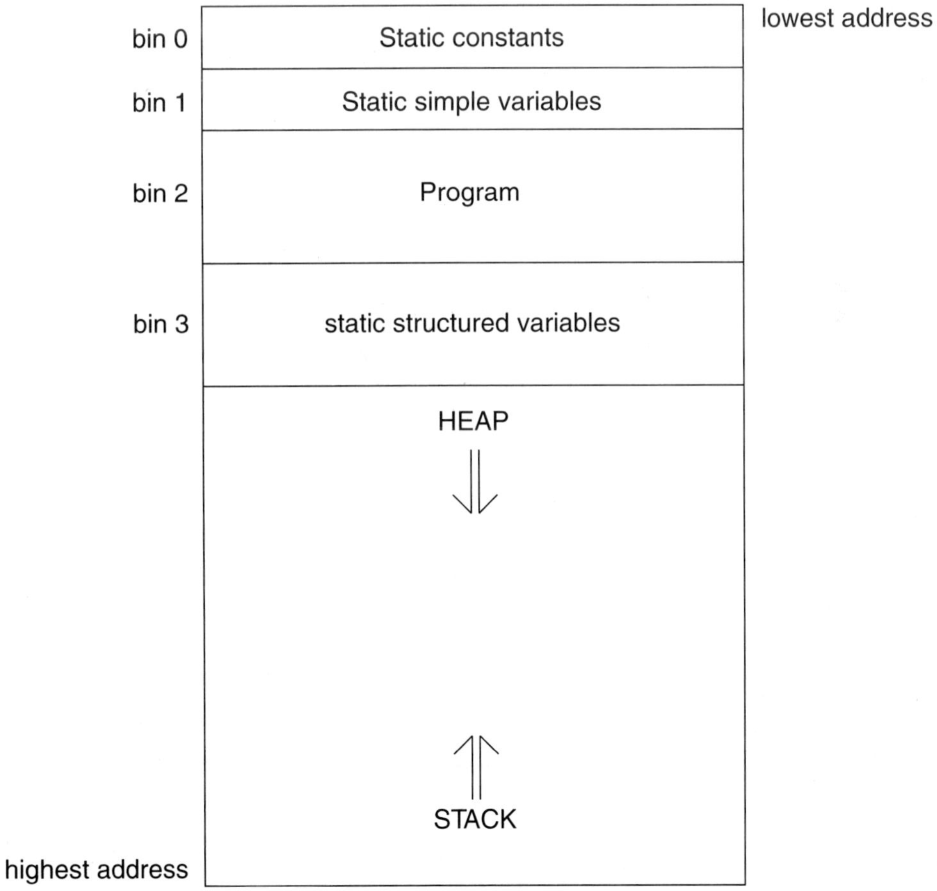

grow and shrink quite independently. By convention and for no other reason, the stack normally starts from the top and works its way down; the heap from the bottom and works its way up.

A stack is a *last-in–first-out* or LIFO queue. Its name derives from the familiar pile-of-plates stack in a cafeteria, where the pile sits on a spring-loaded platform. Only the top plates—the last to arrive—are visible. Take some off, earlier ones appear; add some and the earlier ones disappear.

Heaps can be managed in a variety of ways including piecemeal and LIFO, but they all have one common and important difference from the stack. When a subroutine gets a piece of stack, it holds onto it only while the subroutine is active. Upon termination of the subroutine, the stack space allocated to it is returned—that is, the stack gets shorter. With the heap, the assignment and return of dynamic space are actively controlled by the program itself. The instructions NEW and DISPOSE (or MARK and RELEASE) in Pascal and `malloc()` and `free()` in C acquire and return pieces of memory space in the heap. The reason for having these two different management techniques for structures in the two ends of dynamic memory space is the need for having some things that do go away automatically with the subroutine and others that do not. With a stack, structures created by a parent routine can be passed by pointer to a child of that routine but not in reverse; with the heap, such dynamic structures can be passed in both directions and can remain alive long after the program segment which created them.

Pointing to things on the stack is often thought of as a displacement off SP, but however reasonable, that is a very parochial point of view. What if you are in a C program and you wish to pass a pointer to a stack variable to some routine further down the call chain? What does that routine know about *your* SP? It has its own SP value to worry about. No, the recipient wants an absolute pointer. Similarly, in *heap* or even in the *static* or *program* region, programmers want to pass pointers. So how will we construct pointers? The question is a little tricky only because of our curious way of addressing bytes and halfwords.

Two options commend themselves:

- Use a base of 0. For full-sized things, no problem. You can reach anywhere in the machine. Pointer operations simply translate to *index* mode with a single register set aside for a 0 reference. (Do not, for goodness sake, use NUL! If used as an address base, what you get is PC. Not at all what you should have in mind here.) The only problem is that the byte range is now 4 GB and the halfword range 8 GB. This is hardly a restriction for most programs.
- Use a base of the start of the *static structured* region of Figure 2.12. This means that pointers to lower addresses are negative—so what?—but what you get is a bigger stack and heap range for which byte addressing is possible. The assumption here (and uniformly through the book) is that all items in the *static simple constant* and *variable* regions and *program* region are only word-addressable.

Be aware and beware of casts of pointers between data types of different sizes. They are peculiar enough and architecture-dependent in any case; they are particularly weird on this machine.

2.3.3 Stack Conventions in a Procedure Call

Now consider our example, FFT. When we call it, some space must be made for the local variables defined in the declaration part. We also need some space for parameter passing. One obvious place to put them is on the stack, but another possible one is in register. Which should we use? If we can use registers, it will save us LOADs and STOREs; on the other hand, every part of the program needs some part of the register set and one subroutine does not know what another needs. We will solve some of our problems with the following two rules of usage:

1. r0...r7 and f0...f2 (floating point registers) will be considered "scratch registers" that are available for parameter passing and any other use the subroutine wishes to make of them. By *scratch* we mean that if function *A* calls function *B*, *B* may use the scratch registers without restoring their contents and *A* cannot expect to find the original contents in those registers when it resumes control. If a simple object is returned, then it will be returned in r0 or f0 as appropriate. If the returned object is of a structured type (*struct* or *array*), then function *B* must obtain space for the structure from the heap, place the values in the heap space and return the pointer to the structure in r0. Function *A* has the obligation to free the heap space (*free*(pointer)) when it has finished with the returned object.
2. All other registers *must* be returned with their original contents. This does not mean that other routines cannot use r8...r31. In fact, they all must use r31. What it does mean is that each called routine must save the contents of nonscratch registers before using them and then restore the contents when the routine finishes.

The stack provides an easy way of getting temporary memory space if we accept a simple pair of conventions. These are:

1. The top of the stack (TOS) is defined by register r30 (SP). The TOS is the last location that has been allocated—that is, a program may write into and read from 0(SP). In our machine (unlike many others), the SP has no special stack instructions (e.g., no PUSH or POP), so the only thing that defines r30 as SP is general agreement.
2. If a subroutine needs stack space, it simply subtracts the number of words it needs from the current SP, making the stack longer by that amount. When the subroutine finishes, it is obliged to restore the SP and stack to their former state by adding the same number to SP. This simple convention takes care of both stack allocation and garbage collection. Note that when a subroutine begins, it has no stack space allocated to it. As the program enters the subroutine, the SP will be pointing to the last word allocated in the *calling routine's* space.

Let us consider the example subroutine from Table 2.5 to see how we will use these conventions and have separate sets of local variables for each incarnation of FFT throughout its life. Since FFT calls itself, the one example contains both the call and response. The assembly code is presented in Table 2.6.

TABLE 2.6 The function FFT of Table 2.5 translated to assembly language. No NOP was necessary to accommodate delayed branching. In all cases, it was possible to move instructions to accommodate delayed loads and delayed branches. These are marked with (*) in the comments.

```
.module fft
.pseg
.G FFT:   ;                          .G puts the address of FFT into global table
          LSUBc r2, 1, NUL                                              ;if (size = 1)
          DJUMPEQ  one               ;
          ;else           BEGIN FUNCTION ENTRY SET UP
          LSUBx SP,5, SP             ;set aside 5 words on stack. (*)
          DSTORE r2,  2(SP)          ;copy of SIZE to stack
          DSTORE r1,  1(SP)          ;copy of INDEX to stack
          DSTORE r0,  0(SP)          ;copy of START to stack
          DSTORE RA,  3(SP)          ;copy of return address
          DSTORE MQ, 4(SP)           ;copy of current contents of MQ
          ;               THIS COMPLETES THE SET UP
          LOAD NTOTAL, MQ            ;data from global table.
          SUBc r4, r4, r4            ;clear remainder register          step := NTOTAL DIV size
          DIV r4, r2, r4             ;repeat 32 times (NTOTAL and size both >0)
          ;...                  There are better ways to code this but the compiler will not know
                                that size is a power of 2.
          DIV r4, r2, r4             ;MQ now contains STEP. Remainder will be 0,
                                     ;but in HLLs, the remainder is ignored for DIV
                                     ;data to be passed is put in r0:r2
                                     ;START and INDEX are already in place.
          DCALL fft, rA              ;                                  even:=FFT( ... )
                                     ;Note that we will do DIV 2 as 1 SHIFT and not 32 DIVs.
          SHIFTsx -1(NUL), r2, r2    (*)                                ,size DIV 2)
          ADDx  nul,r0,MQ            ;move EVEN to MQ (used as regular register)
          DLOAD  1(SP), r1           ;INDEX back in r1
          DLOAD 2(SP), r2            ;SIZE/2 in r2
          SHIFTsx -1(NUL), r2, r2
          DLOAD 0(SP), r0            ;START in r0
          DCALL FFT, RA              ;ODD will be in r0                 odd:=FFT( ... )
          ADDx r0, r1, r1            ;INDEX + STEP in r1   (*)          index+step,
          ADDx r0, NUL, r2           ;ODD into r2
          DLOAD 0(SP), r0            ;new copy of START in r0
          LOAD butterfly, r4         ;address of butterfly from global table
          DLOAD 2(SP), r3            ;SIZE into r3
          DCALL 0(r4), RA            ;FFT will be in r0                 fft:=butterfly( ... )
          ADDc MQ, NUL, r1           ;EVEN into r1  (*)
          DLOAD 4(SP), MQ            ;restore old MQ
          DLOAD 3(SP), RA            ;restore original return address
EXIT:     ;                           RETURN TO PREVIOUS CONTEXT
          DJUMP 0(RA)                ;back to calling program
          LADDx 5, SP, SP            ;restore SP to previous value. (*)
 one:     ;                          then fft:=index
          DJUMP EXIT                 ;return
          ADDx r1, NUL, r0           ;INDEX put in r0 to be returned (*)
                                                                        ;end
```

This example is packed with different things to observe. Let us begin with the several issues of working space. Notice that we can do this none-too-simple subroutine with only two "permanent" registers. These are RA and MQ. Everything else fits into the "scratch" registers. RA must be saved whenever there is to be a subsequent call; MQ must be saved if MUL or DIV is used in the routine. In most cases, r0...r7/f0. . .f2 is more than enough working space for a routine. However, by defining these eleven as "scratch," we have no idea what will be in r0...r7/f0. . .f2 when a parent routine calls a child routine. Every CALL instruction must be thought of as likely to obliterate all eleven. The save-and-restore operation can be seen as comprising four steps:

1. Obtain enough space on the stack for all of the storage needed throughout the life of the subroutine. If we need a total of m spaces, then we obtain the space by executing

   ```
   LADDx -m, SP, SP.
   ```

   5 was subtracted in this instance.
2. Save register contents as needed by storing them in the stack using *stack-relative* addressing. All such addresses are of the form n(SP), where 0 <= n < m. A very common alternative with much to recommend it is to establish a *frame pointer* (FP), which contains the value of SP on entering the routine. The advantage of FP is that throughout the life of the routine it is a static reference to the stack and allows easy use of a dynamic SP.
3. Restore register contents by loading them back from the stack, once again using stack-relative addressing. In this case, only MQ and RA need be restored.
4. Remove the space from the stack by executing LADDc m, SP, SP.

This sequence of steps is shown in Figure 2.13. The setup comprises moving the stack pointer and then putting values into the area just opened up on the stack. The restoration has the computer copying the nonscratch values (MQ and RA) back to their respective registers and then moving the stack pointer back again.

With this scratch/permanent setup, the compiler (or assembly language programmer) must make its own judgment on whether to put something into a permanent register (and thus be obligated to later restore the contents of that register) or to keep a copy of the datum in the stack and to load it when a new copy is necessary. As we discussed in Chapter 1, the best allocation can be found by the map-coloring algorithm, where best is defined as having the minimum memory traffic. The idea of the scratch registers is to permit passing of parameters without matching pairs of loads and stores.

It is worthwhile to compare the setup/closedown burden in this machine with those of SPARC and the VAX. The VAX appears to do the save-and-restore painlessly with the mask at the top and the RET instruction at the bottom. (You can refresh your memory by looking at INNER in Section 1.3.1 on page 18.) However painless it looks, all of the registers saved are moved to memory and then restored therefrom. We use 7 registers; the VAX C compiler saved 10. On the other hand, the three CALLS would all involve setting up a call block on the stack. We need only put the proper values in

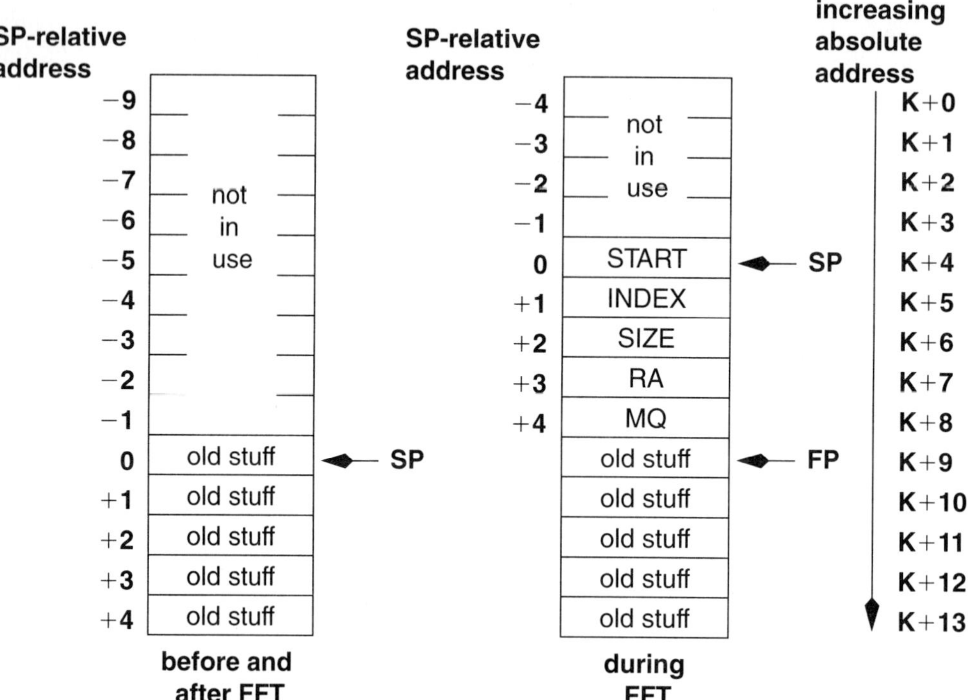

FIGURE 2.13 The stack at three points in the program of Table 2.6. The numbers on the left are stack-pointer relative addresses, whereas the numbers on the right and the position on the page represent the absolute addresses of the memory locations.

register. Count the explicit memory operations. We do 14. Compiling the same C program on the VAX yields a routine which consumes an average of 27.5 memory references in each instance. (Why "average"? Because the compiler improves upon our hand translation by unrolling one level of recursion, so each instantiation of the function accomplishes two passes through the routine. This saves the overhead of the extra CALL and RET.) Now for the real champion. SPARC, with its marvelous MORS, does one memory reference! That's it—at least until the MORS fills. The only memory reference is to the global NTOTAL.

Some other details are worthy of note. One is the difference in the calls to FFT and BUTTERFLY. The starting point of FFT is known to the assembler of FFT. It is, after all, the first instruction in the current routine. Accordingly, the assembler (or compiler) can do a PC-relative jump without any further information. The location of BUTTERFLY might or might not be known to the assembler/compiler and might be out of range of a PC-relative jump (±64K). The sure method of getting to BUTTERFLY is to load its address and then do a DCALL directly off that address. While this clearly works to address any location in all of memory space, you might wonder how the assembler/compiler knows where to find the address of BUTTERFLY. This is handled by common convention among all compilers and assemblers which would run on our machine. The convention uses the *linker* as the arbiter of where things get placed in memory. Once the linker has accomplished this allocation task for all of the modules in the program, it goes back into the code and replaces names with addresses. This is how all linkers work, but each machine handles the linkage in a manner appropriate to its own architecture. Briefly, ours works something like this.

Notice the format of LOAD BUTTERFLY, r4. It is *absolute*. Look at Figure 2.12 and note that there are four static regions of memory—constants, simple variables, program, and structured variables. The first two are guaranteed to lie within the 4-MW absolute address range. (That is, the linker would report an error if that were not the case.) The others are presumed to lie outside this range, though for most programs they will not. To guarantee accessibility to any location which might lie outside the absolute addressing range, we must use either base-index or base-displacement addressing. To do that, the assembler or compiler places a pointer to (address of) the labeled object in the constant region. Thus, one label generates two addresses: the *address* and the *address of the address*. These two addresses do not get assigned to the label until the linker is invoked.

To keep track of the two related entities during assemble or compile time, what the assembler/compiler programs do when they come to a line such as .G FFT:, which means "global label FFT," is to create two 13-character entries in a table. The first 12 characters comprise the label itself plus spaces (chr(32)) to fill in. The labeled object then gets an entry with a 13th character "^" (chr(94)) while the pointer to the pointer gets another space. Accordingly, indicating spaces by underscores, the line .G FFT will create two table entries:

```
FFT__________
```

and

```
FFT_________^
```

The table will tell the linker to assign `FFT__________` an address in the constant area. That is, `FFT__________` is the address of a constant. The value of that constant, also assigned by the linker, is `FFT_________^`. `FFT_________^` itself is the address of the object that the programmer wanted labeled. Thus, if the subroutine, `BUTTER-FLY`, was placed at address 3F0004 and if `BUTTERFLY____` was assigned 40C, then at location(40C), one would find 003F 0004. The line

```
LOAD BUTTERFLY, r4   translates to   00010 00100 0000000000000010000001100
                                     LOAD   r4,             40C
```

After executing this instruction, r4 would contain 003F 0004, the pointer to the function.

The linker's task of assigning appropriate absolute addresses to all the labels and then going back and filling in the "blanks" in the instructions themselves is really rather mechanical. It gets all of the data it needs to do the assignment in the tables from each module (one or more). It does these assignments first and then goes back to look for references to those labels, which it then replaces with the absolute values it has just assigned.

The last big item to note at this time in the program listing is how parameters are passed. Parameters can be either pointers (addresses) or values. Pointers are integer, but values can be floating point or integer. The first eight integer parameters and the first three floating parameters are passed through r0...r7/f0...f2 in the order in which they are listed in the HLL call. While rare indeed will be the function that needs more, if a call involves more than eight integer or three floating parameters, the remainder are passed on the stack starting at the current TOS and at increasing addresses from there. To illustrate that point, consider an absurdly long parameter list:

```
void silly(int0, int1, fl0, fl1, int2, fl2, fl3, fl4, int5...int9, fl5, int10);
```

There are 6 floats and 11 integers. `silly()` can find these parameters in the following locations:

int0...int7	in order in	r0...r7
fl0...fl2	in order in	f0...f2
fl3, fl4, int8, int9, fl5, int10	in the order shown	on the stack

We have three parameters passed to FFT and four to BUTTERFLY. The program saves the input parameters on the stack (because it calls other routines before it is finished with them) and then goes about its business. It sets up each call by putting the parameters in the right place. Upon return, the result is in r0. At the end, it puts its own reply in r0 and returns through the address in RA.

Observe how the call/return operation is handled. The CALL instruction deposits the return address in RA (by convention); the return is then simply DJUMP 0(RA). This copies the value in RA into PC and the machine is back in the caller's space. The internal mechanics of setting off in the direction indicated by the new address is covered in Chapter 6.

2.4 INTERRUPTS, TRAP, AND RFI

One of the pleasures of a chapter on RISC instruction details is the limited number of instructions. We are almost done. The coprocessor instructions are done in the next section. That leaves us only TRAP and *return from interrupt* (RFI). These are concerned with interrupts. Interrupts are intimately associated with the OS and the CPU, but even though we have whole chapters on the OS and the CPU, we need a little understanding of the OS at this point to see how interrupts fit into the processing environment of most computers.

Interrupts are predominantly a methodology for a computer to handle asynchronous events—that is, events which have no orderly place in the currently running program. These events can arise from computer activities or they can be entirely external. If a single computer is doing *multitasking*, the OS makes the several tasks take turns. Do not confuse multitasking with many users. One user will often have several tasks running at once. For example, there is the user's command process—the one that takes the OS commands from the keyboard—and from that command process subsidiary processes can be generated. For example, you might type RUN *program_name* on a VAX or just *program_name* on a UNIX-based operating system. That generates a new process. Another important example is the print-spooling process. When you send something to the printer, the file is put in a queue for a process that puts files out in the order in which it receives them. The sending process is done with the printing as soon as the file is transferred, but the printing process is busy as long as there are files waiting to be printed. To give all processes a chance to move forward, processes get a "turn"—a quantum of time or until they temporarily run out of work—and then get back in either the ready queue or the waiting queue (the bench). They repeat until done (which for some is never).

Often, as in the running of a program above, one process depends on another. For example, the execution of the instruction READLN(string_variable) would have to wait until the I/O process had a string for the program to consume. There is no reason to run a stalled program, so the OS would put the process to sleep until its I/O buffer has a full line for it to process. It would have previously put the command process to sleep, waiting for the program to conclude. Once the daughter process completes its task (or ends ignominiously for want of proper programming), the parent process is reactivated to received the next command.

This all sounds very orderly, but sometimes a dormant process wants service. A user waiting for his program to finish concludes that it is in an endless loop. He hits a key. That keystroke could be input for the program or the user saying: "Trash it!" The system must intercept each keystroke and examine it. If it is "just another letter" destined for the program's *input buffer*, then it should be put in the buffer and control returned to whatever was running at the moment. On the other hand, if it is <CR>, that completes a line and the line should be delivered, with a wakeup if appropriate, to the target process. Finally, if it is the *trash it* character or command, the operating system must suspend the process for which *trash it* was destined.[7]

Enough of background. Let us consider the mechanics of how the machine will pick up the letter. When you strike a key, there is some monitoring hardware connected directly to the keyboard that records the keystroke and notifies the host that a key has been struck. The notification comes about by having the keyboard monitor *post an interrupt*. Each type of interrupt has an *interrupt level* and may even be prioritized within a given level. The CPU has control over whether it is looking at interrupts of a particular level, but assuming that it is, once one or more interrupters post interrupts, the CPU receives a signal of an interrupt pending. The machine stops processing instructions and executes a *vectored* interrupt at the highest pending level. By *vectored* it is meant that the interrupter specifies the location of the starting address of the correct interrupt service routine. Once the machine is working at level k, no interrupt below k+1 will be accepted. When it returns from an interrupt, the level goes back to its prior value.

[7] On the VAX-VMS system, *trash it* is ^Y; on the IBM PC, it is ^C.

The vectored interrupt works much like a CALL instruction but with some important machine-specific differences. The *vector* is a displacement from a base register which resides in the data-cache memory management unit (D-cache) (see Figure 1.1). When an interrupt is accepted, the interrupter puts this displacement (the vector) on the bus. The D-cache forms the complete address, fetches the contents at that address, and puts it in the PC. Accordingly, the next instruction to be executed will be located at the address pointed at by (base+vector). Up to that point, the interrupt has acted like a JUMP. The problem that remains is: How can you get out so that you can get back?

From a hardware perspective, getting back is always done the same way, but from a programmatic perspective there are two very different views of getting back. In one, the interruption is completely independent of the current context—a peripheral needs some data or has something to report—while in the other, it has implications for the context—for example, your slice of time has run out and it is now someone else's turn. The desirable response from the orthogonal interruption is that it should finish quickly and then leave the original process running as if nothing had happened. The desired response from the second is that the original process be arrested in midstep, put out in the appropriate queue of continuing contexts, and then run again when its next turn comes up. The first class of interrupts calls for an essentially pure-hardware response to the end of interrupt; the latter calls for the interrupt service routine to "unload" the current context, load the next context to run, and then drop back by hardware return.

In our machine, there are eight levels of interrupt. Associated with each level are six registers: *instruction*, *previous instruction*, PC, latch C (*intermediate result*), SP, and STATUS word. These six define the essence of a *current state* and from them, the system can get back quite quickly to "what it was doing" before a single interrupt or chain of interrupts. Basically, the hardware must be told where it had been working and what it had been doing. The hardware details of recovery from an interrupt come up naturally in the discussion of pipelining (Chapter 6).

Let us assume that hardware recovery can be solved and turn to the issue of the stack. How does one keep the several interrupts from stepping on each other? Let us consider just three of these six multiply-defined registers. Each SP and PC register is like the one that we have been using up to now, SP0 and PC0. The STATUS register has 8 bits which do not change with level and 24 which do. The 8 bits are the IL active bits; the individual 24-bit registers contain the flags that we discussed above and several other bits. When the CPU accepts the interrupt, the host signals the interrupter to put its interrupt vector on the address bus. The interrupt vector is a 12-bit index into an array of addresses in memory. The processor takes the address indicated from the array and puts it into the PC for that level of interrupt; it sets the appropriate active bit in the common part of the STATUS word; and then it uses the *interrupt* SP and the new level STATUS word for continued processing at the new level. Figure 2.14 shows the relationship between the regular registers and this trio which change with interrupt level.

Before burrowing into some of the details, note that while handling an interrupt at level 3, the machine might be interrupted at level 6. It would switch from 3 to 6 right in the middle of handling 3. The process at level 0 would be waiting as well. The problem that is solved by RFI and the arrangement in Figure 2.14 is how to get back in correct precedence, finishing each task in order of priority before returning to a lower level.

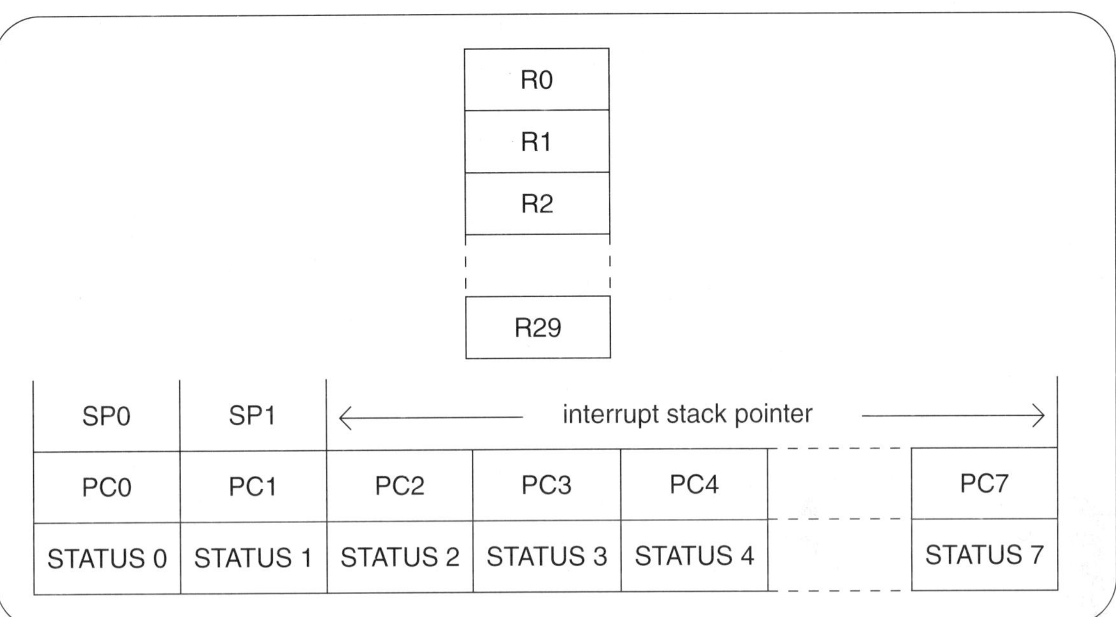

FIGURE 2.14 The eight levels of PC/STATUS pair and the three levels of SP with respect to the other 30 registers. The system is shown at interrupt level 3.

What RFI does is quite simple. It resets the active bit in the current status register. That, in turn, automatically switches the computer to the next lowest active level. For the example given, if RFI were executed at level 6, the machine would take its next instruction from whatever location PC3 was pointing to. Executed again, the machine would be back in PC0. This technique for handling interrupts is very fast, but the interrupt routines still have the task of saving and restoring whatever registers the interrupt handler routine must use. Machines which carry interrupt handling to the limit switch whole register sets so that no saving and restoring of registers is necessary. However, the more common method (e.g., VAX) would be to push both status and PC on the stack upon interrupt, then load them with values appropriate to the interrupt, and finally, when the interrupt has been serviced, restore them both with RFI. This is distinctly slower but cheaper. However, one of the payoffs in RISC design is the extra space (or money) that simplicity in processor design delivers. If one then wants to spend a little of these savings on an extra register set (note that we have just added 43 registers), one has the wherewithal to do it. Now let us look at the interrupt and return process in a little more detail. (We will treat the interrupt process from the perspective of the peripheral devices in Chapter 7.)

Consider that keystroke mentioned above. Assuming that this computer is in a multiuser environment, the keystroke might have come from any one of a couple of dozen keyboards. The server handling one group of keyboards has one interrupt level and one vector. Once the computer has acknowledged that one interrupt and switched, say, to level 3, it enters a routine which "knows" the particular keyboard server that has called for service by which interrupt vector was employed. The routine clears out a few registers by saving their contents on its own stack and then starts to process the interrupt. The computer queries the server (whose I/O registers look like memory to the computer) to find out which keyboard is sending something and which character was sent. The processor must treat each character to see if something special is required—a <CR> or control character from the user to call for some action—or if they are just to be pushed into a buffer for later digestion. If it is something special, then the interrupt routine will post a message—not an interrupt—for the OS. The interrupt does whatever is required of it, restores the saved registers, and does an RFI. The interrupted process recommences without ever missing a step. In fact, apart from a delay, the original process is totally unaware of the interruption. As soon as the current process's current turn finishes—within the next 10 ms if not sooner—the OS will look for any mail in its mailbox. If there is some—such as a request to kill a process—it will do what is requested, and then start (or restart) the next process in the ready queue.

Interrupts are not uncommon. In a multiuser environment, these brief interruptions may occur a hundred times a second, with each interrupt consuming from tens of microseconds up to a millisecond. As you can see, this would comprise a significant fraction of the whole processing burden, and it behooves us to try to reduce the time spent in handling interrupts. Both the use of vectors and the quick context switch aid in reducing the interrupt delay. Let us consider how vectors work and then see how TRAP fits into this scheme.

The vector itself is simply a 12-bit unsigned index into an array. Thus, it can specify one of 4096 elements. This block of addresses serves all of the interrupts. Along with setting up the vector array itself, the boot process must set up a pointer to the base of the interrupt array and also tell each potential interrupter which vector(s) to use.

When the interrupt comes, the base and the vector itself are appended together to form the complete 32-bit address as shown in Figure 2.15. The memory responds with the value stored at that address, which in turn is the address of the first instruction in the

FIGURE 2.15 Forming the pointer to the address in the interrupt or trap address array.

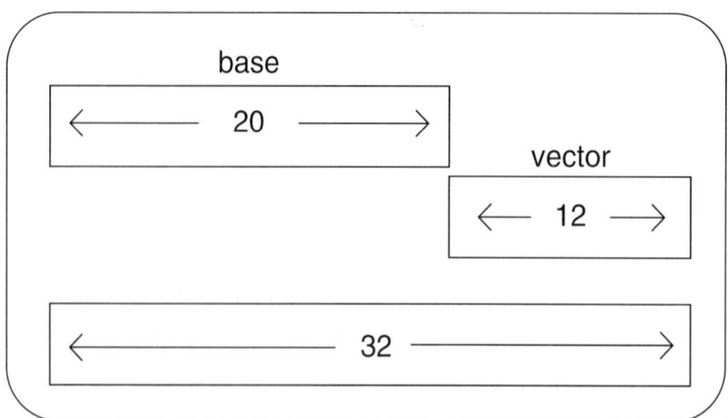

interrupt handler. If the character were ^C or ^Y, the handler would remove the program you had started from the list of current processes, post a notice to your program's parent process (the process which submitted the program) that the child process had been canceled, close any files opened by the process being eliminated, and then execute RFI to return to whatever else it was doing (which probably had nothing to do with your program). When next your turn on the operating system came up (several interrupts later), you would see on the screen a notice that your program had ended in a user abort. This would be fast enough that you would perceive it as an immediate response to your keystroke.

Now we are ready for TRAP.

2.4.1 TRAP, Protection, and OS Services

There are many services which an operating system provides to its client programs. Some of these must be accessed by user programs—I/O routines and memory management routines, to name two obvious classes—but one would not want just anyone mucking about down in the very bowels of the computer. He who has free access to the memory and the I/O processes has the power to snoop, modify, and destroy any data or process carried on by the computer. Even without assuming evil intent, people do trip over their own shoelaces at times. You do not want an error in judgment to become a catastrophe. As a barrier to misuse or error, most computer systems above the level of a simple PC are equipped with a *memory management* system which includes access control. Each *segment* or *page* of memory has an access code which specifies who may read and who may write to that page. The "who" ranges from[8]

- nobody, to
- kernel (level 1...7), to
- process (level 0)

A proper view of the playing field is many independent processes using and being controlled by a single kernel. Each process carries with it the access privileges appropriate to the individual process. In our machine, we refer to these levels as *interrupt levels* (ILs). For the active process, the IL is contained in the status register. For processes waiting to run, the value is retained in a copy of the last current status register. While there are eight ILs in our machine, they are segregated into two rings of security. The outermost ring is the normal *process mode* of operation. All levels above 0 are inside the security zone, or *kernel*. At any one time, any process can be operating at any level, although a process's right to move upward in level is restricted to a step of one

[8] These choices for names are from the PDP-11. Having only two levels of access is typical of UNIX, which saw much of its early development on the PDP-11. Some machines have many more classes of access. For example, the VAX system includes four, labeled USER, SUPERVISOR, EXECUTIVE, and KERNEL. We consider having two levels of security sufficient, though the hardware could support a total of eight.

level. The instruction which accomplishes this increase in privilege is TRAP. Thus, a process wanting a kernel service at level 2 must pass through the kernel level 1 (and ask politely). The reasons for and uses of security will be addressed in some detail in Chapter 3. We will flesh it out in hardware principally in Chapter 5. What we need now are the instructions which permit interrupt handlers and regular processes to move up and down in level as the need arises. An example is in order.

Consider what happens when a program running at process level wants some more memory. The program in HLL contains a statement:

```
NEW(pointer name);  or  b= (structure type)malloc(structure size);
```

These calls in Pascal and C generate code to invoke a system routine which returns a pointer to the new memory area. The routine might be able to fit the structure into a page of the heap that this user process already owned, but it is equally likely that it will need some space not yet allocated. At this point, the routine must ask the operating system to allocate another page (or more). Such an operation is not permitted at the process level. In fact, calls for assigning a new page require changes in the process page-table, a step permitted only at IL1 or above. The system routine begins at IL0 and traps into IL1 to ask for heap space. The operating system at IL1 makes sure that the request is legitimate. Satisfied, it switches to IL2 to change the current process's pagetables. That done, it must pass the pointer down through the ranks and return to the user program in IL0. The question we now wish to answer is: How does the hardware permit this process to get service from the operating system? Closely coupled is the question: How can a process go up and down the protection ladder?

Both questions are answered with the paired instructions TRAP and RFI shown in Figure 2.16. TRAP is nothing more than a programmable interrupt which raises the interrupt level by one; RFI is the instruction which returns to the most recently interrupted instruction stream, whether that be at IL0 or IL6. Our instruction must "tell the D-cache" it is trapping and give the D-cache the trap vector. After that, the D-cache treats it *almost* as if it were a real interrupt. A real interrupt accomplishes two things. It increases the interrupt level by interrupting at a specific level, and it issues an interrupt vector. It would never do, however, to have your average fumble-fingered programmer setting the IL to just any old value. Accordingly, the TRAP instruction provides a vector (i.e., the displacement off the trap base address), but the IL is simply incremented by 1.

The trap vector is the rightmost 12 bits of the instruction, as shown in Figure 2.16. The value of the vector is passed *as an address* to the D-cache. The D-cache, informed by a control line that this is a TRAP, appends those 12 bits to the trap-table address. That base address is (4096+interrupt base), where interrupt base is stored in a register available only to the operating system, so the user is not free to make it point at any old table. The D-cache fetches the desired trap routine address from the trap-address table.

An important restriction must be observed. The system must guarantee that trap-handling routines at or above the page-fault handler are always in central memory. We say that such routines cannot be *swapped out* to disk to make room for other things. This restriction comes about because if one got a page fault while in the page-fault

TRAP / RFI

assembly notation

machine format

	31 27	26 16	16		11 0
TRAP vector(0..4095)	OP		0 / 1		vector
RFI					

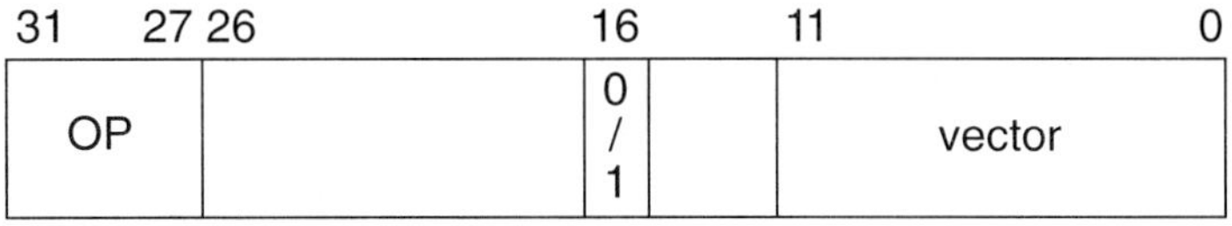

example:

assembly	binary machine code	hex code
TRAP 437	01110 00000 00000 00000 000110110101	7000 01B5

Bit 16 is set for RFI and reset for TRAP. The TRAP instruction signals the D-cache that it is trapping and puts its vector on the p-bus. The D-cache adds the vector to the trap base (interrupt base + 4096) and fetches the word at that address. The D-cache increments the IL by one. It puts the newly fetched word into the now current PC. If a TRAP is executed at IL 7, the IL is unchanged, so the instruction would behave simply as an indirect jump. It is strongly recommended that this not be done.

The RFI instruction resets the highest active bit in the status register. This deactivates the current IL, automatically moving to the next lowest IL with its active bit set. This instruction works equally well with interrupts and TRAPs. Every RFI *must* be followed with 2 NOPs.

FIGURE 2.16 Description of the TRAP and RFI instructions.

handler, the interrupt for page faults would be ignored and the system would process garbage or hang.

How will the routine to which the trap is directed know what to do? The usual interrupt is from a device with a very limited vocabulary and its own set of known memory locations through which data can be passed. The vector itself is enough to say what to do next. TRAP is a little different in that it must use registers or the stack to pass parameters. In that sense, it is really a form of CALL with very special side effects. To allow the vectored routine to know what to do, values are passed, when necessary, just as in the CALL routine—that is, they are put in the registers.

The critical difference between TRAP and CALL is the very side effect that causes us to put the instruction in the instruction set. We get an increase in privilege—we get into OS turf. Needless to say, there ought to be an ogre standing there with a big club, ready to devour any interloper that doesn't belong in this inner sanctum. The ogre must check the parameters passed and verify that they are proper values and that they come from a legitimate caller. If the TRAP proves faulty in any way, the ogre trashes the whole process which generated it, leaving behind a smudge in the process log explaining as politely (and often as obscurely) as possible the process's sudden demise.

After all of this discussion of TRAP, RFI will seem delightfully simple. What RFI does is simply to reset the most significant 1 in the status register. This immediately transfers operation back to the most recently active level. There is one curious little detail, which comes out of the hardware in Chapter 6, but RFI is inherently simple and delightfully quick in this machine. That curious detail is that the RFI instruction *must* be followed by two NOPs. The NOPs prime the pipeline at the IL level of the trap routine. Since IL0 is the basement in this hierarchy, one might ask what happens if the program issues an RFI at IL0. While one option would have been to pass over it as if it were a NOP, we make use of the incongruity of asking to descend from the basement. In Chapter 4, we introduce the concept of a *virtual machine* wherein one often is testing a new operating system by running it as a process under a proven operating system. Having the hardware take exception to RFI at IL0 and thus invoking the real operating system proves useful in implementing a virtual machine.

There is nothing more to TRAP and RFI than learning how they can be helpful. This is left to Chapter 3 on the operating system which makes extensive use of both of them (and a couple of exercises in the problem set).

2.5 SHAKING HANDS AND OTHER POLITENESSES—LODSET

In any processor intended for use in a multiprocessing environment, the instruction set must include at least one atomic (i.e., indivisible) operation which leaves a permanent mark, sign, or flag which can be observed by any other process. Why? The issue is discussed in fuller measure in Chapter 3, but basically such visible signals are necessary wherever shared resources contain critical paths which must be traversed completely by one process before being entered by another. These processes can be running alternately on the same processor or simultaneously on different processors. The possibility of conflict arises only when they share some modifiable data structure or some controllable piece of hardware. All of us have had the experience of attempting inadvertently to share passage in opposite directions through an opaque swinging door. If there is no warning of the other person coming through, somebody gets a flattened nose.

A similar problem can occur in a variety of ways in multiprocessing computer systems. A typical case would be that of two separate processes attempting to remove the first element on a linked list. A simple linked list can be made by having the first word in each element point to the next element of the list. This is shown in Figure 2.17. Notice that the list is started by a permanent *header*, which is simply a pointer to the first element in the list. The act of removing an element is simply changing the header pointer to the first element so that it points to the second element (while the process removing the element holds onto the pointer to that first element). If *process A* attempts to remove the first element at approximately the same time as *process B*, the first one should get element 1 while the second should get element 2. However, if B got started just after A, both might end up with element 1, or, possibly worse, they might interfere with the change of address in such a way that the header would end up pointing at nothing in particular. In other words, somebody gets a flattened nose.

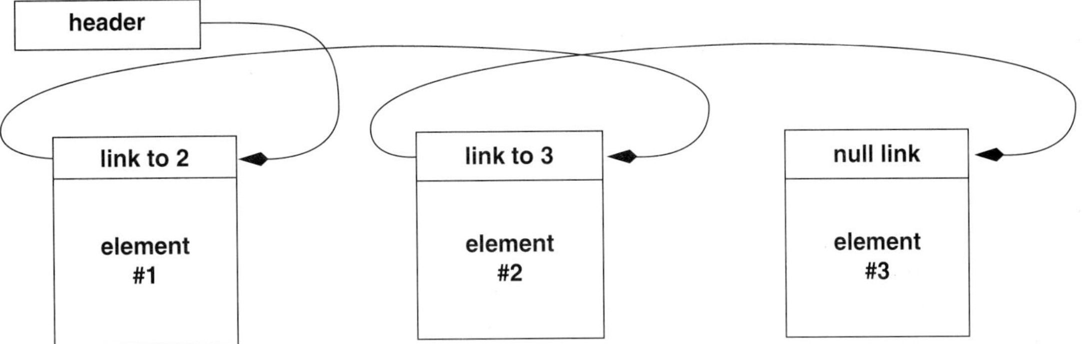

FIGURE 2.17 A simple linked list of blocks of data.

The way to avoid this situation with doors or queues is to have a well-recognized indication that the shared resource is in use. In the computer, this is done by having a *semaphore*, some indicator that all processes will recognize. One neat way to do this is to use the low-order bit of the header as the semaphore bit. What we would do is to guarantee that all elements begin on an even address. In that case, the header's low-order bit would be 0. If you read it and it isn't 0, you know that the list is "in use."

The obvious problem with this scheme is that the header is itself a shared resource. To be able to serve as an inviolable indicator, we must be able to guarantee that any process or processor which inquires about using the queue not only get the current value of the header but also *in the very same single stroke* set the semaphore to *busy*. This must be an indivisible hardware operation from the perspective of any observer (e.g., process or processor). Since the only access to memory is through the central bus, if we can do both the steps of reading the word from memory and writing it back with its LO bit set while never releasing the central bus to any other process, we will have accomplished the task of isolating the use of the resource. Such an operation is known as a read-modify-write bus cycle. They are a common capability of many busses including the VMEbus and Futurebus, one of which we will adopt for our processor.

To see how the semaphore works, consider what happens if two processors attempt to access that same header, one right after the other. Presume that the queue is initially unused. The first process reads the header and simultaneously returns it with its LO bit set. It tests the word it read and observes that the queue is unused. The second processor could begin its bus cycle immediately after the first finished. It too reads the header and sets *the already set* LO bit. Nothing has changed, but that is all right because the bit is still set. The second process observes that the queue is in use and is bound by the rules of good behavior to go away.

The first process can proceed at will, compute the new address for the header, and store it back in a conventional store operation. Since the new address will have the semaphore reset, the queue then becomes available to any other process.

What is left for us is to create an instruction which will accomplish this "atomic" transition from unlocked to locked (and also locked to locked). It is inherently different from the other LOADs because it does modify the word in memory. In our system (see Figure 1.1), all central bus operations ordered by the CPU are handled by the MMU/-DATA CACHE board. It is relatively simple to add the READ-MODIFY-WRITE cycle to that board. Accordingly, the instruction looks almost like a normal LOAD with the added proviso that the MMU board will set the LO bit and immediately return the word to the memory (as well as passing the unmodified word to the CPU). As usual, when we have only one version of a memory instruction, we use the most versatile addressing scheme—base-index. That leads us to the instruction format shown in Figure 2.18 for LODSET. (In an effort to keep the instruction name in six or fewer characters, we chose not to spell it LOADSET.)

2.6 TALKING TO THE NEIGHBORS—CP

The precise use of this coprocessor instruction is, of necessity, left to the design team on the coprocessor(s). What we must specify here is the interface standards to the CPU. That will remain invariant from coprocessor to coprocessor. We will also specify a sample set of floating-point coprocessor instructions which are representative of what one finds in some that are common today. Their opcodes are recognized by the assembler and they are developed in Chapter 9, which treats the floating-point coprocessor

FIGURE 2.18 Description of the LODSET operation.

Base-index Format, LODSET Operation

assembly notation

`LODSET RC, (RB, RI)`

machine format

31–27	26–22	21–17	16–12	11–0
I_OP	dest Reg C	base Reg B	index Ri	unused

example:

assembly	binary machine code	hex code
`LODSET (r6,r5),r25`	10110 11001 00110 00101 0—>	B64C 5000

The contents of the memory location specified by (RB, RI) is loaded into RC. At the same time, the value of that word in memory is ORed with the value 0000 0001 (hex) and put back into memory. The operation uses a bus READ-MODIFY-WRITE cycle which excludes any other processor from memory and guarantees that the modified word will be returned to memory before any other process or processor can read what is there.

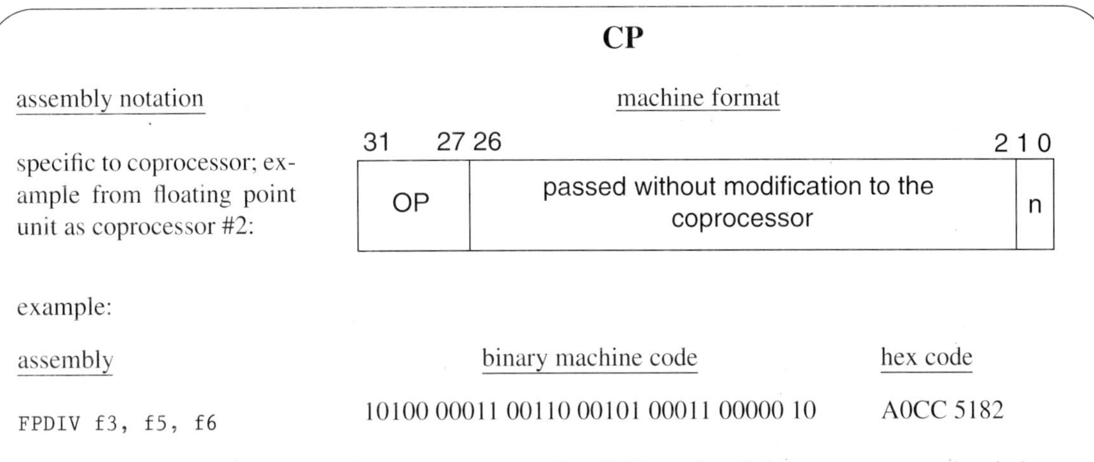

With reference to Figure 2.1, the opcode causes the CPU to signal the coprocessors that it has a coprocessor instruction on the private data bus. Bits 1:0 specify the particular coprocessor selected. Bits 26:2 are the instruction for the coprocessor.

The FPDIV command for the coprocessor happens to have code 3 followed by the coprocessor registers in the usual order (i.e., f6 = f3/f5). Bits 6:2 in this particular instruction are don't-cares.

FIGURE 2.19 Description of the CP instruction.

itself. We begin with the CP instruction as viewed from the CPU's vantage point. CP is quite simple. The 5-bit opcode says to the CPU, "Give this to coprocessor number *n*," where *n* is encoded in bits 1:0. The format is shown in Figure 2.19.

It is important to understand that the coprocessor number is not the slot or socket in which it is installed. It is the unique chip identifier. The architecture does not specify whether the chip has a permanent or a downloadable ID. This allows a single processor to control four coprocessors of the same type or four quite different ones. For our discussion here, we will presume a unique number for each type of coprocessor. Thus, if the floating-point unit was #2, then the assembler will put 10 into the last 2 bits of all instructions that it recognizes as belonging to that chip. One can change what the ID bits mean (by changing assemblers as well as chips) but a single system could have at most four of them at a time. Obviously, code generated with the expectation of a particular coprocessor on line would be fooled if run on a machine with another type of coprocessor with the same identifier. Generally, systems today are autoconfiguring. To accomplish that, chips have readable internal ID numbers which give not only their type but their version number. In that way, the boot software can provide both systems and processes the necessary information to run properly on all flavors of the platform. Generally, this is done by running slightly different code depending on what the application finds when it gets there. However, what about the machines which have no coprocessor of the type specified?

The need to have code run on all machines of a given type is a serious concern. Not only that, but the owner of the machine might want to take advantage of higher processing speed by adding the coprocessor to a machine he or she has already purchased. If changing to a coprocessor requires buying new code or even recompiling all old code, the price of changeover could be overwhelming. How can one accommodate the same code on a machine with or without the coprocessor? The answer harks back to our discussion of interrupts.

When the CPU sends out the control code *coprocessor n*, coprocessor *n* must reply: "Here I am!" on another control line. This is referred to as *handshaking*. If the handshake is not received, *n* isn't there, so the CPU receives an *invalid instruction* interrupt. The operating system picks up the offending instruction and examines it. If the invalid instruction turns out to be valid for a coprocessor known to the operating system, the OS simply performs in software what the coprocessor would have done in hardware. While this is a bit more complicated than it sounds at first—for example, a set of "coprocessor registers" for each known type of coprocessor that the OS does not find must be created in memory to provide storage for variables and intermediate results—the idea is reasonably straightforward. The difference in speed between emulation in software and execution in hardware will be somewhere between 100 and 1000 times. However, it is important to see that only speed is dependent on the physical presence of the coprocessor. The code would still run.

The CPU must be able to test status bits in the coprocessors in order to be able to branch intelligently on the basis of coprocessor results. If you will recall (Table 2.2 on page 70), jump instructions test many combinations of the five CPU flags. To test coprocessor flags, these must first be made accessible to the CPU. The mechanism we will employ is the control-line bus attaching the CPU and the coprocessors to transfer flags (five or less at a time) to the CPU. In other words, the flags that usually represent HvVNZC will now represent five coprocessor flags. Their meaning will depend on the coprocessor and the command that causes the transfer. Consider the following example.

The IEEE floating-point standard [IEEE, 85] requires that the coprocessor have four flags to indicate the result of a comparison of two numbers and at least five flags to indicate various problematic conditions or results (e.g., divide by zero or square root of a negative number). Our coprocessor will have two flag commands, each transferring five particular flags. Upon receiving such a command, the coprocessor pulls up a control line indicating that status is being transferred. The CPU then latches the 5 bits (on five other control lines) into HvVNZC. In other words, HvVNZC now would represent five other conditions, ABCDE. If fewer than five flags are transferred, the unused flags are reset. Immediately following this instruction, a standard JUMP instruction may be performed. This is the only command in which the processor and the coprocessors communicate *data* directly. To accommodate the user, the assembler may recognize mnemonics which are appropriate to different coprocessors, but in all cases, the JUMPs work as they always have—the JUMP tests 0 to 5 bits. The jump may be taken on either a TRUE or FALSE result of the test.

A most interesting question is: How do we get data into and out of the coprocessors? This question brings up the issue that there are differences between the internal representations of data within the coprocessors and those same data in the memory itself. Consider our paradigm coprocessor—floating point. The internal representation of *all* numbers within the coprocessor will be a double-precision format containing 64 bits. In memory, on the other hand, numbers are stored in one or more words which may represent integers or any of the IEEE floating-point formats.

We will find it necessary to be able to save and recall the contents of the coprocessor registers. The need for a method to store the contents of internal registers directly in memory arises in multiprocessing. When one process is to be swapped out and another brought in, the operating system must save the *state* of the current process and then load the state of the subsequent one. This necessitates storing all coprocessor registers. This literal copy of a coprocessor register will have the 64 bits, or two words. The other part of the state of the coprocessor is the status word. That too must be storable and reloadable (FPLOADS and FPSTORES). The ability to store a particular value in the status word provides the operating system (or program) the opportunity to initialize the coprocessor to a known state; being able to save and then restore the status word is required for a context switch.

The basic principle of any load or store operation is that an address must be issued along with a specification of the data direction (READ *from* or WRITE *to* memory). The data source then puts the data on the bus and the data destination reads it from the bus. In most cases, this set of operations is essentially atomic. For example, DLOAD 286(r12), r9 will form the address specified and put it on the bus. Since it is a LOAD operation, it will leave the READ/WRITE line unasserted.[9] Accordingly, memory will write the desired data to the bus and the CPU will read it from the bus and load it into register 9. For our CPU loads and stores, we simply separate the command from the address. Included among the CPU instructions will be all of the LOADdatatype and STOREdatatype instructions that the particular coprocessor needs. The instruction will include a source or destination register in the coprocessor but it will not include a memory address. The length of the data in memory is implied in the instruction. For example, a *double* requires two words. This instruction is delivered over the data bus to the coprocessor of choice. Let us say that the instruction was FPSTORED (floating-point store double). Following this instruction, the coprocessor expects to transmit two words of data. But where? The address function belongs to the integer CPU. Accordingly, the instruction stream to store that double comprises

```
FPSTORED        F3              ;issue the command
DLOAD           0(r9),nul       ;issue sequential addresses
DLOAD           1(r9),nul
```

Double is the easiest one for the coprocessor. No conversion is required. On the next clock stroke, the coprocessor must pull down the READ/WRITE line. Note that the

---

[9] As discussed in Chapter 8, shared bus lines are usually connected to a *pull-up* resistor, which passively holds the line high if no driver is *asserted* (pulling down). If any or all drivers are asserted, the line goes low. The bar over the WRITE indicates that when the line is asserted, the data direction is toward memory.

CPU is not asserting the READ/WRITE line, so the data direction is determined by the coprocessor. During the data phase of the first DLOAD, the coprocessor must write its first datum to the data bus. The CPU would ignore it (the NUL destination), but if the programmer desired (and some certainly will), a real register could have been specified and the data would end up there as well as in memory. On the second clock, WRITE is asserted again by the coprocessor and the second datum is driven onto the data lines. As a general rule, the program should use LOAD with the NUL destination as illustrated above, but since the coprocessor ignores the READ/WRITE line, it is possible to transfer data in both directions between CPU and coprocessor by getting clever with the addressing. However, if a datum is written out of the CPU with the WRITE line asserted, then that datum is going to memory, whatever the coprocessor may do with it. Thus, he who gets clever had better be careful with the side effects.

Along with problems of being too clever, we must consider the consequences of not being clever enough. What happens if some turkey does only one DLOAD after FPSTORED? How could this happen? Well, for starters, it is hard to keep someone else from writing an assembler even if you do not. Once a programmer has an assembler, any arrangement of instructions is possible. Even if an assembler is not used to get around the protection offered by a HLL compiler, people do write new compilers. A compiler bug could cause such an error. So then what happens?

The result of this failure to provide the needed address depends entirely on what happens in its place. Some instruction will be issued. Three possibilities arise for the FPSTORED instruction (none of them benign):

- (CPU does a STORE) The next datum coming out of the CP will get ORed with CPU data and sent to a memory address for which it was not intended.
- (CPU does a LOAD) The next datum coming out of the CP will get read by the CPU as the datum or *instruction* it was requesting and the memory will store the CP datum at the memory address for which it was not intended. An illegal access exception may be taken.
- (CPU does something other than a LOAD or STORE) If the bus is not used for a LOAD or STORE, it is always used for a fetch. Should the I-cache be looking for an instruction at that moment, it would swallow the OR of the D-cache instruction and the coprocessor data. A protection error is likely since code is normally read-only and the coprocessor would be asserting the write line (discussed in Chapter 4).

These errors would be devilish to find without a debugger or with only a HLL debugger. With a low-level debugger, long latency between the evil act and its discovery could still make the bug quite hard to uncover. Those who play at the assembly level must be prepared to live and die at the assembly level. We need not feel too sorry for them.

One issue should concern us, however. The ORing referred to in the first potential result comes about because two entities are writing to a bus at the same moment. If one can drive a bus line high and the other low, we have just arranged a short circuit. This particular problem will not occur in our design even if we do arrange to have two drivers competing on the bus. We are using a *pull-down* design in which each driver is really only a switch to ground. One driver or ten, you are still connected to ground. The two states are *no drivers* and *some drivers*. More than one active driver will be a logical problem, not an electrical problem.

Concluding this section, we propose a reasonable but not vast set of CP instructions for the floating-point coprocessor. These are a subset of what one would find on the Motorola 68881/2 or the Intel 80x87, but they are a powerful subset which meets most of the requirements of the IEEE standard. As you will see in the discussion of the coprocessor in Chapter 9, no great effort would be required to change the set. To see what really ought to be in there, one would need extensive studies of coprocessor use not unlike the CPU studies of Chapter 1. The instructions that we have included comprise almost all of those required by the IEEE standard (0...5, 14...18, and 1A...1E). This set, plus a few of the standard elementary functions found in Pascal and C, comprises the 29 instructions of Table 2.7. The instructions are encoded using 5 bits for each opcode or register field.

While most of the instructions listed in Table 2.7 are self-explanatory, several deserve at least a little comment. The instruction FPMOVE provides the mechanism for register-register transfers within the coprocessor. FPFLAGS performs the transfer of flags from a FP coprocessor to the CPU for subsequent testing using the standard JUMP instructions. FPLOADS/FPSTORES are the instruction pair for storing or

TABLE 2.7 **The 32 floating-point coprocessor instructions and their assembler formats.** Instruction 14 transfers flags from the FP coprocessor to the CPU for testing. F0...F7 are the FP registers. Instructions 15...19 are the LOAD instructions, with the order being single, *integer, double, reserved*, and *status*. 19 and 1E load and store the status word.

0	FPADD	Fx,Fy,Fd	10	FPATAN	Fs,Fd
1	FPSUB	Fx,Fy,Fd	11	FPMOVE	Fs,Fd
2	FPMUL	Fx,Fy,Fd	12	FPABS	Fs,Fd
3	FPDIV	Fx,Fy,Fd	13	FPNEG	Fs,Fd
4	FPREM	Fx,Fy,Fd	14	FPFLAGS	n
5	FPCMPR	Fx, Fy	15	FPLOAD	Fd
6	FPSIN	Fs,Fd	16	FPLOADI	Fd
7	FPCOS	Fs,Fd	17	FPLOADD	Fd
8	FPTAN	Fs,Fd	18	reserved	
9	FPSQRT	Fs,Fd	19	FPLOADS	
A	FPLOG	Fs,Fd	1A	FPSTORE	Fs
B	FPEXP	Fs,Fd	1B	FPSTOREI	Fs
C	FPLOG10	Fs,Fd	1C	FPSTORED	Fs
D	FPTENTO	Fs,Fd	1D	reserved	
E	FPASIN	Fs,Fd	1E	FPSTORES	
F	FPACOS	Fs,Fd	1F	reserved	

loading the coprocessor's status register (32 bits wide). FPCMPR sets four flags based on a comparison between two numbers in the coprocessors registers. These flags indicate the result =, <, > and *unordered*. The *unordered* flag would be set if an attempt was made to compare data which are not comparable, such as a pair of positive infinities. FPREM delivers the difference between the rounded quotient which one would obtain from FPDIV and the *nearest* integer. *X* REM *Y* differs from the more traditional non-integer form of *X* MOD *Y*. For both, $r = X - Y \times n$, but the two differ in how they select n. In MOD, you must always determine n by truncation to the integer nearer to 0; in REM, you must *round to nearest* to get n. For example, 8.6 MOD 3 is 2.6 while 8.6 REM 3 is -0.4 (because 3 is closer to the exact answer than 2). On the other hand, 7.4 MOD 3 and 7.4 REM 3 both yield the answer 1.4. For details on REM see Section 9.4.4.

2.7 A COMPARISON BETWEEN "OURS" AND "THEIRS"

We have reached the point where we should compare what we did above with something somebody built with the intention of making money. The RISC instruction set that is arguably closest to what we have come up with—none of them are grossly different—is SPARC. SPARC (a creation of Sun Microsystems and now the property of the SPARC International Consortium) certainly has made money and history. While it is not currently the absolutely-fastest-ever-since-the-beginning-of-time or necessarily the absolutely biggest bang for the buck, SPARC has been an enormous commercial success for all the reasons which have marked any and all successful machines: reliability, support, lots of software, and a cost/performance ratio which meets or exceeds their customers' current needs.

All right. If SPARC is at least one measure of success, how well did we do with our design heuristics? Table 2.8 presents a side-by-side comparison using the data from the Cypress manual [SPARC, 90]. The similarities are powerful, but the greatest interest is in the differences. What did we put in that they left out? What did they put in that we left out? The differences are small, but for some users, they could be important. The biggest differences are found in two places:

- **Addressing.** We have chosen word addressing; SPARC uses byte addressing. The advantage seems clearly to rest with our choice. We have four times the address space and no *odd-address* exceptions. While our method of byte and halfword addressing sees only one-fourth or one-half the address space at any one time, these ranges are one or two times their whole address space. We also provide a much more regular absolute addressing format. They sneak one in by using their 13-bit displacement on r0 (their NUL). Since the displacement is signed, that gives you access only to the bottom 4096 and top 4096 bytes. Useful perhaps, but not nearly so useful as the bottom 16 MB that our method addresses. Our displacement mode also covers a larger range, providing 17 bits of displacement to SPARC's 13 bits. We also provide greater variety in that absolute addressing is available with all instructions which use addresses except for the byte/halfword pair and LODSET. The greater displacement range is obtained at a cost of fewer bits for opcodes and opcode modifiers. We discuss these below. The benefit is probably small—long displacements are reasonably rare—but the cost seems tiny as well.

- **The MORS.** There is little doubt that a MORS cuts down memory traffic and saves time on function calls. We have chosen to put similar effort, in the sense of devoting lots of extra silicon, into rapid interrupt and trap response. Our observation is that one of the other principal RISC competitors—MIPS, IBM, Hewlett-Packard, and now DEC—has almost always owned the machine with the best cost/performance ratio and none use a MORS. The conclusion seems to be that compiler technology can make a MORS less important, encouraging the designer to use silicon to better purpose. Whether that purpose should be for fast interrupt and trap response probably depends on the expected applications.

Some other small but important differences exist. SPARC has included *tagged* addition and subtraction instructions. These were added to improve the speed in running programs in LISP and Prolog. The idea is that bits 0:1 serve to tag nonnumeric data. If arithmetic is attempted on them, it either sets the overflow bit or traps directly to an overflow handler. From the sources quoted in their analysis, it seems clear that these tag-checking arithmetic operations would definitely accelerate programs in these two languages.

The SPARC also offers somewhat greater variety in their logical operations. They add the possibility of doing a complement on one of the operands, so that you have instructions to do both $A \cap B$ and $A \cap B$. Complementing in our machine requires a separate instruction (LXOR -1, rB, rD). Should we change? Actually, if one is getting down to counting hairs to see whose head is baldest, our machine's literal-format logicals already have all the complementing power that the SPARC provides. Since we supply a 16-bit literal which is sign-extended and SPARC supplies a 13-bit sign-extended literal, we can set the literal bits above and below the 13th to be whatever we wish. Accordingly, to gain absolute equivalence with SPARC, we need change only the register forms. There are extra bits already available in the register forms, so adding the facility for complementing the second term would involve only a little bit of interpretive logic. Essentially, it is a no-cost option. A similar argument would apply to whether the inclusion of a zero-extension loading option on bytes and words is of great assistance. If the argument is yes, we could easily include it without expanding our instruction set, since there are unused bits in LOADH/B. It can be done with essentially no cost. That being the case, could it not have a net benefit?

On coprocessors, our approach is similar though not exactly the same. We allow four different coprocessors, at least one of which we expect to be an FPU. SPARC expects an FPU and allows one other coprocessor. Two small advantages derive from our method of address generation:

- We can move data between the coprocessors and the CPU.
- We have a much larger range of displacements.

Other small issues include:

TABLE 2.8 **Comparison of the instruction set developed in this chapter with the set specified for the SPARC chip**

F&R	SPARC	SPARC Address	Comments
JUMP			
DJUMP	Bicc	22_bit(PC)	16-MB range
IJUMP			
CALL	CALL	30_bit(PC)	4-GB range (whole memory)
DCALL	JUMPL	disp(13)	
ICALL	"	index	
LOAD	SETHI	literal	sets upper 22 bits of register
DLOAD	LD	disp(13)	
ILOAD	"	index	
STORE			
DSTORE	ST	disp(13)	
ISTORE	"	index	
SHIFTyz	SR/SL	static or dynamic, not both	
ADDz	ADDcc	rd=r1+r2	
LADDz	"	rd=r1+const(13)	
	ADDXcc	rd=r1+r2+C	includes carry bit
	"	rd=r1+const(13)+C	includes carry bit
SUBz	SUBcc	rd=r1-r2	
LSUBz	"	rd=r1-const(13)	
	SUBXcc	rd=r1-r2-C	includes carry bit
	"	rd=r1-const(13)-C	includes carry bit
ANDz	ANDcc	rd=r1 AND r2	
LANDz	"	rd=r1 AND const(13)	
	ANDNcc	rd=r1 AND r2*	complements second term
	"	rd=r1 AND const(13)*	complements second term
ORz	ORcc	rd=r1 OR r2	
LORz	"	rd=r1 OR const(13)	

TABLE 2.8 *(cont.)* **Comparison of the instruction set developed in this chapter with the set specified for the SPARC chip**

F&R	SPARC	SPARC Address	Comments
JUMP			
	ORNcc	rd=r1 OR r2*	complements second term
	"	rd=r1 OR const(13)*	complements second term
XORz	XORcc	rd=r1 XOR r2	
LXORz	"	rd=r1 XOR const(13)	
	XNORcc	rd=r1 XOR r2*	
	"	rd=r1 XOR const(13)*	
TRAP/RFI	Ticc/RETT	vector	
CP	CPop	allows FP and another CP	
LOADH/B	LDSB/H	index or disp(13) —	
	LUSB/H	"	zero extension
STOREH/B	STB	"	
	STH	"	
LODSET	LDSTUB		
MUL	MULScc	(1-bit Booth's algorithm)	In version 8, SPARC has
DIV			full integer MUL and DIV
	SWAP	index or disp(13)	exchange register and memory
	TADD/TADDTV	reg+reg or reg+const(13)	Sets V if bits 1:0 $\neq$ 0. If
	TSUB/TSUBTV	"	TV form, traps on V.
	SAVE		
	RESTORE		
	8 read/write to special registers	only 2 used by "process" for reading and writing rY	rY is equivalent to our MQ but used only for MULScc

- Our MUL is twice as fast as theirs.
- We support integer division.
- SPARC has a SWAP instruction. As you would expect, it takes twice as long as a regular LD or ST. Accordingly, it serves a useful function only if that specific action is

particularly advantageous. What makes the SWAP different from LD followed by ST (different registers, of course) is that it is *atomic*; nothing else that any other device is doing can get between the two halves of the exchange. It is another version of LDSTOR without the semaphore. We can accomplish the same transaction security as SWAP by using a semaphore to protect the transaction. The question of how much the added speed of SWAP would contribute to system speed revolves about how often different processors in a multiprocessor system need to exchange data. We have no studies which answer this question for us.

- They support the MC68000-like separation of address spaces for memory protection. Spaces include *process-instruction*, *process-data*, *system instruction*, *system data*, and *interrupt*. Almost all loads and stores have an *alternate space* form which may be used only by the operating system. We suspect that this is a leftover of earlier Sun implementations which used the MC68020 processor. Our machine uses a protection scheme (Chapter 5) more like that of the VAX, where several levels of access and different types of access are controlled by data that the system software can change. As a general design paradigm, we have avoided privileged instructions of any sort. Unlike SPARC, there are no special instructions for accessing protected registers or flushing the instruction cache. Nor is an instruction fetch any different from a data fetch. Instead, we control all accesses by standard techniques of memory protection. Then, we *memory-map* all of the hidden registers (i.e., we make them accessible through particular addresses in the standard memory space). If the process is allowed to read from but not write to the status register, then the area of memory into which the status register is mapped will simply be *read-only* at the process level. The reasoning behind this rule of design is to move as much control as possible into the system-software designer's hands. The only instructions of ours which trigger an exception by themselves are the unimplemented ones and the incongruity of RFI at IL0. By clever use of unassigned opcodes, one can use interrupts to do in software what newer versions of the same machine do by assigning those opcodes to specific actions. From that perspective, the *unimplemented instruction exception* is a valuable asset. (SPARC goes so far as to define an instruction, UNIMP, to achieve just this effect.)
- The SPARC allows the branch instructions to skip the bubble instruction if a branch is *not* taken. In some cases, this permits filling a bubble that would otherwise have a NOP in it. It does improve loop efficiency, but its inclusion in our design would not be entirely trivial. At this time in the design, we have found no particular need for resetting one or more stages of our pipeline to NOP. Furthermore, two of our JUMP modes have no "free" bits to make this choice. To make this alternative available generally, we would have either to free up 1 bit in the displacement and absolute modes or make a new set of modes for the JUMP instructions. The former is undesirable in that it would restrict the ranges and the latter is moderately expensive in silicon. This is not to say it is a bad idea, but unless we found ourselves frequently putting NOPs in the bubbles, it does not seem worth installing this particular feature.

In sum, then, our design seems to be pretty equivalent to one particularly successful design. We have a few bells and whistles that they do not and vice versa. As you will observe when we really get down to the nuts and bolts in Chapter 6, our very compact pipeline can complete an instruction every clock cycle, though for some instructions, there will be a "bubble" in which another instruction starts before the results from its predecessor are available. SPARC has instructions listed as taking one to four clocks and uses hardware interlocks to prevent accessing data before it arrives. Where delays exist in our machine, as in loading data, where the data is not available to the successor instruction, it is up to the software to prevent accessing old data.

CHAPTER SUMMARY

The largest portion of this chapter is certainly the detailed discussion of the 30 instructions which make up our RISC machine's vocabulary. Three forms of address specification were defined:

- absolute
- base-displacement
- base-index

as well as two forms for specifying an operand:

- register
- literal

Several registers were given names which are recognized by the assembler. These include

- r31 PC, NUL program counter
- r30 SP stack pointer
- r29 RA return address
- r28 MQ multiplier/quotient

Table 1.8 summarizes the CPU instruction set; Table 2.7 summarizes the instruction set for the floating-point coprocessor. The set of JUMP tests is summarized in Table 2.2.

Along with the instruction set itself, several very important concepts in memory usage and in interrupt handling were brought in, both because their definition was directly related to the instruction set and also because they are critical to the development of subsequent chapters. These included the partitioning of memory (Figure 2.12) into four static areas:

- constants
- simple variables
- program
- structured variables

TABLE 2.9 Summary of the instruction set, grouped by function

Assembly form		Effect
ADDx rX, rB, rC	ADDc rX, rB, rC	rC $\Leftarrow$ rB + rX (no flags); second form changes flags.
LADDx 4, rB, rC	LADDc 4, rB, rC	rC $\Leftarrow$ 4 + rB (no flags); second form changes flags.
SUBx rX, rB, rC	SUBc rX, rB, rC	rC $\Leftarrow$ rB - rX (no flags); second form changes flags.
LSUBx 4, rB, rC	LSUBc 4, rB, rC	rC $\Leftarrow$ 4 - rX (no flags); second form changes flags.
ANDx rX, rB, rC	ANDc rX, rB, rC	rC $\Leftarrow$ rB $\cap$ rX (no flags); second form changes flags.
LANDx 4, rB, rC	LANDc 4, rB, rC	rC $\Leftarrow$ 4 $\cap$ rB (no flags); second form changes flags.
ORx rX, rB, rC	ORc rX, rB, rC	rC $\Leftarrow$ rB $\cup$ rX (no flags); second form changes flags.
LORx 4, rB, rC	LORc 4, rB, rC	rC $\Leftarrow$ 4 $\cup$ rX (no flags); second form changes flags.
XORx rX, rB, rC	XORc rX, rB, rC	rC $\Leftarrow$ rB $\oplus$ rX (no flags); second form changes flags.
LXORx 4, rB, rC	LXORc 4, rB, rC	rC $\Leftarrow$ 4 $\oplus$ rX (no flags); second form changes flags.
SHIFTux -4(rA), rB, rC		rC $\Leftarrow$ rB $<<$ (-4+rA); positive sign is left shift
JUMPGTE 4097		if ((!v && !n) $\|$ (v && n) PC $\Leftarrow$ 0x00001001
LOAD 4097, r5	LOAD *name*, r5	r5 $\Leftarrow$ M(4097), linker replaces *name* with 4097.
STORE r5, 8193	STORE r5, *name*	M(4097) $\Leftarrow$ r5, linker replaces *name* with 8193.
CALL 4097, RA		r29 $\Leftarrow$ PC, PC $\Leftarrow$ 0x00001001
DJUMPLT -129(PC)	DJUMPLT *label*	if ((v && !n) $\|$ (!v && n)) PC = PC-129;
DLOAD 0(SP), r5		r5 $\Leftarrow$ M(r30)
DSTORE r5, -16(SP)		M(r30-16) $\Leftarrow$ r5
DCALL 0(r6), RA	DCALL *name*, RA	r29 $\Leftarrow$ PC, PC $\Leftarrow$ r6; second case PC $\Leftarrow$ PC±*offset in module*
IJUMPLTU (r4, r22)		if (!c && !z) PC $\Leftarrow$ r4 + r22
ILOAD (r4,r22), MQ		r28 $\Leftarrow$ M(r4 + r22)
ISTORE MQ, (r4,r22)		M(r4 + r22) $\Leftarrow$ r28
ICALL (r4, r22), RA		r29 $\Leftarrow$ PC, PC $\Leftarrow$ r4 + r22
FPADD f3, f4, f4		f4 $\Leftarrow$ fr + f3; floating-point operation.
LOADB (r4,r22), r5		loads sign-extended byte into r5. See Section 2.2.2.1.
STOREH r5, (r4,r22)		stores rightmost halfword from r5. See Section 2.2.2.1
MUL r5, r9, r5		one (of 16) steps in forming r5:MQ = r9 * MQ
DIV r22, r5, r22		one (of 32) steps in forming MQ = r22:MQ/r5 (rem. in r22)
TRAP 2022		IL $\Leftarrow$ IL+1; PC_{IL} $\Leftarrow$ M(interrupt base+4096+2022)
RFI		IL $\Leftarrow$ IL-1

as well as a dynamic area, filling the entire space between the static structured variables and the end of memory, containing

- heap
- stack

The critical difference between stack and heap is that stack space is tied strictly to the subroutine which requires it, disappearing just before the subroutine itself. A parent routine can pass pointers to stack space to a child routine, but the reverse operation cannot be done. In contrast, the assignment and release of heap space is entirely at the control of the process. Pointers to heap space can be passed both up and down in the program hierarchy and disappear only when the program chooses to release them.

The instruction set and the hardware support rapid interrupt handling, including the possibility of programmable interrupts (TRAP). While the concept of an external event needing immediate service is self-evident enough to require some form of supervision of externalities (interrupts or frequent polling), the great utility of interrupts in the management of a multiprocessing environment is deferred to Chapter 3. What was presented in this chapter covered the mechanics of switching to the interrupt handler using a vectored interrupt and then returning to the original context using the RFI instruction.

PROBLEMS

2.1. In signed arithmetic with 32-bit words, FFFF FFFF is -1. In unsigned arithmetic, it is the largest possible 32-bit number (4 G). Using 2s-complement arithmetic and 32-bit registers, show that signed and unsigned addition of index FFFF FFFF to any base address leads to the same memory address—the predecessor to the base word. (Words may be more valuable here than numerical examples.)

2.2. Hand-compile the code to do the operation A = A+B; into assembly and machine code. Let A and B be at locations 1390 and 1391 respectively.

2.3. Hand-compile the following statement using shifts rather than MUL/DIV operations. Let unsigned int *a*, *b*, *c*, *d* lie in successive words with the address of *a* in r26. r2 through r7 are available to you, but use as few registers as possible without wasting instructions. Remember to work in appropriate delays for LOADs and JUMPs.

```
If (a==b && c==d) a = a/2;
else a = a*4;
```

How many registers and how many instructions did you need to do this one complex HLL instruction? (The best solution we have received uses 12 instructions and no NOPs, though you may be able to do better and can certainly do worse.)

2.4. A full multiply takes 16 instructions. Let us hypothesize that 80 percent of integer multipliers are less than 32768 and therefore can be multiplied in 8 steps. Write an assembly-language multiplication routine which takes advantage of this and then determine if the overhead of making the choice and cleaning up afterward has really saved you anything over just doing 16 MULs.

2.5. We chose to give our processor the ability to read 1 byte at a time, arguing that it was a nuisance to program unpacking and packing bytes out of and into words. To prove the point, write two sections of assembly code: one that takes the word in r2 and puts its bytes, starting with the rightmost one, in r3…r6; and one that reverses the process. Be sure to sign-extend the results of the unpacking. (In our solution the combined operations of unpack and pack take 17 instructions. We have room for more instruction types since creating another LOAD and STORE pair still only gives us 30 instructions total. With these new byte instructions, handling 4 bytes takes four LOADs and four STOREs. Case proved.)

2.6. A literal in an instruction is almost always sign-extended to a full 32 bits before it is used in an operation. With this sign-extension idea in mind, what logical operation on the contents of r5 does one get from the instruction

```
LXORx -1, r5, r5?
```

2.7. There is a programmatic quirk to having byte addresses which are intrinsically different from word addresses. To see the issue, let us say that you have two different base addresses, one in r9 and one in r6. Base addresses, of course, are always word addresses. The offsets then count bytes. Now let us say that there are two offsets associated with the two bases. These are in registers r10 and r7, respectively. Write a small assembly program section which determines whether the r6:r7 pair are pointing at the same byte as the r9:r10 pair.

2.8. The choice of JUMP never as the NOP was based at least in part on the ease of recognizing it in doing *disassembly*, that is, changing machine code back into assembly code. There are certainly lots of different instructions in this machine that can fill a hole and do absolutely nothing. Find one from each general group of instructions in the instruction set and establish that, in the words of Gilbert on the House of Lords, it "did nothing in particular and did it very well."

2.9. Coding which requires you (or a compiler) to keep track of delays—that is, *delayed branching* or *delayed loading*—undoubtedly provides traps and pitfalls for the unwary. Consider the perfectly reasonable construction:

```
if (a>b){ … };
else if (a==b) { … };
else { … };
```

You might translate it as follows, with *a* in r6 and *b* in r7:

```
if_1:
    subc r6, r7, nul
    djumpgt bigger
    djumpeq equal
less:
    instruction X
    ;block of code
    djump done
    ;bubble filler (either a NOP or a worthwhile instruction)
equal:
    instruction Y
```

```
    ;block of code
    djump done
    ;bubble filler (either a NOP or a worthwhile instruction)
bigger:
    instruction Z
    ;block of code
done:
```

(*a*) Explain the consequences of this coding scheme for the three branch possibilities.

(*b*) Code it properly with the fewest possible NOPs.

2.10. It would not take too long for hackers to discover that you can use STORE to move data from CPU register directly to a coprocessor register in action similar to snatching the data from the data bus on a coprocessor store instruction. Create a sequence of instructions which passes the data in R8:R9 as a double-precision floating-point number to F4. Also, show that the READ/WRITE line does work as it should for this sequence. For purposes of making all answers the same, let the pointer to the address in memory for storing the data be in R14.

2.11. Hand-compile the following small Pascal function, VECTOR_LENGTH, into assembly code for our machine. Recall that a function which returns a floating-point variable leaves it in floating-point register f0. Remember that r0...r7/f0...f2 are scratch registers.

```
type
    vector = array[0..99] of DOUBLE;

Function VECTOR_LENGTH (here: vector; length: integer): double;
    var
        index: integer;
        sum: double;
begin
    sum := 0;
    for index := 0 to length do
        sum := sum + here[index] * here[index];
    vector_length := SQRT(sum);
end;
```

2.12. C includes *unsigned* as an integer type. On our machine *unsigned integer*, for example, will be 32 bits wide and span the range 0...0xFFFFFFFF. How will you realize proper unsigned multiplication on our machine? Consider the 32-bit case and allow results of any length that C would admit including a 64-bit *long*.

2.13. While we are considering unsigned operations, we should not leave out addition and subtraction.

(*a*) Show that the arithmetic operations are identical with signed arithmetic but that the meaning of the results may be quite different.

(*b*) If *unsigned overflow* is defined as meaning going over the top or out the bottom of the unsigned range, write functions in our assembly code to which are passed the two parameters, which perform the arithmetic, return the sum or difference, and set the V flag if an unsigned overflow occurs.

REFERENCES

[IEEE, 85] *IEEE Standard for Binary Floating-Point Arithmetic*, **ANSI/IEEE Standard 754-1985**, IEEE (1985). This document defines the IEEE floating-point standard. It specifies the required formats, operations, rounding, and exceptions. It does not explain the reasons for these choices.

[SPARC, 90] **SPARC RISC User's Guide**, 2nd ed., Ross Technology, Austin, TX (1990). See also **The SPARC Architecture Manual**, version 8, SPARC International, Prentice Hall, 1992.

CHAPTER 3

OPERATING SYSTEMS

THE INTERFACE BETWEEN THE HARDWARE AND THE REST OF US

3.1 OBJECTIVE

For those who have had a course in operating systems, you might wonder why an architecture book should have a whole chapter on this "software" topic. The answer is that the operating system requires well thought through hardware support. Most operating system courses do not get down into the trenches to see how operating system concepts are carried out. The designer had better get into that trench or the computer will not work well. The operating system is intimately involved in productivity. From Chapter 1 onward, productivity has been the theme. It behooves us to have a good if rather limited look at what the operating system will need from our machine. This chapter marks the beginning of that study. Two especially important subjects which are essential parts of the operating system and of the hardware get their own chapters. These are memory management (Chapter 4) and input/output (Chapters 7 and 8). For those who have not had a course in operating systems or who are curious about the details, we provide a *down in the trenches* discussion of process creation, pipes, and process termination in Appendix IV.

Most processors never see a keyboard or a screen—such processors support embedded applications in cars, washing machines, tape drives, and TV sets—yet the machines we all have in mind when we say "computer" interact with human operators. While we are not yet computing through such endearing fellows as R2D2, the interface that greets us as we try to log in and get something done is far friendlier than the bare and empty computers that were common in the '50s. In those beasts, you started by cranking loader instructions into memory *one bit at a time*.

```
repeat
    put in an address;
    put in a datum;
    hit the enter button;
until done.
```

Then set the starting address and press go. You would be amazed or amused by how few instructions can be used to create a *rim loader* whose only task in life is to load a bigger loader (from punched card or paper tape) and then the bigger loader would load the real program. The real program would run until it issued a HALT instruction. If you had anything else to do, you could repeat the process. *Multiuser* back in those days meant that someone else took over on the next eight-hour shift.

Consider the difference today on a typical multiuser machine on a college campus. You go to the terminal of your choice, hit a few <CR>s, and type in the name of the machine that you wish to use. Up pops an invitation to log in. Once on, you can invoke a host of different activities—word processing; mail; program creation, compilation, and linking; debugging; data base creation, editing, and querying; spreadsheet operations; mathematics programs . . . the list is certainly long and varied. But that is not what we want you to consider. Whether you work on your own personal computer or the school's megamonster, getting there, getting on, and invoking the application of choice is easy. Something is "in there" handling your queries, providing services, making the computer work for you. That something is the *operating system*. In the most fundamental sense, an operating system is a set of programs or applications like any other program. The most conspicuous part of the operating systems with which you interact is the *command interpreter* or *shell*. Whether you issue commands by pointing and clicking or by typing obscure strings of pseudo English, the operating system responds to the command(s) by making something happen. This most conspicuous of attributes, however, is one of the more peripheral of the operating system's tasks. As much as the operating system serves to make things happen, perhaps its most important function is to be sure that some other things *don't* happen. If they do happen, the result is likely to be a *system crash*. Generally, that calls for a manual or automatic reboot to put the system back together again. Data will be lost, tasks will be delayed, valuable man hours and machine time will vanish. This suggests that the operating system is as essential and central part of the computer as the CPU. That view is quite correct. From here to the end of the book, we will see that the operating system dictates hardware decisions.

3.2 FUNCTIONS OF AN OPERATING SYSTEM

It is not only possible to use a computer without an operating system; it is done quite regularly. The typical embedded computer usually runs *bare*. It has a program in ROM and runs that program forever. Even big, multiuser computers have some programs, typically diagnostic programs for testing the hardware, which can run entirely by themselves. However, as soon as we want our computer to handle multiple tasks, whether sequentially or concurrently, good reasons appear for having an operating system. A class of such reasons can be grouped under the rubric of *providing services*. For example, most programs need to access input/output devices—disks, terminals, and printers. There are two reasons for moving the I/O routines into the operating system. The first is that such drivers can be fairly complex. Rather than oblige every program to supply these complex I/O routines, simple economics suggests including them in the operating system. The second reason is one of enforcing discipline. One of the things that every user wants is to be able to carry disks from one machine to another, to write on one and read on the other. Users also want to be able to put multiple files on one disk. In order to do that, it becomes necessary for all applications to obey certain rules for reading and writing. The only sensible way to enforce such rules is to make all reads and writes pass through the same driver routines. Again, this argues for putting those routines in the operating system.

In this one example, we have the essential reasons for having an operating system to

- provide a single, easily accessed source for common software needs
- maintain discipline in the use of shared resources, which include I/O, memory, and the processor(s)

Consider a *timesharing* system, where many unrelated programs run concurrently on the same machine. *Concurrently* here implies that the several programs take turns on the processor(s), that they are resident *simultaneously* in memory, and that they share access to I/O devices. There must be some way to

- decide which program will use the processor(s) at a particular time
- switch between programs
- prevent users from interfering with each other in use of
  the processor
  memory
  I/O devices and disk files
- protect *the protector*—the operating system

3.2.1 Flavors of Operating Systems

Operating systems are available for a variety of special purposes. The earliest operating systems were called *batch* systems. In batch systems, a sequence of programs was presented to the operating system, typically using large decks of punched cards. The operating system simply executed them one after the other. There was essentially no sharing of anything. While batch processing in some sense still persists, it gave way in the 1970s to *timesharing*. Interactive timesharing systems allow users to treat the machine as their own personal computer. (The PC as a real thing did not appear in force until the '80s.) Users communicate with the computer through *terminals*, with input going in through the keyboard and responses being returned on a video terminal. Except for links through computer applications such as *mail* or *phone*, no user is aware of any other one. Yet all of the users are simultaneously connected to one machine. However transparently, they are sharing the use of resources such as the processor, memory, and disks. With the advent of cheap microprocessors, true single-user systems have become remarkably common. On a single-user machine, it is possible to use a very simple operating system, such as MS-DOS, which is essentially an interactive batch processor. One thing gets done at a time. However, single users can have multiple tasks, so sophisticated single-user machines use a *multitasking* operating system, which can share the resources of the machine among different programs, even though all of the programs may be serving the same user. In this chapter, we will assume that the operating system is capable of handling both multiple tasks and multiple users. Typical examples of multiuser, multitasking operating systems are DEC's VMS for the VAX, IBM's VM/CMS for the 370, and UNIX for almost any type of computer.

We have mentioned several times that most computers spend their waking hours in embedded applications. More and more frequently, these applications are complex, multitasking problems which have the added constraint that certain external stimuli require prioritized, predictable, and rapid response. Human beings are marvelous examples of such *realtime* operating systems. Eyes must blink before the owner is aware that something has intruded into his or her peripheral vision and the eye response to something alarming (or exciting) normally precedes the response to the smell of smoke or the calling of a name. In order to satisfy these kinds of constraints, realtime operating systems must provide some way to guarantee that a particular program will remain in memory even when it is not using the processor, and it must guarantee fast prioritized response to external interrupts.

A major application of large computers is called *transaction processing*. For example, the computer systems which are used for airline ticket processing may have thousands of I/O devices, all of which are attempting to update information in the same data base. A transaction is a combination of computations and data base accesses which must be done as a single "atomic" operation in order to keep the data base in a self-consistent state. No other transaction can be allowed to interfere. Only one person may buy a particular seat on a particular flight. (Ah, would that were true!) A machine used for transaction processing clearly requires a very efficient I/O system, must access data bases very well, and often must be robust enough to function in spite of major component failure. Operating systems for transaction processing must provide reasonable response times for all queries and guarantee self-consistency in the data base and noninterference between transactions. Frequently the computing power to achieve these goals leads to systems with multiple machines joined together to serve a common if diverse set of tasks. Achieving self-consistency and noninterference with multiple machines working on a common problem is certainly a nontrivial objective.

Operating systems which support multiple users or multiple tasks are often called *multiprogramming* systems. We will soon define an entity called a *process*, which is almost but not quite equivalent to a *program*. Unfortunately, this leads to confusion between *multiprocessing* as a synonym for *multiprogramming* and *multiprocessing* systems used to describe a computer system with more than one processor. We will attempt to maintain the distinction by using multiprogramming or multitasking for running several programs/processes and multiprocessing for machines with two or more processors working in parallel. Since most multiprocessing systems do multiprogramming, you can see the need for care.

Parallel processing is quite the buzzword today but even if you use *multiprocessing* to mean that the system has several CPUs, that does not define a unique class of machines. The simplest multiprocessor contains a single central processor and one or more I/O processors (IOPs) or I/O channels. In this case the operating system is mostly on the central processing unit, and only the routines which control I/O devices run on the IOPs. More complex conceptually is the multiprocessor system called *master-slave*. Here there is more than one CPU running user programs, but the operating system runs on the master CPU and simply assigns certain user programs to the slave CPUs. An even more sophisticated arrangement is a *symmetric* multiprocessing system, where both operating system routines and user programs run on all of its principal CPUs. Multiprocessors which share a common memory are called *closely coupled*; those which communicate only through some kind of communication channel are called *loosely coupled*. Loosely coupled computer systems often have independent operating systems running on each computer and the cooperating systems can be hundreds or thousands of kilometers apart. If the communication channel is fast enough, it is also possible for loosely coupled processors to share a common distributed operating system.

3.2.2 Hierarchies and Services

Now let's look at the services provided by an operating system in more detail. The most fundamental functions of an operating system all involve the allocation and protection of resources. These resources include the processor(s); the memory; I/O devices such as terminals, printers, and disks; and files on the disks, or even records within files. It is the function of the operating system to share the resources among users or programs and to protect the resources assigned to one user or program from other users or programs. Notice that protection is required not only from malicious users or programs containing malicious features (such as viruses), but also from programs which simply contain errors that might cause damage.

Although this allocation and protection function is the raison d'être of an operating system, most systems provide other functions simply because they are things that many programs or users require. Examples include

- libraries of subroutines which can be linked with user's programs
- programs that the user can invoke or that the system invokes in the user's behalf:
  the login program
  mail services
  command interpreters (*shells* in UNIX)
  directory services including creating, deleting, and copying files
  compilers, assemblers, and linkers
  editors
- I/O services to and from disk, tape, printers, and displays

You may not have been aware that so many of these services really result from the launching of specific programs, but in multiprogramming operating systems, that has been the popular way ever since UNIX appeared in 1970. The truly central and essential services of allocation and protection are grouped into a relatively small program called the *kernel*. All other functions are provided in separate programs, stored in disk files, and executed as needed, just as if they were programs written by users. This provides complete flexibility; users can buy or write programs to provide the services that they want. For example, three different command line interpreters are commonly found on UNIX systems, and each user can choose which one to use at any time. Some operating systems include the essential functions in a kernel, as in UNIX, but provide additional functions as another layer of the operating system, which may be called a *supervisor* or *agent*. This layer has more privileges than an ordinary user program, but fewer than the kernel. The grandfather multiuser operating system of them all, Multics, carried this layering to remarkable depths, as we will see in the next section.

This chapter and the next will describe most of the important features of operating systems. Our focus will be on the UNIX kernel. UNIX is a particularly appropriate operating system to use for our RISC machine, since it was designed to be portable, is widely available on virtually all classes of computers, and is reasonably simple and compact. While "small," it includes most of the more complex features we would like to implement (and discuss), such as protection and communication between asynchronous processes. We will stress those features which affect the design of the hardware.

The layout and parts of a UNIX-style kernel are shown in Figure 3.1. The position of a particular service or action in that diagram indicates in some sense how close the routines are to direct hardware transactions. All software runs on hardware, of course, but the hardware in Figure 3.1 is a restricted subset of the whole machine. In many machines access to this hardware is limited to privileged instructions; in our machine, the restricted hardware items are assigned privileged addresses. In either case, only software running in a privileged state can access the special hardware itself. In machines which have only two states—*user* (unprivileged) and *kernel* or *system* (privileged)—those system routines which lie outside the inner circle are not intrinsically different from any process started by an identifiable user. They are called *system processes* because they were started by and support the work of the system. At the outermost ring, the process ring, all the computation is done at *user* level. The processes—the individual programs—whether their origins are users or the system, are unprivileged. They obtain privileged system services either by trapping into the kernel (deliberate requests) or by causing a fault or exception which causes an interrupt into the kernel.

To understand the entire panoply of hardware mechanisms, we would have to understand large pieces of the operating system. The essence of the issues, however, can be found in four critical areas:

- mechanisms to enter and leave layers of the operating system
- interprocess communication (IPC) mechanisms
- memory management
- the context switch (processes taking turns in using the CPU)

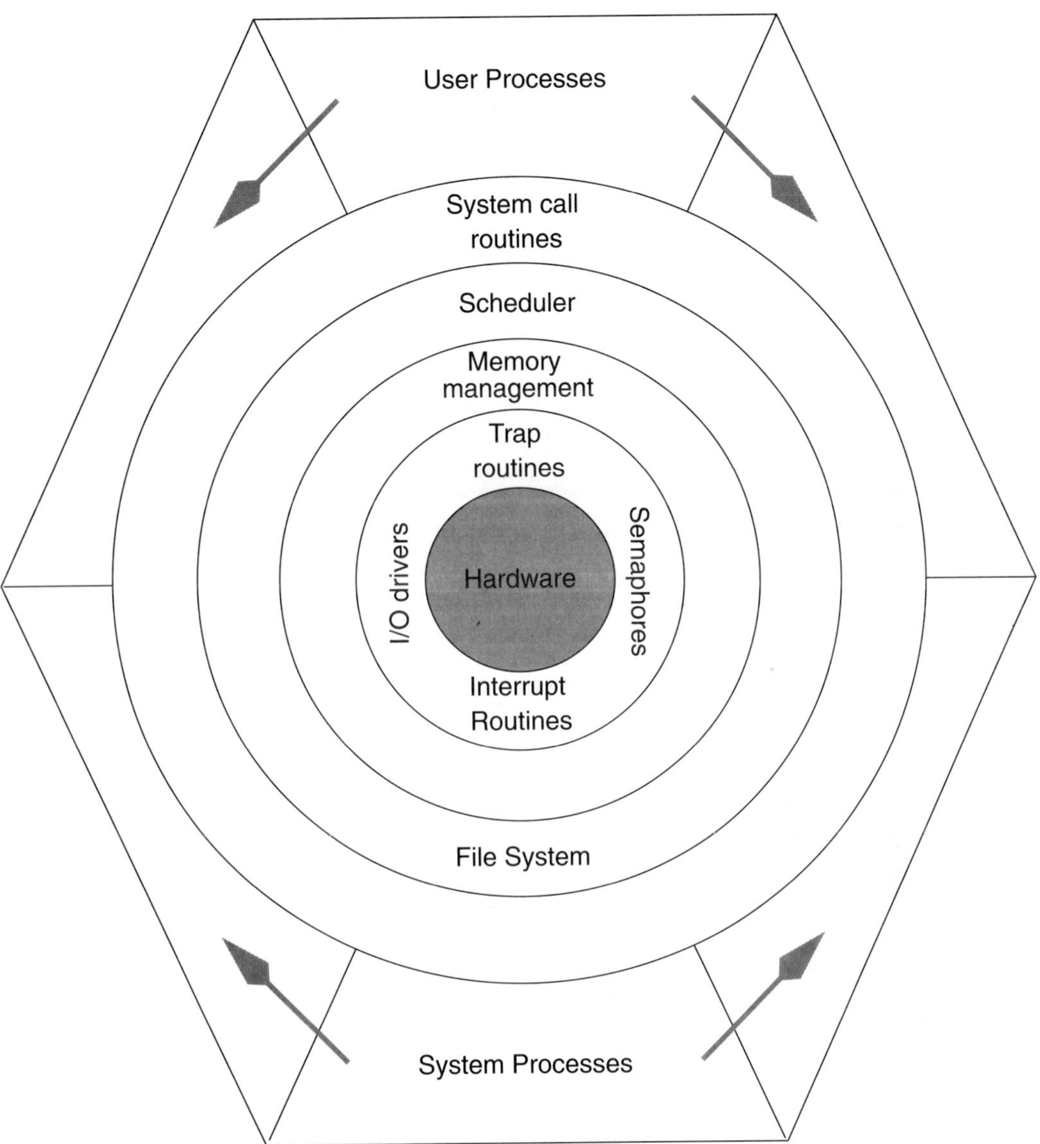

FIGURE 3.1 Elements of a typical system kernel in a multiprogramming environment. Hardware connection to the kernel through traps and interrupts is at the center of the diagram. The kernel ends at the outermost ellipse. System processes differ from user processes only in terms of origin. Processes all share the same kernel. They obtain direct system services through traps and indirect system services through interrupts.

These four will motivate the hardware that we will develop in this and the next two chapters. We will also delve into layers that deal with different hardware, particularly the file system, which are critical both to system performance and to data security.

3.3 ALLOCATION OF THE PROCESSOR

In this chapter and the next we deal throughout with the issue of dividing up the machine's resources among the several programs running concurrently on the same machine. The resources of principal interest are the central processor(s), the primary memory or memories, and secondary memory. Two themes should be before us constantly:

1. What division should we make of any resource at any particular time to optimize the throughputs we deem to be most important?
2. How well, in terms of hardware and running-time expenses, can we afford to do this allocation?

The first item that we will deal with is the allocation of running time on the central processor(s). The kernel is the 800-pound gorilla in this operation. What it wants, it gets. But the system's only raison d'être is to provide for swift and safe computing by all who need and want it. Accordingly, the people whose work counts are the users. They and the system both generate *processes* and the allocation problem on the CPU(s) is to determine which process gets the CPU(s) next and for how long. We begin, as we should, by considering just what it is that is "getting" the CPU(s).

3.3.1 Defining a "Process"

Let us differentiate between a *process* and a *program.* Let's assume that you are using a large timesharing system. You might be editing a program. At the adjacent terminal someone else is using the same editor program to write the great American novel. Although both of you are using the same program, something in there must be able to distinguish what you are doing from what your neighbor is doing. The system must be able to switch back and forth fast enough to convince both of you that you are getting a prompt response. And it must be able to separate your work from that of your neighbor. (Consider trying to compile the great American novel or getting Ballantine Press to publish your C program.) In order to accomplish these things, the operating system provides a mechanism for separating distinct tasks into quite independent *processes.* A process is a program *in the process of being executed.* Multiprogramming operating systems can execute more than one process concurrently. That may mean that two or more programs are actually running simultaneously, if the system has more than one processor, or it may mean that they only appear to run simultaneously, with a processor switching back and forth between various processes. Since different processes may be executing the same program—two people using the same editor—to avoid wasting memory, the operating system should keep only one copy of the program's instructions in the memory. It is inevitable that the two users of this one program will be in different parts of the program at any one time, and since each will certainly have different data files—the texts being edited—something reasonably clever must be going on to keep all of this sorted out.

A program which can be being executed from different points by different users at the same time is said to be *reentrant.* It isn't all that hard to write reentrant code, but clearly one of the things you would have to do is to isolate the data of the several users. These data include not only the text files themselves but pointers, stacks, heap, and global variables. Doing this proves to be simple, though the concept is not. Basically, each process gets a separate address space, called a *virtual address* space, which has no direct connection to the physical memory. The novel writer may insert his sexiest character at exactly the same address where you are working upon a `do ... while` construction. No doubt those two should never mix. The operating system maintains structures for the hardware system to translate your data addresses and his or her data addresses to different physical addresses, while at the same time translating both of your program accesses to the same physical addresses. These different translations are attached to the processes by the operating system. That said, we doubt that this brief description makes the separation understandable to you. To solve that problem, we provide the entirety of Chapter 4 and then flesh it out in hardware in Chapter 5.

The term *process* is used to mean slightly different things in different operating systems, but it always involves the idea of a program in the process of being executed. That is, a process includes the instructions, data, contents of registers, and the current value of the PC—everything that is going on in the computer which is related to the execution of a particular program. Typically, more than one process exists at any time. On a uniprocessor, only one process can be active at a particular time, but others may be waiting to get their turns on the CPU and still others may be waiting for something to happen before they get back into the *waiting-to-run* queue. On a multiprocessor, different processes can be active simultaneously. Notice that different processes can be running the same program, possibly even with some of the same data, but tables within the operating system keep track of the fact that they are distinct executions of the program.

Processes are normally created by other processes. For example, if you are at a terminal using the UNIX shell (command line interpreter program), the commands you type are delivered to a process which is executing the program *sh* (or *csh* or *ksh*). If you type *emacs*, which is the name of an editor program, the shell process will ask the operating system to create a new process which will execute the emacs program. The shell process will then tell the operating system that it wants to sleep until the emacs process is finished. There is a child-parent relationship between a process and the process that created it. The operating system not only distinguishes all of these processes, but it remembers their relationships and notifies the parent when any of its children finish their programs. It is not necessary for a parent process to sleep while its child process is executing. Instead, it may continue and even create more child processes. Thus there can be a large tree of coexisting processes emanating from a single user. In UNIX, all of these processes are descended from a first process called *init*, which is created when the system starts. Init creates a number of other processes, one of which allows users to log in on the various terminals on the system. User processes get initiated as children of the login process. How this gets done is developed in moderate detail in Appendix IV.

Some operating systems distinguish between the terms *process* and *task*. The reason for a distinction is that some programs can be written which involve asynchronous routines (routines that respond to external events) which share a common address space. We could call each asynchronous routine a *task*, and the whole collection sharing the address space a *process*. The Ada programming language allows the creation of asynchronous tasks like this. In some systems the two terms are used in exactly the opposite sense. Another fine distinction is whether the operating system routines which are being executed on behalf of a process (e.g., to find a disk file) are part of the process. Sometimes the term *thread* is used to mean a flow of control through a program.

The *context* of a process is the current state of all of the things that make up the process: the instructions and data in the program, the contents of the registers, condition codes, and all of the information which is maintained by the operating system, such as the tables of physical memory locations being used by the process, any files being used and pointers into those files, connections to terminals, and so on. The collection of principal elements of a context is shown in Table 3.1. For the processes waiting in queues for their turn, context information is kept either in the memory or on disk, but for the active process, much of the context data is in processor registers. In order to stop executing one process right in the middle and start or resume executing another, the contents of those registers must be saved in the memory tables of the old context, and then the new context's values must be loaded from memory into the registers to start (or resume) the next process. This operation is called a *context switch.*

While a context switch is definitely an interruption in the forward progress of the active process, we wish to use the word *interrupt* to mean something quite different. An *interrupt* is a momentary diversion in the process's normal progress, something rather like answering a telephone call while watching a rented videotape. You stop the tape, answer the phone, hang up, and restart the tape. Of course, the call can make you decide to go do something else entirely—a context switch—but the call itself was only a momentary diversion. Interrupts come principally from external devices asking for attention. Examples include

- a call by a SCSI host adapter to inform the host that the last transfer is complete
- a signal from the clock that a time interval has elapsed
- a signal from the memory management unit (MMU) that the last address violates protection restrictions

TABLE 3.1 Elements in the process context

Process context
Contents of the virtual address space:
Program
Data (includes heap)
User stack
Kernel stack
Contents of the user registers
Contents of the privileged registers
Memory management pointers to pagetables, resident list, etc.
File descriptors, pointers, buffers
Terminal descriptors, pointers, buffers

A program may cause interrupts by doing something egregious such as issuing an illegal address, dividing by 0, or causing a floating-point overflow. Whatever the cause of the interrupt, the response is developed without disturbing the current context, and unless the current context must be switched because of the interrupt, the system should finish the business of the interrupt quickly and then seamlessly return control to the active process. Since interrupts can occur frequently, the hardware normally provides an efficient method for an interrupt routine to be started without saving and restoring very much data. It goes without saying—at least we hope it does—that if the interrupt routine is to remain invisible to the current process, it must save and restore any regular registers which it uses. Most machines use the same registers to handle interrupts as regular processing. CISCs traditionally save the current *state of the machine* by pushing the contents of the process PC and the status register onto the stack and then use a vectored interrupt to generate the new contents of the PC. Upon a return from interrupt, the CISC will put back the saved values of PC and status register and restart where it left off. This sounds easier than it is, particularly in modern *pipelined* machines. Since the pipeline contains instructions in various stages of completion, saving the current state of the machine is considerably more complicated than meets the programmer's eye. Other machines, like ours, provide *shadow registers* to save the machine state automatically. We introduced the idea of *interrupt levels* in the last chapter with a different set of critical registers for each IL. Included in that list of critical registers are the pipeline contents. Accordingly, an increase in IL automatically saves the current state of the process; a decrease restores it. The downside of shadow registers is that if a context switch occurs while shadow registers have active data in them, those data must be saved as part of the context. More context makes a context switch more expensive.

3.3.2 Protection Domains

One of the major functions of a multiprogramming operating system is to protect the resources of the computer system from processes that might cause some kind of damage. Without this protection, a rogue program containing an error or a nasty virus might cause a disaster like erasing all of the information on a disk. Protection against hostile users is particularly critical on systems connected to telephone lines. Most computers divide their operations into two or more protection domains. The protection domain in which a process is executing currently determines which privileges it has. These privileges determine

- the set of instructions that can be executed
- the memory areas that are accessible
- the process's ability to move into other domains

Operating systems protect resources by limiting direct access to them. Making access indirect is making access slow. To prevent protection from being such a burden that users will opt to ride without their crash helmets, the first layer of protection—violation detection—is provided by hardware. Normal instructions and normal memory references pass through at full speed. Yet any attempt to execute a privileged instruction from a less privileged domain or to access memory areas reserved for more privileged domains results in an exception and interrupt. If the intrusion is unacceptable to the operating system, the operation will be prevented and in most cases the offending process will be terminated (with prejudice). However, the intrusion can be the timid knock at the door by a restricted process seeking some legitimate service from the operating system. In that case, the operating system will respond by doing what is required and then return control to the restricted process.

Let's consider a simple but increasingly dominant example first. UNIX divides its computational world into only two domains. While some hardware is built to support more than two, almost all machines support at least two. The kernel (and only the kernel) operates in the more privileged domain; all other programs operate in the less privileged one. A quick review of Figure 1.1 would be useful here to establish what we mean by *hardware* in Figure 3.2. Obviously, both kernel and user run on the CPU. Furthermore, hardware gets software (system) attention by interrupting the CPU and directing it to an appropriate interrupt service routine. What is meant by saying that "only the kernel can access the hardware" is that access to the control registers is restricted to programs running in *supervisor* or *system* mode. These control registers are part of all the devices on the right side of Figure 1.1 as well as the MMU/D-cache, the coprocessors and even the CPU itself. In our machine (and many others, such as the MC68000 family), processes needing system services *trap* into the kernel. The TRAP instruction both sets the host into its supervisory mode and calls the routine in the kernel that provides the desired service. It is critical to this discussion that you understand that the TRAP instruction has a *vector* as its operand. (See Section 2.4 on page 90.) The trap vector is simply an index into a table of destination addresses. *The right to change that table of addresses is restricted to the kernel.* The kernel and only the kernel determines where any program can trap to. Thus, when your program arrives at the august state of *supervisor* with all the rights and privileges therein appertaining, it has entered through a gate prescribed by the kernel. Sitting at that gate is the very ogre we specified in Chapter 2. If the ogre doesn't like what your program is trying to do, squish—terminated with prejudice. The kernel is in complete control. For example, if the system needs only 500 of the 4096 trap vectors, it sets all of the others in the table to point to a routine which handles *illegal traps*. All of those gates go directly into the cobra pit. If you have read about breakins to secure computer systems, many have been accomplished by finding *trapdoors*. These are unpublished traps into the kernel which return control to the process code, but with kernel privilege. The trapdoors were put there to permit system developers to observe and even modify the system while it is being used by others. If the uninvited find such a trapdoor, the entire system is available to them.

Most of the time, you are comfortably unaware of your process's need for system services. They "happen" as needed in the normal course of your program. For example, if one issues a READ or WRITE command in a HLL, that may require a transfer of data between memory and disk. Disk transfers are performed by the disk controller and DMA controller, and they in turn are set ("programmed") to doing a particular task by writing appropriate numbers into their control registers. It is this type of transaction which is permitted to the kernel and forbidden to the processes. Some typical system calls are shown at the top of Figure 3.2.

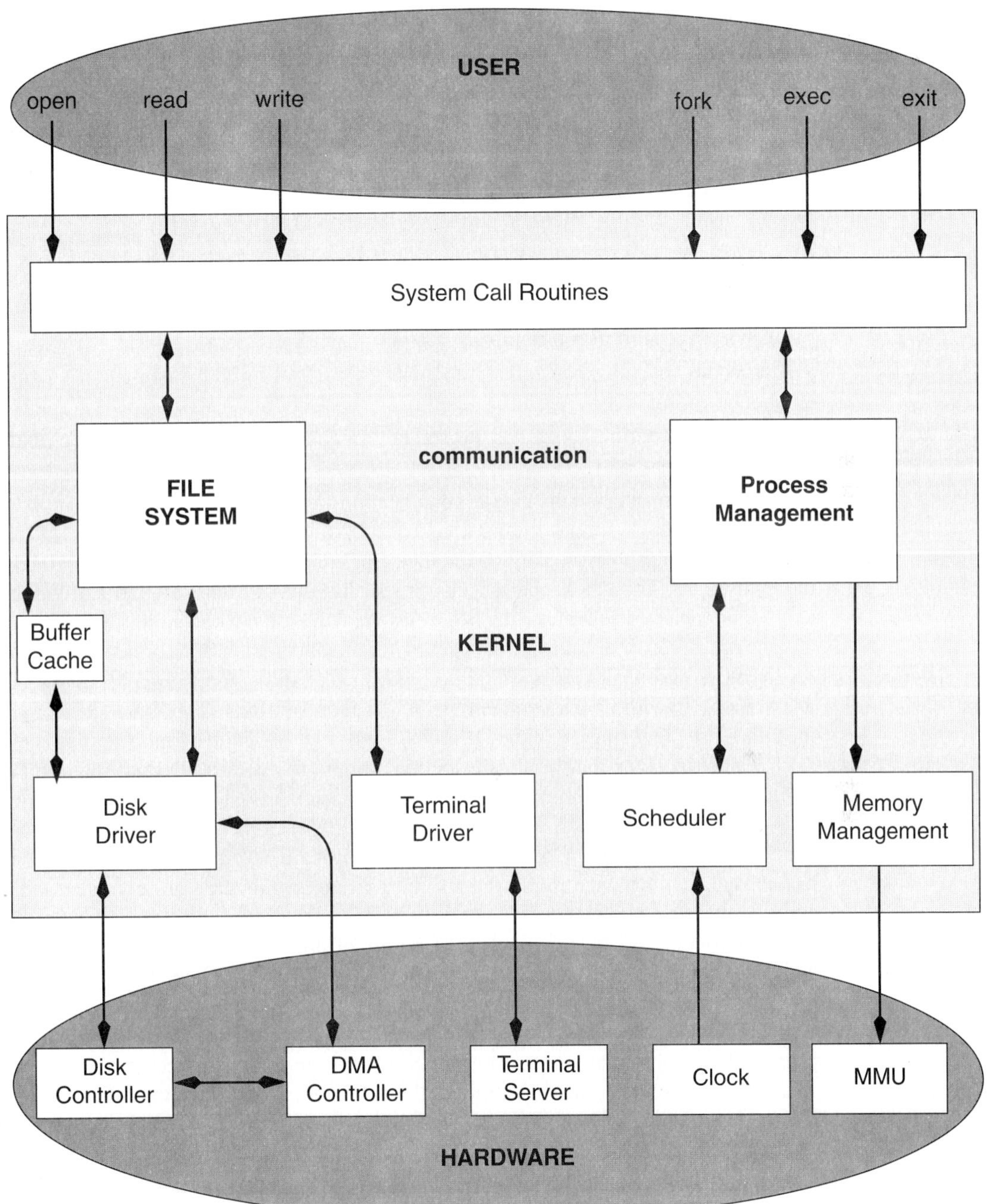

FIGURE 3.2 Block diagram of a simplified UNIX kernel sitting between hardware devices and processes. "Hardware" is a little misleading here since all levels use the CPU in one way or another. Entries into the kernel from USER level employ traps to access the higher state; the hardware gains entry into the kernel through interrupts. After [Bach, 86] with permission of Prentice-Hall.

The Multics operating system, which was the product of an early research effort on multiprogramming at MIT and which preceded UNIX by some years, created a much more general version of this mechanism [Organick, 72]. Instead of having only two protection domains, the design of Multics allowed for up to 64 concentric protection rings. The innermost ring, number 0, is the most privileged, and the outermost ring, number 63, is the least privileged. This allows the assignment of different procedures to different rings depending upon what privileges they need and how much they can be trusted. The rings tend to correspond in a natural way to the layers of an operating system, as described in Section 3.2. The rules for inter-ring accesses are as follows:

- A procedure in ring n can call any procedure in rings $\geq n$. (This is used by the operating system to start user programs.)
- A procedure in ring n can access data in rings $\geq n$, if allowed by the memory management hardware.
- A procedure in ring n can call procedures in rings $< n$ only through special entry points called gates.
- A procedure in ring n can never access data in rings $< n$.

Any attempt to cross ring boundaries results in a trap to an ogre in ring 0 called the *gatekeeper*. The gatekeeper checks to see that the rules are obeyed and validates any pointers passed as arguments. Most systems which have copied this design use far fewer rings. Even for Multics, this strict hierarchical ordering of rings proved to be too restrictive, so groups of rings called *access brackets* and *call brackets* were defined to allow more freedom of movement within groups of rings. The Data General MV machines use eight rings, and the DEC VAX and Intel 80386 use four.

If it strikes you that Multics is the maximum of whatever UNIX is the minimum of, that object was in the minds of those who devised UNIX. UNIX was made to run on little machines (which in the '60s meant *really* little machines). The name was a deliberate jest that UNIX was "one of" whatever Multics was "many of." Lean-and-mean has carried the day once more, though the reasons in this case are complex and not entirely due to technical merit.

Although most machines use a hierarchy of protection domains as pioneered by Multics, whether 2 or 20, sometimes this leads to giving unlimited privileges to a process simply because it must access some special hardware device. Granting carte blanche to some process that is not really part of a coherent operating system is unappealing. One horizontal solution to this problem is to define an access matrix, which specifies exactly what each process is allowed to do. This is not very different from memory protection where a different domain of access to memory is provided for each process, with all of them running at user level. In fact, with memory-mapping of the hardware control registers,[1] the memory protection scheme can also serve to support

[1] In memory mapping, hardware registers get assigned to addresses in the physical address space and can be accessed as if they were part of normal memory. This is discussed in Chapter 4.

the access matrix. However, for machines which have privileged instructions as well as or instead of privileged locations, some other mechanism must be used to achieve a horizontal distribution of privilege. See Chapter 8 in [Maekawa, 87] for details of this and other complex protection mechanisms.

3.3.3 The Scheduler

In Section 3.3.2 we introduced the concept that all processes are descendants of other processes. Yes, there is an identifiable Adam. In UNIX, the *init* process is created when the operating system is started. All other processes are derived from *init*. *Init* creates processes which watch the terminal lines, waiting for someone to log in. When a successful login has been achieved, the *login* process creates a shell (or command line interpreter) process. The shell process then creates other processes for each command the user types. Along with creation there is process termination. For example, if you typed *ls* (for "list"), your shell would *spawn* a process (create a separate process which runs the program you have requested) which reads the current directory and writes it in standard format to your screen. Having completed your request, the spawned process terminates itself, returning control to your shell. Process in; process out. On the right side of Figure 3.2 at the top you will see the three basic UNIX commands for creating a process, launching the specific program that the process should run, and then terminating the process—*fork*, *exec*, and *exit*. Each effects a trap into the kernel.

This cascade of processes, some with long lives and some with short, presents an obvious problem of fair allocation of processor time among the many concurrent processes. It is the job of a kernel routine called the *scheduler* to decide which process should be run at any time. The task is handled much as you would handle giving turns at the water fountain to the kindergarten class. You line them up in some sort of order, and after that, each child gets a turn of reasonable length before any gets a second turn. You queue your kids; you queue your processes. A *queue* is nothing more than an ordered list. What makes the scheduling more complex than simply calling the next number at the bakery is the many reasons for getting on or off the list and the possibility that some programs are made "more equal than others." Let us begin with the simplest of models—a single queue of programs ready to run.

When a new process is added in UNIX, it emerges like Athena from the head of Zeus, fully armed and ready to roll. The new process will be attached to the end of the *run* queue. Its parent, who just executed a *fork* command to create the new process, either continues to run (it was inevitably the active process when creation occurred) or more likely opts to wait for the child process to complete. If it is to wait, it is taken out of the *active* position but not placed at the end of the *run* queue. It cannot be left dangling, so there must be other lists, lists of processes waiting for particular events. Notice that the process which is waiting was in kernel mode when the transition to a *wait* queue occurred. While it is not immediately obvious to the casual observer, a process is inevitably in kernel mode when it is *not* running. The reason is that any act which results in moving the active process off the processor is carried out by a kernel routine *running as part of the active process*. This may seem a little strange, but it is an important issue, so let us pursue it a bit.

Let us say that your process is chugging along happily in a *preemptive* multiprogramming environment. By *preemptive* we mean that the active program can be displaced from its *running* status by an external event. The event we have in mind right now is the clock interrupt. After roughly 10 ms, the clock signals *time-out* and the scheduler changes the process to the next in line. We all know about taking turns, but what does the interrupt routine which causes this switch have to do with the process that is running? After all, you never wrote any such thing into your code. The answer is: It has nothing to do with your code, but it does have everything to do with your process. Each and every process shares the kernel. The kernel in most interactive computer systems is *nonpreemptable*, *unswappable*, *unpageable*, and *shared*. That is, it is always there, in memory, and it will not be interrupted by any process-related operation. Sharing is a curious thing to consider on first approach. It means that all processes in kernel mode are using the same addresses in memory when running the same subroutine. The trick in getting the same code to handle different users is to have the process data on which the kernel works be attached to the process, not the kernel. Those data, or, where necessary, the pointers to those data, are stored in each process's process control block (PCB). Since the PCB is attached to the process, the code in the shared kernel always works on the process at hand and since the kernel itself is nonpreemptable, the process at hand never changes except when the kernel makes it change.

When an ongoing process is switched out of the active position it must go to the end of either the *run* queue or one of the *wait* queues. While it is waiting, the kernel may find that it is short of memory and decide to free up some space at the expense of waiting programs. It does this by *swapping* out to disk processes that are waiting. Before these processes come up again for a turn, the swapper must bring them back into main memory, sometimes at the cost of swapping something else out. The way that the system keeps track of the state of each process is by putting its PCB in the proper queue or list. (The queues themselves are all in memory.) Accordingly, upon swapping a process out, the swapper will move the PCB from the *run* or *wait* queue to the *swapped* or *out* queue. These transactions are shown in Figure 3.3. Notice that there are six states, two ready queues and a pair of wait queues for each event that can be waited for, and this is a *simple* round-robin scheduling algorithm.

3.3.4 Context Switch Out and Context Switch In

Looking at Figure 3.3, consider what sort of events would cause a process to switch from one state to another and also what transaction must be accomplished to get all of the process baggage on the right flight.

Let us say that the active process, running in user mode, wants to read a file from disk. The program does the C call `fopen(filename, "r")` which uses `open()` to access a disk file, *filename*, for reading. From the program's point of view, the function returns a pointer to the first item in the file. Let us consider what really must transpire to carry this programming construct through to having a datum in memory to point to. `fopen()` simply "calls for" the required system service, which in our machine and many others is a TRAP into the kernel. The TRAP instruction accomplishes several tasks:

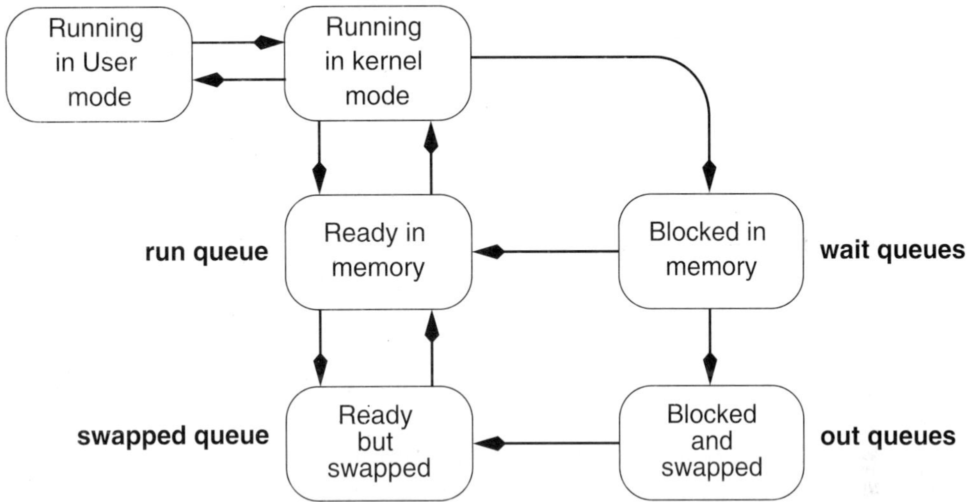

FIGURE 3.3 Process state diagram. The two running states are for the single process running on a processor at one time. The other four states represent both where the process resides and what it is waiting for. The four waiting states are each served by one or more queues. To change a process from the *blocked and swapped* state to the *ready but swapped* state, the scheduler moves the process control block from an *out* queue to the *swapped* queue.

- It changes the mode to kernel.
- It saves all of the information necessary to return to the user state. In our machine, this is done by switching to another set—a *shadow set*—of critical registers; in most other machines, the critical data are pushed onto the *system* stack. Note that this means that most machines have at least one shadowed register—the stack pointer—to provide hardware isolation between *user* and *system* modes. We have simply carried this isolation fully into hardware.
- It does a vectored call to the correct handler.

The fact that the active process is now in kernel mode increases its privileges, but it is important to recognize that this power to do anything is not granted to the writer of the user-level program. The TRAP carried the program through the trap-vector table to a system routine. It is the system routine that has the privileges, not the user program. The same process still prevails, but the process will now be executing inviolate system code, not user code. You may write your own version of **fopen**, but you will not be allowed to access the requisite hardware. To gain that privilege for your process, you must turn over control to the appropriate operating system routine.

Before executing the TRAP, `open()` will have put a pointer to the file name into, say, register 0 and any other necessary data (e.g., open for READ, APPEND, or WRITE) into subsequent registers (or in most machines, the stack). The system routine can pick up the file name directly, but finding the disk address structure calls for a look at the hierarchical file directory. In general, this is out on disk, though the directory sections needed may be resident by happenstance in memory when the request comes in.

Generally, only the small, top directory, brought in when the disk was *mounted*, is kept permanently in memory. Let us assume that the directory pieces needed are out on disk. Consider what must be done:

- Open up buffers in memory to hold the directory or directories and the file descriptor.
- Go down the hierarchy of directories until the file name in question can be found. This can require one or more disk accesses. The file name in the directory identifies the location on disk of the complete file descriptor. The descriptor contains all of the file data including access permissions and an index locating all of the blocks in the file itself.
- If the operation is allowed by the permissions, read the first section of the file into the buffer.

The disk acccsscs will bc accomplished by a system call. To get the directory data, the process, operating at system level, must set up an I/O request through one of the disk drivers. Because of its mechanical nature and the possible queuing of many requests, a disk access is an extremely lengthy affair—in units of processing time on our machine, 50,000 to 1,000,000 instructions. Not only does the current process have to get off the CPU to let the file process run, but it is clear that there is likely to be a hiatus of many milliseconds until the file descriptor can be delivered. It is definitely time for a nap. During the nap, the interaction between system and disk driver will be interrupt driven. Our state diagram of Figure 3.3 shows what to do. The current process, running this system I/O routine, will ask to be suspended (another TRAP). The system will switch this process from the *running* position to the tail of the appropriate *wait* queue. The queue chosen identifies the event which all this queue's members are waiting for. (While the usual case will have one process awaiting one event, a group of processes could be stalled waiting for some particular resource such as free buffers. As these become available, all processes in the waiting group would be awakened at the same time. As each process gets its turn to run, it must check that the resource is still available. If not, it goes back to sleep. This *test-and-sleep-on-failure* activity is programmed as a simple `while...` loop.) Once the current context is switched out, the next process in line can be served. Let us examine some of the details, not so much to create the system routines but rather to show how processes can move about the state diagram.

The kernel function which is attempting to get the needed file will get its buffer space from a queue of free buffers—a quick operation—and then start down the disk directory. The kernel will have a pointer to the top of the directory. That uppermost directory will be cached in memory, but as the function walks down the hierarchy, it may hit an entry which is marked as *on disk*. That causes the function to tack a request for the needed block of entries onto a queue of requests for the interrupt-driven disk-handling routines. This diversion is part of a programming loop which is of the figurative form:

```
queue_IO(block);          /* the working end of open() */
sleep(event);             /* the "event" is a specific instance */
                          /* of a static list of system events */
next_operation;
```

The `sleep(event)` call is part of a pair of system functions, `sleep()` and `wakeup()`, which move processes into the *wait* queues and back to the *ready* queues. The routine which finished the read does `wakeup()`, using the same *event_identifier* as the `sleep()`. This tells the *scheduler* process to move the next element on the queue in question onto the appropriate *ready* queue in Figure 3.3.

The changing of the current process or *context switch* is a rather mundane affair. We will develop most of the important details in Chapter 4, but we should provide the first insight here. When our process is running, all of the registers contain data associated with our process. The set of registers includes everything that the process sees—R0..R31, FP0..FP7, and so on—and all of the control and data registers which are associated with the process. Each process has a PCB to store these data in when the process is dormant. The system stores a pointer to the active process's PCB in a fixed location in memory. When it is time for a process switch, the system will copy the contents of the register set into the PCB whose pointer it holds, then it will get the pointer to the PCB of the next process to run and put that in the "current PCB" location. Finally, it will copy all of the relevant PCB data into register and drop into the new process right where it was before. The VAX, designed under the CISC microcoding paradigm, has a single machine instruction to do all the copying. The copying part is easy. Let us consider for a moment the "dropping into" part.

Figure 3.4 illustrates the relationship between concurrent contexts and the context switch. In our machine, the system might have just three calls which initiate a context switch: `sleep()`, `timeout()`, and `terminate()`. The first puts the current process into the *wait* queue and brings in the next process; the second puts the current process back at the end of *run* queue and brings in the next process; and the third, which is the very end of the *exit* call, simply brings in the next process, with the PCB, now detached from any process being queued on a *free-PCB* queue. All of these routines will be running at IL1. The routines attach the PCB to its designated queue and then, when the routines reach the point where the context switch itself must be done, they will issue a TRAP instruction vectored to the context switch routine. The TRAP will raise the IL to IL2. At that level, the shadow registers for IL2 are active; those for IL1 and IL0 are dormant. The copying required is of all of the registers associated with IL0 and IL1 as well as the visible registers (R0..R29, F0..F7, etc). The context switcher will copy out the current process state to its PCB, obtain the pointer to the next-to-run PCB, and copy in the data last stored there. In Figure 3.4, the TRAP reverses the arrow in process A and the copying out and in moves the switch contact from A to B. Once that little chore of copying out and copying in is done, the context-switching routine simply does:

```
RFI
NOP
NOP
```

The NOPs simply clean out the pipeline, an issue to be covered in detail in Chapter 6. The RFI (see Figure 2.16 on page 97) puts the processor back in IL1 (arrow down in process B), running the line after the TRAP instruction which process B issued the last time it was running. We have indeed dropped in exactly where we were the last

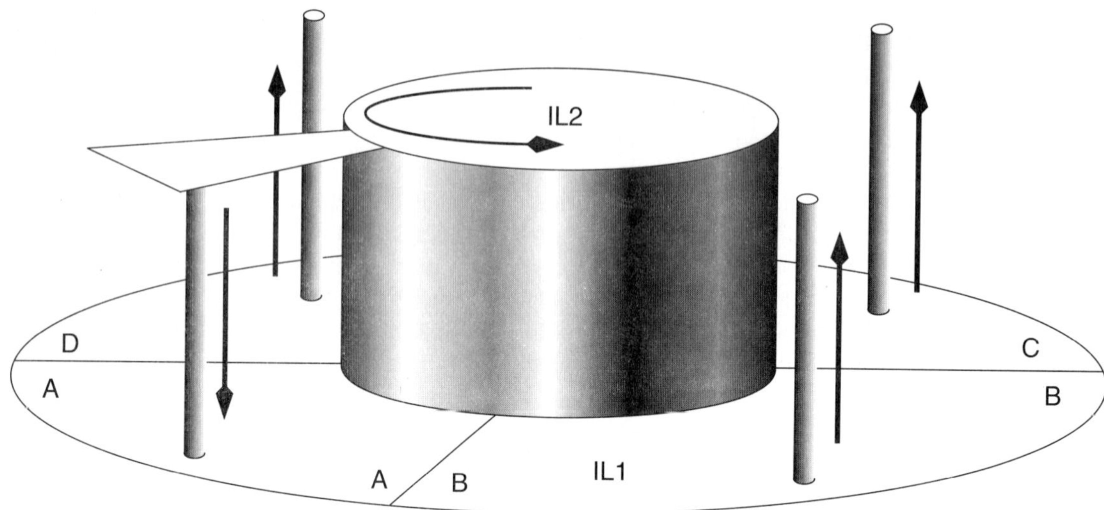

FIGURE 3.4 Illustration of the context switch in our machine. Four processes, A..D, run concurrently by using context switching. B..D are in the *run* queue and A is running. B..D were all last operating at IL2. A is running at IL1 or IL0. Events which cause a context switch, such as timeouts or I/O requests, inevitably move the current process into IL1. From there the current process does a TRAP into IL2, reversing the arrow in the figure. The operating system saves all of A's current data in its PCB and then queues that PCB in either the run or wait queue. It then takes the next process to run (B in the diagram) and copies its current data into the appropriate registers and places it in memory. This, in the diagram, rotates the tab to the next process. It then reverses the arrow by doing an RFI and resumes doing whatever B was doing by executing the instruction after TRAP *in process B.*

time that process B was running. It is as if B had never stopped. Notice that the instruction returned to is always some routine in the kernel. That routine will finish its business and do another RFI, NOP, NOP to get back to user level. And thus the circle goes. Or does it? Can any other event intrude into the orderly process we have just described?

For UNIX, the answer is: "No." UNIX has a *nonpreemptive* kernel.[2] Preemption implies an essentially immediate context switch. A nonpreemptive kernel can be interrupted, but it cannot be preempted. In a nonpreemptive kernel, an interrupt of the kernel always returns control to the interrupted process. In a preemptive kernel, a second interrupt can cause a context switch during the first interrupt, returning not to the interrupted process but to a new one. The nonpreemptive kernel allows a context switch

[2] UNIX provides a preemptive multiprogramming environment for processes even though the kernel itself is not preemptable. The difference is illustrated in the response to the clock interrupt, which is the event that causes process preemption. If the process is running in user mode, the clock interrupt puts it into kernel mode running the clock-interrupt routine. If a time slice has expired, the clock-interrupt routine does a call to `timeout` which in turn causes a context switch. Had the process been running in kernel mode, the clock interrupt, which runs at IL1, would have been ignored until the process dropped again into user mode (IL0). Accordingly, the clock would never interrupt the kernel but the processes (in user mode) can be preempted.

only at certain times, which simplifies the problem of keeping all of its tables and lists consistent. Consider a system which allowed preemption of the kernel. How can you assure file and table consistency if you allow the kernel to be interrupted in the process of changing a table or file? If the newly invoked process uses a table rendered inconsistent by the interrupt, your machine is in deep trouble. Designing a successful preemptive kernel is hard. Getting one to work with no bugs and really fast response is even harder. Why would you try? Well, such systems get installed where real-time control of multiple independent processes is the objective. (See Chapter 7 of [Auslander, 90].) The need to have independent processes respond with great speed to critical events is an essential feature of such systems.

The two *swapped-out* states in Figure 3.3 occur when the memory manager gets starved for space. Swapping sounds simple enough. To make room for a new process or to allow active processes to grow, the system can take processes that are waiting in line and ask them to wait on disk rather than in central memory. Unfortunately, disk is out at the end of a subway line, not right outside the door. It takes a long time to transfer a large set of blocks to or from disk. To use swapping effectively, the operating system must recall swapped-out programs from time to time, putting them into the *run* queue soon enough so that they get a reasonable measure of service. To make room for the incoming process, another may have to be swapped out. While all of this swapping is costly in I/O, it does provide the system with the ability to run more processes concurrently than its physical memory would allow. In having the four queue groups shown in Figure 3.3, we guarantee that a process is in before we let it try to run. This reduces the queuing problem to one of shuffling programs around so that all programs get an equitable slice of run time. The cost of increasing memory availability by swapping is that swapping consumes a great deal of bus bandwidth. (See Figure 1.1 for connectivity and Chapter 8 for a discussion of bus bandwidth.) That too is one of the resources an operating system must husband and equitably distribute.

There are many different algorithms used to order the processes to determine which one will be executed next. *Round-robin* is the simple algorithm we just described. It uses only a single *run* queue so that each process gets to use the CPU once and then wait for all of the other processes which are ready. More sophisticated algorithms assign priorities to the processes, based on such things as CPU time used, I/O operations, or priorities chosen by the user (e.g., *interactive*, *fast-but-short batch*, *slow-but-long batch*). (See Chapter 1 in [Finkel, 88] for descriptions of some of these algorithms.) By adjusting priorities properly, a system manager can better satisfy the disparate needs of various users.

3.3.5 Queues Shared between Processes

We have been using the word *queue* without bothering to define it. Since everyone has been in queues at bakeries, banks, and ball games, the general concept is well known. Less obvious are the constructs which make queues workable in computers. This topic includes not only the mechanics of manipulating queues but the absolutely essential topic of how independent processes can share a queue and ensure that the queue is always *coherent*. (An *incoherent* queue would be one with a break in it or with an element in the queue that should have been removed.)

People think of queues as arrays of elements ordered by physical position: "Lined up like ducks," or "I stood in a line for two hours." Such queues have the inconvenience that all elements must move in order to advance the queue (although it is rather spectacular when ducks queue up in the air). Other queuing arrangements are often employed to provide order independent of the physical location. Queuing by taking a number as you enter or by the order of appointment at a doctor's office allows the participants in the queue to move about freely or remain in fixed positions while still advancing in the queue. Although we most often use FIFO queues, where one adds at the tail and removes from the head, a queue can also be simply an ordered collection of items which can be searched for special subsets. This takes place at the supermarket when the 10-items-or-less checkout line opens. Those in adjacent queues are invited to step out and join the new queue *if they meet the special criterion*.

In computers, queues usually comprise ordered arrangements of structures or records. Were one to order the queue by physical location, one would be obliged to continually shift blocks by copying them in their entirety. It is much less expensive to assign one or two locations in each queue element as pointers to the adjacent elements in the queue. This is shown in Figure 3.5. Now the queue elements remain fixed in memory but can be added or removed from the ends or the middle by the change of only a few pointers. Since a queue is one type of ordered list and since these pointers provide links to their nearest neighbors, we are wont to say that computer queues are most often implemented as linked lists. Generally, one has a known place where the pointer to the first element can be found. That place is called the *queue header*. The header is not an element in the queue; it is there even if the queue is empty. The simplest version of a linked list is just a collection of elements, each of which contains a pointer to the next. The header could be simply a pointer to the head of the list or, for convenience in adding elements to the tail, it could have a pointer to the tail as well. To differentiate between the two directions, we will use DEC's notation: The forward link will be called the *flink* and the backward link the *blink*.

FIGURE 3.5 The structure of a doubly linked list. For complete regularity, the tail flink and head blink can point back at the header. Alternatively, those two pointers can be `null` pointers. The neat ordering reminiscent of a queue of people is entirely artificial. The system is really more like the take-a-number queue where the customers get their relative position upon entering and then mill about, with numbers clutched in anxious palms.

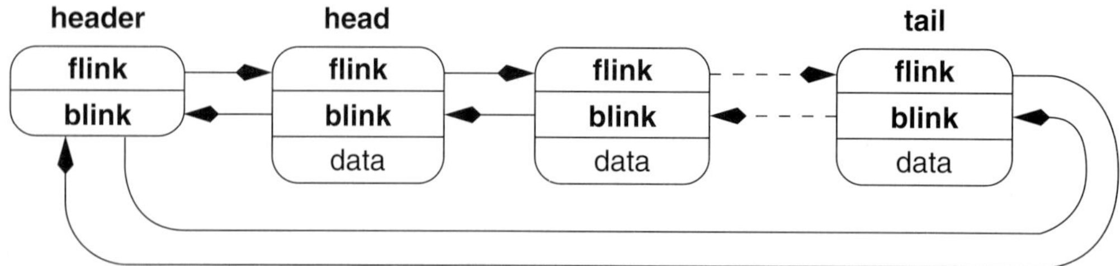

If one uses only flinks in the elements themselves, a basic asymmetry exists. Such a list is said to be *singly linked*. The header's flink makes it easy to add or remove entries at the head of a linked list; the header's blink makes it easy to add entries to the tail. What is not so easy is to remove entries from the tail, since we have to find the next-to-last element to do that. The only way to do that in a singly linked list is to go through the entire list starting from the head. If this kind of operation is used frequently, if we need to add or remove elements from the middle, or if we need to be able to search through the list in either direction, it is better to use a *doubly linked* list. That is, each element has both flink and blink. This is the arrangement shown in Figure 3.5.

While any process is entitled to create its own queues, our principal interest here lies in queues used by the operating system. Often these must be shared between quite independent processes. An example is found in the I/O queues. In many systems, the actual I/O operations are done by an independent process; in big, multiprocessor systems, that process is often running on another processor. When a process needs a disk operation, it not only does not do it at the user level, but it does not do it even at the system level. Instead, at the system level, it *posts* a request for the operation. To be precise, the I/O driver in the requester's kernel writes out a transaction request and enqueues it on a *command* queue in system space. The other processor (or in a smaller system with only one processor, another process), which may have a very different perspective on memory, will go independently to that same queue and remove requests one at a time. If this is a multidisk I/O channel such as SCSI (see Figure 8.1 on page 406) where a group of smart controllers share a common communication line, the other processor is either a *host adapter* or the disk controller itself. To get a picture of the layout, look at Figure 8.1. There you see several hosts attached to several disks and a tape drive over a common SCSI bus. That bus is connected to the two host busses through host adapters (SCSI adapters in the figure).

Whether smart or simple, the host adapter is acting essentially as mailman. It takes off the elements from the command queue and transmits the data therein to the target device. The target device chews on the request for a while and then, when it is ready, it does a data transfer through the host adapter. Now it must tell the host that the transfer is complete. It does this by modifying the very command itself and then enqueues the *response* on the *response queue*. The process which handles replies will dequeue the response and take whatever action the response requires. In most cases, the response will be to prepare a reply that can be read by the process which ordered the action and then to move the waiting process onto the "ready" queue.

Note what we have just described: Packets of data are "moving" from queue to queue. Each packet will occupy a small piece of memory and stay fixed in place. Only the connecting links and the data in the packets will be changed. Since the system will need many such packets and since the data structures are inevitably of standard form, the system will create blocks of memory to hold some fixed number of packets of known size. The actions we just described have processes and processors grabbing a packet, processing it (reading, writing, or modifying the data therein), and then disposing of it. But you do not want to lose the memory associated with that packet, so the used packet should be recycled. These are all *returnables*. The place to keep spares is on the *free queue*. Figure 3.6 shows a single block of memory linked to these three queues.

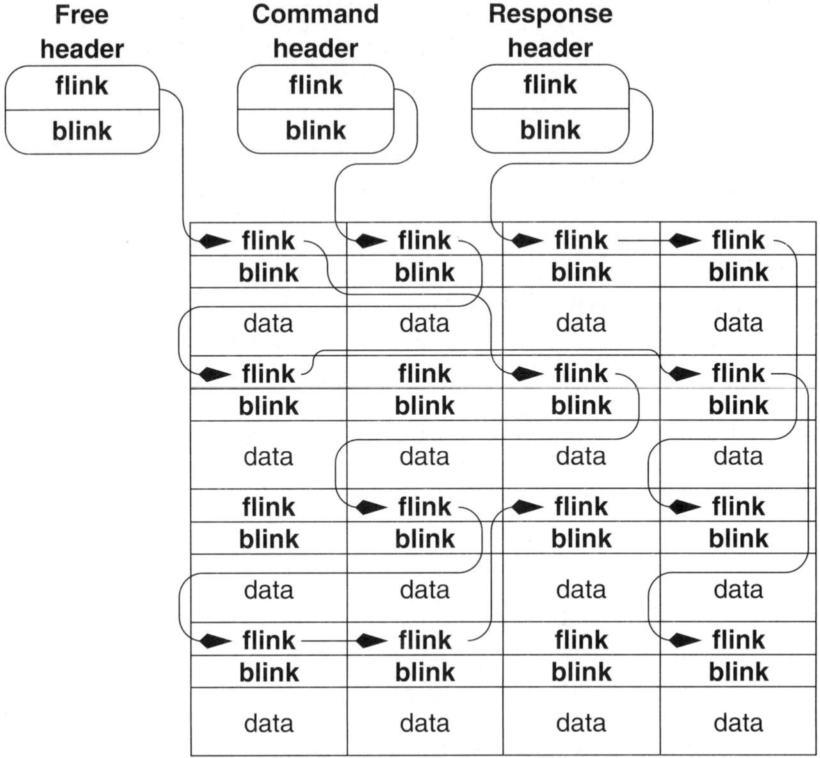

FIGURE 3.6 A contiguous block of memory divided into 16 envelopes. Thirteen of them have been attached to one or another of the three queues. Only the forward links are shown.

These pieces of memory are analogous to interoffice mail envelopes. They get stuffed, sent, emptied and reused. Whenever any process wants to talk to this disk group, it grabs an envelope from the free queue, stuffs it, and puts it on the command queue. When the process or processor which handles I/O is ready, it removes the envelope from the command queue and "empties it." It then puts the envelope back on the free queue. When the I/O process or processor finishes the task, it grabs a free envelope, stuffs it, and puts it on the response queue. When the process which handles responses is running, it takes response envelopes off the response queue, "empties them," and puts them back on the free queue. One curious effect of all of this is that while a process or processor is holding an envelope, no other process or processor "knows" about it. It is lost to the general system until the holder returns it by enqueuing it. Three such "missing" envelopes are included in Figure 3.6.

The structure of the queues is reasonably obvious. What is not obvious are the problems which arise because all the processes and even different processors share these structures. One peculiarity is that different processes may refer to these queue headers by different addresses *even though one object must be of necessity in one physical location*. The problem arises because in most multiprogramming systems, the different processes use different mappings of the physical memory into a *virtual address space*. Chapter 4 explores the way that hardware translates the program addresses to their proper physical counterparts, but for the moment, all that is necessary to understand is that not all the players in this game are using identical decks. When different users manipulate the queue, they all must come up with identical flinks and blinks. With that in mind, what algorithm for calculating the links would be independent of a process's concept of the address space? A simple solution is first to put all the envelopes into a contiguous block of physical memory and then to make the links *displacements* rather than absolute addresses. That is, each link field contains only the relative distance to the next element, rather than an actual pointer to it. No matter how you get to the header, subsequent displacements will be the same. Stepping through such a list is almost as simple as in the case when the links are pointers. Instead of just reading the next address, add the link to the current address to get the next address. A queue which uses displacement addressing is called *self-relative*. One that uses addresses is called *absolute*. Note that all users of a self-relative queue must have an address of the header which is correct in their own address space. An I/O processor might be using a physical address (PA) while a user process might be using a system virtual address that gets translated by hardware into the PA. Once at the header, however, all may proceed by displacements from the starting address.

Letting all comers get to the same doorway from different starting points is one thing; keeping them from stepping on each other's toes is quite another. One of the services which must be provided by the operating system is to maintain mechanisms for independent processes and processors to communicate with each other. This is called *interprocess communication* (IPC). When two asynchronous processes share data structures, it is an understatement to declare that very complex and unexpected problems can occur. For example, consider what happens when we insert or delete an envelope in the doubly linked list shown in Figure 3.5. In order to make such a change, we must change four links. That will require at least four instructions. But suppose that an interrupt occurs before completion of the four instructions, and that the interrupt results in a context switch. If the new process tries to access the same doubly linked list, it will find that two different elements are half-linked into the list. Both processes could end up writing to the same envelope, an envelope or even a whole list could be lost, or the list may be defined differently depending on the direction of transit. Such a queue is said to be *incoherent*.

If you think that you can beat this simply by preventing interrupts while doing queue-changing operations, ponder the multiprocessing situation. There you can have both processors—the host and the smart peripheral—attempting to access the same queue at the same moment. No interrupts are involved. Disaster awaits. Only one process may pass through the door at a time. The solution to door problems is a doorkeeper. "One at a time now, and step lively, please." In the computer and in numerous examples in real life, the doorkeeper maintains order by signaling when it is safe and when it is forbidden to enter. The earliest such problem solved in a regular way was on single-track railroads. The signaling device was called a *semaphore*. We explore this critical topic in our next and final section of this chapter.

3.4 SYNCHRONIZATION OF ASYNCHRONOUS CONCURRENT PROCESSES

Many a farce has been constructed on the violation of synchronization rules. A delightful example is *Cox and Box* by Burnand and Sullivan, in which an audacious landlord rents a single room independently and at full rent to each of two gentlemen, one of whom works days and the other nights. This arrangement is fine until Cox gets a day off—a rare and unexpected event in Victorian times. Confusion and hilarity reign till all is revealed and the none-too-sheepish landlord is confronted.

It is less funny when process A and process B inadvertently get into the same bed together. In this section we explore solutions to collisions between asynchronous concurrent processes in their use of shared resources. While in its simplest form the solutions amount to an orderly taking of turns, the two processes which are sharing the resources are generally completely unaware of one another's existence. What makes farce funny is that the audience sees the unsuspecting players moving toward the unavoidable collision. Real life has no audience. Shared resources are generally subject to corruption if the competing users can interfere with the protocols of using the resources. To prevent corruption, a computer system—in both hardware and software—must be capable of excluding intervention or interference whenever a process is in a *critical section* in the use of a shared resource.

The resources that we wish to consider in this section are shared memory structures: lists, queues, and buffers. The routines which are sharing the structures may be running concurrently on a single processor or running simultaneously on multiple processors sharing a common memory. When otherwise asynchronous processes are forced to wait until a resource is freed, we say that they are *synchronized*. The word synchronized gets a little bent here because there is really nothing more here than waiting your turn at the bakery, but synchronized is what it is called. The question that we wish to examine is: How can they be synchronized efficiently and reliably? *Reliably* is fairly obvious; you wish to prevent collisions, to ensure that shared structures do not become disordered. *Efficiently* has a good gloss to it—everything computational should be efficient—but we have something particular in mind: the issue of deadlock. If A ties up resource X and then looks for resource Y while B ties up Y and then looks for X, neither can be satisfied so both stop dead. Unless there is a mechanism for not only breaking out of the *deadlock* but also assuring that one of the processes can proceed, the efficiency goes to 0!

The data-sharing routines that we are attempting to synchronize are any routines which operate asynchronously, whether they are part of the same program or not. Terminal I/O routines (discussed in Section 7.2.1) are an example of asynchronous routines which share data structures with each other within one process and also with other unrelated processes. The input routine must echo most input characters by feeding them to the output routine. These two routines are interrupt-driven and, at least within a single process, very infrequently invoked. They are thus totally asynchronous and unaware of the other's state of activity. Other processes may insert a message right in the middle of this stream: "*newline* New mail from TSMITH@NORTHEASTERN.EDU *newline*."

That would have two or more processes queuing output and one process dequeuing output. They have nothing to do with each other other than sharing the output buffer queue. The input routine must also deliver its input to the user process. The characters could be arriving with the user program awaiting each and every one or the person could be typing ahead, queuing input which the user program will find when it looks in the buffer. The input routine does its transfer without any connection to the whim or will of the user program. Once again, the two programs are asynchronous and unrelated except for a shared buffer.

These terminal I/O routines are typical of a general class of cooperating routines called *Producer-Consumer* transactions. In this case, one or more processes produce some data items (such as characters being put in from the terminal), and another process (or processes) consumes them. To see what kind of synchronization is required, consider actual routines using a fixed ring-buffer, a structure particularly suitable for the very low data rates of terminal I/O. The concept of a ring buffer is shown in Figure 3.7. It is easy to write routines to insert and extract data from such a structure. While it is helpful to think of the structure as a ring, in reality it is a linear buffer with a wrapping algorithm. Simple read and write routines which insert or remove integers from a ring buffer comprise:

```
int *read_ptr,*write_ptr,*start_ptr,*round_ptr;

int readbuf()
    {int not_ready, item;

        do {not_ready = (write_ptr == read_ptr);}
        while (not_ready);
        item = *read_ptr++;
```

FIGURE 3.7 A ring buffer containing eight storage locations. The rule of operation is that the write pointer points to the next location to be filled; the read pointer points to the next location to be read. You may read if write ≠ read; you may write if (write+1) ≠ read, where the sense of direction is as shown. In the figure, you have room to write one more datum; there are currently six data waiting. An empty queue has read=write.

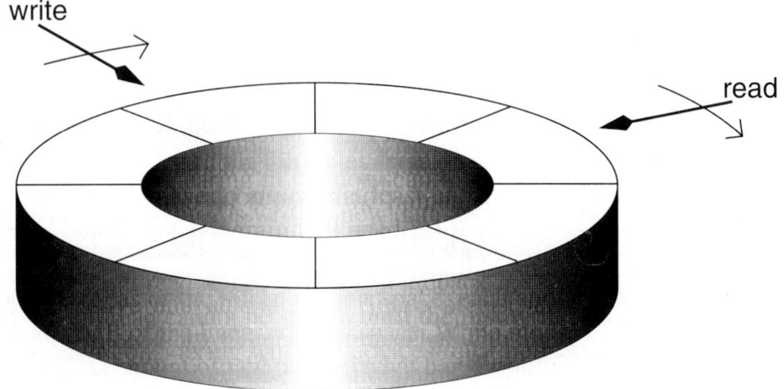

```
        if (read_ptr > round_ptr) read_ptr = start_ptr;
        return item;
    }

void writebuf(int item)
    {int not_ready;

        do {not_ready = (write_ptr+1 == read_ptr) ||
            ((write_ptr == round_ptr) && (read_ptr == start_ptr)); }
        while (not_ready);
        *write_ptr = item;
        if (++write_ptr > round_ptr) write_ptr = start_ptr;
    }
```

These work, but as interrupt-driven routines running on the same processor they contain a serious bug. Since both of these routines "hang" there until they get the resource each needs—a datum for `readbuf()` and a place in the buffer to put a datum for `writebuf()`—and since each in turn makes the resource for the other, they can get into irrevocable gridlock. You might think that by having one at a higher interrupt level, we could avoid locking up, but since either can go into an endless loop and only one can have a higher interrupt level, there is always the possibility of an endless wait. Without even half trying we have come up with a deadlock. What could we do to prevent painting ourselves into this corner? The obvious problem is that, once frustrated, the routine guarantees continued frustration by excluding the very event it is looking for. The resource it needs is either space [`writebuf()`] or data [`readbuf()`]. The resource that each holds is access to the processor. The other function, which has or eventually will have the resource being sought, cannot make that resource available until it gets the resource of access to the processor. The cure, as it always will be in deadlock problems, is to make one or more of the players release the resource(s) that will enable progress. Here the problem is conspicuous a priori, and we will fix it by doing the obvious—eliminating the repetitive inquiry. Instead of the `do ... while` loops, the routine must report its failure and finish. The device or process which caused the interrupt will have to try again, but in the meanwhile, progress can be made.

Not all deadlocks are this easy to spot or to fix. Let us say that process X takes commands off queue A, processes them, and then puts the result on queue B or C. Independent process Y takes items off B and on rare occasion finds reason to post something on A. Now if X and Y were poorly written, X might gain exclusive privileges to A and then try to acquire B while Y might try to gain exclusive privileges to B and then make a try for A. If either is frustrated in its effort, it will invoke the `wait()` option. This pair runs happily for years until one day, X gets A and Y gets B and then each tries for the other. Now both get put to sleep with no chance that the event that each is awaiting can ever occur. They are not asleep. They are dead! How does the system break this deadlock? How can a system programmer prevent it in the first place? If your first answer is "Eliminate the exclusive access for X and Y," you have done exactly what any instructor would want: You have brought up the heart of the problem—synchronization. Exclusive access is synchronization. Why synchronize?

The synchronization problem occurs when two independent and asynchronous routines use the same structure. The reason why X or Y must have exclusive access is that if both could be modifying the queue at the same time, they are likely to break the queue—that is, render parts of it inaccessible.

Look at Figure 3.5 and Figure 3.6. Removing the first element of one of those queues requires changing its header flink and the second element's blink. If two independent processes are mucking about in there at the same time, you can end up with both owning (and independently manipulating) the same queue element or with the header pointing at a first element that is not even in the queue. The number of different primitive operations in pulling off the first element of a self-relative queue may be greater than you envisaged (Figure 3.5):

```
Header_Flink := Header_Flink + First_Flink;
Second_Blink := First_Blink + Second_Blink;
```

There are four reads and two writes. Let us consider a couple of disaster scenarios with X and Y hacking away at the same time. Let us assume that both X and Y are running on one CPU although they are different processes, either of which can be context-switched. Figure 3.8 illustrates what might transpire if the context switch occurred at an inopportune moment.

Two simply unacceptable results arise in this illustration. To begin with, two different processes have ended up with the same queue element. This is the Cox and Box

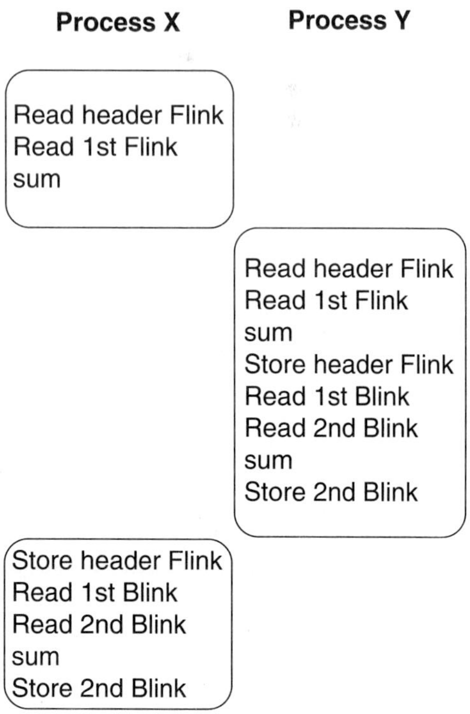

Process X	Process Y
Read header Flink Read 1st Flink sum	
	Read header Flink Read 1st Flink sum Store header Flink Read 1st Blink Read 2nd Blink sum Store 2nd Blink
Store header Flink Read 1st Blink Read 2nd Blink sum Store 2nd Blink	

FIGURE 3.8 Two unsynchronized processes reading from the head of the same queue. In this example Process X is context switched out in the middle of the operation, Process Y runs to completion, and then X completes. The result is to have both X and Y owning the same queue element and to break the queue linkage.

scenario: Two *exclusive* owners of the same piece of turf, totally ignorant of one another's presence. The other bad end arises because both modify Second_Blink *using* Second_Blink as one of the inputs. This results in Second_Blink being twice incremented by First_Blink. Who knows where that points? Certainly not back at the header. By moving the timing of the context switch a little bit, we can

- keep the queue whole but give the same queue element to both processes
- give each its proper element but break the queue
- break two queues at once by allowing Y to reenqueue the element it took onto a different queue

Queues are not a special problem. We could build equally awful consequences on any shared data structure, even if only one process writes to that structure. All of these problems have something in common. In each case, shared data are damaged because one process interrupts the action of another process on those data. The part of each process which manipulates a shared data structure is called a *critical section*. If we can find a way to guarantee that only one process can be in a critical section at any time, we will have made data sharing robust. This one-at-a-time requirement is called *mutual exclusion*. On a uniprocessor, we could guarantee mutual exclusion simply by preventing interrupts during each critical section, but in many cases that solution is not acceptable. For example, user programs may not inhibit interrupts, since an error in a user program might get stuck in an endless loop with interrupts disabled and bring the entire system to a halt. While inhibiting some, most or all interrupts from within the operating system is allowed, external devices which depend on interrupts often require a very prompt response. If interrupts are to be suspended, it must be for only the briefest time—a few instructions at most. It is generally a technique to be avoided. On a multiprocessor system, inhibiting interrupts on one processor has no effect on the others, so for most modern multiprocessor machines, it does not provide mutual exclusion. Another solution is required.

Our problem is to find a mechanism to enforce mutual exclusion between two or more asynchronous concurrent processes. The processes may run

- on the same machine, or
- on different *tightly coupled* processors (i.e., distinct CPUs which share a common memory), or
- on different *loosely coupled* processors (i.e., distinct CPUs which communicate by sending messages over a network

Several assumptions are required to assure mutual exclusion:

1. The processors execute instructions in the order that they occur in the program.
2. The memory transactions from any process are strictly sequential. That is, if one processor does a write to location A followed by a write to location B, no other processor will ever see B change before A. Some large multiprocessors violate this assumption, so they must be more careful in synchronization.

Notice that we make no assumptions about the relative speeds of the processes. Because of interrupts, context switches, and other events, one process may execute many instructions in between any two instructions of another process. To be explicit about this generality:

1. In the case of a uniprocessor, we will assume that a context switch can occur at any time that an interrupt can occur.
2. In the case of a multiprocessor, the two processes may be running simultaneously, and their accesses to memory may occur in any order.

In addition to guaranteeing mutual exclusion, we should prevent deadlock. We would like to have a reasonable degree of fairness—one process should not be able to lock out another indefinitely.

As long as we meet the two assumptions, we can solve the mutual exclusion problem strictly in software. It's harder than it looks. In most cases, a little help from the hardware will speed things up, so we will finish up with considerations of hardware and of mutual exclusion in loosely coupled processors.

3.4.1 Mutual Exclusion in Software

Mutual exclusion is neither a new problem nor one reserved to the world of computation. The first railroads comprised long sections of single track separated by short sections of dual track (the *siding*). The possibilities for collision were all thoroughly explored and after enough metal got bent, some reasonably reliable methods for guaranteeing mutual exclusion were developed. In the absence of rapid signaling (the telegraph), the railroad problem is less obvious than you might suppose. How, for example, do you prevent a faster train from overtaking a slower train? Any train can become slow or be forced to a halt. Scheduling itself is not a solution in an uncertain world. This is our reason for proscribing any assumptions on processor speed. A reliable method must depend on signaling entrance and exit from the critical sections. In railroading, the signals were called *semaphores*, a name which has moved into many other fields that needed the same sort of mechanisms. Picture the problem in light of railroading with all of the problems which can beset both the train and the communications, and you will start with a good picture of the problem. Now to the solution.

Were we simply to set before you a functional software solution to mutual exclusion, you would scratch your head a bit as you tried to fathom why we made it so complicated. To appreciate what is being done, we have to shoot down a few of the more "obvious" solutions. Let us consider some possibilities.

Try 1. As a first attempt, we might create a shared variable called LOCK, which each process sets as it enters a critical region and resets as it leaves. LOCK is simply a location in a shared memory. Now suppose that one process reads LOCK and finds that it isn't set, so it is about to set LOCK and enter the critical region. But before it can set LOCK, an interrupt occurs and another process begins executing. The second process also finds that LOCK is not set, so it sets LOCK and enters its critical region. Then another interrupt occurs, and the first process resumes where it left off, by setting LOCK and entering its critical region. We now have two processes in critical regions at the same time. Bent metal.

Try 2. Let's try to modify the algorithm to get around this problem. Suppose for the moment that we have only two processes, and that we provide a lock variable for each of them. Process1 will set LOCK1 (not a *test and set*, just *set*) when it starts to enter the critical region; process2 will set LOCK2 when it starts to enter the critical region. However, in this case we will have each process test the other process's lock variable just before it enters the critical region. If the other lock is set, it waits until the other process leaves the critical region and clears its lock. Now we have made possible a classical deadlock. Entering the critical region requires two resources. Each can be held by a separate process. Each waits for the other to clear its lock. It never happens.

Before abandoning this scheme because of the deadlock, try breaking the mutual exclusion by causing interrupts at any point. You cannot violate mutual exclusion, simply because no matter where you interrupt in the process of acquiring both locks, the other process is either already excluded or is still capable of excluding the first. So this two-lock method works for mutual exclusion but suffers from potential deadlock.

Try 3. Let us say that if a process finds itself blocked, it must clear its own lock briefly before trying again. In the interim, the other process has a chance to find the lock clear. Unfortunately, since we can't assume anything about the relative speeds of the processes, it is possible that each process will test the other's lock only during the time when it is set. In that case, both processes will be blocked for such a long time that it is effectively still a deadlock. Random, unexpected deadlocks can be the very devil to detect, but if you know that there is a potential deadlock, you can set up a deadlock detector and an orderly recovery upon detection. Breaking the deadlock is done by setting a rule for who goes first, by prioritization. Prioritization can be fixed—the king goes first—or round robin—"Your turn." Priority matters only if both processes are trying to enter critical regions at the same time; we never want one process to prevent another from entering when there is no conflict.

Try 4. Let us add another shared variable, PRIORITY, to the scheme of try 3. A process may enter the critical region if *either* it finds that the other has not locked its lock *or* it finds itself favored by the PRIORITY. The method, an improved version of *Dekker's algorithm*, is illustrated in Table 3.2 [Peterson, 81]. It guarantees all of the good things, to wit:

- mutual exclusion
- escape from deadlock
- perfect turn-taking under conditions of contention

There is only one caveat with Peterson's solution. You must be able to guarantee that both processes are looking at the *same* version of the shared variables. If the

TABLE 3.2 **Peterson's version of Dekker's algorithm for two processes.** The *enter* routines are purely software-driven. The context-switch call simply gets the blocked process off the processor to allow another process—ideally the one blocking progress—to run. If the events were going on on different processors sharing memory, then if the critical section were always short (no interrupts), it might pay to just "spin lock" by excising "context_switch."

```
int lock1=0, lock2=0, priority=1;

void critical();
void context_switch();
```

```
void enter1(){
    lock1=1;
    priority=1;
    while (lock2 && priority)
        context_switch();
    critical();
    lock1=0;
    }
```

Process 1

```
void enter2(){
    lock2=1;
    priority=0;
    while (lock1 && !priority)
        context_switch();
    critical();
    lock2=0;
    }
```

Process 2

different processes can cache a local copy, the two copies could be simultaneously 0 and 1. The way we will deal with this particular problem is to set certain sections of memory as *uncacheable*. If `priority` were in such a section, each time that the process loaded the variable, it would get the current value from memory. The ability to so mark a variable is essential to both hardware and software solutions to the mutual exclusion problem.

Dekker's algorithm can be generalized to the case when there are more than two processes, but turn-taking becomes more complex. If there are only two in competition, then if you have to wait, you know that you are next. The algorithm shown takes explicit advantage of that fact. With more than two processes, fairness is no longer easy. In the problem set we ask you to do mutual exclusion without deadlock for three processes *without worrying about fairness*. [Dijkstra, 65] discusses generalizations and the fairness problem. See [Raynal, 86] for details of other improvements and variations of this algorithm.

3.4.2 Mutual Exclusion with Hardware Assistance

Dijkstra later proposed a general simplifying mechanism for problems of this type, but one which requires some assistance from the hardware. The idea is to make try 1—the trivial solution with a single lock variable—work correctly. Recall the only reason why that solution fails: Between testing the lock and setting it, another process may enter its critical region. If we can somehow make this test-and-set an *atomic* operation, then a single LOCK variable will work. The meaning of *atomic* here is the original Greek concept: indivisible. There will be a *before* and an *after* but no *while* or *during*.

It was here that Dijkstra started calling the locks *semaphores*. His semaphore had the opposite sense of the locks in that it represented permission to enter when set. In discussions of the hardware method, the atomic operation is often described as TEST_AND_CLEAR or TEST_AND_SET, depending on the sense desired for assertion of the semaphore. What is really critical is not that the test be performed and acted on in an atomic fashion, but that the old value gets read and that the *deassertion value* gets stored as an atomic operation. The test of the old value can proceed in stately fashion thereafter, since the semaphore has been lowered for any other process. With atomicity assured, we can go back to try 1 and still admit any number of users.

We could stop here, making this the shortest subsection in the book, were it not for the fact that some of the same subtleties which led us to consider four tries for the software methods beset the hardware solutions. There are lots of different nominally atomic instructions for performing what appears to be a read and in-place modification in memory. We will describe a few of them in a moment, but the potential problem with all of them is that if you design the system to do its modifications in the CPU, it may be possible for another processor to slip between the READ and the WRITE operations. If that can happen, you are back to the problems which beset the software versions of mutual exclusion. Let us look at one conspicuously CISC instruction from the VAX which would appear to be subject to this problem and then consider how the problem is avoided in hardware. The solution that DEC employs brings up an interesting question of proper behavior when confronted with a busy signal.

Consider the problems of safely manipulating a queue as described in Section 3.3.5. The VAX supports both *absolute* and *self-relative* queues, but with a curious dichotomy. The self-relative queues support multiprocessor environments; the absolute ones do not. While the usual actions are to add elements to the tail and take elements from the head of the queue, the VAX instruction set allows you to add or subtract at either end. The four interlocked self-relative queue instructions are

INSQHI element_address, queue_head_address	insert at head
INSQTI element_address, queue_head_address	insert at tail
REMQHI queue_head_address, element_address_destination	extract from head
REMQTI queue_head_address, element_address_destination	extract from tail

These are truly glorious examples of CISCiness. The description of each instruction in the *VAX Architecture Handbook* (1981 edition) goes on for more than two pages of quite small type. Let us look at the essence of, say, REMQHI, and see what the *interlocked* business is all about. The steps and the problem are shown in Figure 3.8. The *interlock* is supposed to eliminate that problem by keeping everybody else out of the queue while each of the two critical sections is traversed. Note the plural "sections." The truly critical sections where interference would occur are to be kept extremely short. To that end, the VAX architecture defines two forms of lock:

- There is a *software lock*, which is simply a bit in the header flink. The self-relative queues on the VAX require that the header and all queue elements be *quadword aligned*. That is, their addresses must have 0's in the low-order 3 bits. The low-order bit in the header FLINK is used as the software lock, but to provide some security against accidental manipulation of nonqueues the quadword alignment is obligatory and is checked each time one of these instructions is done.

- There is a single *hardware lock*, which applies to *all* queues simultaneously. You lock that baby and nobody gets to any interlocked queue until you are done! It is this hardware lock which provides the protection for an extremely short critical path.

Figure 3.9 shows the principal steps. The critical paths are those between LOCK and UNLOCK. The LOCK bit is a flipflop right in the memory hardware. If you attempt to LOCK an already locked bit or to UNLOCK an already unlocked bit, the memory manager signals a *bus error.* What happens next is determined by the routine which handles the bus_error exception. Generally, for bus errors on LOCK, the routine recognizes that it was shut out and should simply try again. Failure on an UNLOCK operation is far more serious. It indicates that that bit was not set when it should have been. This is either a hardware failure or the consequence of a rogue program, but if this is a system queue, the system is now in trouble.

The first use of LOCK in Figure 3.9 is obvious: Grab hardware control of all queues, set the software lock bit in the header FLINK, and UNLOCK all queues except for the one on which you now have a software lock. After that very brief episode (three elementary operations) queues are enabled again.

The necessity for the second use of LOCK is much less obvious. The problem here is that regular reads and writes are not inhibited by the hardware lock; only the

```
LOCK & read header FLINK
        Set software lock in copy of FLINK
UNLOCK & Store copy of FLINK in header
If lock bit set in FLINK then begin
        Set carry flag
End else if (FLINK=0) then begin
        Set overflow flag       ;queue was empty
        LOCK (& read header FLINK)
        UNLOCK & Store old FLINK in header
End else begin
        sum header address plus header FLINK
        Read 1st Flink
        add 1st FLINK to previous sum
        Read 1st BLINK
        Read 2nd BLINK
        sum
        Store 2nd BLINK
        Store address of first element
        LOCK (& read header FLINK)
        UNLOCK & Store FLINK in header
End
```

FIGURE 3.9 The principal operations performed by the VAX instruction REMQHI. The hardware recognizes two different forms of READ and WRITE. The usual READ and WRITE as well as READ_WITH_LOCK and WRITE_WITH_UNLOCK. The last two instructions test_and_set or test_and_reset respectively *in hardware*. If the test fails, the system executes a bus exception which forces a retry. In the second LOCK operation, the data that are read are discarded and the newly calculated header FLINK (with lock bit reset) is stored.

interlocked instructions are blocked. Accordingly, some other processor might execute the first READ_with_LOCK and get the still-locked FLINK; you could then write back the unlocked FLINK that you had just computed by using a regular WRITE; then the other processor reinstalls the old FLINK with lock-bit set. The other guy abandons the access because his software lock bit is set. You go away because you just reset the bit. The queue is now forever locked! The key is lost. System checkmate.

You might wonder at the elaborateness of all of this. Is it necessary? Well, no, but before dismissing it, let us see what the VAX designers had in mind. There are two parts of this scheme: having two locks and tying the hardware lock to special instructions. These instructions are all uninterruptable, so there is no issue of intrusions on a single processor. All of this complex locking is done to allow multiprocessing. Apart from variations on Dekker's algorithm, a hardware lock is a must for that. However, one need not limit the hardware lock to a single flipflop. There is a widely used, simple but crude method of doing the same thing. The hardware exclusion is done by hanging onto the central bus and not letting anyone near memory while the read_modify_write operation is conducted. That is cheap and functional in systems which use a single backplane bus to talk to memory. It is found in Intel's 80x86 and Motorola MC680x0 processors and many other machines. This approach is appealing because it admits all sorts of operations for the *modify* part. It also allows one to use commercial busses which do not have signals for the special memory operations. However, some machines—the VAX being an example—find themselves with multiple flavors of backplane busses in a single machine and many different busses across the whole family of processors. The busses in a single machine do talk to each other, but hanging on to them all to ensure no interference becomes more and more intrusive as the complexity of the machine grows.

To avoid this traffic jam, one may do the required operations at the memory unit itself. Here you have the choice of doing something complicated, such as a local read_modify_write operation, or something simple, such as a single flipflop that can be set and reset. The latter is clearly easier and cheaper, so the VAX solution is the low-cost one. If you look at our LODSET instruction (Figure 2.18 on page 100), you will see that we opted for a "hold the bus" version, though it would be quite simple to modify the memory controller to provide the *modify-write* function at the memory itself. We chose not to in order to make our machine compatible with the Futurebus specification, reasoning that lock operations are not that extraordinarily common and that the burden of a read_modify_write operation (less than two full memory cycles) is not an extreme burden.

3.4.3 To Be Pushy or Polite

A question that we have not dealt with so far is: What is good behavior if our program finds itself with a busy signal? The choice is between sitting on the sidelines until called (the *wait* paradigm) or the rather insistent paradigm: Keep trying until the sucker lets go. This pushy behavior, called a *spinlock*, can waste a lot of CPU time, but if the competing processes are on separate processors and the critical region is short, then the question is: Does it pay to do a context switch? Obviously, this is a question to answer only after examining the process interactions on a particular installation. In Figure 3.9, the regions constrained by a hardware lock are so short that a spinlock is clearly called for. By the time that you get back from handling the first exception, you will find that the lock is free. (Furthermore, the hardware lock must *never* be set by a process which may be preempted, so all processes that can compete explicitly for the hardware lock will be on separate processors.)

At the next level up, it is not so obvious. User processes generally should not use spinlocks and certainly should not lock out all queue operations because they cannot control their environments. One solution for user processes is to avoid semaphores altogether, at least apparently, by introducing complicated instructions which effectively shrink the critical section down to a single, apparently atomic instruction. This is what the VAX does, although deep down inside, the interlocked VAX queue instructions actually set the hardware lock twice in the course of the complete execution of a single instruction. For the user of one of these instructions, only the software lock bit is visible and that only by reflection. For example, on doing a REMQHI, the process gets three flag bits to ponder:

- If the carry flag is set, the queue is temporarily busy. Finishing a queue operation takes just the time to run through the steps listed in Figure 3.9. The process should choose to spinlock in software if the other competing process is running on another processor or do a `sleep()` if it is running on the same processor. Note that if a context switch occurs in the midst of the spinlock, other processes will find the hardware lock reset. That is because all interlocked commands are atomic *on a single processor* and the context switch is always at the end of such an instruction.
- If the overflow bit is set, there is nothing on the queue. Unless the process has something else to do, it is certainly time for a nap.
- If the zero flag is set, the element removed was the last element on the queue.

Interrupt routines have very different problems when they use semaphores. An interrupt routine usually must not be blocked and resumed later, as a user process may be. In fact, to satisfy latency requirements, it may be required to complete within a specified time. Spinlocks may work, if they can be certain that only a small delay will occur. Bach and Buroff consider solutions to this problem [Bach, 84]. In our machine, with its hierarchy of interrupt levels, the system programmer must be sure that no deadlock can occur as a result of resources shared between programs running at different ILs. A safe scheme is to have all processes and programs which share data structures operate on those structures at the same level. Otherwise, the higher-level program could get stuck in a spinlock with the lock being held by another program at a lower level. Another system checkmate.

3.4.4 Sharing Resources over Weak Interconnections

Think of having an array of big machines distributed over the country—or the world, for that matter—which share a common resource such as a data base or a queue. How do you handle mutual exclusion when the delay time between machines may be large fractions of a second and where there is no central repository of current information? You cannot count even on all processors staying on the air all the time, though that is something which can be approached asymptotically with great care and lots of money. There is certainly more than one answer to this question and none of them is entirely simple. One whole issue of the *Digital Technical Journal* (September 1987) is devoted to the structures of the VAXcluster. Mutual exclusion is treated by Snaman and Thiel in that journal [Snaman, 87].

The concept of a cluster is to accomplish *symmetric multiprocessing* in which all of the functions of the operating system are distributed over all of the processors in the cluster. User processes run on any of the processors, with much effort in design going into balancing the load so that *N* processors come close to giving *N* times as much processing as one processor. In the VAX system, it is permitted to mix and match many of the VAX models in a single cluster.

In the VAXcluster, the lock manager is a distributed function in which cooperating processes share resources. In the system described in [Snaman, 87], the whole system is divided into hierarchical *resources* where each resource root might be a processor and its descendants the files that can be obtained through that root. The files themselves can be further subdivided into records or blocks which are descendants of the files. By handling things in small pieces, different processes can have exclusive or protected access to different parts of a single file. The lock manager's task is to provide protection services including both mutual exclusion and deadlock detection.

Since the processes are cooperating, there is no reason why the lock manager should reside anywhere in particular. In general, on the basis of the fact that most files or pieces of files will be of interest to only one process, the first to request access to a resource or subresource generally becomes the manager of that resource, regardless of where the resource itself is located. If you are the only one interested in the collection on ancient Abyssinian literature in the library, why should you have to go through the librarian to access the collection? If you are the only user and a trustworthy soul, there is no reason to pass messages back and forth. Even with multiple users, this separation of resource and manager is eminently reasonable, because the request for access is quite independent of the order to read or write some data on the resource. After all, politely cooperating processes will not attempt to access information until they have been granted proper permission. Now if you think of a smart program getting requests and comparing them to the permissions already granted, it should not come as a surprise that it can manage this access to achieve mutual exclusion when that is the objective. The six access modes that the lock manager supports are shown in Table 3.3, which is taken from [Snaman, 87]. With a sophisticated lock manager, a process can put in a request for exclusive control of a resource and ask to be notified when it is granted. The process can then either wait or go about doing something else. In the VAX, it is possible to post a trap for a particular process at some interrupt level and the VAX will handle it whenever it has nothing more urgent to do. This *asynchronous system trap* (AST) is then used by the lock manager to alert the process which wanted it. Nice. You can now have a queue of requests, wakeup calls, requests to relinquish your current mode on a particular resource, and access to resources throughout the entire cluster.

TABLE 3.3 The six modes of access to a resource that a process may request from the VAX/VMS distributed lock manager

Mode	Suggested interpretation
NL	Null mode grants no access to the resource: it is typically used either as an indicator of interest in the resource or as a placeholder for future lock conversions.
CR	Concurrent read mode grants read access to the resource and allows its sharing with other readers. This mode is used when control is exercised with sublocks at finer granularity or when no protection is required.
CW	Concurrent write mode is the write image of CR.
PR	Protected read mode grants read access to the resource and allows its sharing with other readers. No writing allowed by anybody.
PW	Protected write mode grants read and write access to the single user and allows sharing with other users holding CR rights. This allows single user updates but does not guarantee that a reader will obtain coherent updates.
EX	Exclusive mode grants read and write access to a single user.

Any problems? You bet! Consider the possibilities for deadlock. There are two varieties which DEC calls *conversion deadlocks* and *resource deadlocks*. The first is a cinch. Two processes are requesting EX and holding, say PR. Neither will give up its PR till it gets EX, but neither can be given EX till the other gives up all access privilege. This is the conversion deadlock. It is easily observed because the single manager has all the data. Snaman and Thiel then state that "a victim is chosen" and told to let go. The victim has to release its relevant resources, and then the other can go for broke. The hard one is the multiple-resource deadlock. This is a problem which arises when A is holding X and waiting for Y and B is holding Y and waiting for X. Since X and Y can be resources whose lock managers are on other members of the cluster, it certainly is not obvious how you detect the deadlock. As with most obscure-deadlock detectors, the distributed lock manager gets curious when a request has been queued for what seems like an excessively long time. A single request too long delayed must trigger its attention, because it may be totally unaware that the other request is pending. The search algorithm is partially spelled out in [Snaman, 87], which also gives further references and states that the algorithm was discovered independently at both IBM and DEC. Basically, it is a rather expensive tracing of the request up through the root and down through other resource trees looking for closure. That is, the algorithm hopes to find that B, which is holding Y, is the one that is waiting for X, which brings us back to A. Of course, since the resource deadlock could have three or more players, with resource demands on several machines and resources held on still others, lots of messages may have to rattle back and forth before the right victim can be found.

There are many other issues that a distributed lock manager must be able to address. Probably the most interesting conceptually is the idea of recovering from the failure of a single machine in the cluster. There has to be some way to recognize the loss, both to account for the lost resources and to reacquire the current status of any resources which were controlled by lock managers running on the lost machine. Such esoterica as protecting the system from collapsing or breaking into subclusters if the cluster is subject to a "rolling power failure and recovery cycle" illustrate the sophistication of the design and the concern for reliable operation in adverse conditions. But these are beyond our current level of concerns. It is time to sum up.

CHAPTER SUMMARY

This chapter focused on the services required in a multiprogramming environment. The source of these services is the *operating system*. The operating system provides both assistance and discipline. The operating system will provide

- a single, easily accessed source for common software needs
- discipline in the use of shared resources, such as I/O, memory, and the processor(s)

The specific chores performed by the operating system would include

- scheduling of processor time
- allocation of memory, controlling isolation or sharing of memory resources
- I/O services for processes and file system maintenance
- a library of common service programs including
  the login program
  mail services
  command interpreters (*shells* in UNIX)
  directory services including creating, deleting, and copying files
  compilers, assemblers, and linkers
  editors
- mechanisms to enter and leave layers of the operating system
- interprocess communication and synchronization mechanisms
- memory management mechanisms
- the context switch (processes taking turns in using the CPU)

The need for controlling access to certain hardware and memory resources and the concept that there should reside in memory a small, privileged control program led to the idea of a system kernel. The relationship of user and system processes to the system kernel was shown in Figure 3.1.

The concept of a *process* was expressed as a program running in its own isolated environment, protected by the operating system both from external interference and from some of the foolish or clever ways we can shoot ourselves in the foot. The process's *context* was defined and summed up in Table 3.1. An overview of a UNIX operating system was presented and illustrated in Figure 3.2. UNIX's simple worldview with two levels—user and kernel—was compared with its ancestor, Multics, with its rather incredible 64 concentric domains.

To introduce the mechanics of multiprogramming, the *scheduler* function of the kernel was considered. The concept of preemptive multiprogramming was introduced, and Figure 3.3 presented in simplified form the array of queues and states that the scheduler maintains for determining the order in which processes get access to the CPU. The concept of swapping a context out and back in showed a method by which the kernel could accommodate requests which summed to more memory than was actually available as well showing a need for several classes of wait queue. The transactions which comprise a context switch were explored, and through Figure 3.4 and the accompanying text it was shown that all waiting processes are in kernel mode and why. Time slicing and synchronous I/O provided examples of events which induced context switches. The system calls `sleep(event)` and `wakeup(event)` were introduced to provide the tools for putting a process into a wait queue and getting it back out to the run queue.

The last major topic in this chapter was the synchronization problem when asynchronous concurrent processes share data resources. In the absence of such synchronization, data corruption and system crashes are inevitable. The two principal objectives that we sought were *mutual exclusion* and *deadlock prevention*. Our first effort was to develop an algorithm which would permit mutual exclusion strictly in software. This effort finally resulted in Dekker's algorithm. Along the way to that algorithm were revealed some of the difficulties which could arise if mutual exclusion were not obtained or if it were obtained with the possibility of deadlock.

Having struggled to do it right in software, we next turned to the far easier techniques available with hardware assistance. We introduced our simple method—LODSET—which obtains exclusion by hogging the bus. This method is quite common among microprocessors of both CISC and RISC flavors. Then we considered the structure underlying the more complicated VAX *interlocked* queue instructions. This brought up the subject of proper response to finding the way blocked. The choices were spinlock or `sleep()`. The choice was dependent on whether the process doing the test was subject to preemption and whether the process with which it is competing was running on the same processor. The VAX provides some nice alternatives for processes subject to preemption.

Finally, we took a very brief look at sharing resources over weak interconnections. Our example was a VAX cluster using symmetric multiprocessing and a distributed lock manager. This brought up two different classes of deadlocks. We provided a very brief overview of the solutions to both.

We have not finished with operating system issues. In particular, the whole of the next chapter is focused on memory management and Chapter 7 examines I/O from the operating system perspective.

PROBLEMS

3.1. State how you would tell from the header of a queue if:

(a) The queue, which uses absolute addressing, is empty;

(*b*) The queue, which uses absolute addressing, has one element on it;
(*c*) The queue, which uses self-relative addressing, is empty;
(*d*) The queue, which uses self-relative addressing, has one element on it.

3.2. Write functions in C or Pascal and then translate them into our local assembly language to accomplish the tasks of enqueuing and dequeuing an element from a doubly linked list. Assume that the list is a self-relative queue. The dequeue function receives a pointer to the queue header and should return a pointer to the queue element removed from the head (a `null` pointer if the queue is empty); the enqueue function is passed pointers to the queue and to the element to be enqueued and returns a 1 (Boolean TRUE in Pascal) if the element added is the first in the queue. The enqueue function should put the element on the queue tail.

3.3. Assume that the assembly language instructions that you wrote in Problem 3.2 are executed at 10 instructions per microsecond. For how long a period is the queue *incoherent* while you are *enqueuing* and *dequeuing* an element?

3.4. Consider the section of VAX byte-addressed memory containing two doubly linked, self-relative lists below. (Recall that self-relative means that the forward and backward links are relative to the beginning of the current element, whether header or list entry.) Each element is an envelope guaranteed to be quadword aligned; the header is quadword aligned as well. Our envelopes are only 16 bytes. Included in that length are the FLINK and BLINK. The first list is the command list; its header is found at location 20000. There is also another linked list of "empty" envelopes on the freelist; its header is found at 20008. Hex numbers are used throughout.

0000 0018	0000 0048	0000 0030	0000 0010	**20000**
xxxx xxxx	xxxx xxxx	FFFF FFF0	0000 0030	
xxxx xxxx	xxxx xxxx	0000 0030	FFFF FFE8	**20020**
xxxx xxxx	xxxx xxxx	0000 0010	FFFF FFD0	
xxxx xxxx	xxxx xxxx	FFFF FFD0	FFFF FFF0	**20040**
xxxx xxxx	xxxx xxxx	FFFF FFB8	FFFF FFD0	

(*a*) Show memory after the removal of the first (head) element of the command queue.
(*b*) Assume that the process finishes with the message removed in (*a*) and puts it back on the tail of the freelist. Show memory after this operation.

3.5. In the text accompanying Figure 3.8, it was claimed that there were three other possible evil scenarios. Show how to accomplish each of the following scenarios:
(*a*) Keep the queue whole but give the queue element to both processes.
(*b*) Give each its proper element but break the queue.
(*c*) By allowing Y to reenqueue the element it took on a different queue, break two queues at once.

3.6. In Dekker's algorithm (Table 3.2), only two processes may share a structure. Create an extension to Dekker's algorithm to handle three (or more) processes sharing a common structure in which you guarantee both mutual exclusion and escape from deadlock. You need not provide perfect symmetry in access. To make it easy to wake up sleeping processes, you may have more than one signal. For the train analogy, consider bringing three tracks into one track. In the process you would go from 3 to 2 to 1.

3.7. The queues described in the text are doubly-linked lists requiring two link fields in each element. If the elements are short, that is a lot of overhead. Since you almost inevitably arrive at an element by traversing the list from front to back and know where you came from, you really can make do with a single link field from which you *derive* the link displacement. There are several ways to organize such embedded links. Consider this one:

Let the header contain pointers to the first and last elements of the list as before. Then construct a single link field in each element which comprises the XOR of the addresses of the previous element and the successor element (including the header). The links in a three-element list would be:

Header	A	B	C
A	H⊗B	A⊗C	B⊗H
C			

An empty queue is indicated by a header which points only at itself.

(a) How would one identify a queue with only one element?

(b) Write a routine to insert a new element at the head of a queue.

(c) Write a routine to insert a new element at the tail of a queue.

(d) Write a routine to remove the first element from the queue. Return a pointer to the element removed.

(e) Write a routine to remove the last element from the queue. Return a pointer to the element removed.

(f) Write a routine search for and remove an element containing a particular value of the integer *datum*. Search from the head. Return a pointer to the element removed.

REFERENCES

Operating systems textbooks

[Deitel, 83] Deitel, H.M., *An Introduction to Operating Systems*, Addison-Wesley (1983). Good coverage of asynchronous processes (Chapters 3-6), memory management (Chapters 7-9), and VM/370 (Chapter 22).

[Finkel, 88] Finkel, R.A., *An Operating Systems Vade Mecum*, 2nd ed., Prentice-Hall (1988). Somewhat easier to read than the other textbooks. Good coverage of asynchronous processes in Chapters 8 and 9.

[Maekawa, 87] Maekawa, M., A. Oldehoeft, and R. Oldehoeft, *Operating Systems—Advanced Concepts*, Benjamin-Cummings (1987). This book should be read only after one of the others. It includes a good summary of research results in various areas including process synchronization, virtual memory, and distributed systems.

[Milenkovic, 87] Milenkovic, M., *Operating Systems, Concepts and Design*, McGraw-Hill (1987). This book is particularly strong on interprocess communication and synchronization (Chapters 3, 4, and 5). Also includes an IBM PC kernel.

Descriptions of actual operating systems

[Bach, 86] Bach, M. J., *The Design of the UNIX Operating System*, Prentice-Hall (1986). This is the best publicly available description of the algorithms used in the AT&T UNIX kernel, and it is very readable.

[Comer, 84] Comer, D., *Operating System Design, The Xinu Approach*, Prentice-Hall (1984). Revised for IBM PC in 1988. An operating system textbook which contains the source code for a small PDP-11 kernel, or an IBM PC kernel in the 1988 version. A second volume is also available, which covers networks.

[Kenah, 88] Kenah, L.J., R.E. Goldenberg, and S.F. Bate, *VAX/VMS Internals and Data Structures*, Version 4.4, Digital Press (1988). An extremely detailed description of VMS, but not easy to read.

[Leffler, 89] Leffler, S.J, M.K. McKusick, M.J. Karels, and J.S. Quarterman, *The Design and Implementation of the 4.3BSD UNIX Operating System*, Addison-Wesley (1989). A description similar to [Bach, 86] of the Berkeley version of UNIX.

[Organick, 72] Organick, E.I., *The Multics System: An Examination of Its Structure*, MIT Press (1972). A detailed description of Multics and the GE645 computer. Most interesting is the discussion of protection mechanisms.

[Tanenbaum, 87] Tanenbaum, A.S., *Operating Systems, Design and Implementation*, Prentice-Hall (1987). An operating systems textbook which contains the source code for a small UNIX-like operating system called Minix. A fairly complete Minix system is available for the IBM PC, containing the sources for the kernel and most of the utility programs.

[Toy, 86] Toy, W., and B. Zee, *Computer Hardware/Software Architecture*, Prentice-Hall (1986). Chapters 5, 6, and 7 are devoted to operating systems and hardware support for them.

Synchronization

[Auslander, 90] Auslander, D.M., and C.H. Tham, *Real-Time Software for Control*, Prentice-Hall (1990). A text on the general problem of real-time control and operating system issues therein. Covers both preemptive and nonpreemptive multitasking with the constraints imposed by real-time control.

[Bach, 84] Bach, M.J. and S.J. Buroff, *Multiprocessor UNIX Operating Systems*, **AT&T Bell Laboratories Technical Journal 63**(8): 1733-1749 (1984). Covers problems like the use of semaphores in the kernel. There is a similar, but not identical, discussion in Chapter 12 of Bach's book on UNIX [Bach, 86].

[Bourne, 91] Bourne, Philip E., *The UNIX File System*, **DEC Professional 10**(11,12) (1991). A short, two-part discussion directed toward fledgling system managers.

[Dijkstra, 65] Dijkstra, E.W., *Solution of a Problem in Concurrent Programming Control*, **CACM 8**(9): 569 (1965). Reprinted with various responses in **CACM 26**(1) (1983). Gives a software algorithm for multiple asynchronous processes to enforce mutual exclusion. The letters responding to this paper discuss some of the problems with algorithms of this type and propose modifications.

[Dijkstra, 68] Dijkstra, E.W., *Co-operating Sequential Processes*, in **Programming Languages**, F. Genuys (ed.), Academic Press (1968). Defines semaphores and gives some elaborate examples of their use.

[Janssens, 86] Janssens, M.D., J.K. Annot, and A.J. van de Goor, *Adapting UNIX for a Multiprocessor Environment*, **CACM 29**(9): 895-901 (1986).

[Lamport, 78] Lamport, L., *Time, Clocks and the Ordering of Events in a Distributed System,* **CACM 21**(7): 558-565 (1978).

[Lamport, 86a] Lamport, L., *The Mutual Exclusion Problem: Part I—A Theory of Interprocess Communication*, **JACM 33**(2): 313-326 (1986).

[Lamport, 86b] Lamport, L., *The Mutual Exclusion Problem: Part II—Statement and Solutions*, **JACM 33**(2): 327-348 (1986).

[Peterson, 81] Peterson, G.L., *Myths about the Mutual Exclusion Problem*, **Information Processing Letters 12**(3): 115-116 (1981).

[Raynal, 86] Raynal, M., *Algorithms for Mutual Exclusion*, MIT Press (1986). A translation of *Algorithmique du parallelisme*. A good summary of software and hardware algorithms for both tightly coupled and distributed systems.

[Ricart, 81] Ricart, G., and A.K. Agrawala, *An Optimal Algorithm for Mutual Exclusion in Computer Networks*, **CACM 24**(1): 9-17 (1981).

[Snaman, 87] Snaman, W.E., Jr., and D.W. Thiel, *The VAX/VMS Distributed Lock Manager*, **Digital Technical Journal 5**: 29 (September 1987). This whole issue is devoted to communication, file management, and reliability in VAX clusters.

[Stone, 87] Stone, H.S., *High-Performance Computer Architecture*, Addison-Wesley (1987). Chapter 7 contains good coverage of hardware synchronization mechanisms.

General

[Tiberghien, 81] Tiberghien, Jacques, *The Pascal Handbook*, Sybex (1981). An excellent, readable, and rather complete exposition of the instructions of the Pascal current on small machines.

CHAPTER 4

VIRTUAL MEMORY

IN WHICH WE EXPLORE JUST WHERE THE DATA RESIDE

4.1 SHARING THE WEALTH, SUCH AS IT IS

A disparate collection of applications will not, by themselves, share resources on one machine in some safe and efficient manner, yet this is exactly what the user expects and wants to occur. The operating system is supposed to make it happen. It is more than just playing traffic cop at a busy intersection. The operating system must provide both allocation and protection services. The three principal resources are CPU time, memory, and secondary storage (the file system). In this chapter we will consider memory and examine in detail the kinds of memory management functions that are provided by operating systems and the hardware support required to implement them. After comparing some typical mechanisms, we will choose one for our RISC machine, and use it to implement some of the operating system functions. We will use this material in Chapter 5 to develop the details of the hardware design.

A multiprocess operating system is, from its roots to the most modern manifestations, a rather aggressively competitive operation where each process would like to hog all of the resources which help it get its job done. Among the more important resources is primary memory. Every process needs some, but in truth, few need to have all of their programs and all of their data in memory at one time. Do you need a desk which can hold all of your books at one time? Hardly. The usual answer is that you can read only one at a time. While that is true, you certainly encounter situations where you are jumping back and forth between two or three books, but even if your project encompasses 50 references, the number that you need at any one moment is limited. This suggests a desk big enough to keep you busy and shelves or filing cabinets for the references not immediately in use. If you want to bring a reference from the shelves, generally it involves both some trade of space (another volume back to the shelves) and some noticeable delay in bringing the desired text "into the foreground." A full description of the hierarchy of these desk and reader-oriented data structures includes

- book sitting on the desk, open to the desired information
- book sitting on the desk, closed
- book on the shelves
- book in the library
- book obtainable through interlibrary loan

From top to bottom, accessing data requires longer time but far more information is available and storage is generally cheaper per unit data.

A similar hierarchical scheme is employed in computers, where we might assign the five layers as

- register
- cache (SRAM)
- primary memory (DRAM and ROM)
- secondary memory (disk and tape)
- remote hosts connected through a network

Costs go down and delays go up as you move down the list. It is a principal task of the operating system to see that the primary memory is well utilized, that every process gets enough memory to function well, and that the exchanges between primary and secondary memory be accomplished swiftly and with minimum overhead (activity which does not result in user work being done). If people interact with the operating system, then good operating system design will also entail a deft and comfortable interface between users and the file system.

Back in the days when computers were remote and obscure, the remote and obscure people who programmed them worked on machines with minute memories. They had to come up with schemes to make do, to somehow fit their programs and their data into the insufficient space available. A typical example that is neither very remote nor very obscure would be an Apple II, circa 1980. Maximum memory was 64 KB and many of the earlier machines were shipped with as little as 16 KB. Many programs exceeded that range even without their data. Obviously, something had to be done. The solution was called *overlaying*. Programs were constructed in *segments* or *units* which were small compared to the memory size. If the main program said "Do **A** and then do **B**," **A** and **B** would each be a segment. All the segments would reside on disk—generally a floppy in those days—but only a few could be accommodated simultaneously in memory. Let us say that the segments comprised **main**, **A**, **B**, and **C**. When the user launched the program, **main** was loaded and began to run. First it called **C**, so **C** was loaded. Then it called **A**, and that was loaded. Now **B** is called, but there is insufficient room. Accordingly, **B** must be written into the space now occupied by one of the other segments, say **A**. **B** is said to *overwrite* or *overlay* **A**. The original copy of **A** still resides out there on disk, so if **A** is called again, it can overlay another segment, either **B** or **C**. However, as you might imagine, with the slowness of floppies, programs which did a lot of overlays would be remarkably slow and full of whirring and clicking noises. When the system spends essentially all of its time replacing the contents of memory rather than doing "useful" computation, it is said to be *thrashing*. To limit thrashing behavior, the programmer on such primitive systems was usually permitted to tag some segments so that they would be held in memory during certain sections of the program, even when other segments were running.

While programmer-controlled overlays do solve the problem of memory allocation in running a single process at a time or when sharing is done by allocating a fixed and immutable piece of memory upon startup of each application, they become unwieldy to the point of uselessness when applied to noncooperative multiprocess operations. Instead, the operating system, and whatever hardware is necessary to support it, should take the burden of apportioning memory, it should do it dynamically, responding to the needs of the moment, and it should do it painlessly. This chapter is devoted to developing methodologies to accomplish that task.

4.2 FUNCTIONS OF MEMORY MANAGEMENT

Every CPU has some range of possible addresses. This address range is called the *address space* of the machine. There may or may not be anything installed at a particular address. What is installed is the *physical memory*. In 32-bit machines today, the address space greatly exceeds the physical memory. In our machine, the address space is 16 GB, while the physical memory will be a tiny fraction of that, perhaps 8 to 128 MB. If you recall our discussion of program structure in Chapter 2 and particularly Figure 2.12 on page 83, you will suddenly realize that all programs seem to use the same addresses. Furthermore, many processes—100 or more in a big machine—will share that same physical space but each operates independently with little or no knowledge of the other processes. Clearly, there must be a difference between a process address (a *virtual address*), where every programmer is using the same addresses, and a *physical address*, where every process must use different addresses. The operating system provides not only translation between these two addresses but allocation of memory as well.

Let us consider how independent applications can share memory. First we will look at where things are in physical memory; then we will consider (briefly, at this stage) how the program addresses them. We illustrate two quite different paradigms in Figure 4.1. The Macintosh, running under *Multifinder*, can load as many programs *as will fit in memory*. This system is illustrated on the left side of Figure 4.1. Fitting is simple, because each program specifies its memory needs. While the size is specified, location is determined by what is available at load time. No available space, no run. While only one program may run in the foreground at any one time, switching foreground tasks is easy and quick. Furthermore, programs can run concurrently (i.e., alternate turns on the processor in reasonably rapid succession) through cooperation with the operating system. Note that application #1 leaves some of its program or data out on disk, loading some subset of it at any one time. As another subset is brought in, it *overlays* the previous

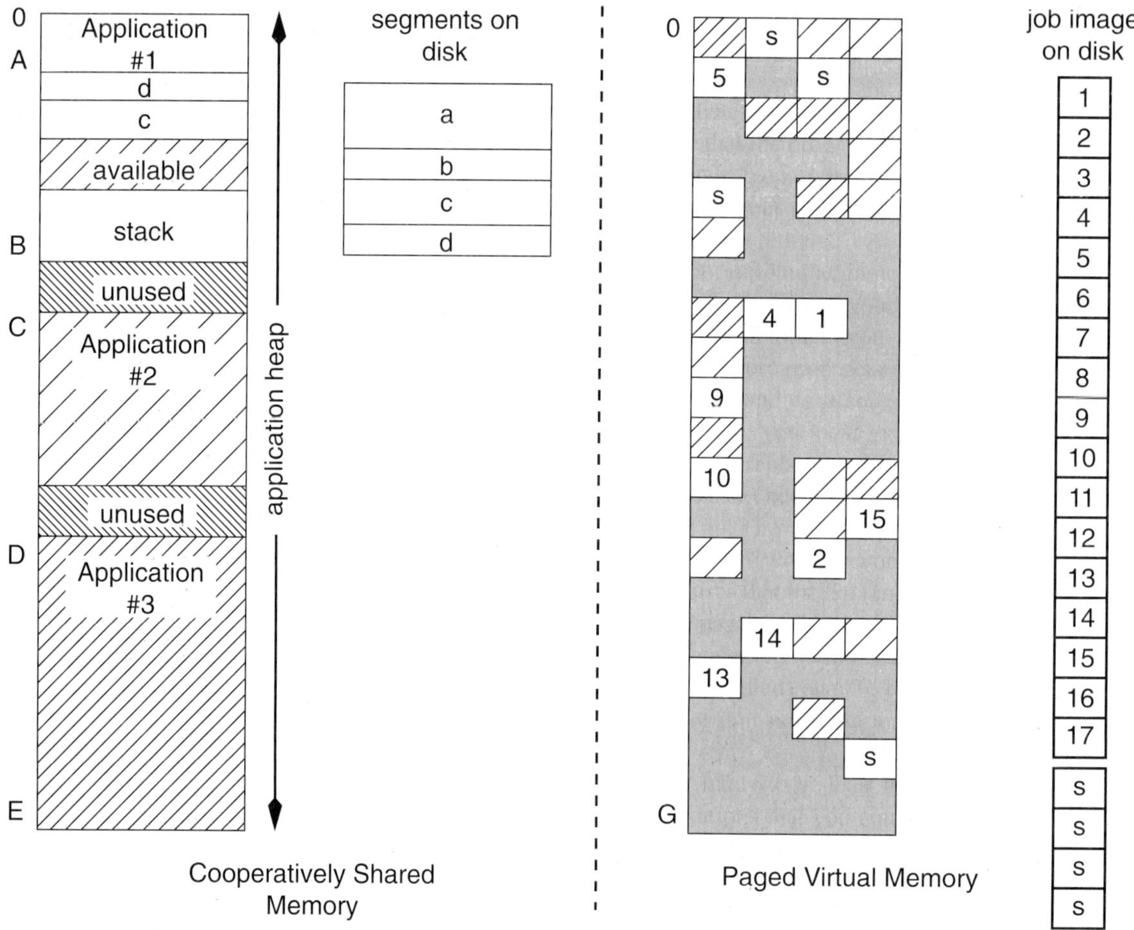

FIGURE 4.1 Two ways to have three applications share a memory of size G. Both leave some portion of one or more of the applications out on disk. In the cooperatively shared memory, each application gets a fixed allocation specified in the application itself. To fit more program or data than that allocation can hold, the application, through requests to the *application manager*, swaps segments in and out. The application itself marks which segments may be swapped. Dynamic structures (e.g., stack or local heap) are simply segments created at run time. In paged virtual memory, the entire job is imaged on disk. The operating system brings in standard blocks (pages) of the applications as it sees fit, keeping track of where it puts them. If the program references a missing page, the operating system fetches it from disk. Note that much less of a given application need be in memory at any given instant, leaving more room for other applications or for one particularly hungry application.

subset. The application itself is party to its memory allocation, but the application manager provides all of the tools for managing the application heap and for keeping track of the segments in memory. Applications must remain within their static allocation, but the system allows great flexibility within that range at quite modest cost.

How different is the paged virtual memory system on the right? The operating system has complete control over what portion of each program resides in memory and where it resides. Memory is divided up into standard-sized blocks called *pages*. Typical page sizes range from 0.5 to 8 KB. The programs are written without knowledge (or interest) in where they will reside. A good view of the application is to see it as basically one or more contiguous blocks of large size that all reside out on disk. Somehow, the operating system determines dynamically how many and which small page-sized pieces of these blocks to load and which to let go or write back. The application just runs, asking for what it needs when it needs it. Somehow, whatever it needs gets into memory and can be used without worrying about where it is resident. The virtual addresses (VAs) are essentially the name of the item; the name gets translated by the operating system to an actual address. If that address is on disk, the page must be fetched and then the datum delivered; if the address is in memory, the datum can be delivered at once.

This observation leads to breaking the memory management task into three almost independent subtasks:

- finding the correct physical address for addresses written at compile time, a time when the physical address is simply unknown and unknowable
- fairly allocating space in the physical memory available on the local machine to the several processes running at any one time
- providing each application or process the ability to acquire space for dynamic data—stack and heap in the most common programming languages

With the Macintosh running under multifinder, *allocation* is handled interactively between application and operating system. When the user launches an application, the operating system checks to see if the memory requirement can be fulfilled *in a contiguous block of memory.* If not, the user gets a dialogue box saying what the deficit is and asking what the user would like to do. With paged virtual memory, allocation is much more complex, but of no concern to the programmer at all. Allocation is both dynamic and generally unrelated to a program's actual size. The concept is illustrated on the right side of Figure 4.1. The dynamism can apply to the amount of memory that the program is holding at any one time as well as to what specific parts of a program's code and data are in memory. It is important to realize that the same machine can support both modes of operation. Running under multifinder, the Macintosh uses static memory allocation per application but provides considerable dynamic flexibility on how that allocation is used. The same machine running under A/UX (Apple's version of UNIX) operates as a true virtual address machine, with dynamic memory allocation. To drive home the difference, operating under A/UX, the machine can run multifinder as one of its applications! Programmers like dynamic allocation, particularly because they do not have to do it. Customers are indifferent to the memory model. They are concerned with performance and reliability.

Let us now demystify the concept of address translation. While the idea of address translation will get more complicated as we delve into virtual memory systems, at least for programs which are loaded as contiguous segments, as shown on the left in Figure 4.1, finding the physical address is straightforward. One simple way to generate the physical address is to write all programs in *position-independent code*, that is, use only base-displacement (including pc+displacement) addressing. In this way, when you move a whole segment, you drag all of the addresses with it. Then the operating system can place each program anywhere in the memory, jump in turn to the now known starting addresses, and the programs run without further translation service. In the Macintosh, pointers to the segments are maintained in an address translation table while the program itself uses pointers to these pointers in the table (*handles*). This permits the application manager to move things about within the static allocation for maximum effectiveness. All that must be changed is the translation table. The handles are fixed.

The Macintosh system is exceptionally efficient in managing multiple applications in relatively small memories. However, it makes application programming much more arduous, and it is less impressive in systems where memory is plentiful and cheap. The paged virtual memory system needs a goodly measure of free space to be efficient, but if that is available, then dynamic allocation is to be preferred. But with dynamic allocation, you really do have an address translation problem! Look at the random scattering of Application #1's pages. To provide the address translation with any facility, a hardware mechanism becomes essential. An address created by the compiler has no logical relationship to the address of the datum in memory. Contiguous sections of program may get distributed hither and yon like a shuffled deck of cards. Addresses used by the program are called *logical* or *virtual* or sometimes *effective* addresses. One primary function of the memory management unit in a virtual memory operating system is to translate logical addresses to physical addresses—essentially to *unshuffle* the deck.

A true virtual memory system provides a great deal more. Along with address translation, we will want

- A *low context-switch overhead.* While a context switch involves several data swaps, here we are concerned that the swapping of address translation tables from one process to the next not consume too much time.
- *Memory protection,* keeping rogue programs in their own pens. This feature is conspicuously absent in the cooperative model on the left of Figure 4.1. If multiple programs are sharing the memory, we should be able to protect them from each other and to protect the operating system itself. This implies that each program should be allowed access only to those areas of memory which are assigned to it. A look at the right side of Figure 4.1 should make you wonder how we will accomplish this task, but it is certainly a task we will want to accomplish. If a program attempts to access a logical address which it was not expected to use, the memory management unit should detect the error and notify the operating system that something is wrong.
- *Access type checking.* Areas of the logical address space which the program needs to read but not change can be write-protected. The logical addresses which contain instructions can be identified as execute-only, so that instruction fetches can occur from those addresses, but no ordinary reads or writes will be permitted. All of these protection functions can be added to the basic translation function of the memory management unit without much extra hardware.
- *Sharing data and program.* There are plenty of cases where two processes could profitably share some part of the memory. A common example is when two or more users are executing the same program. Each could have a copy of the entire program,

but in that case the physical memory would contain two identical copies of the same sequence of instructions. If our translation mechanism is versatile enough, both processes should be able to share the instruction part of the program, while each has its own data region. Programs which can be operating simultaneously in different parts for different users are said to be *reentrant*. In systems with *dynamic linking*, different programs may be able to share common routines, such as library functions—one sin( ) function for all comers. The sharing of data areas, with sequencing regulated by semaphores, can be useful as an interprocess communication mechanism. Accordingly, we want our memory management scheme to have mechanisms for sharing code and sharing data.

- *Dynamic memory allocation and deallocation.* As programs proceed, their memory needs grow and shrink. The program itself may need lots of stack or heap space at one time and later give it up. The range of data references may grow as a program does an operation on large matrices and then shrink abruptly as it cycles through some linear data. The paged virtual memory system should be able to take advantage of one program's shrinkage to accommodate the needs of a growing program. We must ask how the operating system finds out who needs what and we must find out how it can respond.

This is enough of an introduction to concepts. Next we must proceed into details to see what choices there are. Let us summarize the requirements for a good memory management unit:

1. A logical-to-physical mapping mechanism
2. Efficient use of the physical memory
3. Fast context switching
4. Protection within and between processes
5. Sharing of memory regions between processes
6. Dynamic allocation of new memory areas
7. Dynamic sizing of existing memory areas
8. Virtual memory support

In the remainder of this chapter we will look at some specific memory management mechanisms. Since we have so many distinct requirements, we can't expect one mechanism to provide the ideal solution to all of our requirements.

4.3 SEGMENTATION

As Figure 2.12 on page 83 shows, programs do not use contiguous logical address spaces. Rather, they break the logical address space into separate contiguous areas. Flexibility and efficiency suggest mapping each area independently. In the context of virtual memory, each of these areas is called a *segment*.

In a simple case, we might have only three segments: instructions, data, and a stack area. Each of the segments would be contiguous in the logical address space, and each segment would have its own characteristics. For example, the program segment should be write-protected. The data segment should allow reads and writes, but not fetches, and may require dynamic growth toward higher addresses (heap). The stack should allow reads and writes but not fetches. The stack will require dynamic growth toward lower addresses.

More complex systems may allow a larger number of segments, possibly a distinct segment for each procedure and each data structure. This has the advantage that individual areas can have their own protection specified, and individual segments can be shared between different programs. Some operating systems, such as Multics, VAX/-VMS, OS/2, and newer versions of UNIX, apply this sharing to most programs by using *dynamic linking*. With dynamic linking, library routines are not linked into a program when it is created. Instead, they are linked when the program is loaded into memory to be executed or even after it has started executing. This avoids duplicating the library routines in many different programs on the disk and in the memory. If two different programs are dynamically linked to the same library routine, the operating system can load a single copy of it into a segment in the memory, letting both of them share it. The important point is that a segment is a logical unit *of the program*. Each segment has its own starting address, length, and protection. The memory management hardware must provide a mechanism for identifying which segment is being used, checking for protection violations, and finding the location of the segment in physical memory.

It would be easy to modify our RISC machine to use a simple, hardware-driven segmentation mechanism. Were we to adopt this scheme (we won't!), we would end up with a system not unlike the Intel 8086. We would define one group of registers as offset registers for stack references and others as offset registers for each type of data. Special-purpose registers would then become automatic base registers. That is, if you used R3 as an address register, it would automatically call in, say, R20 as a base register. How many segments should we define? Our programming model (Figure 2.12) defines structures for four classes: *absolute* (bins 0 and 1 in the figure), *program* (bin 2), *data* (bin 3 and the heap), and then *stack*. The processor would specify which segment is being used on the following basis:

Address Source	**Segment**
fetching an instruction	program
using the absolute reference mode for a LOAD or a STORE	absolute
using a stack-reference register as base register	stack
any other address	data

Remind yourself that in a RISC, LOAD, STORE, and fetch are the only things which generate references to memory. JUMP and CALL have no impact on segment selection since their actions are entirely within the CPU. They simply set up the next fetch. (All of the fuss in the 8086 about long and short jumps has to do with the fact that registers are too small to hold a whole address, so that to take long jumps in the address space, you must change base and offset simultaneously.)

In effect we would now have four independent logical address spaces, one for each segment. This suggests that addresses coming from the CPU be regarded simply as offsets within the segments. The processor will access memory by specifying both a segment number and a logical address (which is actually an offset within that segment). At the price of giving up completely general registers, this mechanism expands each program's address space to three units of 4 GW. The absolute segment will remain at its diminutive 4 MW, limited by the instruction size, but the address space (not the memory size!) has become enormous. It is as if we had extended all of our addresses to 34 bits. Just this sort of simple mechanism is used in the VAX, where the top 2 bits of the 32-bit virtual address rigidly define a "space" or segment and the remaining 30 bits define the offset within that segment. With both Digital and IBM weighing in on this sort of mechanism, it cannot be all bad. With such a scheme, how would we meet our objectives of rapid address translation and expandability?

A mechanism to translate logical to physical addresses is shown in Figure 4.2. Since a simple segment is a contiguous block of memory, it takes only two numbers to specify it completely: its starting address and its length. Each process will have four such number pairs, and when a process is active, those eight numbers will be kept in registers. The segment number provided by the processor is used to select the base address of the current segment and its length. Then the address provided by the processor is compared with the length of the segment, and a protection fault is signaled if the offset is too large. The diagram seems to have assumed that all segments grow toward higher addresses. However, most comparators have at least two outputs: *greater-than* and *less-than*. *Less-than* is a good address for segments which expand upward; *greater-than* is a good address for a segment which expands downward.

FIGURE 4.2 Structure of a simple segmentation mechanism.

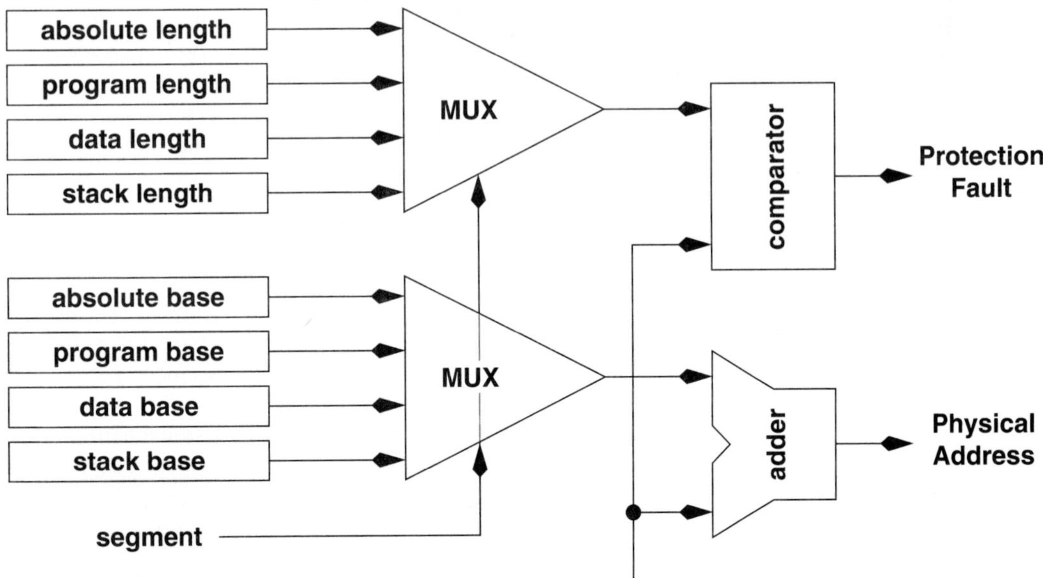

How do you increase or decrease a segment? The obvious answer—change the value in its length register—while true and enduring is not the whole answer. One thing that your operating system will have to worry about is whether that particular chunk of memory that is about to be added is *free*. If a process needs to augment a segment and there is something in the way—a piece of another process—things get a little tacky. Your waiting process either must be put out in the hall to sit until a space opens up, or the whole segment must be copied to another spot in memory where there is room enough for the expansion.

Notice how small a cost there would be to add read/write/execute protection for these contiguous segments. A few bits for each segment would be plenty. They would reside in register and can be checked for every reference to a segment. Such a low cost of protection is one of the most appealing aspects of segmentation schemes.

One of the problems presented when tying registers to specific segments is the natural desire to address a different segment than the one which the hardware defaults to. An example in our simple scheme of Figure 4.2 would be if you wanted to do base-displacement addressing in the *absolute* segment. When default segments are used, some machines allow the program to specify a different segment. The Intel 80386 is a typical example of this kind of overrideable default-segmentation.

How well does a pure segmentation mechanism fulfill the requirements which we listed in Section 4.2? Since segments are logical units of the program, they provide an ideal mechanism for protection and for sharing between processes. Context switching can be performed very quickly since it takes very little information to describe the mappings of all segments in a process. Segmentation also seems to be an efficient way to use the available physical memory, since we can allocate exactly as much memory as the program intends to use. However, the last three items on our list of requirements reveal some problems with segmentation.

We have already raised the issue of finding space to grow into. You might think one could avoid this problem by using a simple scheme which puts open space between a segment that grows upward and one that grows downward—the standard single-process approach for heap (upward) and stack (downward). Unfortunately, the dynamics of multiprocessing prevent so simple a solution. Consider what happens to the physical memory as segments are allocated for processes and then freed as the processes end. We can begin allocating space starting at physical address 0, leaving "adequate" space between heap and stack in each process to allow for growth. When we reach the top of the physical memory, new processes will have to wait until another process completes or gets swapped out. Since space freed by the departing process will not be the exact size required by a new process, gaps will be formed between the segments. This buildup of wasted chunks of space between segments is called *external fragmentation*. The part of the operating system which allocates physical memory must attempt to minimize this fragmentation problem by combining free areas which happen to be next to each other, and by looking for the best-fit free area to assign to a new segment. It may also be necessary to move segments from one area of physical memory to another if there is too much fragmentation (an act called *crunching*). Crunching becomes the only reasonable escape if enough free, contiguous memory is not available for a new segment. The only other choice is to suspend new or growing processes until a large enough piece of memory just happens to open up. If we allowed little processes to start in the meanwhile, that large space might not appear until everyone went home at night. Delays of hours are generally not acceptable, but holding up all new processes until Big George gets a chance to run won't be popular either.

One of the main objectives of a virtual memory system is to make efficient use of the available physical memory, making room for many concurrent processes by loading in only that part of each process that is currently active. Pure segmentation requires that an entire segment either be loaded or not. With only four segments, as in the simple example of Figure 4.2, there would be little chance to swap individual segments to disk and back, since all four segments are required to do almost anything. With a large number of segments, swapping would be more reasonable, but "a large number of small segments" is not a bad description for our next methodology—*paging*. Pure paging is well suited to efficient use of memory but gives up some of the other advantages of pure segmentation. It is possible to mix these metaphors without killing the benefits of either, so let us proceed to paging.

To summarize, a segment is a logical unit of a program which can be mapped to any starting address in the physical memory, and which has exactly the length and protection required by the program at any given moment. Segmentation satisfies our requirements for protection, sharing, and fast context switching very well; it has significant problems with dynamic allocation and growth, and it is not well suited to efficient use of the physical memory.

4.4 PAGING

Since all of the problems we noticed with segmentation were a result of the fact that segments have many different sizes, it is natural to try solving the problems by mapping memory blocks of some constant size. This memory management paradigm is called *paging*. We simply divide the logical address space, the physical address space, and even the disk space into equal-sized blocks, and we provide translation schemes for going from logical to physical and disk addresses. In the translation, those logical pages which are not assigned are marked invalid. The unassigned physical pages are attached to a *freelist*. For a process to acquire a page requires that a page be removed from the free queue, that its address be assigned in the translation tables to a logical page, and that that logical page be marked as valid. The two most important advantages of the paging system are:

- With all pieces of all programs being the same size, perfect packing is achieved.
- With every page getting an individual logical-to-physical translation, there is neither reason to load into memory all of a logical portion of a program nor necessity to make logically adjacent pages physically adjacent.

A simple and direct page-address translation technique is shown in Figure 4.3. The upper bits of the logical address—the *logical page number* (LPN)—are used to select an entry in the *pagetable*. The pagetable entry (PTE) includes the physical page number

(PPN) and also protection bits for the page. Among the protection bits will be the *valid bit*. The lower bits of the logical address become the lower bits of the physical address.

This scheme should seem simple enough, but take a good look at it and think about how you will realize the operation *in the computer*. Start with the idea that hardware has to do the entire translation. As far as the user is concerned, an item was asked for by address and the only thing that happens is that the item appears from memory. Anything that goes on "under the hood" is somebody else's concern. There is no problem for the hardware to pick off the LPN, but what does it do with it? The answer will turn out to get progressively more complex as we move on through this chapter and into the next, but let us consider a simple case—one that was current in the period from about 1975 to 1985. This was a time when many computers had 16- to 24-bit address spaces. If you have a byte offset of 10 to 12 bits, then the LPN for a 16- to 24-bit address space would be merely 4 to 14 bits. For 4 bits, you would have only 16 choices. That sounds more like the segmentation scheme of Figure 4.2. For that case, you would be inclined to use the LPN to choose one of 16 registers to give you the translation. The PDP-11, using only 3 bits, did precisely that. At the other end of the range, the number of choices would be too expensive to put into register. 14 bits would require 16,384 registers. While that is too many by far, it would be just fine for a small RAM. Since the early '80s, fast 4Kb static RAM chips have been readily available. With a 16K RAM—not part of primary memory but a separate RAM that is an integral part of the memory management unit—the LPN becomes simply the address of the PPN, or, in other words, *the address of the address*. With some refinement, this is basically what was done in Data General's Eclipse and in the original Sun. This scheme is neat enough, but notice what happens now on a context switch. Now it becomes necessary to overwrite

FIGURE 4.3 A simple and direct paging mechanism in which the physical page number is obtained by a table lookup on a one-to-one basis.

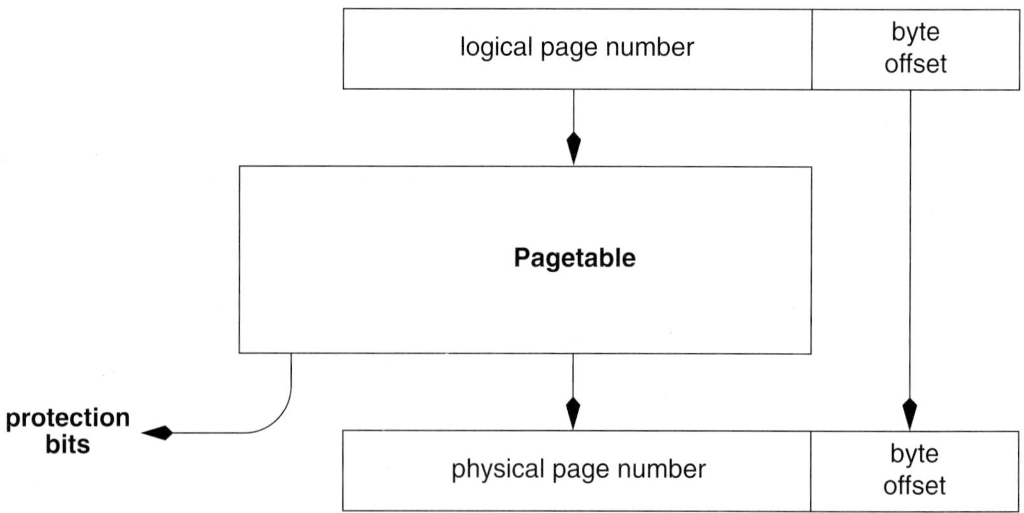

some or all of the 16K RAM to represent the pages of the next process to run. That is no huge burden at 16K, but what will happen when we switch from 24 to 32-bit spaces? That would multiply our effort by 256! No, thank you. That will not do. We will have to be more clever than that.

Before considering what we must do when larger address spaces are used (we are really going to put off the final answer to Chapter 5), let's see how well this paging system satisfies our requirements for a good memory management system. With all pages having the same size, we will have no external fragmentation. Dynamic allocation and dynamic growth are much simpler. Since there is no reason for a logical program unit to be commensurate with the page size, some wasted space will be left in "last pages" of each unit of the program. This wastage is called *internal fragmentation*. It is generally not much of a problem, but it does imply that we should keep pages reasonably small to avoid wasting memory. It is convenient for a virtual memory system to have the size of a page equal to the size of a disk block, so that is a common choice. A small multiple of the minimum-sized disk block size is often used also.

Protection and sharing of pages are reasonably simple, but not quite as ideal as with segmentation. Consider that most library routines are much smaller than a page. If each is extended to a page, internal fragmentation will waste a lot of space. Sharing procedures and data structures between different processes causes similar problems.

By breaking long segments into many pages, we have increased the amount of translation information that must be stored. Let us consider just how large the pagetables are. A typical virtual memory machine today will have a 32-bit address space. If 10 bits are used to index into the page itself, 22 bits will specify the PTE. That is 4 million entries, or 16 MB. Remember that this is only the pagetable. You haven't put a single page into memory and you have 16 MB! Possible solutions include:

- building a hierarchy of translation tables (Only what is used gets created.)
- keeping unused portions of the pagetable out on disk
- grouping pages into segments and using segment length to determine each table's extent

The major problem with the scheme of Figure 4.3 is that the table is *flat*. That is, it has one entry for every virtual page. If one builds a hierarchical set of tables, then whole blocks of unused pages can be rendered *invalid* by a single entry in a high-order table. This very quickly cuts the pagetables for each process down to a size that is reasonable for each process, and it also allows inactive parts of the pagetable set to reside out on disk. That sounds as if we have solved the problem, but in fact we have replaced one problem with another. Now it will take multiple memory accesses to travel down the hierarchy. We might even page fault on a pagetable and then page fault on what it references. Lots of waiting around for disks to do their thing. Lots of references to memory. Not very encouraging. In Chapter 5, we will show how you can limit the impact of having a hierarchy by having a cache of recent acquisitions, but a cache gives symptomatic relief, not a cure.

4.5 COMBINATIONS OF SEGMENTATION AND PAGING

We have seen that a good memory management system should have some of the attributes of segmentation and other attributes of paging. Since segmentation seems to be a better match to the software and paging seems to be more efficient in allocating the physical memory, a common solution is to break the memory management system into two layers. Logical or virtual addresses from a program are divided into segments for protection and sharing. Then the segments are subdivided into pages to allow dynamic allocation, growth, and efficient virtual memory support. Since each segment has a length associated with it, the size of the associated pagetable can be limited, which removes a major objection to flat pagetables. In this section we will examine some ways of combining segmentation and paging. Summaries and diagrams of the mechanisms are grouped at the end of the section.

The implementation of this two-stage memory management system can take distinctly different forms. The Intel 80386 uses simple segmentation followed by a paging mechanism. Each logical address is associated (either explicitly or implicitly) with a segment selector register, which the hardware uses to locate the base address, length, and protection bits for that segment. When the logical address (called an *offset*) is added to the base address of the segment, the resulting "linear address" is sent to a paging mechanism for translation into a physical address. What you get for your trouble are limited-length tables and the possible elimination of protection bits from *each* PTE. Intel got a little bit more from this choice: It got a virtual memory scheme which overlaid the nonvirtual addressing mechanism of the 8086, which in turn evolved from that ancient of days, the 8-bit 8080. While such backward compatibility can be powerful motivation indeed when you own a big piece of the current market, it is a solution to a problem in history, not memory management. (The 80386 attempts to deliver almost any combination of segmentation and paging the system designer could want. The cost for this versatility is that the translation mechanism is not optimized in hardware. If the designer chooses page-level isolation, the machine runs noticeably slower. With this wide variety of choices, you will find the 80386 listed as an example in almost every case that we consider.)

A more common approach is to approximate the segmentation function with a two-layer hierarchy of pagetables. This is illustrated in Figure 4.6. In this case, the upper bits of the logical address (index 1) are used to divide the logical address space into a fixed number of segments, with the segment base addresses and table lengths for the current process kept either in memory or in special registers. Protection information for the whole segment can be kept at this level or it can be stored with each PTE. The advantage of having them at the segment level is a shorter PTE; the advantage of having them with the pages is that single large segments can contain sections with different protection. The middle bits in the logical address (index 2) become the index into the pagetable for the selected segment. The PTE found at that physical address contains the physical address of the page and some or all of the protection bits for virtual memory support. This two-level pagetable mechanism has been very popular. For example, it is used in the AT&T 3B20, Data General MV/8000, IBM 370, and even in the paging mechanism of the Intel 80386. Variations of this mechanism are used in the DEC VAX and the Motorola MC68030.

An important issue in the design of a paging mechanism is the amount of space required for the pagetables. Let's examine a few specific examples of two-level paging mechanisms to see how much space is required.

The AT&T 3B20 computer uses 24-bit logical and physical addresses with two-level pagetables. *Index 1* is 7 bits, *index 2* is 6 bits, and the lowest 11 bits are the offset into the 2-KB page. The segment table will contain 128 entries, and each pagetable 64 entries. An entire 16-MB logical address space can be mapped with only 8320 table entries (segment and page). That is 0.2 percent of the space mapped. While that sounds like an eminently reasonable expenditure, remember that you will be spending physical memory to map virtual memory. If we had but 1 MB of physical memory, we would now be spending 3 percent per process, and if we had 20 processes, 60 percent of physical memory could be devoted to pagetables. That sounds less reasonable. Some parts of this scheme are very appealing. Context switching is done simply by changing a register which holds the starting address of the segment table. Typically many of the processes are small programs with a few scattered segments; we need only the segment table and a few pagetables. For example, if the typical program used only 8 of the possible 128 segments, even with 20 processes and 1 MB of physical memory, we would need only 1.2 percent. Once again, that sounds like a reasonable apportionment.

Let's try the same exercise for the Intel 80386. In its full glory, the 80386 uses six 16-bit segment registers. The segment register used is determined by the instruction. The value in the segment register is an offset into a table of segment descriptors, each of which contains the 32-bit base address and a 20-bit length for a segment. The length can be in units of bytes or 4-KB pages, giving upper bounds of 1 MB and 4 GB respectively. The logical address and the base address are added to form what Intel labels a *linear address*. That 32-bit linear address is then used in the manner shown in Figure 4.6 to index into a two-level pagetable. To select from the 80386 panoply of translation modes a pure two-level scheme, one simply loads the same value into all the index registers. That turns all of the 4-GB address space into a single segment. Intel calls its outer pagetable a *directory* rather than a segment table, but it has the same function as the segment table in the 3B20. The upper 10 bits of the linear address are *index 1*, the next 10 are *index 2*. The PTE contains a 20-bit physical page number, which is concatenated with the lowest 12 bits of the linear address to form a 32-bit physical address. The remaining 12 bits of the PTE contain the protection bits. With each table entry being 4 bytes, the size of each page and directory table is exactly 4 KB, which is also the size of the pages themselves. Memory is always allocated in 4-KB pages, even the space for the tables themselves.

Since we have to allocate at least enough space for the directory and one pagetable, even a small program will need 8 KB for tables. But that is sufficient to map all linear addresses up to 4 MB (1 KP). If the program uses more space than that, or uses scattered areas of the linear address space, each additional 4-KB pagetable is sufficient to map 4 MB of the linear address space. While moderately large programs require only a moderate amount of table space, what happens with a very large program? A program which uses the full 4 GB of linear address space will require a directory and 1024 pagetables, or 4 MB of tables (0.1 percent). Main memory would not be large enough to hold more than a small fraction of the entire 4 GB of the physical address space, so most pages of all sorts would be kept on disk. This includes the pagetables *but not the directory table*. It is fundamentally necessary for a logical address to have a destination in reality. That reality can be a statement that the translation table needed for this address is out on disk, but sooner or later every address must end in reality. The directory is the first layer in translation, the key to reality. It must reside in memory. Probing that first and obligatory level gives one of three answers:

- The necessary pagetable is in memory at location xxxxx000.
- The necessary pagetable is out on disk at location zzzzzz (page fault).
- This pagetable is forbidden or does not exist (drop dead).

With some pagetables now in virtual memory, the directory entries must contain the appropriate information to support virtual memory, such as referenced and modified bits.

To clarify the operation of this paging unit, let's follow the process of Figure 4.6 for translating a linear address. The processor contains a register pointing to the start of the directory. Using that register and the upper 10 bits of the linear address, we can read the directory entry. If the directory entry specifies a memory address for the pagetable, we can continue and read the pagetable entry. However, if the pagetable is on disk, the resulting page fault tells the operating system to suspend the current (faulting) process, retrieve the page from the disk, find a place for it in the memory, insert the address into our directory entry, and reactivate the suspended process. Upon restarting, with a valid address for the pagetable, we can append the middle 10 bits of the linear address to find the pagetable entry. Reading the pagetable entry should produce the address of the physical page we are trying to access. However, that page may not be in memory. If it isn't, we again page fault, causing the operating system to get the target page from the disk. More detail will be included in Section 4.8.

This paging mechanism is quite efficient for large programs. Using relatively large pages reduces the amount of space required for tables, at the cost of exacerbating the internal fragmentation problem. Some space is wasted both in the data pages and in the pagetables.

Making everything fit within single pages is a little too neat. It hides some problems. Let's see what happens if we try to create a two-level paging mechanism with very small pages. Let's modify Intel's paging unit to use 256-byte pages. The lowest 8 bits of the linear address will be the byte offset. Since a pagetable itself should fit into a page, only 64 entries would be in each pagetable. Thus, the middle 6 bits would be used as an index into the pagetable. That leaves 18 bits of the linear address for the directory index, so the directory would require 1 MB of space, contiguous space in physical memory! Obviously, we wouldn't want to devote that much table space to a small program. A partial solution to largely unused directories is a length register as in the 3B20. Unfortunately, that fails if the program uses widely separated areas of its logical address space. Probably the worst aspect of this little-page–big-directory problem is that each process would have its own directory. If large directories are required, it will limit quite drastically the number of independent processes which can share the machine.

There is a fairly obvious solution to this problem: Add another level of pagetables. In fact, let's carry this even further and add two more layers. Examine the diagram of the four-level pagetable mechanism (Figure 4.7). Up to four levels of pagetables can be used with the Motorola MC68030 (or MC68851), which allows the number of bits used at each level to be programmed. Notice that each pagetable now fits into a page and a rather small one at that. All but the top one can be kept on the disk and brought into memory only when needed. There is never a problem allocating space for the pagetables, and there is much less wasted space within the tables and within data pages, since the pages are so small. On the other hand, it may take as many as five disk accesses to find the data word we want. The search begins with a register, called a root pointer, which locates the top level pagetable. It then proceeds through a tree of tables leading to the actual data page, which can be thought of as a leaf.

There are situations that can benefit from a complex mechanism like this. Consider a large LISP interpreter, which is constantly allocating small areas of memory, many of which are later freed by an independent garbage collector. After this program has been running for a while, it will be using a large number of small areas scattered around its logical address space. A simple two-level pagetable mechanism might have to allocate tables and memory pages for a large fraction of the entire address space. But a three-level or four-level paging mechanism can pick out those areas of the address space actually being used. The tree of tables contains only those branches which lead to valid leaves. Much less space is wasted, both in the data pages and in the pagetables.

Consider an interesting question about pages and pagetables. How does the operating system load them initially and modify them when necessary? Pages can be more than one thing at a time. When the kernel clears your page or writes an address into your pagetable to make the page accessible to your program, both your page and your pagetable look like data pages to the kernel. It uses system VAs to address both. The kernel's pagetables are also kernel data pages. It is not out of the question that in the process of address translation, a system VA could pass through the page it addresses. On the way to understanding this arcane (weird?) blending of perspectives, let us consider the VAX which will allow us to look at yet another version of the 2-layer hierarchy of pagetables.

The VAX segments its logical address space into four 1-GB segments (or *spaces*, as DEC refers to them), the top one of which it simply discards. The top 2 bits of a logical address specify the segment. The remaining bits are used as illustrated in Figure 4.8. For each process, segment 0 contains program and data and segment 1 contains stacks, buffers, and some tabular process information. All processes share segment 2, which contains the operating system. Each segment has its own single-level pagetable, with all processes sharing the table for segment 2. That is, on context switches, the base and length registers for segment 2 *do not change*. What is two level about this scheme? Each current process has its own tables for segments 0 and 1 and those tables are mapped into the system's virtual (i.e., logical) address space. Pagetables must be contiguous, but because all of these process tables are in system virtual space, they are contiguous in logical, not physical address. Only the system pagetable is contiguous in physical memory. Space for that table is allocated at bootup time and remains constant. Space for process pagetables, on the other hand, is created and expanded as the system is running. Since the system table provides the requisite first taste of reality, any portion of the process pagetables can be out on disk. The reason for having two segments is to accommodate the fact that stacks grow down while heap grows up. The huge space in the middle—usually almost all the address space—does not have to be mapped at all.

Let us follow through Figure 4.8 to see how this virtual pagetable functions. First an overview:

$$dataVA \Rightarrow ptVA \Rightarrow ptPA \Rightarrow dataPA$$

Notice that there are three steps in the address translation, but only the last two require reading from memory. The first operation in the figure simply uses the original VA in segment 0 to generate a VA in segment 2. Each translation requires that bits 29:9 of the VA be right-shifted seven places and added to the base specified by bits 31:30. In the first case, this operation yields another VA, but one in segment 2, not 0. Repeated for the new VA, the translation yields a PA because the base address of the system pagetable is a PA. At that PA is a PTE whose low-order 21 bits are the page address the 50 pagetable page. By appending the byte offset of 9 bits, one obtains a PA of 30 bits. That first PA is the address of the PTE which will (finally!) point to the data page. Again, the byte offset is appended, and you have in hand the PA of the datum whose VA started all this scurrying back and forth to memory.

The VAX process is very similar to the two-level pagetable, but decidedly more convoluted, as the figure shows. Notice that it is very easy for the operating system to access the process pagetable, since it is already contiguous in the system's virtual address space. All that it needs to know is the base address and length of the process's segment. That data is part of the every process's control block. While the basic translation mechanism might seem convoluted, access to the tables themselves is particularly direct. In the system that we shall employ, translation will be simple and hierarchical but the access to process tables much less so. From a machine point of view, how it looks to the reader is irrelevant. The principal criticism of the VAX scheme is that the system pagetable must be large and resident. Some fraction of that table is probably not working hard or at all most of the time. It could free up memory space if that low-utility section of the system pagetable could be farmed out to disk.

As a really different solution to reducing the amount of space needed for tables consider the IBM mechanism called an *inverted pagetable* (IPT) [Hester, 86]. The pagetable is inverted because it contains one entry for each *physical* page, rather than one entry for each virtual page. Since the virtual address space is normally much larger than the physical address space, the size of an inverted pagetable can be much smaller than a direct pagetable. In fact, the size of the IPT is a small fixed fraction of the physical memory. An entry in the IPT identifies the virtual page number being represented in that physical page. The problem, of course, is that the MMU starts with the virtual address and must find the physical address. Searching through all of the entries in the IPT would take too long, even if we cache the most frequently used entries. We need a fast way to find the entry in the IPT which contains a given virtual page. The solution employs *hashing*. The concept derives from a common human experience: There is no need to sort a short list, since you can scan it fast enough to make you indifferent to its order. A hash function is an easy-to-compute number that spreads a list or collection of data in uniform and relatively random fashion into many small lists. For virtual page numbers (VPNs), we might make the hash function the low-order 12 bits. Adjacent pages would then end up with different—adjacent—hash numbers. We would then create a table of pointers called a *hash anchor table* where each pointer starts a linked list of all the entries which have the same hash number. The relationship between the hash anchor table and an IPT is shown in Figure 4.9. Each entry in the IPT contains

- the VPN assigned to the physical page
- the link to the next element on the list associated with that particular hash number

The entries are organized according to physical page number (PPN). Thus, if you find the VPN that you are looking for, its PPN is simply the position in the table; for example, the 10th entry is PPN 10. Finding the entry of choice is done by starting with the hash function. That tells you which list to search. If an element on the list does not match your address, it will tell you where to look next. If you get to the end of the list and find no match, you have either a page fault or an invalid address.

To keep the number of memory references in the worst case reasonable, the linked lists must be kept very short by having many hash numbers. On the average, the number of memory references need be no larger than the number in the hierarchical schemes.

The advantage of using an inverted pagetable is that the tables are reasonably small, even for very large virtual address spaces. In fact, the tables may be small enough to be kept in fast static RAM. You can cache the whole table. However, before we all sign up for IPTs, note that the hash anchor table should be larger than the IPT to keep the average length of the linked lists very short. Also remember that the operating system must keep track of all virtual pages being used by processes, whether they are in memory or not, so the operating system must contain tables of the disk addresses of pages not in memory. With most other pagetable mechanisms, these disk addresses can be kept in the invalid pagetable entries, but with an IPT they must be kept somewhere else. Another problem with the IPT is that it provides no mechanism for two processes to share a page, as can be done with multilevel pagetables. Sharing on the S/38, RS6000, and ROMP is done only at the segment level.

The mechanisms we have discussed are summarized in Figures 4.4 to 4.9. You should examine them and understand the tradeoffs involved. See [Rachid, 87] for a discussion of how easily the various memory management mechanisms can be adapted to the portable operating system MACH. In the next section we will choose a mechanism for our RISC machine and examine it in more depth.

4.6 A MEMORY MANAGEMENT MECHANISM FOR OUR RISC MACHINE

Having looked at some commonly used memory management mechanisms, we must now pick one for our RISC machine and start thinking about how we will use it. From the previous discussion, it seems clear that some multilevel pagetable mechanism is the

FIGURE 4.4

Pure Segmentation

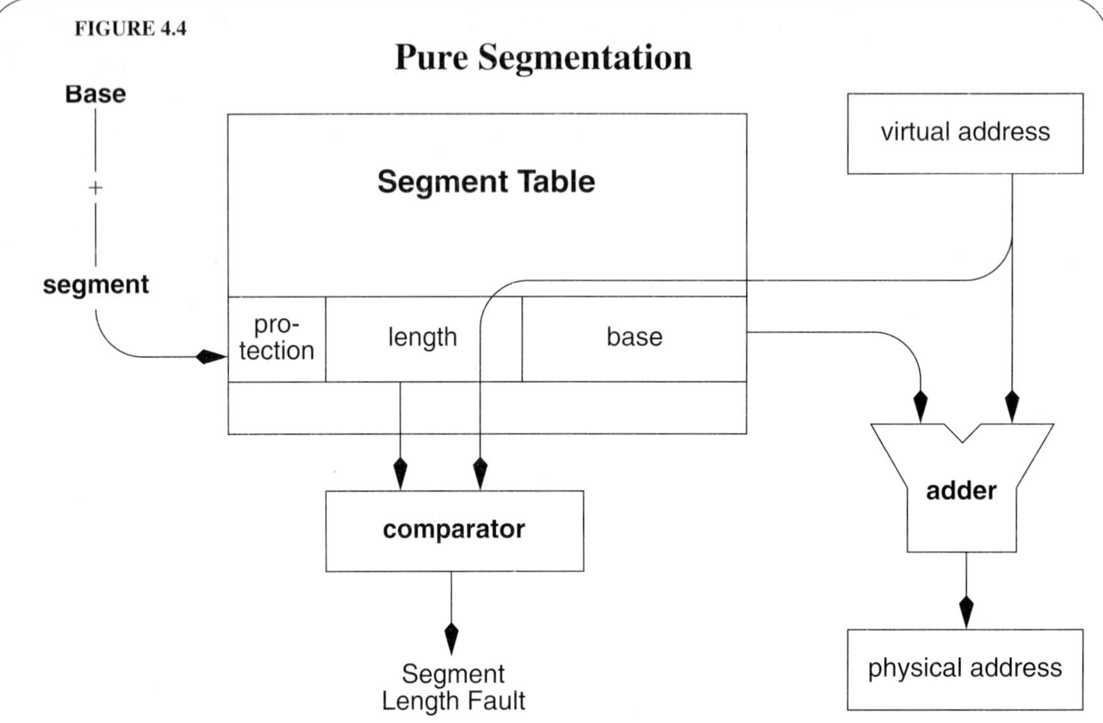

Description:

Hardware assigns each memory reference to a particular segment. The choice of segment can be made by any combination of the following: the instruction, the leading bits of the address, the target of the address (program or data), or current status (process, system or interrupt). The virtual address is the offset within that segment. Each process has a segment table. When the process is running, the table's starting address is loaded into a base register. The segment number is used to locate a segment descriptor in the segment table, which provides the starting physical address of the segment, its length, and protection bits. The physical address is calculated by adding the segment's base address to the virtual address. Note that segments can start at any byte in the memory and extend for any length.

Advantages:

Segments correspond to the natural units of a program, so they are ideal for protection and sharing. Typically each program uses only a few segments, so little space is required for the tables and the descriptor information may be kept in registers within the memory management unit.

Disadvantages:

Variable size segments lead to external fragmentation and make it difficult to provide dynamic growth. Segments do not map naturally into disk blocks for virtual memory.

Typical Example:

The Intel 80386 can implement pure segmentation if segments are less than 1 Mbyte each. For larger segments, the length must be a multiple of 4 KB. Note that the 80386 also contains an optional 2-level pagetable mechanism which can be used after segmentation.

FIGURE 4.5

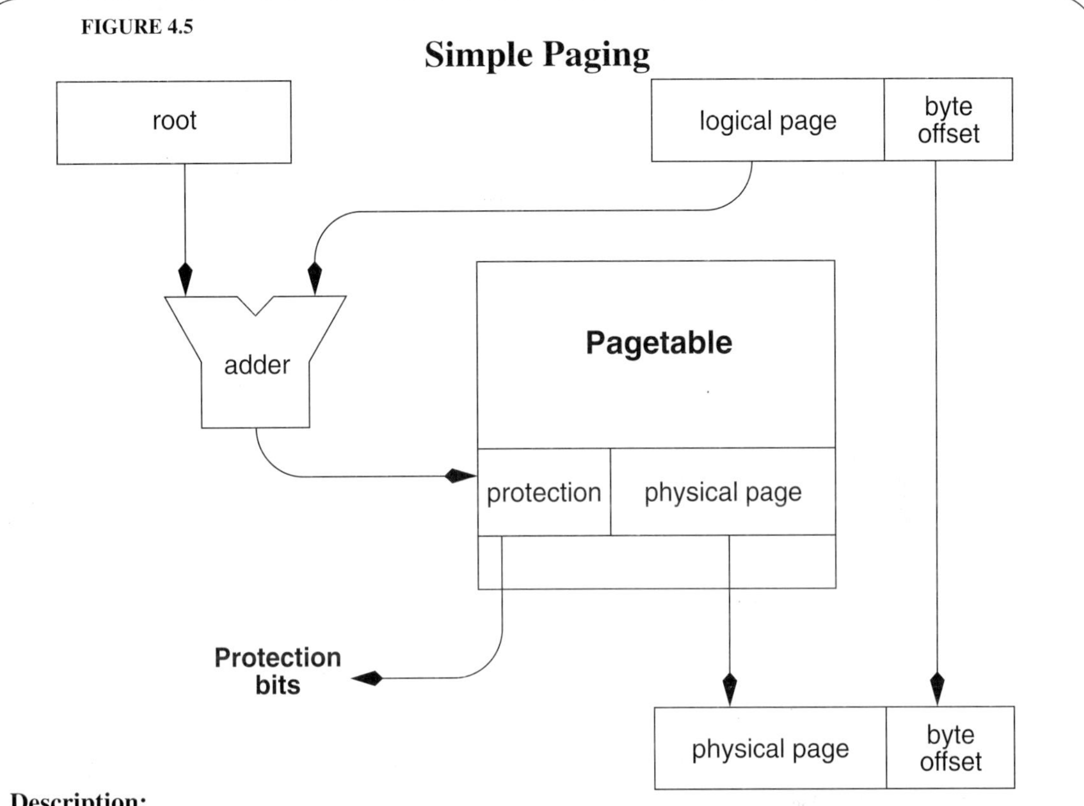

Description:

The virtual page number is used as an index into a pagetable usually located in the main memory. The pagetable entry contains the physical page number and protection bits. The offset within the physical page is the same as the offset within the virtual page. In some cases, a length register is used to establish the end of the pagetable to avoid wasting space for unused entries.

Advantages:

All forms of paging eliminate external fragmentation and simplify dynamic allocation and growth. Table size can be kept reasonable either by using large pages or by restricting the maximum size of programs. The complexity of table-search is low, since only one memory access is required to find the pagetable entry.

Disadvantages:

A huge amount of space in the main memory must be reserved for the pagetable if it is necessary to provide a large virtual address space with pages of a reasonable size. Dynamic allocation and growth of a large pagetable can be a problem, since it must be contiguous in the physical memory. Sharing is possible only by pages, and the pagetable entries must be duplicated for each process.

Typical Examples:

The DEC VAX uses this mechanism for system space. Data General Eclipses use this mechanism for programs smaller than 1 Mbyte. The Motorola MC68030 can be programmed to use this mechanism.

FIGURE 4.6

Two-Level Pagetable

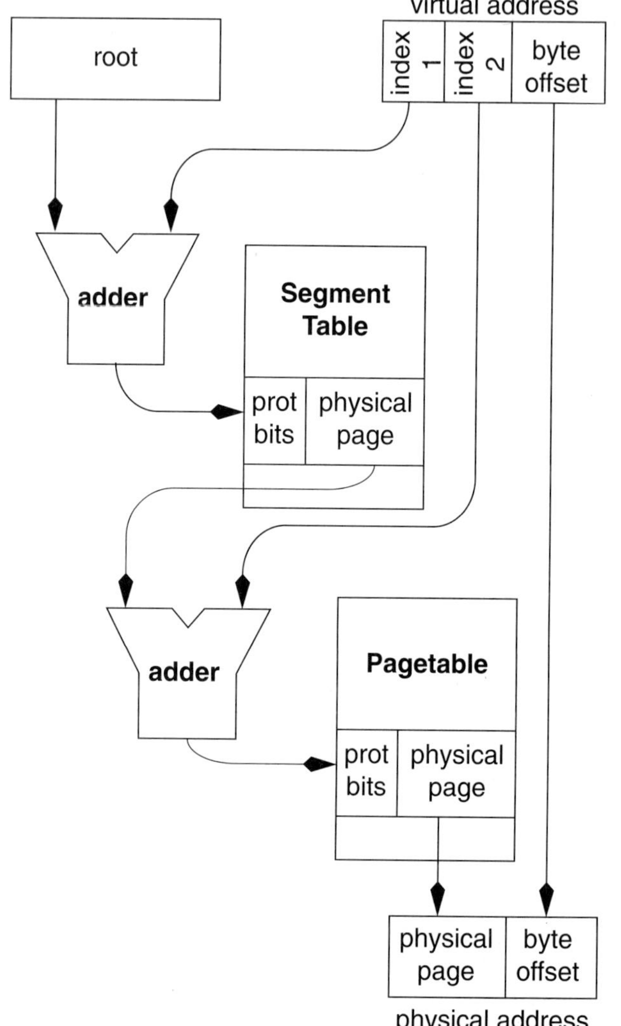

Description:

Translation of a virtual address to a physical address is clearly a labor intensive affair. First, index 1 is added to the *root* or base address of the segment table to obtain the address of the segment table entry (STE). The STE is read from the memory, and its base address is added to index 2 to obtain the address of the pagetable entry (PTE). Then the PTE is read from the memory to obtain the physical page number. This is appended to the byte offset to form the full physical address.

Advantages:

This mechanism combines some of the advantages of segmentation and paging. Sharing can be done at the segment level, reducing the need for redundant pagetable entries. The pagetables need not remain in the main memory and need not be contiguous when they are in the main memory. This allows simple allocation and growth of pagetables and makes it possible to use relatively large virtual address spaces.

Disadvantages:

Very large virtual address spaces (e.g., 4 Gbytes) require a large amount of space in the segment table, which must be kept in the main memory, and must be contiguous. This makes dynamic allocation and growth of the segment table difficult. Translations take forever unless we can be clever. The rather standard cleverness which solves translation lethargy is covered in Chapter 5.

Typical Examples:

The IBM S/370 uses this mechanism. Data General's 32-bit Eclipses use this mechanism for programs larger than 1 Mbyte. The Motorola MC68030 can be programmed to use this mechanism with various page sizes and segment sizes. The Intel 80386 can use this mechanism after its segmentation mechanism.

FIGURE 4.7

Four-Level Hierarchical Pagetable

Description:

Translation of a virtual page number to a physical page number requires four steps. Each index field is added to the base address of the corresponding table to find the next table entry. Then the table entry provides protection bits and the base address of the next table.

Advantages:

This rather extreme subdivision is useful for programs which use scattered areas of a very large virtual address space. Large Lisp programs which continually allocate and release new areas of memory are a typical application. The tables may be viewed as a tree which contains only those branches necessary to reach the pages actually being used at each level. This can greatly reduce the amount of space required for tables. In addition, all tables except the root table can be kept on disk. Typically, no individual table is larger than one page, so dynamic allocation and growth of the pagetables is easy.

Disadvantages:

In the worst of all possible scenarios, it is possible for a translation to require as many as four memory references, each of which may result in a page fault. Also, since most of these pages will have only a few entries, the tables will have a great deal of internal fragmentation.

Typical Example:

The Motorola MC68030 can be programmed to use multiple level pagetables with up to four levels and any number of bits in each index or offset field.

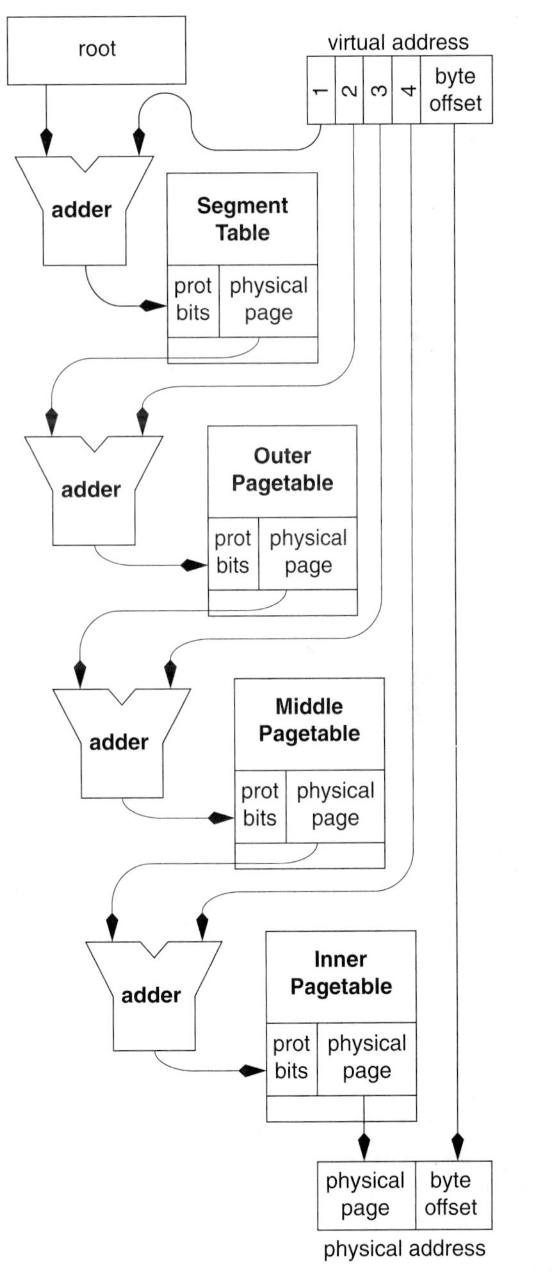

FIGURE 4.8

Virtual Pagetable

Description:

This mechanism, while similar to a 2-level pagetable, is clearly a maze-maker's delight. Process and system spaces are identified by the leading 2-bits of the virtual address. Process pages are listed in *process pagetables*. The process pagetables are virtual because they exist as blocks only in the system *virtual* address space. A process virtual address is added to the process pagetable base to form the system virtual address of the pagetable entry. Then that virtual address is translated using the system pagetable to find the physical address of the PTE. Finally, the PTE is read from the memory to obtain the physical page number and protection bits. A length register is used to specify the size of both pagetables, to avoid wasting space for unused entries.

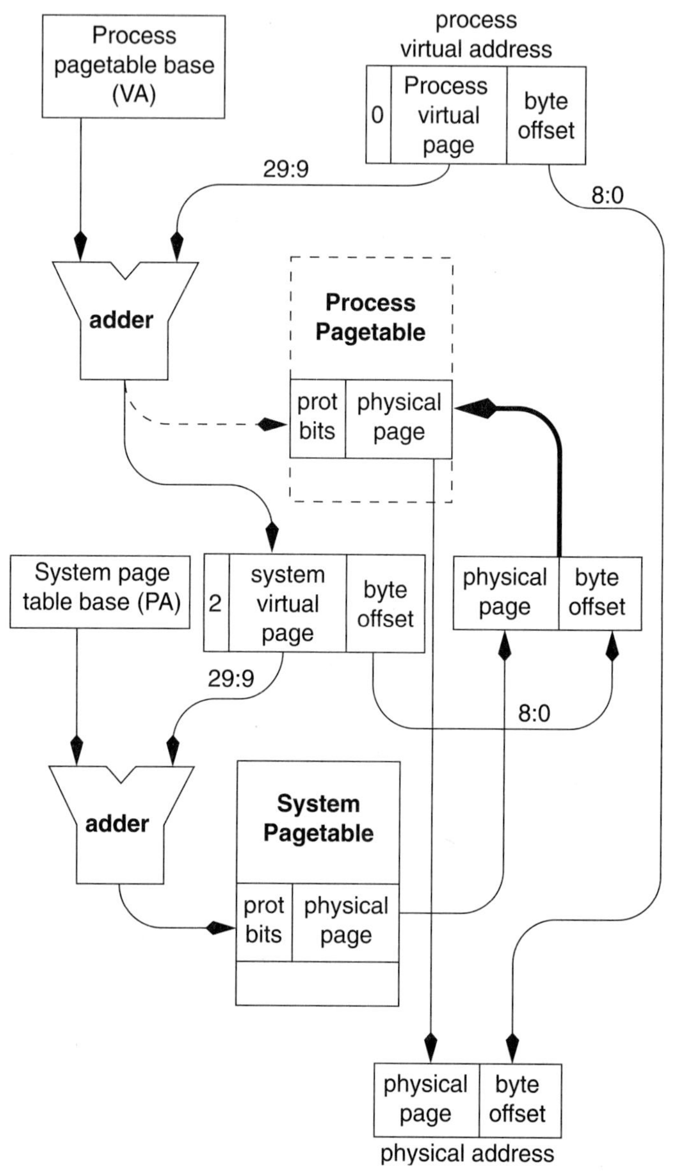

Advantages:

The virtual pagetable has the advantages listed for the 2-level pagetable and also allows a sharp delineation between system space (shared) and individual process spaces. This has considerable advantages in caching strategies.

Disadvantages:

Very large virtual address spaces (e.g. 4 Gbytes) require a large amount of space in the system pagetable, which must be kept as a contiguous *unpaged* block in the main memory. As with a 2-level pagetable, translations can require two memory accesses.

Typical Example:

The VAX uses this mechanism for both process spaces.

Description:

This IBM scheme is quite different from all of the others we have considered. The segment number is used as an index into an array of segment registers. The contents of the segment register are concatenated with the page offset to form a virtual page number. The virtual address is considered to be the VPN plus the byte offset. A hashing function is applied to the VPN to access the hash anchor table, whose output points to the head of a linked list in the inverted pagetable. Entries on the linked list are read until one is found that matches the desired virtual address. The index of that entry in the IPT is the physical page number. A page fault occurs if the linked list has no match.

Advantages:

The IPT requires only a small, fixed fraction of the physical memory, since it contains one entry for each physical page. All processes share the same IPT. The tables are small enough to be kept in fast static RAM. Segments are easily shared. A major advantage of the large address space is the ability to keep pieces of different programs simultaneously in cache.

FIGURE 4.9

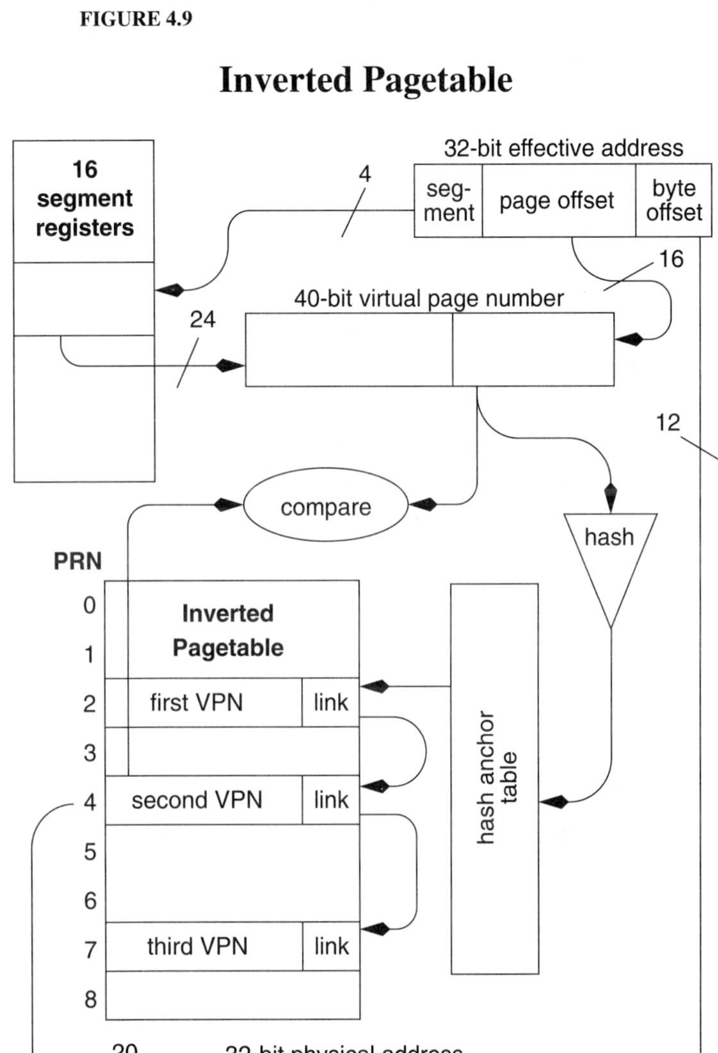

Disadvantages:

Sharing is done only at the segment level. A varying number of memory accesses may be required for a translation, depending on the length of the linked list.

Typical Examples:

This mechanism is used by the IBM S/38, the IBM PC-RT microprocessor, and the IBM RS-6000, using respectively 48, 40, and 52 bits for the full virtual address. Bit widths shown are for the RS-6000.

best choice, particularly if we intend to implement virtual memory. To provide the flexibility to use very large virtual address spaces without huge pagetables, we have chosen the three-level mechanism shown in Figure 4.10.

This mechanism works in the same way as the multilevel pagetables described in the previous section, except that a separate root pointer is provided for each of the protection domains, process and kernel. This doesn't force the operating system to keep two separate trees of pagetables. The system designer could simply put the same address in both root pointers, but it does allow them to be different. There are both general and special reasons why we would like to keep them separate. Among special reasons is that the absolute addressing mode used by our RISC machine works only for low addresses. Since we would like both process and kernel programs to be able to use absolute addressing, both must have those addresses in their logical address range. However, we do not want to be required to make common the first 4 MW of address space.

We have chosen a page size of 256 words or 1 KB, which is in the middle of the range of typical paging systems. Since we will be using very simple descriptors, one word each, exactly 256 descriptors will fit in a page. As we have seen, page-sized pagetables are a great asset to the virtual memory system. It makes the pagetables themselves eminently pageable.

This system has a number of advantages:

FIGURE 4.10 The three-level pagetable system we will use in our system for translation of virtual addresses into physical addresses.

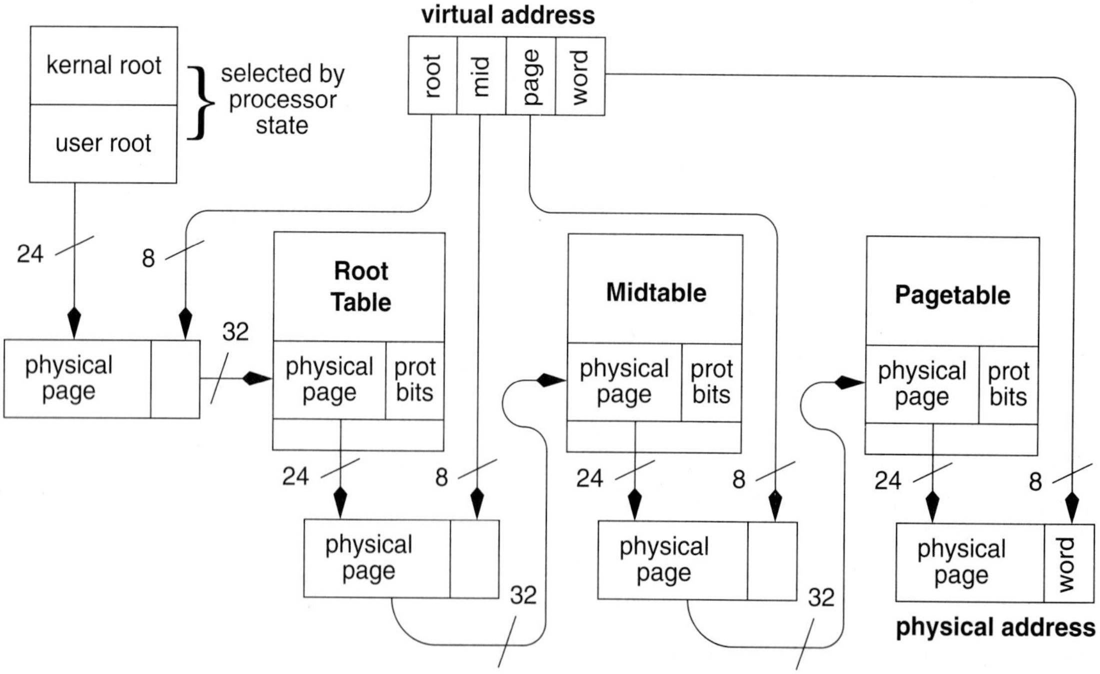

- With page numbers 24 bits wide and the word offsets 8 bits wide, the addresses do not require an addition operation to form the 32-bit physical addresses. Appending is an order of magnitude faster.
- Every table takes exactly one page of memory. There is no need for limit values or direction in the descriptors; every entry in a table must be marked either valid or invalid. Those marked invalid can contain information on why the page is currently invalid.
- The pointers to pages on disk are stored in the same array, so that when a page fault occurs, the location of the desired page is immediately at hand.

How much space will our pagetables require? Let us assume that there would be some shared system tables at high address numbers and then stack, some absolute address space, some program, and some data at low addresses and that a typical application requires a total of 1000 to 3000 pages. Twelve pagetables are needed to cover 3000 pages, but that assumes tight packing. Probably a few more would be used. Then, at midlevel, if we limit the size to 16 MW (64 MB) we will need only one table. Finally, there is one and only one root table. In total, then, a typical program can be handled nicely with fewer than 20 pages of pagetables or less than 1 percent of application space. The percentage improves (decreases) as program size increases and deteriorates for very small programs. All in all, table size looks like no problem.

Each pagetable entry (PTE) for a page in memory (a *valid* page) will have the format shown in Figure 4.11. The upper 24 bits of the PTE are the page number and the lower 8 bits are for protection and miscellaneous functions. Bit 0 will be 1 with this configuration, indicating a valid page. If that bit is not set, three alternatives are possible:

- the address points to an unassigned page
- the page is in transition (locked for input or output)
- the desired data is on disk

If the valid bit is not set, all of the other bits are ignored by the memory management hardware, so they can be used by software for other purposes, such as a disk address. With the valid bit set, the PTE contains 4 bits which determine access permission for both process and system modes. The table in Figure 4.11 shows the 14 states which are defined. Defining protection for both modes would not be necessary if we always used separate trees of tables for process mode and supervisor mode. But to allow the possibility of one common tree, we need a way to specify who may do what with the data in the page. Note that it is possible to inhibit system access to *read only* or *execute only*. This is protection against rogue routines or damaged code. Since the system ultimately has authority to change protection bits, it can do anything it wants to, but it has to do it deliberately. The ability to provide such protection is important enough that the VAX, for example, supports four levels of system privilege. Only the highest level—kernel—can change protection. Ours supports only two levels, which is usual with UNIX, but should a third layer become important, the two unused states could be defined for operations at IL2.

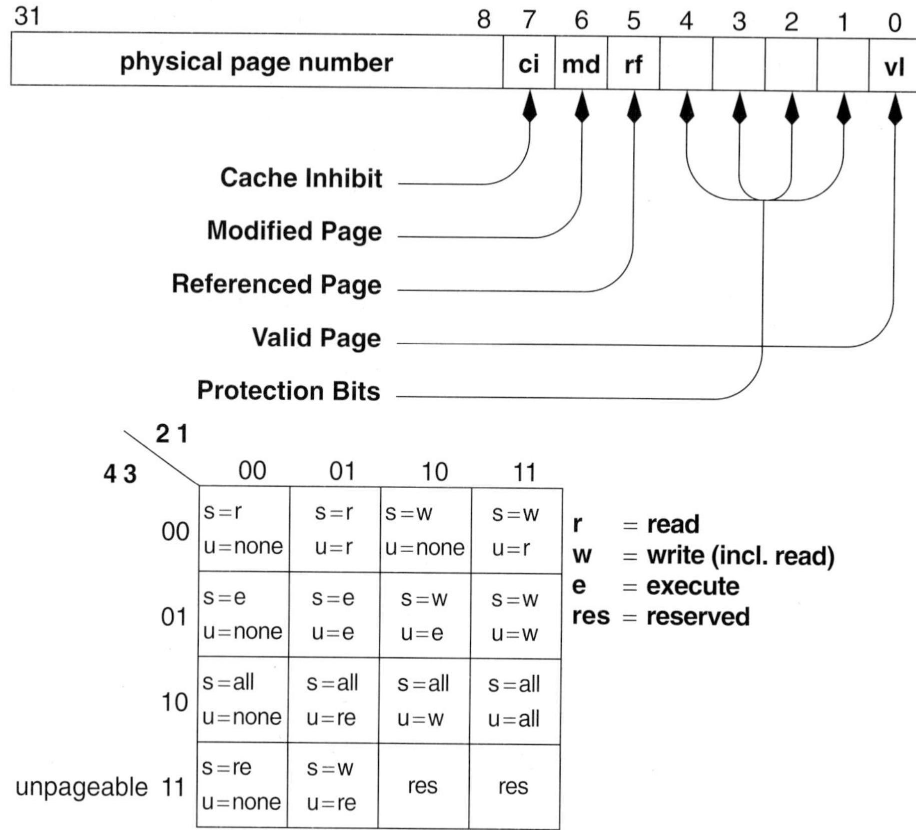

4 3 \ 2 1	00	01	10	11
00	s=r u=none	s=r u=r	s=w u=none	s=w u=r
01	s=e u=none	s=e u=e	s=w u=e	s=w u=w
10	s=all u=none	s=all u=re	s=all u=w	s=all u=all
unpageable 11	s=re u=none	s=w u=re	res	res

FIGURE 4.11 Pagetable entry for a valid page. The assignment of the protection bits to the 14 assigned protection states is shown in the table. When the valid bit is 0, the same space identifies why it is invalid (page on disk or unassigned). If the page is *on disk*, the remainder of the word is a disk and record specifier. Note that entries in the bottom row identify pages which may not be removed from memory (unpageable).

The *referenced* and *modified* bits are used by virtual memory routines to be discussed in Section 4.8. Just briefly, the *referenced* bit gets set every time the page is addressed and the *modified* (or *dirty*) bit indicates that the program has written into the page. The *cache-inhibit* bit is used to guarantee that references to semaphores or other shared data structures go directly to main memory, which ensures that they will be shared with other processors, and also to force accesses to peripheral devices to access the device itself rather than data in cache.

4.7 MEMORY ALLOCATION AND SWAPPING

When the memory management hardware supports paging, as ours does, the kernel software for memory allocation is fairly simple. After the kernel sets up its own data structures and reserves space for such things as disk and terminal buffers, it constructs a queue of the free physical pages that remain. This list is used by the memory allocation routine to find free pages when they are needed. For example, when the kernel is asked to create a new process, it will determine how much space is needed for new data areas, remove the corresponding number of pages from the free page list, and load the pagetables for the new process. When the process terminates, the kernel will reclaim the memory pages by queuing them to the freelist. Similarly, if the program needs more memory while it is running, to increase the size of its stack or heap or to add more pages of program to a process which seems to need them, the kernel can easily obtain pages from the freelist and insert the appropriate values into the pagetable.

We should consider two models of management: *whole program* management and *virtual memory* management. In the former, a program gets almost all of what it needs right at the start; a big program gets lots of space, a small program gets little space. The only space that gets allocated during program execution will be stack and heap. This contrasts sharply with virtual memory management, which uses *demand paging*. Here, a new process is given a page limit at startup but its pagetables are set up initially as *invalid* (*not in memory*) with the PTEs being addresses of the pages on disk. As the program starts, it page faults and the operating system responds by fetching the page referenced and usually a few linear successors. In this way, pages are added only as they are needed. That works until the set of in-memory pages—the *resident set*—reaches the *resident-set limit*. At that point, the system will take one page away for every new one that is added. Virtual memory operation clearly involves more "thinking" on the operating system's part. We save a more thorough development until Section 4.8. Here let us continue with the simpler *whole-program* management.

All of these generous allocations of pages assumed that free pages of memory are available. What happens when the freelist begins to look like Old Mother Hubbard's notorious cupboard? To alleviate the shortage, the operating system attempts to reclaim some pages from processes that are currently queued up in the machine. One particularly choice target are processes that are waiting for some event, like an editor waiting for your next keystroke. Why not let them wait on disk and give some other programs a chance? Waiting processes can be copied out in whole or in part to a special area on a disk and brought back when they are ready to run. This is called *swapping*. A procedure called the swapper periodically checks on processes which have been swapped out, checks to see if the events they are awaiting have occurred, finds the one which has been on disk for the longest time, and if enough memory is available, swaps it back into the memory. If there isn't enough memory, the swapper ups the ante and takes the process which has been in memory for the longest time and swaps it out to the disk. Should a running process try to expand and the memory allocation routine discover that there is not enough physical memory available, it has the process swapped out to disk. Eventually, the swapper will obtain enough memory for it and swap it back in. Of course, if any process tries to expand enough to require more pages than are available in the entire process part of the memory or more than some preset quota, it will simply be terminated. Indeed, the whole-program management scheme is really not intended for immense programs or programs which change size drastically as the program progresses. Processes which require large address spaces or critical care in memory management should use virtual memory systems, as described in Section 4.8.

In Appendix IV, we use the memory management mechanism we defined in Section 4.6 and write some of the basic routines in a simple, whole-program operating system. Following through the code, which we have written in C, will show the details of the decision process. Here in this chapter, we will simply describe what is carried through in detail in Appendix IV. The address translation mechanism we have chosen is intended for a more complex virtual memory system, which will be covered later, but we can still use it for a simple swapping kernel. In this case, we can simply set the maximum size of a process's address space—the resident-set limit—to some fixed subset of a reasonable physical memory, such as 2 or 4 MW (8 to 16 KP). Let us view all processes as comprising four segments at fixed logical starting addresses. The lengths of the segments will vary, but only in page increments, and of course they will not be allowed to overlap the next segment. We will restrict the absolute segment to the first 1 MW to fit our limited range of absolute addressing. All of the other segments can be of any length.

Absolute data	from	0x00000000	
Executable text	from	0x00100000	
Data and heap	from	0x00500000	increasing upward
Stack	from	0x00FFFFFF	increasing downward

Each of the three upper segments can contain 4 MW, or the full allocation, without intruding on its neighbor. Stack and heap, of course, divide 8 MW between them. Since we have limited the logical address space to 24 bits, we need only the root table and a single midlevel table to span the full address space. With our upper bound on the total page count, 64 pages should suffice, though if someone works at scattering heap pages hither and yon, that count could increase a bit.

Now let us consider the kernel and its connection to each of the processes it might be handling in concert. The kernel will contain similar segments for its program, but the kernel's logical address space should also contain three other areas. First, the kernel must be able to access peripheral devices through memory addresses. We will map these at the top of the logical address space. Second, the kernel should be able to access the process pages easily. Since we have limited the size of process address space to 16 KP, we can fit the entire process space into the kernel space. With its 24-bit address range, it occupies precisely 1/256 of the kernel's logical address space—one entry in the kernel root table. Finally, it simplifies memory management if the process pagetables are easy to find in the kernel address space. Since all of our descriptors have exactly the same format, we can easily insert the process's tree of pagetables into one branch of the kernel's tree. That makes the process's pagetables accessible to the kernel, and it also makes it very easy to switch from one process to another. Since the relations among all of these tables is far from obvious, examine Figure 4.12.

All of the tables above the dashed line are part of the kernel, and they are created when the system starts. The tables below the dashed line represent the process, and they are allocated from free memory and initialized when the process is created or when it is swapped in from disk. The system can access data both above and below the line using *system virtual addresses* (SVAs); the process, limited to *process virtual addresses*

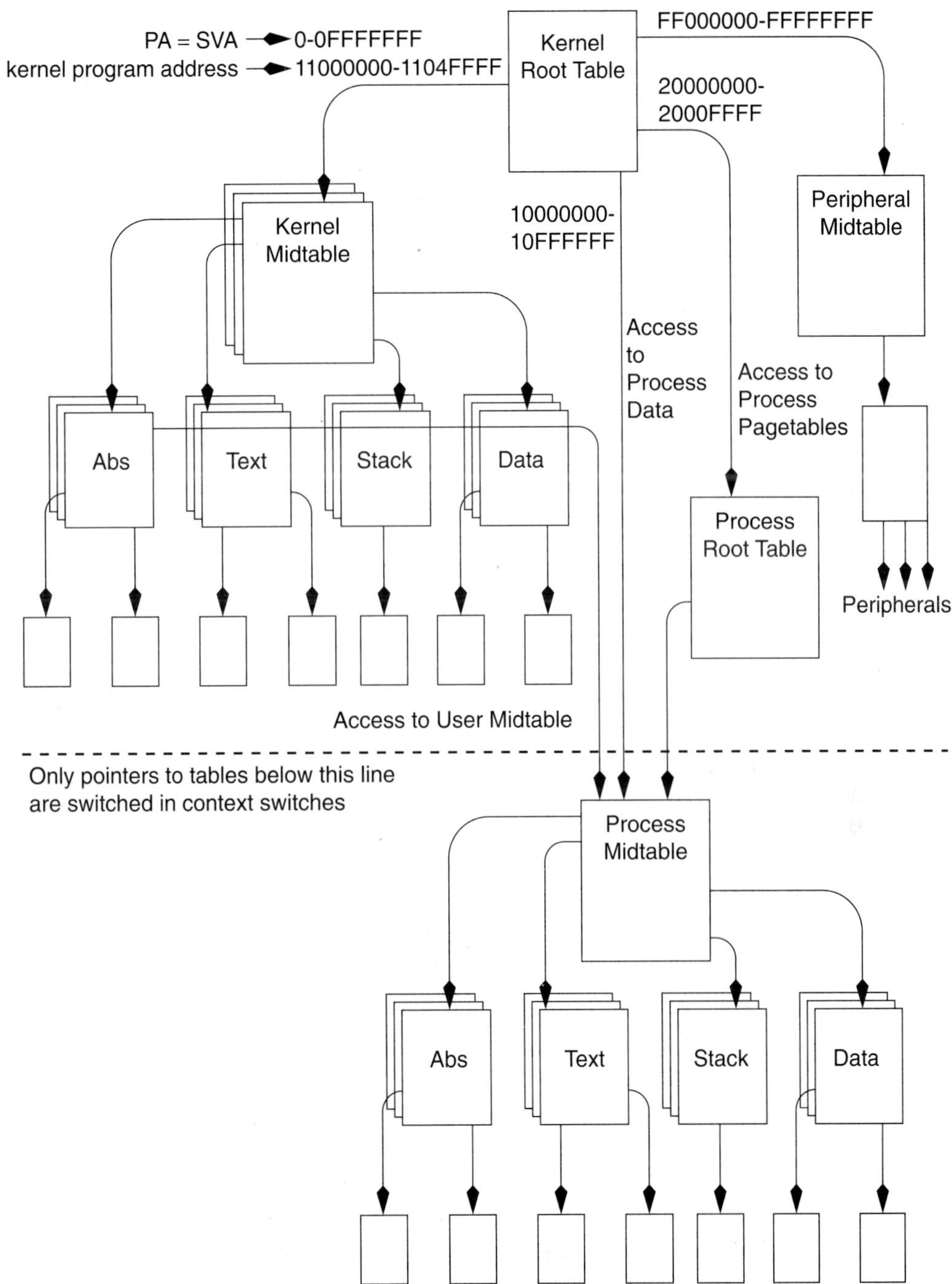

FIGURE 4.12 Pagetable tree for a moderate-size operating system. Each process has a single process midtable. Upon a context switch, the three PTEs giving access to the process tables and pages are switched. All PAs are directly mapped into the address range 0-0FFFFFFF, allowing 1 GB of physical memory. You may find it helpful to examine Figure IV.4 on page 593. That figure expands and explains the features of this figure.

(PVAs), can access only the data in the bottom line. Normally, a number of processes will be in memory at the same time, and we would like to be able to switch back and forth between them quickly. Very few values have to be changed in the tables to do this. To switch processes, we insert a descriptor pointing to the three page layers in the new process in three locations in the kernel. By *pointing* we mean that the PTEs we are inserting provide the SVA ⇒ PA translation at the correct point in the chain that leads to one of the three bottom layers in Figure 4.12. After changing values in the tables, we also must flush the translation cache to remove the old values, as we will explain in Chapter 5.

Begin looking at Figure 4.12, thinking of inserting a word into any page below the dashed line. The basic key to all transformations of VAs to PAs is:

> Every VA ⇒ PA translation requires three memory references—root table, midtable, pagetable—though the particular table's name may not always seem to be in agreement with this hierarchy.

Let us say that you wanted to put an entry in the process data pagetable. Observe that there is only one process root table and that at any one time, there is only one entry in that table—the PTE at displacement 0. All the other slots will be marked *invalid & unassigned*—numerically 0. What this says is that only the *currently active* process is in position to have pages added or deleted from its tables. After you believe that concept, you should be ready for the next: While the figure shows three arrows to the process midtable, and while all those pointers must perforce arrive at the same physical address for that table, none of the three will access it in the same way. With reference to Figure 4.10, both process and kernel will consider the process midtable as a midtable (a table immediately below a root table) when they access process pages but they will use different logical addresses (VAs). When used as a midtable, the process midtable provides access to the process data at the very bottom of the chart. The kernel, as the figure shows, has access to the process midtable through two other paths. In one, the process root table is the midtable, the process midtable serves as pagetable, and the data being addressed is in the process pagetables. Finally, there is the link running through the kernel absolute pagetable. In that case, the process midtable is the data page itself, equivalent to any of those shown in kernel space directly below the kernel pagetables.

The tale goes on. The kernel requires access to its own tables. It must be able to add and change entries. An obvious example at this point is changing upon a context switch the three pointers which reference the current process. Writing into the root tables to make this switch requires that the kernel have a logical address (VA) to write to. While we will map all SVAs directly to PAs (i.e., SVA = PA), the address goes through the normal translation mechanism even though the result is an identity. With the address translation mechanism shown in Figure 4.10, that requires that the kernel root table be a table of data at the end of the chain, so you should envisage pointers from the kernel absolute pagetable to every pagetable above the dashed line *including itself*. This is expanded upon in Appendix IV and particularly in Figure IV.4 on page 593. As we will discuss in a moment, it will be quite profitable to make the entire mapping of the *physical memory* correspond to the structure from system midtable down. In other words, the lower array of system virtual addresses from 00000000 to whatever the maximum physical address is will translate into itself. VA 00000000 will be PA 00000000. This thought leads us to assignment of PAs to VAs. Let us consider the orderly and purposeful construction of pagetables.

4.7.1 Address Translation

The first issue to consider here is the idea of SVA = PA. This idea is put into action each morning when the computer wakes up from its evening's slumber. After a reset, the computer has no operating system and no operating MMU. In fact, the only thing that is in memory is whatever is in ROM. In setting itself up, the initialization system must build the structure above the dashed line in Figure 4.12. What is different about the system structure compared to any process structure is that the system is almost completely specified at boot time. The amount of physical memory (PM) is readable at boot time. Even the maximum extent of the system stack can be specified.

Just as an example, let us say that

- Absolute data occupies 64 KW or 256 pages. Much of this is ROM.
- Text data occupies 2 MW or 8 KP.
- Stack data requires 2 KW or 8 pages.

While these numbers are arbitrary, they are eminently reasonable. The absolute and stack pages can be referenced from a single pagetable. Text, on the other hand, will require 32 pagetables. Each page occupies, not surprisingly, one physical page. We have just specified about 8 KP. Now comes the big move. *All the rest of the physical pages constitute the system heap or data area.* That data area includes everything except the pages specified by the bullets. Even the pagetables that we just specified will come out of the data area.

Keep in mind that the kernel is *always* in memory. It is never paged out. Thus, the boot process loads it right away and there it is, ready to start working as soon as the boot process launches the initialization process. Let us look at the address translation process for this one-to-one identity mapping.

Let us say that the system maintains a list or bitmap of all unassigned pages. If the system text wants a free page (page-aligned) in heap, it does `p = pagealloc();`. The value of p that is returned is a PA, but in our system PAs are also system VAs. Let us let it be 0024E300. The last two hex digits of 00 show that the pointer is indeed pointing at the first word in a page. The translation process is as follows (and takes place in hardware in the MMU):

1. 00 (leading byte) is the offset into the system root table. That table's PA is stored in a register in the MMU (part of the boot process setup). Accordingly, we get a PTE that has protection bits and the leading three bytes XXXXXX of the PA of one page of the system midtable.

2. The MMU appends 24 (second byte) to those bytes to make XXXXXX24. This is now the PA of the second PTE. This PTE has protection bits and the leading 3 bytes YYYYYY of the PA of the appropriate system data pagetable.
3. The MMU appends E3 (third byte) to those bytes to make YYYYYYE3. This is now the PA of the third PTE. This PTE has protection bits and the leading 3 bytes ZZZZZZ of the PA of the appropriate system data page. As it happens, ZZZZZZ = 0024E3! How did that happen? It happened when the boot process created these tables. In other words, whoever wrote the boot code that installed the PTEs of each PA into the correct system pagetables generated the PTEs using the reverse of the algorithm we just constructed. See Problem 4.4 for a chance to play this game yourself.

Of course, if the system programmer who is using this system wants the physical address, he or she need not go off to the MMU to get this translation. The programmer can know that the PA = SVA and just use it. Why would he or she want the PA? Because the PA is exactly the item that your system must build PTEs from. Whenever the system wants to install a page in a process's space, this is central to the activity. There are lots of places where this duality is convenient. What is the cost? Practically nothing. Only that your system devote 0.4 percent of its physical memory to pagetables to map all pages.

Creating a new process under this system is an interesting exercise, one that is considered at some depth in Appendix IV and in the problem set. If you have not had a course in operating systems and particularly UNIX, we recommend a diversion at this point.

4.8 VIRTUAL MEMORY

We keep saying, ". . . if we were doing virtual memory management. . . ." The time has come. Let's do it. Virtual memory management is an effort to micromanage one particular resource, primary memory, to achieve one or more of the following goals:

- allowing a program whose address space is larger than the physical memory to run without requiring the programmer and compiler to do explicit *overlays* of subsections of the program or data
- allowing many programs to share memory and the other system resources in an equitable and efficient manner
- minimizing the amount of bus and disk traffic that is necessary to run many programs concurrently

These objectives may seem useful enough in an abstract way, but they are anything but abstract goals. Consider the first goal: making a program "fit" regardless of the physical memory complement. If you write a program of some heft for a VAX or SPARC, for example, how much memory can you assume will be there? These machines exist with as little as a couple of megabytes of RAM and as much as several hundred megabytes. How big a machine does your program need? On those two machines and any others using a true virtual memory management system, you do not have to ask. Your program will run. Maybe not with the blinding speed that you or your customer had hoped for, but run it will. On a machine using whole-program management with a small memory, your program simply may not load. If it will load, it may do so only at the expense of swapping everything else out. That situation would result in "sharing the computer" by losing most of the compute cycles to waiting for the disks to do their thing. Even your fastest disks are dreadfully slow when compared to computer processing speeds. One of the major issues in sharing resources is to let *ready-to-run* processes run while *waiting-for-I/O* processes get disk services. Efficiency in multiprogramming requires the ability to have many processes simultaneously in memory and to load and swap small blocks of code at a time.

Along with the other applications of the adage that there is no free lunch, virtual memory management (VMM) requires considerable amounts of system management overhead. System management activity is "unproductive" delay as far as a user is concerned. In systems used where the three goals stated above are only weakly compelling—for example, systems which run modest-sized programs one at a time—the benefits of VMM do not always outweigh the costs. But as programs grow ever larger to do things that we want them to do and as we find ourselves using the computer concurrently to do different tasks, VMM becomes more and more compelling. Consider the fact that in the system which will supersede System 7, VMM with all its benefits and liabilities will be included.

VMM works like this: As the current process is executing, it generates virtual addresses to fetch instructions and to read or write data. These virtual addresses are translated by the MMU. If the page being referenced is located in physical memory and there are no protection violations, then the corresponding physical address is generated and the fetch, read, or write takes place. If the page is not in physical memory, the memory management unit will cause an exception (*page fault*). The *page-fault handler* must decide whether the page that is not there is out on disk or simply not assigned. DEC calls the latter a *demand-zero page*, meaning that it will be delivered, full of zeros, on demand. That kind of page represents new turf added to stack or heap. The other kind represent pages of data or program that have not been loaded yet or were swapped out. Note that the hardware cannot simply retrieve the desired page and resume. The minimum time to fetch a page from disk generally exceeds a whole process time slice. Instead, when a page fault occurs, the page-fault handler does three short tasks:

- It posts a request for the kernel's *pager function* to fetch the desired page and add it to this process's resident set.
- It recovers any special information that will be necessary to restart the current (faulting) process (not necessary in our RISC design because instructions cannot "break" in the middle).
- It causes a context switch, which brings in the next *ready-to-run* process and puts the current process in a queue of *waiting-for-I/O* processes.

Since it takes so much time to read a block from disk into memory, it is very important to keep in memory those pages which are most likely to be used next. That is a curious quest! How do you know—better yet, how does a system which has no idea what you had in mind when you wrote this program—know what will be used "next"? The short answer is a direct derivative of the classical response to: "What will the weather be tomorrow?" The best bet is: "Whatever it is doing today." The equivalent answer for the computer system is to assume that the program will continue to do what it just did. The long answer—how the system keeps track of what the program did recently—we develop later in this section. First let us consider the transaction of bringing in a page.

The game of memory replacement is not unlike the game of poker. You get five cards. To get more, you must first discard a subset of what you have in hand. You may not have more than five. Furthermore, if you intend to win, you will want to discard the cards least costly to your success. Similarly, the program gets a resident set, which is almost always much less than the whole program and its attendant data (the *job image*). To read in a page from disk, if your hand is full, you must give up one of the pages already in memory. Naturally, you would like to replace the page which will cost you the least. It is cheapest to yield a page which hasn't been modified; it is cheapest to discard a page which will not soon be needed again. The data in an unmodified page is still on the disk, so "giving it up" is simply moving the PPA from your resident set to the list of free pages. Releasing a modified page requires that the data in the page get preserved by writing it out to disk. Thus, bringing in a page would require the paging process to both read and write a page. All things being equal, you will always choose to discard a *clean* (unmodified) page rather than a *dirty* (modified) one. To be able to tell one from the other, the hardware memory management unit normally maintains a modified bit for each page in memory.

When you guess which cards are most likely to be least useful, you should base the guess both on the possible useful combinations that you could make with the hand (*recent actions*) and the probabilities dictated by what comprises the known remaining deck (*typical deck behavior*). In order to guess which pages to discard, we should look both at the recent actions of the program at hand and at the behavior of typical programs. The address stream generated by a program normally exhibits a set of properties known as *locality of reference*. The general idea is that addresses tend to be clustered. In fact, they tend to be clustered in several ways. Because programs often contain loops which produce very similar sequences of addresses over and over again, they exhibit *temporal locality*; addresses which occurred in the recent past tend to occur again. Since procedures have their instructions clustered together and usually refer to data structures that are stored close together, they also exhibit *spatial locality*; addresses tend to occur which are close to addresses that have occurred previously. A more specific example of this is called *sequentiality*: When address **n** occurs, the most probable next address is **n+1**. Sequentiality has two obvious causes:

- The instructions in a program are usually fetched sequentially.
- Data in the form of arrays, text, and structures are often accessed sequentially.

Locality of reference is the principal tool with which we may choose which pages we should bring into the memory and which we should discard. Temporal locality—tomorrow's weather will be like today's—suggests that we discard the pages least recently referenced. While looking out the window will do for weather, it is going to take some hardware and some cleverness to pull this off in the computer at low cost. Spatial locality, on the other hand, leads to a rule that is easy to implement: Since each read has almost the same amount of overhead regardless of its length, when you find that you need page **n**, read in pages **n** to **n+m**. One of the choices often left up to the system manager (in contrast to the system *designer*) is the choice of **m**. The best value can often depend both on the local disk configuration and the programs typical of the local site. The range depends on page size, but likely values will be 1 to 8.

Reading in **m** sequential pages is simple enough, but discarding the *right* **m** pages leaves about as much room for cleverness and error as poker. Needless to say, the game of page replacement has led to many strategies, several of which we now consider. As with any game, one should proceed from an overview of the rules, resources, and objectives to a consideration of strategies of play. The first question to be answered here is the size of the principal resource: How much memory do we have to work with? You do not get the whole deck. The house holds a considerable portion of the physical memory for its own critical use. What makes these data and this code critical is that they must always be available. They may not be paged out; they must be in memory and not out on disk. An obvious example of such an unpageable item is the *page-fault handler*. How could the system handle a page fault in the page-fault handler? That is rather like climbing out of a hole to get the ladder with which to climb out of the hole. There are lots of similar examples:

- any form of interrupt handler
- the vector tables for interrupts, exceptions, and traps
- the root table(s) for translating VAs to PAs
- the areas set aside to contain linked lists of commands and responses for I/O processes (discussed in Chapter 7)
- lists of free and dirty pages
- lists of processes such as the *ready-to-run* list, the *waiting-for-event* list, and the *waiting-for-I/O* list
- system processes involved in I/O such as the pager, the swapper, and the several device drivers

What remains of physical memory is available for assignment to virtual memory pages. The first problem to be faced is how to divide this resource among the various pageable processes. Flexibility demands that some free pages be kept available, so that an empty page can be obtained immediately when one is needed. But how should we divide the available pages among the processes? The question has both static and dynamic parts. How big should the resident set be for each process? There is nothing carved in stone which states that all processes must be created and kept equal. Poker would become a curious game if you could have as many cards as you could coerce from the other players, but in computer operation it is often beneficial to all to let resident sets grow and shrink—within limits—as the need arises. A typical way of running a VM system is to start a process with some very limited number of preassigned pages—maybe only some header and pagetable information—and then let it grow into its initially assigned *resident-set limit* by requesting what it needs through page faults. If a process is tiny, it may never hit the limit. Inherently big processes, on the other hand, might not fit well within the initial limit. They will have a tendency to *thrash*, that is, to keep changing pages to access the program and data that it needs all the time. Thrashing causes lots of I/O and context switching, devoting more of the computer time to nonproductive work. Everybody suffers. It would be far better if the big guy could get a chair big enough to sit down in. To see how this unequal but efficient division of the memory resource can be accomplished, we must consider what our paging process might do when a page is demanded by a process which has reached its current working-set limit.

When a page fault occurs, one strategy is to remove whichever page has not been used for the longest time, regardless of which process owned that page. This is called *global replacement*. If we do this, the demanding process will grow. Another strategy is to make the complaining process replace one of its own pages. This is called *local replacement*. Local replacement holds the process to its current resident-set limit. Note that even a huge program that marched in simple, linear fashion through its code would not benefit from more memory. It would never return to a page once it finished with it. On the other hand, a modest-sized program which accessed a huge data base might well benefit by having all of the active parts of the base simultaneously in memory. It is easy enough to think of mixing the two strategies to fit the individual program needs—a strategy called *variable local replacement*—but how does the system keep track of who needs what?

4.8.1 Replacement Algorithms

The answer—at least the initial answer—is as obvious as you think it is. The system must count page faults per unit time. Counting is not a perfect algorithm, since random selections from a data base too huge to contain in memory would defeat its intent, but without inquiring into why the program is so piggy, counting is the best we can do. However, counting determines who needs more pages and who could afford to give some back. It does not point to the specific pages to take. Let us first consider how we will acquire pages for our freelist, deferring for a moment how we will count to determine the best objects for our later largess.

To be able to deliver free pages on demand, some minimum number of pages is kept free. Naturally, as page faults occur and the free pages are consumed, the number of free pages will decrease below the minimum. When this happens, a system routine called the *page stealer* is invoked to take some pages from the rich processes and put them on the *free-page list*. This *steal from the rich and donate to the poor* is the essence of a global replacement strategy. Assume that counting has pointed to a dozen process which apparently could afford to spare a few pages each. Which pages does our page stealer steal? Each of the following algorithms (in order of increasing performance) can be used either globally or locally. Our poker analogy will serve us in good stead as you think about whether you would adopt such an algorithm if you had money riding on it.

Random replacement. This is simple to implement and there are constructible examples in which it can be shown to be *best*, but in situations where order exists and we have some sense of usual order of events, we can almost always get better performance from a nonrandom algorithm. If your poker hand had nothing of value in it—no pairs and no more than two of any suit—*and if you had nothing but your own hand's history to judge what is in the deck*, random replacement of cards is probably as good as any other scheme.

First-in first-out (FIFO). This is also very easy to implement. The pages of each process are kept on a linked list. New pages are added at the tail, and pages are removed from the head. The biggest problem with this algorithm is that we will steal pages which have been in memory for the longest time, even if they have been used constantly during that time. This algorithm, taken at its most primitive, is little better than random replacement. Whatever improvement results would derive from the tendency of a program to proceed from beginning to end, making early pages less valuable than later ones. However, many programs are constructed of many interacting pieces hung off a central skeleton. FIFO is not a good model of that structure and may be worse than random replacement for many programs. However, a simple trick can make FIFO a very effective replacement strategy. The trick is to hang onto the stolen pages to see if the process from which they came notices the theft. If so, your page stealer apologizes and gives the pages back. In the card-playing analogy, this would be like giving the player the opportunity to change his or her mind on discards *after* getting the new cards. Now wouldn't you like that! The VAX/VMS operating system does this. It uses local FIFO replacement, delivering the pages retrieved to a deliberately long FIFO *freelist*. Then when a page fault occurs, the system can scan the pages on the freelist before starting to read from disk. If it happens to find the correct page, it can grab it back and put it into the faulting process's resident set; no disk read is necessary. Simply change a few table entries and resume the process. This is called a *soft page fault* to distinguish it from *hard page faults,* which require disk accesses. In effect, we are using the list of free pages as a *disk cache*—a handy collection of likely-to-be-referenced pages that the system can acquire at much lower cost than a true disk access. See Chapter 15 of [Kenah, 88] for details.

First-in not-used first-out (FINUFO). This algorithm adds a *utility* factor. In the poker analogy, it is equivalent to keeping those cards that already have some intrinsic value—three 4's or four hearts, say. You certainly don't want to chuck your better cards onto the waste heap. In cards, the value of a card depends on the other cards in the hand and on the (variable) probabilities of drawing the card(s) necessary to complete a competitive hand. Pages are useful if they are about to be used, but since one cannot look into the future, the best guess is that the most favorable pages are the ones most recently active. This data requires keeping track of page references. For FINUFO, the use data is reduced to binary states of *referenced* or *not referenced.* The hardware sets a *referenced bit* in a PTE whenever a reference is made to that PTE. Then, whenever the page stealer (global replacement) or the pager (local replacement) wants to take a page, it starts down the list in order, checking and resetting the referenced bit for each PTE. It takes pages from those whose *referenced bit* is not set. Note that if all bits are set, all will get reset. If a page must be taken, that would lead to taking the first in the list on the second time around. While this algorithm requires a little hardware assistance, it is still pretty cheap and almost as effective as our next and last *realistic* replacement strategy, LRU.

Least recently used (LRU). This algorithm simply refines the values used in FINUFO from the binary classifications of *referenced* and *not referenced* to a multivalued rating of worth. Two kings are a pair no less and no more than two 2's, but they do not have equal value. We can assign an *age* to each page which indicates the time since last usage. Several schemes are possible. A simple method depends on periodic sorting of the page list based on the *referenced bit* for each page. Referenced pages move to the start of the list. Then all of the referenced bits are cleared and the process continues until the next clock interruption. Pages which have not been referenced recently move to the end of the list, from which discards are taken. A similar idea, which is faster than sorting, is to increment an age counter associated with a page if it hasn't been referenced and to reset it if the page has been referenced. This algorithm is used in UNIX System V.3. See Section 9.2 of [Bach, 86] for details. Note that the burden of LRU over FINUFO is that the system must provide intermediate interrupts to evaluate the LRU data. For FINUFO, the data can be collected at the same time that a context switch is executed.

Perfect prediction (PP). This is not a real method since it requires the system to peer into the future. If you find that your poker partners seem to have this ability, take up another form of entertainment or move to another table. Our reason for considering it here is only to compare look-backward prediction methods with what really happened. If you know the actual sequence of page calls, PP allows you to set the standard by which all of the other page replacement schemes can be judged. What PP requires is that you replace the page that is furthest away from your current position in the sequence of pages. Obviously, if a page is never referenced again, it is a prime target for replacement.

We must consider one final issue before doing some examples of replacement algorithms. Stealing a *dirty* page is not the same as running off with a clean one. A dirty page must be rendered clean by writing out the data in that page to the process's job image on disk. Only then may the system reuse the page for either local or global replacement. Since a write followed by a read is twice as much work as a read alone, some systems shy away from modified pages entirely. Others, like the VAX/VMS, provide one more layer of buffering to try to save the double work of reclaiming dirty pages. In VMS, pages are taken without looking at the *dirty* bit, but once taken, if they are dirty, they are put on the long *dirty page list*. Dirty pages are written out at a lower priority than reads from the disk. Accordingly, these writes are done as a background job. That makes their stay in memory rather long. They move to the *freelist* with their *dirty bit reset* only when the data is backed up to disk. Then they dwell on the freelist until they get to the front of the line. In this way, there is a relatively long interval during which a process can reclaim a dirty page with the very low cost of a soft page fault. A distinct benefit of this double buffering of dirty pages is that it gives preference to dirty pages but those which are really not being used do not continue to dwell in memory.

Although any of the previous replacement algorithms can be applied to either global or local replacement, for variable local replacement we also need a method for adjusting the *resident-set limits*. These algorithms often work by applying purges to the resident set when conditions seem to warrant. Once again, there are a number of algorithms for trying to make the resident-set limit fit the varying needs of each process.

Working-set replacement (WSR). Each process will use only a limited number of its pages during a given interval of CPU time. The idea is to let processes page fault and add pages, growing for some given interval, and then take away from a process all pages unused in the interval. The set of pages used by a process during the most recent interval is called its *working set*. The referenced bits can be used to determine which pages each process has used in the most recent interval, and any pages not being used are simply moved to the freelist. This method then allocates to each process as many pages as are in its working set. Note that to run a working-set replacement algorithm, the system must maintain both *referenced bits* and *process CPU time*.

Page-fault frequency (PFF). This is simpler to implement and almost as good as working-set replacement. The PFF of a process is the number of page faults per unit CPU time for that process. A high PFF usually indicates that the process needs more memory. A low PFF may mean that the process could afford to give up some memory. If the time between page faults is small, the system increases the process's resident-set limit. If the time is large, the referenced bits are checked for all pages assigned to the process, and any pages which haven't been used since the last page fault are released to the freelist. An example of a page-fault handler using PFF is given at the end of this section. There are some types of programs which do not work well with PFF. In particular, a program which made unrelated references to a large data base could have a high PFF but would not benefit from keeping the old references in memory. There are also some of the usual problems in determining a rate from a brief observation of a sequence of events. A simple-minded PFF can be obtained simply by storing the clock time of the last PF. If it has been only a brief interval since the last one, you have a high PFF. A better indicator can be obtained by taking the time interval for the last three or six PFs, using a moving-average low-pass filter to avoid overreacting to short bursts of requests. Note that once again, to run this algorithm, we will need both clock data and *referenced bits*.

Clocked LRU. Both of the previous algorithms work well, but some machines, such as the VAX, don't have referenced bits. They must use different algorithms or software-maintained referenced bits. Berkeley's version of UNIX creates software referenced bits on the VAX with an algorithm called *clocked LRU*. In this algorithm, the software bit serves as the *valid bit*; the PTE valid bit is used by the system as a software setable referenced bit. A system *clock routine* periodically runs through each process's page-tables, resetting the valid bits in the PTEs. After that, if a page is referenced, a page fault will occur. The page-fault handler will check the software valid bit and find that the page is actually in memory. If that is the case, the page-fault handler sets the PTE *valid* bit and resumes the process. On the next round of the clock process, if it finds an invalid page with its software bit set and its PTE valid bit reset, that page hasn't been referenced. The page is removed from the working set and transferred to the freelist. See [Quarterman, 85] or [Leffler, 89] for a description of this and other features of Berkeley UNIX. Other versions of clock algorithms are described in [Maekawa, 87].

VMS soft page fault frequency. VAX/VMS uses still another algorithm, one that depends rather heavily on its long freelist. It has three different *working-set limits* and keeps track of soft page faults. If it finds that the process is shuffling pages between the resident set and the freelist, it assigns that process the next higher working-set limit. If a process seems too content with its working-set limit, the operating system moves it down to a lower one, forcing it to give pages back. Again, the long dwell time on the freelist allows the process time enough to find which pages it really wants to keep. While not as regular as WSR, this process requires essentially no hardware support beyond that required for handling normal PFs.

4.8.2 Thoughts on a PFF Page-Fault Handler

In Appendix IV we develop a system routine to create a new process using whole-program memory management. Here we want to build routines which use demand paging. Both systems use the same table tree (Figure 4.12). Here however, since we can limit the resident set to modest proportions whatever the program size, we would like to allow a process to access the full 64 MB of virtual space that is available from a single midtable. With the potential for 256 pagetables, both pagetables and pages will be pageable. Now, with but one process midtable per process, it makes sense to mark midtables as unpageable. The process creation routine will be cheaper than the one in Appendix IV, since it will be necessary to create only the pagetables. Nothing else need be loaded. As a process is created by the `fork()` call, it emerges as a duplicate of the parent process, the only difference being the value that is returned by `fork()`. Based on that return, the parent process continues what it was doing while the new process calls the system routine, `exec()`. `exec()` changes the new process to make it do what has been asked for. The installation of the new application is preceded by returning all the old pages and pagetables to the freelist. The midtable is retained—every process needs one—but blanked after it has served to dump all the old pages. Then the loader can start afresh building the process tree.

The process of building the tables is an outgrowth of the linking process. The *linker* will have packed together a file containing a header and all of the bins in order. Most linkers will paginate the bins so that each bin will be an integer number of disk blocks and memory pages. Others will pack words together to give a smaller disk image. The length of each bin in words or pages and the starting virtual address of each bin are part of the header. The *loader* can convert words to pages, but the loading information is much more direct if pages are employed all the way through. Let us assume page mode. Upon getting that data, the pagetables become a direct map of the data on disk plus *demand-zero* pages allotted at load time to the *data* segment. Pages for stack and heap will be added as the program requires. A new process normally gets arguments passed to it, so on many machines a process will start with a page of stack. As the midtable and pagetables are constructed, several items for the process control block will be developed or read in from the header. One is the entry point to the program itself. Starting is then accomplished essentially as a function call to that address in the process space. This will cause a page fault, which will bring in the first page of program. Pages are delivered on demand; hence the name *demand paging*. Smart paging algorithms may cache a few succeeding pages on the premise that pages are often accessed sequentially, but this caching is transparent to the page-fault handler. The program is concluded by a JUMP back to the calling address where a TRAP to the system initiates program termination. Termination proceeds in orderly fashion, closing any open files, returning to the freelist all of the process pages including the midtable and pagetables, and deleting any temporary files on disk. Now that we have considered birth and death, let us have a look at the program in middle age.

Using PFF replacement, all of the interesting parts occur in the page-fault handler. Let us consider a simple version of such a system function. Several structures would be defined for the system and for each process. On inception, each process gets a process control block (PCB) and a process ID (PID). The PID is an index into a table of current processes and the table entry is the system VA of the PCB. PCBs are unpageable. Among the many items in the PCB are:

1. The PTE containing the PA of the process midtable.
2. A pointer to the list of pages in the process's resident set. Each entry in the list includes
   - *a.* the SVA of the PTE for this page (possibly null).
   - *b.* the disk address of its image (possibly null).
   - *c.* the disk location of the swap-out image (null if not swapped out).
   - *d.* the PA of the page.
3. The time of the last page fault for this process.
4. The moving average of the time between page faults.
5. The current size of the resident set.
6. The program starting address (entry point).
7. Limits of the fixed and variable segments as follows:
   - *a.* Start and end of the absolute segment.
   - *b.* Start of the writeable pages in the absolute segment.
   - *c.* Start and end of the text segment.
   - *d.* Start of the data segment and the top of heap (TOH).
   - *e.* Bottom of the stack. (Top is specified by R30.)

There are a lot of entries in the PCB, including all of the data stored for a context switch, but this list of seven items covers our needs in the page-fault handler.

The pagelist entries themselves are constructed on the *page_ID* template:

```
struct page_ID
    {   struct page_ID *link;       /* link to next page */
        int *pte;                   /* system pointer to PTE if mapped*/
        int image_blk;              /* disk image block number */
        int swp_blk;                /* swap disk block number */
        int pa;                     /* physical memory address */
    };
```

Consider the transaction that must go on to deal fully with a page fault (PF). A process running at IL0 sends an address to the MMU. The address being sent resides in register in the CPU at this moment. The MMU checks the address by accessing the pagetables. The translation is there or it is not. If it is not, then we have a page fault. The page fault could be either at the pagetable or page level, but not (in our tree) at the midtable. There is also the possibility of an access exception such as trying to write to a read-only page or trying to access a page which is not *yet* in the process set. This last one is tricky to handle because such an error flags either an egregious error (an address which does not exist in the process's panoply of legal addresses; e.g., using a NULL pointer) or an innocent request to use a part of the stack which has not been allocated yet. You are asked to judge between error and innocence in the problem set.

The interrupt transaction for a page-fault/access-error will take place at the lowest real interrupt level, IL2. The page-fault interrupt handler will start running with several questions to ask:

- What was the faulting address?
- Where was the program when it issued the faulting address?
- Was it a page fault or an access error?
- If a page fault, what sort of page fault was it? Possibilities include:
  page out on disk
  page on freelist or modifiedlist
  demand-zero page
  address out of bounds (access error)

The task of the PF handler is to answer these questions and then to take the appropriate corrective action. Corrective action can range from supplying a free or cached page immediately, to putting the process into a *wait* state and requesting the data from disk, to handling a fatal error as the process or system demands.

Consider how the interrupt handler will get the data to answer its questions. All currently active ILs are identifiable by bits set in the CPU status register. In many machines, an interrupt pushes the current value of the status word and PC onto the stack where they are accessible to the interrupt handler; in our machine, as we detail in Chapter 6, we use *phantom registers* with each IL having its own PC, SP and several hidden registers. The active set of registers is determined by the IL. Inactive registers are accessible through a memory-mapping scheme. If we are in the PF handler, we must be active at IL2. A simple bit test tells whether IL1 is active. If so, we have one of the rare kernel page faults and the faulting address is in IL1 registers; if not, it is a normal process page fault with the faulting address in the IL0 set.

Determining the type of PF or access error requires data that are held in the two MMU registers, MMU_STATUS and FAULT_PTE. As usual, the registers will be accessible to the CPU through memory mapping. These data will include:

- In the MMU *status register* we have the data shown in Figure 4.13.
- In the MMU *PTE register*, the PTE of the page which faulted. This could be an attempt to access a nonextant or paged-out pagetable as easily as the page of data or text. Whenever the bone gets stuck in the MMU's craw, that PTE is in the PTE register.

For purposes of responding to the fault, the page address (top 24 bits) is sufficient. If an error handler must inform the user of the offending address in all its particulars, then the error handler must be able to recover those missing low order 8 bits. The MMU status register shows both the type of operation and at what stage the fault was exposed. From these data, the system software can find the offending address in PC or hidden register at the proper IL.

The issue of finding the offending instruction on a data operation or branching operation is made more complicated by the combination of pipelining and branching. Recollect the issues of delayed branching and instruction-stream bubbles which were introduced in Chapter 2 and how they arose. In our machine, every instruction takes 3 clocks to execute and at any moment, there are three instructions in the pipeline. The problem that arises is that the instruction which generated the address will be two places along in the stream by the time the address emerges from the CPU. Were the address always two places in back of the current PC, no problem. All that you must do is subtract 2 from a readily accessible value. However, how do you step back 2 with the

FIGURE 4.13 The MMU status register. The register is loaded whenever the MMU determines that it has an access error, bus fault, or page fault.

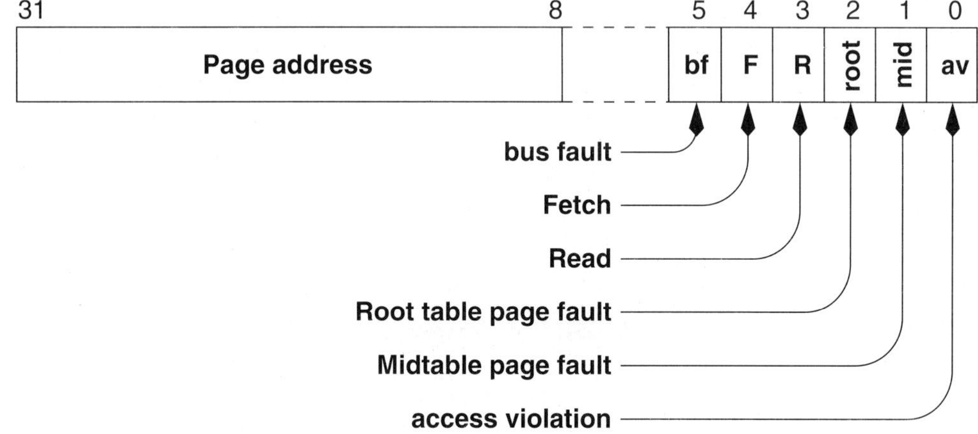

gulf of a branch between the current address and the offending one? The real problem is not the JUMP or CALL instruction itself. If that address is unsuccessful, you can still do PC-2 to get the address of the JUMP or CALL that caused the exception. The problem occurs with its successor, the bubble instruction. That is often a LOAD or STORE instruction, a typical source of an access exception. By the time that instruction actually delivers an address, the PC will no longer hold a useful reference. The issue is shown in Figure 4.14.

Since this problem is inherent in our design, the solution requires some help from the hardware. The only device which will always have the correct stream of instruction addresses is the CPU. Accordingly, we have put in a FIFO buffer with a depth of 2 for IL(0) and IL(1). This buffer stores the last two PC values, making it possible to pick up unambiguously the instruction address for the instruction causing a fault.

We have said most of what the page-fault handler must do, but it is often a good dose of reality to look at code which details the steps. The function `page_fault()` below is a simplified PFF handler. To smooth performance, we have used a *moving average* of the time between PFs over the last four faults and added that as a parameter stored in the PCB. To give a starting program a jump start, the initial value of the average time is set to 0.

Reading code being what it is, we have chosen to break the program up into chunks of modest proportions, with a paragraph of description preceding each chunk. There are relatively few comments, but the paragraphs break both the visual ghastliness and the necessity to wade through too many lines at a time.

We begin with a set of definitions of constants, structures, and system routines. Remember that this function is a kernel routine and will be running at IL2 with full WRITE access to anything its little heart desires. The constants through PWSWV are masks which fit the PTE and MMU status register definitions (Figure 4.11 and Figure 4.13). PTBASE is an address base which will pick up the first PTE in the pro-

FIGURE 4.14 Address in the PC as a JUMP is executed. Note that the address **b** never appears in the PC and that **a+3** does appear even though **X** is not fetched and **QA** is. When **b** was used, it came from a hidden CPU register. The only "unretrievable" address is **a+2** since a faulting address caused by the bubble instruction will be issued when **b+1** is resident in the PC.

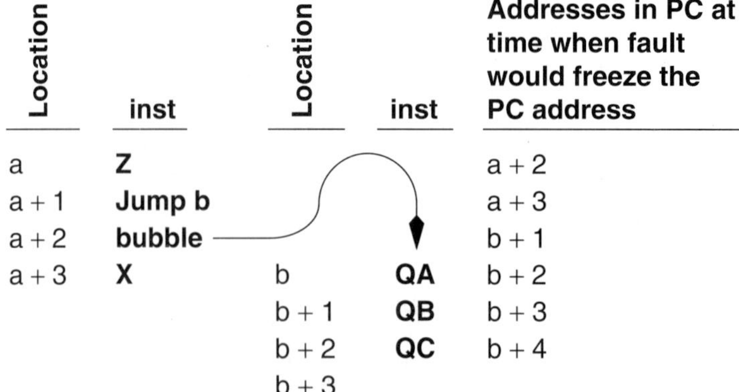

cess root table (Figure 4.12). Our presumption here is that the process will always be the active process when a page fault is being serviced at IL0. Accordingly, that location can be set aside for the PTE which accesses process pagetables.

```
#include <stdlib.h>
#define PROT_FAULT     0x00000001
#define REF            0x00000020
#define MOD            0x00000040
#define MIDFAULT       0x00000002
#define PRSWV          0x00000007          /* process read, system write, valid */
#define PESWV          0x0000000D          /* process execute, system write, valid */
#define PWSWV          0x0000000F          /* process write, system write, valid */
#define PTBASE         0x20000000          /* access to process pagetables, valid */
#define SIGSEGV        11                  /* "signal segment violation" defined elsewhere */
#define ABSR           1
#define ABSW           2
#define TXT            3
#define DAT            4
#define STK            5
#define MMU_STATUS     ((int *)0xFF000001)
#define FAULT_PTE      ((int *)0xFF000002)
#define PROCESS_MID    0x00120300          /*see Figure IV.4*/
```

The definitions below derive from the objects we have defined in the text. They include the entries on pagelists and the subset of entries in the PCB which are relevant to this subroutine. Since every page—that is, every piece of memory which is handled as a page entity—will have a `page_ID` and since these IDs will be in unpageable memory, it is important to keep them as small as possible. Accordingly, certain entries may serve more than one function. For example, since an unpageable page has no need for a swap block address, we have assigned the address 0xFFFFFFFF to mean an unpageable entry.

```
struct page_ID
    {   struct page_ID *link;
        int *pte;
        int image_blk;
        int swp_blk; /* 0xFFFFFFFF is unpageable */
        int pa;
    };

struct pcb            /* called PROC and found in <sys/proc.h> in UNIX */
    {
    struct page_ID *rsqueue;
    int last_pf, avgTime, rssize, midPTE;
    int botABS, botWRT, topABS;
```

```
int botTXT, topTXT, botDAT;
int TOH, botSTK;
int *midtable;
};
```

The following definition produces a "macro." The preprocessor will simply replace `zero_pag(x)` with the line below with `x` substituted for `adr`. Variables used inside macros are normally preceded with underlines to avoid conflicts with other variables in the functions they are used in. This macro will put zeros into all addresses in a page. The masking operation ensures that the clearing operation stays within page boundaries even if the macro is passed a midpage address.

```
#define zero_pag(adr)\
{ int _n, *_p; for (_n=256, _p= (int *)(adr & 0xFFFFFF00);_n>0;_n--) *_p++ = 0;}
```

The block of externals below are system routines and variables. In UNIX, everything about the current process is described in a huge structure called u. It resides at a fixed virtual address in the kernel space, and the structure for a new process is mapped there during context switches. This definition would be in <sys/user.h>. Our use of it here is to get the pointer to the PCB so we include the definition of a small piece of the structure. `Seg_type()` returns the numerical value of the segment in which the address lies. Note that this includes a check for stack or heap extension. If the address is not legitimately in any of the segments, the function returns 0. The ranges for the segments are given in the PCB. `Valid_address()` checks that the segment number is legal and that the PTE, which will be invalid in a page fault, has a legal form of invalidity for the segment in question. For example, *unassigned* (i.e., PTE = 0) would be legal in the STACK or DATA segments but a reference to an unassigned TEXT page is an *access exception*. `Getblk()` takes either a 0 or a disk reference (invalid PTE right-shifted by 1) as input and returns either the first page on the freelist (0 input) or the page specified by the disk address. This process will search the freelist and dirtylist before issuing a disk transfer request and putting the user process into a wait state. By "return a page" we mean that the program returns a pointer to the `page_ID`. Note that the `page_ID` is the only handle on that physical page. It gets moved from list to list as the page gets assigned or removed from processes. Before `Getblk()` returns the pointer to the `page_ID`, it updates or zeros all entries in the `page_ID` except for the critical physical address of the page. If a new page is issued, it will be assigned a place in the disk image. The PTE of a new page should be marked as *referenced*, since no copy of it yet exists on disk. It will be up to our `page_fault()` routine to put this `page_ID` into the process's resident-set list and to update the pagetable entry which makes the page visible. The last function, `psignal()`, is the standard kernel mechanism to send a "signal" to a process.

```
struct user { int u_pid;          /* process id number of current user */
              struct pcb *u_pcb;  /* pointer to pcb of current user */
```

```
            /* etc */
        };
extern struct user u;
extern int pff_threshold;
extern struct page_ID *dirtylist,*freelist;
extern int pff_threshold;

extern int valid_adr(struct pcb *process, int pte, int segment);
extern int system_clock();
extern void enqueue(struct page_ID *dest, struct page_ID *item);
extern int seg_type(int address, struct pcb *pcb);
extern struct page_ID * getblk(int blk);
extern void psignal(struct pcb *process, int signal);
typedef long page[256];
```

Now we begin the function itself. First we get the pointer to the PCB of the current process. Then we bring in the data from the MMU by referencing its internal registers. The first test is to find out if the user process has issued an illegal request, either a violation of protection or address exception. If that occurs, a call is made to an error handler (by `psignal()`) which will respond according to the protocol set up by the program. Whatever the protocol, this will terminate this function without any changes to the user process pagetables.

```
void page_fault()
{
        int n,adr, type, pte, paddr, seg, time, elapsed;
        int reducing, modified, *pte_adr;
        struct pcb *pcb;
        struct page_ID *pp, *oldpp, *unref;
        page *pg,*clr;

    pcb = u.u_pcb;
    type = *MMU_STATUS;
    adr = type & 0xFFFFFF00;
    seg = seg_type(adr,pcb);
    if ((type & PROT_FAULT) || !valid_adr(pcb,*FAULT_PTE,seg))
        {psignal(SIGSEGV); return;}
```

At this point, the subroutine knows that it has a legitimate page fault. However, before responding to that "request," it updates and checks the PFF and if it is low, it *cleans out* the user process by removing all unreferenced pages. This is the only transaction (other than ending a process entirely) which makes a process shrink. Swapping simply moves an active process in part or whole out to disk. The process does not get smaller when swapped; it just waits somewhere else. The system will swap it back in before it tries to run it. Here, however, we shrink the process. Pages are removed from the resident set and put on the freelist or dirtylist for later reassignment. All later sections of this page fault handler will add a page to the resident set. Note that the update of the time between page faults executes a very simple moving average filter.

```
time = system_clock();
elapsed = time - pcb->last_pf;
pcb->last_pf = time;
pcb->avgTime = (pcb->avgTime<<2 - pcb->avgTime + elapsed)>>2;/* moving average filter */
reducing = pcb->avgTime>pff_threshold;
pp = pcb->rsqueue;
oldpp = (struct page_ID *)&pcb->rsqueue;                /* points to pp's predecessor */
while (pp!=NULL)
    { if (((*(pp->pte) & REF) == 0) && reducing &&
        (pp->swp_blk != -1))                            /*-1 = unpageable */
        {   unref = pp;                                 /*dequeue page */
            pp = oldpp;
            pp->link = unref->link;
            pcb->rssize--;
            modified = *(unref->pte) & MOD;
            *(unref->pte) = unref->image_blk<<1;        /* the shift makes PTE invalid */
            unref->pte = 0;
            if (modified) enqueue(dirtylist, unref);
                else enqueue(freelist, unref);
        }
    else *(pp->pte) &= ~REF;                            /* reset REF bit in PTE */
    oldpp = pp;
    pp = pp->link;
    }
```

Now we add the needed page. Whether it is a pagetable page or a user page is readily determined from the MMU status register. There is a status bit which is set if the fault occurred in the midtable. Faults can be either unassigned or paged-out pages. For an unassigned page, we must get a free page and zero it; a paged-out page must be retrieved from disk or freelist or dirtylist. Demand-zero pages must be marked as *modified* and *referenced* in order to assure that they survive the next page fault and also that an image copy be preserved. While this will happen normally since page faults to unassigned pages almost always are to write something into the page, in the case of a new pagetable, the restart of the program will cause another fault, when the same address which faulted at the midtable now faults on the empty pagetable. Since we hit the shrinking actions before the building actions, our fresh new pagetable could vanish before we get the chance to fill it with its first datum.

Take a good look at the address construction. We use the fact that the high order 3 bytes in the VA are displacements into particular pagetables. For example, if VA 00QQRRSS were our target, we could find a PF either at the QQ'th PTE in the process midtable or at the RR'th entry in the process pagetable whose PA we got from the process midtable. Let us say that we are adding a process pagetable whose PA is XXXXXX00. We must put some protection bits into the 00 part and store the resulting PTE in the process midtable at a displacement that we know—QQ. From Figure 4.12 and Figure IV.4, you can see that the SVA of that PTE is simply 110003QQ. Similarly, once we have this new process pagetable in place, we must add the appropriate process page. We obtain another free page whose PA happens to be ZZZZZZ00, put some protection bits in the rightmost byte and simply put it as the first entry in the new pagetable—that is, the PTE goes in address 2000QQRR. Now we can go back to the original request, and the data page is there.

This section ends with the command `flush_tlb()`. The TLB (translation lookaside buffer) is a cache of recently done address translations. Since this program will have changed one of those entries, it is proper to flush the cache and let it build up again with all current translations. We have set up the kernel pagetables so that the PAs map into the SVAs. (See Problem 4.4.) Since we are running in the kernel, this allows `zero_pag()` to use PAs.

```
if (type & MIDFAULT)
{   pte_adr = (int *) PROCESS_MID + (adr>>16 & 0xFF);   /* get midtable PTE */
    pte = *pte_adr;
    if (pte)
    {   pp = getblk(pte>>1);                             /* shift out "valid" bit */
        *pte_adr = pp->pa | PRSWV | REF;
    }
    else
    {   pp = getblk(0);
        *pte_adr = pp->pa | PRSWV | MOD | REF;
        zero_pag(pp->pa);                                /* It seems easier to use PA */
    }
    pp->pte = pte_adr;
    enqueue(pcb->rsqueue, pp);
    pcb->rssize++;
    flush_tlb();
    return;
 }
```

Now we know that it is a process page that is to be added. This is very much like the adding of the pagetable except that the PTE is put into a pagetable and the address constructions are working out one more step in the address hierarchy. There is also the issue of different protection for different segments. We have assumed no reads from the TEXT segment. Assembly language programmers often stuff constants—a construct supported by HLLs—and sometimes even local variables into the code segment (above the entry point or below the return point). If data exist in the code segment, the protection for the TEXT segment must be changed appropriately. If you look back at the PTE definition (Figure 4.11), you will find provision for READ and EXECUTE in the lowest row.

```
    pte_adr = (int *) (PTBASE + (adr>>8 & 0xFFFF));
    pte = *pte_adr;
    if (pte) pp = getblk(pte>>1);
    else
        {pp = getblk(0);
        zero_pag(pp->pa);
        }
    pp->pte = pte_adr;
    enqueue(pcb->rsqueue, pp);
    pcb->rssize++;
    switch(seg)
    {   case ABSR: *pte_adr = pp->pa | PRSWV | REF; break;
        case TXT: *pte_adr = pp->pa | PESWV | REF; break;
        case DAT:
        case ABSW:
        case STK: *pte_adr = pp->pa | PWSWV | REF; break;
    }
    flush_tlb();
}
```

As in the example of the swapping system, we have ignored many practical issues, such as locking data structures, handling shared segments and shared pages, copy-on-write, and the possibility of kernel page faults. (Kernels, as their name implies, are usually pretty tight, small structures. As such, they can be marked as unpageable and no page faults will occur—unless they try to reference a paged-out process page. In general, that should never happen *as a surprise*. In `page_fault()`, if a pagetable was out on disk, `page_fault()` found out about it without suffering a fault itself. The kernel code is unpageable, but each process's system stacks can be swapped with the rest of the process.) Notice that two processes can share a page simply by having their PTEs point to it. But if one of them modifies it, the change will not be reflected in the modified bit of the other process. To use shared pages, we need not only a way of finding one and sharing it, but also a way of releasing it safely. One technique for doing this is to enter sharing information in the `page_ID`. For example, if we had a pointer to a count of co-owners, the page could be unpageable until the number of owners decreases to one. The price would be one more test in our reducing routine and one more word in the `page_ID`. If we get clever, we could use the `swp_blk` or `image_blk` for this extra service since there is no need for the disk address on unpageable pages. We could also share whole segments by having both midtables point to the same pagetables, with similar problems. Another issue we have ignored is the question of how `getblk()` can determine whether the requested block is on the freelist or dirtylist. This should be done quickly, since it can significantly affect the performance of the system. Hash tables can help shorten the search. An interesting question is: How do we identify the page when it is on the freelist or dirtylist? The answer is by the `image_blk` entry. That is unique and it is what is left in the PTE when a page is being put out to pasture.

We have been toddling along fat and happy with a virtual space of 64 MB. Not bad, but many large applications require more memory than that. Consider what changes would be necessary to allow processes to access the full 16 GB in their virtual address spaces. The pagetables for such a process would occupy 64 MB. Naturally, most of the pagetables would be on disk. We would require 256 midtables instead of 1, so we would want to allow midtables to be paged. The process root table would then become part of the process context instead of being fixed in the kernel. Note that we have included the **root** bit in the MMU_STATUS word (Figure 4.13) so that the hardware is prepared to support page faults on PTEs in the root table. The only significant problem we would face in using the entire 16 GB is that it would be impossible to map the process's virtual space into the kernel's virtual space. That can be a slight inconvenience, but we can easily map a 64-MB window from the kernel into any 64-MB midtable in the process's tree, so it's not much of a problem. The principal uses for kernel access to the process's virtual address space are:

- to read system call information, which might be on the process's stack
- to transfer blocks of data to or from the file system
- to manipulate pages and pagetables as we just did

The algorithms to accomplish these tasks and the data necessary for each process become a little more complicated when we expand our tree, but they do not become insuperable.

Enough said. Yet, if we have convinced you that pretending that you own the entire address space can improve the utility of a computer's physical memory resource, you must be wondering if turning the entire machine into make-believe might not work real wonders. The answer: "Yes it can," though the wonders are of the limited sort. As our final topic, we briefly consider the *virtual machine*—not to be confused with the *vaporware machine*, one that is much touted but *still* not delivered. Virtual machines have been running real code for better than two decades. The very first RISC—IBM's 801—ran initially as a virtual machine. Now how does that work?

4.9 VIRTUAL-MACHINE OPERATING SYSTEMS

Most instruction sets include instructions which are *privileged*. That is, they may be invoked only by a process operating at a privilege above that of mere user. An example of a privileged instruction is the somewhat old fashioned command HALT. It would never do to have some turkey bring to its knees a system serving 100 different users, so only a kernel process can issue a HALT. Many CPUs have instructions for direct I/O. These are frequently privileged to keep control of the I/O hardware and all of the data structures in the capable hands of the kernel. Now let us say that you want to test a new kernel that you are writing. You want to discover the bugs in this kernel, but you do not want to discover them by finding that you have destroyed the disk file system. Those who have I/O privileges can wreak all sorts of havoc. Our machine takes a rather different tack for providing a barrier between processes and system functions. All privileged registers including those of I/O devices are mapped into the address space. Processes are given no access to these privileged addresses. Accordingly, if a process includes an operating system under test with that operating system running at IL0, any attempt to access privileged addresses will cause an exception and bring on an inquiry from the real operating system. Since exceptions can be directed back to the process which caused them, the opportunity is there for getting whatever operation is needed from the real system. The *virtual machine* lets you run your new operating code in a protected mode where all dangerous operations must be passed through an old, well-debugged operating system. The virtual machine can also let you run under the operating system of your choice and even on a "machine" that differs from the real hardware. In a sense, the system that you are really on will be simulating the system you would like to be on.

Since simulation is generally a pretty slow affair, you might despair of such a plan for any computation-intensive task. However, if the hardware you wish to simulate is not too different from the hardware you are running on, the simulation can be as fast or even faster than the native system! Faster? How can it be faster? Well, let us first consider "as fast" and then slide into "faster."

If all you want to do is protect the other processes and the file system, and if the simulated (virtual) instruction set is identical or almost identical to the real one, then privileged instructions provide a simple mechanism for supporting the virtual machine. The program operating on the virtual machine runs in native code until it attempts a privileged operation. The attempt produces an exception. The real operating system picks up the issued instruction and handles it in software. For example, a virtual HALT stops only the virtual machine. All other processes go right on. While this may seem both reasonable and somewhat less wondrous than you had expected, stay with us. It gets better.

Virtual-machine operating systems provide each process with a virtual copy of the actual hardware of a machine—often but not necessarily identical to the real machine on which the code is running. This includes all of the instructions (even privileged ones), the entire virtual address space that the hardware can use, and the appearance of direct access to I/O devices.

The normal way to use a virtual-machine operating system is to run an operating system on each of the virtual machines. This can be useful in several different ways. The most common example is VM/CMS. This consists of a *control program* (CP), which runs on an IBM 370 and creates multiple virtual 370s. The *conversational monitor system* (CMS) is a simple single-user operating system, which runs on any of these virtual 370s. When a user logs in to a VM/CMS system, he is using the console of a virtual 370 running VM. If he types "IPL" for "initial program load," the CMS operating system will be loaded onto his virtual 370. From the user's perspective, it is a normal operating system. Notice that this is an even more extreme division of functions into layers than with systems that separate the command line interpreter from the kernel.

It gets still better. One user can debug an operating system on the same machine on which other users are doing normal editing or other jobs using CMS. The control program in VM provides debugging features so that a user can monitor the actions of her virtual machine. One may run a copy of VM on one of the virtual machines, and use it to debug itself. Or one may run an earlier version of the same operating system to avoid having to upgrade old (useful) programs. Finally, some operating systems are reported to run better on one of VM's virtual machines than on the actual 370 being used. That can occur if VM's demand paging algorithm is better than the one used by the other system. If you wanted to check your new operating system's ability to handle the creation of virtual machines, could you run another virtual machine on the virtual machine that you get when you logged in on VM? Yes, indeed, recursive virtualization is supported, but things slow down as you begin to lose the hardware support provided to the first layer of VM.

A major issue in a virtual-machine operating system is the efficiency of the simulation. Some IBM 370 processors include hardware features to be used with VM, and some other IBM operating systems include features to improve their performance when they run on VM's virtual machines. See Chapter 22 of [Deitel, 83] for a summary and additional references. Things get harder when you go across hardware lines. Nonetheless, there exists an operating system, *Soft PC*, which runs under the Macintosh operating system and supports any DOS-compatible 8086 program. File I/O is fine, though printing founders on the gross incompatibility of DOS and Macintosh printing algorithms. Speed loss across the emulator is roughly a factor of 4 to 16, depending on how you want to count it. Essentially, a 16-MHz Mac becomes a 4-MHz 8088. However, if you have a DOS program or DOS program data that you cannot or do not want to convert and you own a Mac, this program/operating system is a remarkable winner.

The Intel 80386 includes a mechanism to implement a slightly different type of virtual-machine operating system. Instead of creating multiple virtual versions of itself, the 80386 is designed to be able to create multiple virtual 8086s. Since the 8086 instruction set is essentially contained within the 80386, 8086 instructions run at 80386 speed. MS-DOS is a single-user operating system without demand paging or protection features, but just as with VM/CMS, the several concurrent users can be nicely isolated from each other by the overlying operating system. The paging mechanism is used to provide each virtual 8086 with its own 1-MB virtual address space, and all privileged instructions are trapped into the control program. The control program can implement time sharing, file protection, and demand paging.

Our machine includes only one mechanism that is incorporated specifically for running virtual machines. Traps provide the normal method for processes to obtain system services. TRAP at IL0 puts the CPU into IL1 as well as achieving a vectored jump. If the real operating system is supporting a virtual operating system, its response should be to return control to the virtual system's trap handler but at IL0. It does this by swapping values in the shadow registers at IL0 and executing an RFI. Back now in IL0 but with the trap handler address in the program counter, the virtual operating system may run the trap handler in protected mode. The handler inevitably finishes with RFI, NOP, NOP. While the RFI normally carries the CPU back to the last active IL, that sequence at IL0 would fail to get back to the program which invoked the trap. In order to reinvoke the operating system to reinsert the proper instructions in the pipeline and the proper value in the PC, the execution of RFI at IL0 must cause an exception. The hardware is so constructed and in that sense, RFI is a privileged instruction.

What is missing from these show-and-tell examples is the set of hooks and handles which interlock the virtual and real machines and the myriad software and hardware tricks for making virtual machine operating systems fast and safe. We do not intend to pursue them further in this text, interesting as the topic is, because it is too wide a digression from our central theme. Nonetheless, it would have been a shame to have so thoroughly pursued the topic of virtual memory without at least hinting at the possibility of virtualizing the other parts of the machine.

CHAPTER SUMMARY

The chapter introduced the concept of memory as a resource to be husbanded and apportioned to allow the computer to handle programs that were larger than the available memory space and to allow more than one application to run concurrently on a single machine. We began with the historically first method of management, which arose when memories were tiny and expensive. It delegated to the user the task of breaking his or her program up into a set of pieces called *overlays*, which the user, with a loader's help, shuffled in and out of memory as needed. In a single-user, single-process machine, this method sufficed to get relatively large programs onto relatively small machines. The first problem with such solutions is that they must be either directed at the smallest machine in the field or tailored at the local site to fit the particular memory at hand. Neither is very viable in today's huge market of highly variable machines. Overlays are also impractical in any environment in which more than one independent application is to be simultaneously in memory. The need for some general solution which was reasonably independent of the program size and memory size led to the development of a number of schemes that permitted programs to coexist in memory without any care or concern by the authors of those programs. The systems which handled the automatic allocation of memory were called *memory management systems*. While these systems varied enormously in their sophistication and in the services they supplied, all shared certain goals, among which would be:

- finding the correct physical address for addresses written at compile time, a time when the physical address is simply unknown and unknowable
- fitting the programs and static data into the physical memory available on the local machine
- providing each application or process the ability to acquire space for dynamic data—stack and heap in the most common programming languages

The methodologies ranged from simple *position-independent code* in which addresses were all relative to the program counter and in which dynamic growth was not supported to *demand-paging virtual memory* systems in which program addresses at compile time have no known relationship to each other or to physical memory and in which the portions of a program that are resident in memory at any one time are variable and unknown. These latter operating systems and their associated hardware provide dynamic growth, dynamic and efficient address translation, and protection services which keep errant programs from hurting those who share the computer with them.

A series of memory division schemes for accomplishing the three objectives were presented. These included:

- pure segmentation
- pure paging
- paged segmentation

Segmentation provided the least costly address translation and memory protection system but suffered rather severely from problems with external fragmentation and abrupt limits on dynamic growth. Paging provided the easiest tools for memory allocation and dynamic growth and did a good if expensive job with address translation and protection. It is possible to combine the methodologies to achieve some of the benefits of both, and although we use a pure paging methodology for the direct management of memory resources, we have adopted a memory management scheme which is at least conceptually very definitely a paged-segment methodology in which each process gets four segments, two of which are intended for dynamic growth.

In all of the operating-system memory management schemes, memory management is done in a manner completely transparent to the user and the application. As far as the process is concerned, when it asks for data or program by VA, the data or instructions arrive. When it puts data back by VA, they can be retrieved by the same VA (even if the PA has changed in the meanwhile). Except for explicit reading or writing of separate data files on disk, the program/user never brings program in from disk or does any form of overlay. And whenever the program needs more stack or asks for more heap, it is always there.

Six different schemes for address translation and protection management were presented, all of which had some commercial application. These included (Figures 4.4 to 4.9)

- pure segmentation
- simple paging
- two-level pagetable
- four-level hierarchical pagetable
- virtual pagetable
- inverted pagetable

Selecting elements from that panoply of techniques, we developed the details of our own memory management scheme. We began by specifying a page of 256 words (1 KB). We selected a three-level hierarchy of pagetables. Each table filled one page, and only the root table had to be kept in memory. The PTE was defined (Figure 4.11). If the page is valid (bit 0 = 1), the PTE contains the physical page address and protection and control bits; if the page is invalid (bit 0 = 0), then a 0 PTE indicates an unassigned page, while any other entry references a disk block.

With these definitions in hand, we first considered an operating system which did *whole-program* management. Programs were loaded in their entirety; they could be swapped out while still active to make room for other waiting processes, but a program was either all in or all out. Paging avoids external fragmentation, but with whole program management, a process can enter the stream or be swapped back in only if there are enough pages on the freelist to accommodate the whole program. The principal weakness in this approach is that large fractions of a whole program are inactive in any time slice of its activity. This means that a large fraction of the memory is storing inactive data.

To improve memory utilization, we turned to *virtual memory* management (VM). Having decided to manage by page rather than by program, we had to weigh the many schemes for page replacement and for setting the *resident-set limit*. Among those considered for fixed-size resident sets were:

- random
- FIFO
- FINUFO
- LRU
- perfect prediction

If one allows the resident-set size to float according to demand, two other schemes suggested themselves. In *working-set replacement* (WSR) one pages out unused pages at regular intervals and adds pages on demand. In *page-fault frequency* management (PFF), processes with a long time between page faults are shrunk by removing all unused pages before their request for a new page is answered. Both are attempts to accomplish the same goal, but WSR requires regular inspection of all processes while PFF depends on page faulting itself to trigger shrinking. WSR is probably more accurate in trimming unused pages but it will cost more in processor time. PFF depends on page faults being frequent enough to serve as a trigger. In all but peculiar cases (e.g., an endless loop with no page faults), that is a pretty good assumption. We adopted PFF for our model.

We chose to simplify our pagetables by limiting each process to a virtual space that could be commanded by a single midtable. That space is 16 MW or 64 KB. In that way, each process had but a single midtable and that table was tagged to be unpageable. The address manipulation which allowed the system access to the process midtable, pagetables, and pages was developed and illustrated in Figure 4.12 (see also Figure IV.4 on page 593).

The last topic that we covered in depth was the simplified PFF page-fault handler. In full detail, we showed the function

- doing a check for an illegal access attempt
- updating on the PFF (or, really, the moving average of the time between page faults)
- paging out all unreferenced pages in the resident set if the PFF was low
- adding the requested page to the resident set:
  if the fault was at the pagetable level, a new pagetable was added
  if the fault was at the page level, a new page was added

The chapter concluded with a brief look at the possibility of virtualizing not only memory but the whole machine. The IBM 370 VM/CMS system was discussed, showing some of the uses of virtualization and why virtualization need not slow down program execution. Applications to a few other machines were considered as well. To make it possible to run our machine in a virtual-machine mode, we made RTI a privileged instruction. This enabled the virtual operating system running at IL0 to execute trap and exception handlers, concluding them as usual with RTI, NOP, NOP, using the exception on RTI to get back to the appropriate place in the instruction stream.

PROBLEMS

4.1. One of the important considerations in choosing a translation scheme is the size of the unpageable tables. Another consideration is the amount of disk traffic that *translation* might entail. Sometimes, to avoid excessive disk traffic, VAX system managers set the process pagetables (PPTs) so that they may not be paged and then limit the length of those tables for each process so that only a modest amount of physical memory is used for process pagetables. Let us consider the implications of such a move. Consider the VAX represented by Figure 4.8. The VAX divides its address space of 4 GB into four regions of 1 GB: P0 (program and heap), P1 (stacks), S0 (system), and S1 (unused). Each PPT is contiguous in VM. The unpageable SPT is contiguous in physical space. Addresses are translated as shown in Figure 4.8 with two provisos:

- The top 2 bits of the address determine the space. Each space has its own base address and length (in register). The top 2 bits are not part of the page number (PN).
- While the rules for address translation are spelled out in Figure 4.8, the tests for a valid address are different in the two P regions. For P0, the PN*4 may not exceed the length; for P1, which grows upward, PN*4 *must* exceed the length.

Let us say that the space allotted to each process in the *system pagetable* is 1 page where each page is 512 bytes long. (This was the allocation at Northeastern University on the VAX 8650 that we used through 1990.) Each PTE in a VAX is 4 bytes long. Determine the maximum total number of pages of program and stack that a process could obtain. Show how to select the base addresses P0BA and P1BA so that the two tables can fill a single, contiguous region in system virtual space with no constraints on the sizes of the two regions except on their sum. Finally, describe how the system could detect a stack:heap crash.

4.2. With reference to Figure 4.8 and the outline of a C program below, write the code to return the correctly translated address for a VA from any of the three allowable segments (0:2). The code should be recursive for VAs in segments 0:1. Do a proper length check before translation. If an address fails in length call `error()` with argument 2. Note that lengths are measured from low address and that segment 1 grows down from high address.

```
typedef unsigned long ADDRESS;

extern ADDRESS pm[];        /* memory modeled as an array of longwords */
extern void error(int);     /* terminates process with prejudice! */

ADDRESS vatopa(ADDRESS va){
```

```
    ADDRESS base[] = {0xB238A598,0xA56D92B4,0x3600,0};
    ADDRESS length[] = {1223,496,4095,0};      /* lengths in longwords */
    ADDRESS pn,pa, offset;
    int index;

    index = va >> 30;   /* values 0 to 3 possible */
    if (index > 2) error(1);
/*************** your code goes here ***************/
    return pa;
    }
```

4.3. With reference to Figure 4.11, develop the logic—PLA or gate logic—to determine if an access violation has occurred. Presume that the logic has the PTE, the seven upper IL bits; and a pair of bits which indicate a fetch, a read, or a write (10, 01, 00 respectively). Assert the error line low if an access violation occurs.

4.4. Let us contribute to the process of waking up our machine by writing the boot routine that makes it possible for the system to use PAs and system VAs. Since this boot routine will run in ROM, we want to keep it short. Let us allocate a contiguous block of PAs to cover the whole translation. For purposes of this problem, let us say that the machine has a 64-MW physical memory.

(a) How many pages of kernel data pagetables will be required to map the VA to PA translations for this size of PM?

(b) How many pages of kernel midtable will be required *just* for the mapping of these data pagetables?

(c) How many entries will be required in the kernel root table to cover the midtable entries of *(b)*?

(d) Write the tiny routine which generates the pagetable entries. Let us start the pagetable space at 00000000. You are to map the entire PM space from 0 to upper bound of PM specified in the problem introduction. (In the real machines, the size of PM can be read by software.) The machine will be running *bare* (no address translation) while your program is doing this job so the addresses that you are writing are PAs.

(e) Now, with the results of *(d)* in hand, extend the routine to build both the midtable and the root table. One item that you will generate and which should be returned by this routine is the PA of the system root table.

4.5. Let us say that the system grabs a page from the freelist to add to the stack of the currently active process. The system VA of the first word in this page (and thus its PA) is 0103C900. When the system sets out to acquire the page, the system knows that process VA which caused the page fault is 00FFFD3C. Pages in the process stack should be w/w for system/process respectively.

(a) How many changes to the pagetables of Figure 4.12 must be made to put this page into the process's domain? Be specific on what those changes are but save specific table entries for *(b)*.

(b) Now, for each of the changes specified in *(a)*, give the specific values that will be entered in the table and say at what address you will deposit each one.

4.6. (With due credit to the author of "As I Was Going to St. Ives.") Consider the VAX instruction which increments a word in indirect stack-relative format (mode B in this case):

```
ADDW2 #1, @16(SP)     ; note that this is mode B.
```

This instruction occupies 4 bytes. Since the VAX does not require one to keep things word-aligned, anything longer than 1 byte can be split between two pages; conversely, anything shorter than 258 bytes can be split at most over two pages. This includes any VA at all, whether pagetable, instruction, stack, or data. However, PTs are guaranteed to be long-word-aligned. The question is:

(a) Considering the worst possible case, how many page faults can this one specific instruction evoke? (*Hint:* Build a tree of the memory references.)

(b) Of course, everything needed could be in the several caches. The two extremes suggest a comparison of execution times. If a page fault takes 100 ms to retrieve the page, a memory reference 200 ns, a cache reference 50 ns, and the instruction execution for this instruction 100 ns, what are the extremes of the real time that this one instruction could require for completion?

4.7. Consider the following sequence of page references:

ABACDCABEBFBEGHBACDIJCBKLBABEGHBACDIJCBKLBA

Take four pages as the resident set for each of the replacement algorithms you are asked to check and use a purely local replacement strategy. Begin by finding the *perfect prediction replacement number* by using your ability to look into the future of this sequence. Then report the result as a fraction of this perfect page number (perfect page number/actual page number). Determine this ratio for:

(a) random replacement (any method for generating random numbers will do, but run it a few times to be sure that you have reasonable statistics)

(b) FIFO without caching

(c) FIFO with a cache of one page

(d) FINUFO without caching

(e) FINUFO with a cache of one page

(f) LRU without caching

(g) LRU with a cache of 1

4.8. Write the function

```
void enqueue(struct page_ID *dest, struct page_ID *item);
```

which was defined for `page_fault()` assuming that it deals with a FIFO list.

REFERENCES

Operating systems textbooks

[Deitel, 83] Deitel, H.M., *An Introduction to Operating Systems*, Addison-Wesley (1983). Good coverage of memory management (Chapters 7-9) and VM/370 (Chapter 22).

[Finkel, 88] Finkel, R.A., *An Operating Systems Vade Mecum*, 2nd ed., Prentice-Hall (1988). Somewhat easier to read than the other textbooks.

[Maekawa, 87] Maekawa, M., A. Oldehoeft, and R. Oldehoeft, *Operating Systems—Advanced Concepts*, Benjamin-Cummings (1987). This book should be read only after one of the others. Chapter 5 summarizes research results on virtual memory.

[Milenkovic, 87] Milenkovic, M., *Operating Systems, Concepts and Design*, McGraw-Hill (1987). Chapters 6 and 7 cover memory management and virtual memory.

Descriptions of actual operating systems

[Bach, 86] Bach, M.J., *The Design of the UNIX Operating System*, Prentice-Hall (1986). This is the best publicly available description of the algorithms used in the AT&T UNIX kernel, and it is very readable.

[Kenah, 88] Kenah, L.J., R.E. Goldenberg, and S.F. Bate, *VAX/VMS Internals and Data Structures*, Version 4.4, Digital Press (1988). An extremely detailed description of VMS, but not easy to read.

[Leffler, 89] Leffler, S.J, M.K. McKusick, M.J. Karels, and J.S. Quarterman, *The Design and Implementation of the 4.3BSD UNIX Operating System*, Addison-Wesley (1989). A description similar to [Bach, 86] of the Berkeley version of UNIX.

[Organick, 72] Organick, E.I., *The Multics System: An Examination of Its Structure*, MIT Press (1972). A detailed description of Multics and the GE645 computer, including the segmentation mechanism and the hardware to support it.

[Quarterman, 85] Quarterman, J.S., A. Silberschatz, and J.L.Peterson, *4.2BSD and 4.3BSD as examples of the UNIX System*, **Computing Surveys 17** (4): 379-418 (1985). A good description of the clock algorithm used for paging on the VAX.

Memory management and virtual memory

[Denning, 68] Denning, P.J., *The Working Set Model for Program Behavior*, **CACM 11**: 323-333 (1968).

[Denning, 80] Denning, P.J., *Working Sets Past and Present*, **IEEE Transactions on Software Engineering SE-6**: 64-84 (1980).

[Furht, 87] Furht, B., and V. Milutinovic, *A Survey of Microprocessor Architectures for Memory Management*, **Computer 20**(3): 48-67 (1987). Reprinted in slightly different form in *IEEE Tutorial on Computer Architecture*.

[Goldberg, 74] Goldberg, R.P., *Survey of Virtual Machine Research*, **Computer 7** (6): 34-45 (1974).

[Hester, 86] Hester, P.D., R.O. Simpson, and A. Chang, *The IBM RT PC ROMP and Memory Management Unit Architecture*, **IBM RT Personal Computer Technology**, IBM SA23-1057 (1986). Reprinted in *IEEE Tutorial on Reduced Instruction Set Computers*.

[Levy, 82] Levy, H.M., and P. Lipman, *Virtual Memory Management in the VAX/VMS Operating System*, **Computer 15** (3): 35-41 (1982). Reprinted in *IEEE Tutorial on Software Oriented Computer Architecture*.

[Levy, 89] Levy, H.M., and R.H. Eckhouse, Jr., *Computer Programming and Architecture: The VAX*, 2nd ed., Digital Press (1989). Chapter 12 covers many of the same topics that we have pursued but from the perspective of the VAX/VMS operating system.

[Rachid, 87] Rachid, R., et al., *Machine-Independent Virtual Memory Management for Paged Uniprocessor and Multiprocessor Architectures*, **Proceedings of the Second International Conference on Architectural Support for Programming Languages and Operating Systems (ASPLOS-II)**, 31-39 (1987). Describes memory management in the MACH operating system and compares the hardware memory management mechanisms of various machines.

CHAPTER 5

THE DESIGN OF LOCAL MEMORY

A BIRD IN THE HAND

5.1 OBJECTIVE

In Figure 1.1 we show a computer layout containing two *caches*. In Chapters 3 and 4 we talked about *caching* in discussions of operations as disparate as address translation and reads or writes to disk. The time has come to define what we mean by a cache in the ultimate engineering sense—by designing one. We have chosen the data cache of Figure 1.1 as our target. The cache is intimately connected to address translation and protection. A most sensible approach is to design both the cache and the MMU together. That is what we shall do in this chapter. This is the first of our four hardware chapters.

A cache memory is a small, fast memory which should contain "the most frequently accessed words" from a larger, slower memory. The idea of a hierarchy of memories, with memory speed and memory size being the tradeoffs, was discussed explicitly in John von Neumann's report on the design of the EDVAC. Essentially, the idea was there right from the beginning. The "slower" memory may only appear to be slower because of competition for the communication channel (the *von Neumann bottleneck*) or it may be inherently slow (disk or tape). Whatever the reason, standing in line waiting for data transfers gets old very quickly. As early as the 1960s, CPU speeds could exceed *core memory* speeds by a factor of 10. Perhaps the earliest proposal for what we would today call a cache is found in [Bloom, 62]. The idea quickly took hold. To get around the inherent disparity in speed between CPU and memory, both the 360/370 design group at IBM and the 6600 design group at CDC developed methods for acquiring instructions at speeds which matched the CPU's swiftness. The regularity and linearity of programs allowed both companies to interleave memory modules so that a request for one instruction could elicit not only that instruction but a long string of its successors from adjacent modules. In the IBM 360/91, the CPU cycle was 60 ns while the core memory rumbled along at 780 ns. The interleave factor was 16! Were memory response and not bus bandwidth the limit, the interleave factor would provide the needed speedup. While interleaving matched the delivery speed to the CPU, it left the designer with the problem of providing fast temporary storage for the sudden dose of data. That local store had to be constructed from the same sort of components as the CPU—class-A or unsaturated electronics. This made the storage very expensive, very hot, and very fast. The cost and heat constrained the designer to use as little of this superfast memory as possible, but another factor said: "Do not make it too small." This other factor was the high frequency of small loops in most programs. If the whole loop could reside in this local memory, the program could avoid:

- the up-front addressing delay of starting each block of instructions from memory
- the energy (heat dissipation) inherent in core memory accesses
- the bus traffic to repetitively fetch the loop instructions

The team at CDC used this local store for instructions, visualizing what they were doing as hanging on to the last few instructions in case they were useful again. The local instruction store was called a *look-backward buffer* in contrast to Bloom et al.'s name, *look-aside buffer.* At almost the same time, IBM introduced a local memory for data and instructions into the IBM 360/85. It was first named a *muffer* (for *memory buffer*) by Donald Gibson, but no one liked that name. In search of a better name, Lyle Johnson, the editor of the *IBM Systems Journal*, went to a thesaurus. *Cache* is the name which emerged and swept all other candidates before it [Pugh, 91] [Conti, 69].

In most cases the words in cache memory are copies of words in a larger memory. The principal function of the cache is to make these copies accessible more quickly. This sounds like a simple idea, but caches are neither entirely simple nor obvious. The problems which must be addressed form the matter of this chapter; they are:

- how to tell which words will be needed most frequently (cache replacement policy)
- how to fetch data into the cache
- how to arrange access to the data in cache (addressing)
- how or whether to deal with virtual addresses
- how to keep cached data consistent with memory data

A central theme of RISC philosophy, "Do not do forever in hardware what you could do effectively once in software," suggests that we look first to solutions to these problems in software. This may sound strange, but compilers normally decide which information will be kept in the CPU's registers. A compiler should try to keep *the most frequently used data* there. This makes cache manipulation sound like the register allocation problem once removed. In some restricted circumstances, a compiler can do the cache allocation job quite expertly. For example, compilers often can predict how much stack space will be needed by each procedure, which makes it relatively easy to design a cache memory for the stack. The cache allocation is controlled by the software when procedures are called and when they return [Ditzel, 82] [Ditzel, 87a] [Ditzel, 87b] [Eickemeyer, 88] [Stanley, 87]. In fact, the MORS described in Section 1.4.2 on page 38 is a register version of software-controlled storage allocation.

While there is certainly some appeal to moving cache control over to software, a major practical engineering issue pushes most cache designs in the other direction. Commercial history teaches that if a design is successful, it undoubtedly will have successors whose user architecture remains the same. The VAX, IBM 370, Motorola 680x0, and Intel 80x86 are clear cases in point. One item that undergoes frequent upgrading in successive generations and variations among the models is the cache. The repeat customer buys these upgrades with the perfectly reasonable expectation that currently operational software will remain operational. He or she will not care if the new machine requires an upgrade in the operating system, but if payroll, accounts receivable, and the critical data base applications do not walk comfortably from old machine to new, the user may buy elsewhere. In most cases, the users do not have the application source code. They simply cannot recompile. Even where recompilation is possible, if hardware changes must be accommodated by software updates, remarkable bugs can be expected to float to the surface. Software manufacturers undertake such upgrades with trepidation and only because customers expect their software to work. Customers don't want to hear about compilation or about bugs. It was this very independence of the software from the underlying engine that empowered it which led IBM to appropriate the word *architecture* to describe those programming features which would remain ever constant and compatible as the engine continued to evolve. It is thus no surprise to find that most cache memories rely on hardware to decide what to keep in the cache and to control the cache's operation.

In this chapter we will describe some of the organizations used for cache memory. Then we will see how various factors influence performance. Finally we will design the data cache of our RISC machine. Let us begin by looking more closely at the principle of locality of reference.

5.2 REFERENCING DATA IN A CACHE

5.2.1 Locality of Reference

A central pillar in Chapter 4 was that the addresses generated by programs normally exhibit a set of properties know as *locality of reference*. Addresses tend to be clustered. They tend to be clustered in several ways:

- Because programs often contain loops which produce very similar sequences of addresses over and over again, they exhibit *temporal locality*; that is, addresses which occurred in the recent past tend to occur again.
- Since procedures have their instructions clustered together and usually refer to data structures that are stored close together, they also exhibit *spatial locality*; addresses tend to occur which are close to addresses that have occurred previously.

- The two combine to exhibit *sequentiality*; when address n occurs, address $n+1$ is likely to occur in the near future. Sequentiality has two obvious causes: the instructions in a program are usually fetched sequentially, and arrays are often accessed sequentially.

Temporal locality suggests caching words which have been used recently. Spatial locality suggests transferring a block of information, rather than just one word. This, of course, was precisely what UNIX was doing in Chapter 3 when it brought in and cached the successor to a block requested from disk. Finally, sequentiality suggests that if word n is requested by the CPU, reading word $n+1$ from the main memory into the cache will be beneficial. Real cache memory systems use some or all of these techniques. The success of each form of look-ahead or look-backward will depend quite strongly on the application that is running and the size of the cache. After we have discussed the general design of cache memories, you will be able to understand the alternatives that are possible and the tradeoffs involved.

5.2.2 Associative Memory

The information in the cache will be a subset of the information in the main memory. In memory, at least conceptually, each datum has a unique address. If these same data map from a large memory into a small cache, there must be a multiplicity of memory addresses mapping into one cache address. How can we identify which words are in the cache? If the cache were used to contain one contiguous block of addresses, it would be fairly easy to identify it from its starting address. In fact, were we to require the block to start on a convenient boundary, we could identify it simply by the upper address bits, as is done in the CRISP stack cache [Ditzel, 82] [Ditzel, 87a] [Ditzel, 87b]. The stack, of course, is both small and programmatically unique. In general, locality has its limits. For any particular system and application, one can generally define a best block size for caching. Many parameters enter into determining the optimum. Particularly important are:

- the cost of starting a transfer from the large memory to the cache
- the cost of holding onto the bus
- the cost of storing unwanted or low-use data in the cache

Cost is a general description for the pain and suffering or delays caused to other operations. The numbers can be wildly different for different systems. For example, it is quite right and proper to hang onto a peripheral bus, such as a SCSI bus, for milliseconds, while a few microseconds of unavailability on the main bus of Figure 1.1 can cause calamitous delays for I/O chips such as ethernet adapters. The allowable range of transfers—the block size—for a cache such as those shown in Figure 1.1 range between 1 and 16 words.

It is important to be able to visualize the cache as a small set of blocks where any block in the cache maps to many blocks in the much larger main memory. The mapping may be orderly or essentially random—*if you have a club, put it in this slot* versus *if you have a card, put it in a slot.* We will consider examples of both organizations. A cache of any considerable size will contain many unrelated blocks. How then can the hardware know if a particular address identifies data now resident in the cache? "Does anyone have the 2 of hearts?"

For our first example, let us consider a random arrangement in the cache—any card in any slot. Assume that the main memory contains 16 MB of dynamic RAM (DRAM) and the cache contains 64 KB of fast static RAM (SRAM), or 16 KW. Let us presume a block size of 1 word. In the deck-of-cards example, we might select 8 random cards from the deck of 52, holding them in whatever order we happen to have selected them. The question to be answered is: If I need the 5 of spades, is it in the cache? Obviously, we could answer that question by looking at the faces of the 8 cards in the cache. Such a labeling scheme is called *content-addressable memory.* So how do we put faces on memory data? Since each of the 16,384 words could have come from anywhere in the main memory, we have to store an address identifier with each of them. The most obvious *face* is the address. It must be stored along with the word itself.

A cache is useful only if it is fast. When the CPU wants to read a word from a given address, the cache must compare each address in the cache to see if one of them matches the requested address. To be useful, it must complete this search and deliver the data in a time that is short compared to the orderly access to directly addressable memory.

The cache certainly cannot afford to look through its slots one at a time. That would take too long. To be competitive, it will have to do all of the comparisons at the same time. Consider coming to your 30th high school reunion. You see someone you have not laid eyes on for 30 years. He is now bald and paunchy and yet you can say: "Hey, George! How've ya been?" The subtle clues to Georgeness allow you to do a broad, parallel memory search and come up essentially in real time with an identification from an enormous array of possible choices. Clearly, your brain did not do that by serially comparing the data you are confronting with all data acquired in 48 years. Somehow, you are able to *associate* the characteristics you are observing quite directly with the data corresponding to George, lo these 30 years ago. Brains are clearly better at this than computers. How then would such an associative search be done in relatively simple hardware?

The logical organization for such a search is shown in Figure 5.1. This structure is called an *associative memory.* It is clearly *content-addressable memory,* with the content being the address. For each word kept in the cache, an address and a *valid bit* are also stored. A set of comparators is provided to check all stored addresses against the requested address. When a comparator indicates a valid match, it is called a *hit.* In that case, the datum is transferred to the output. The data replacement mechanism must guarantee that there will never be more than one hit at a time. (There are more general forms of associative memory, used for other purposes, which allow multiple hits.)

A miss requires that we obtain the word from the main memory. It will take longer to obtain the word, so some mechanism has to be provided to tell the CPU to wait. When the word is obtained from the main memory, it is given to the CPU and also

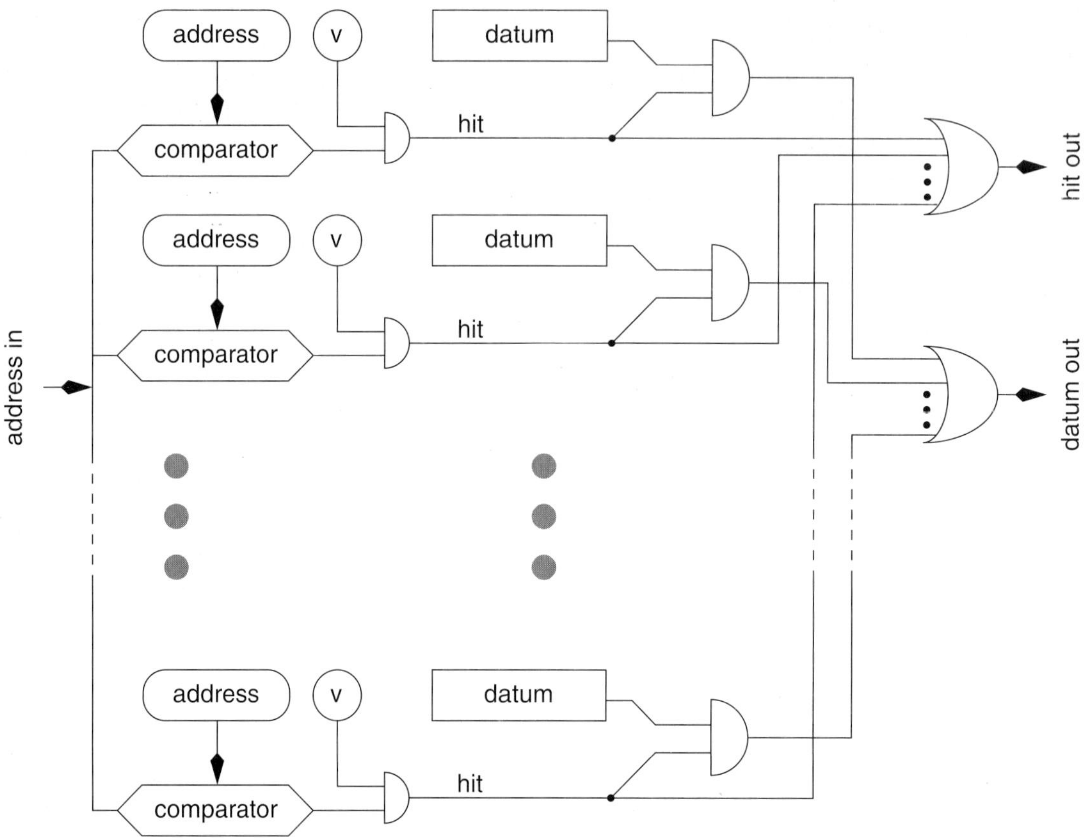

FIGURE 5.1 The logic of a fully associative memory. Each datum is stored with its address and a *valid* bit. If an address matches the *address in* and the valid bit for that datum is set, then one has a hit and that datum is presented at the output. It is up to the replacement hardware to guarantee that there are never two valid entries with the same address. The mechanism for data replacement is not shown.

written into one of the cache locations with its address. Ah, but where shall we put it? If one of the address-data pairs in the cache is unused, that would be a good place to store something, but in most cases they will all be used. While the object is to replace the pair which is least likely to be needed in the future, a sure mechanism for picking that place is anything but obvious. We take up that issue in Section 5.3.2.

A more serious problem with the organization in Figure 5.1 is how to build it. The data registers form a more-or-less conventional memory. There is excellent technology for building very compact and rather large, fast memories. But the address registers and comparators do not fit in these schemes. If we want to include a small cache in a custom integrated circuit, we could build this kind of associative memory, but it just isn't practical for scaling to large sizes. Somehow we have to find a way to remove those comparators from the memory. In fact, we would really like to reduce drastically the amount of hardware per datum. Let us consider being a bit more orderly.

5.2.3 Direct-Mapped Cache

The associative memory has a comparator tied to each address because any address could be in any location. A simple way of avoiding all of those comparators is to restrict the possible places where a given address could be stored. Maximum specificity would map each address in the main memory to a particular location in the cache. Many addresses will map into one location, but any specific address requires only one test. Consider our cache of playing cards of Section 5.2.2. An example of this one-to-one mapping would be to reserve the first space in the cache for clubs between 2 and 7. Note that 6 cards are mapping into one cache location. Only 1 of 6 may reside there at a time. If you insert the 4 and then draw the 6 of clubs, you must put back the 4. The *replacement policy* is simply "last to arrive gets it." Figure 5.2 is a block diagram for this kind of cache.

This layout of the *direct-mapped* cache is general, basic, and widely used. Let us explore how it works by considering structure, loading data into that structure, searching for a datum from the structure and finally, should we need to, invalidating the data in the cache:

- *Structure of the cache.* The figure shows eight rows. Any integer power of 2 would do, but the rest of the example will assume 8. Each row has room to store 4 words of data, one *tag* and one valid bit. The 4 words of data are not just any 4; they are contiguous in memory. The tag identifies which large block of memory this particular line was extracted from. The same tag can appear in any or all rows, as shown in the figure. Note that the full address is there; some bits are determined by position in the cache and the rest are in the tag.
- *Loading data into the cache.* Whenever a search of the cache misses, whether because the tags do not match or the data is invalid, a whole row or *line* is replaced. If we assume a 32-bit address and 4 words in a row, then whenever the memory management unit goes to memory, it uses only the top 30 bits and fetches all 4 words with those 30 bits as the upper part of the address. The 4 words are brought in in order, the valid bit is set, and the tag field is replaced with the upper 27 bits of the address.
- *Searching for a datum.* The address of the desired datum is broken into three fields. The lowest 2 bits specify which of the 4 words in (any) row is desired. Those 2 bits go to control the data MUX. The next lowest 3 bits specify the row. They go to the cache structure to select both data and tag. Note that this is a regular memory operation in the sense of addressing a particular line of bits in a large array of lines. The tag in the selected row is compared with the tag of the address. If they match and the valid bit is set, we have a hit. The data emerging from the MUX is valid.
- *Invalidating the cache.* If the addresses in a process are not unique to that process—for example, if you were using virtual addresses with no attached process tag—then the operating system would be obliged to "flush" the cache on a context switch. The structure shown in Figure 5.2 makes this easy to do. A single reset line is attached to the entire column of valid bits. The system simply "writes" to that memory-mapped line. All the bits will reset together. They will be set one-by-one as the new process loads blocks of words into the lines.

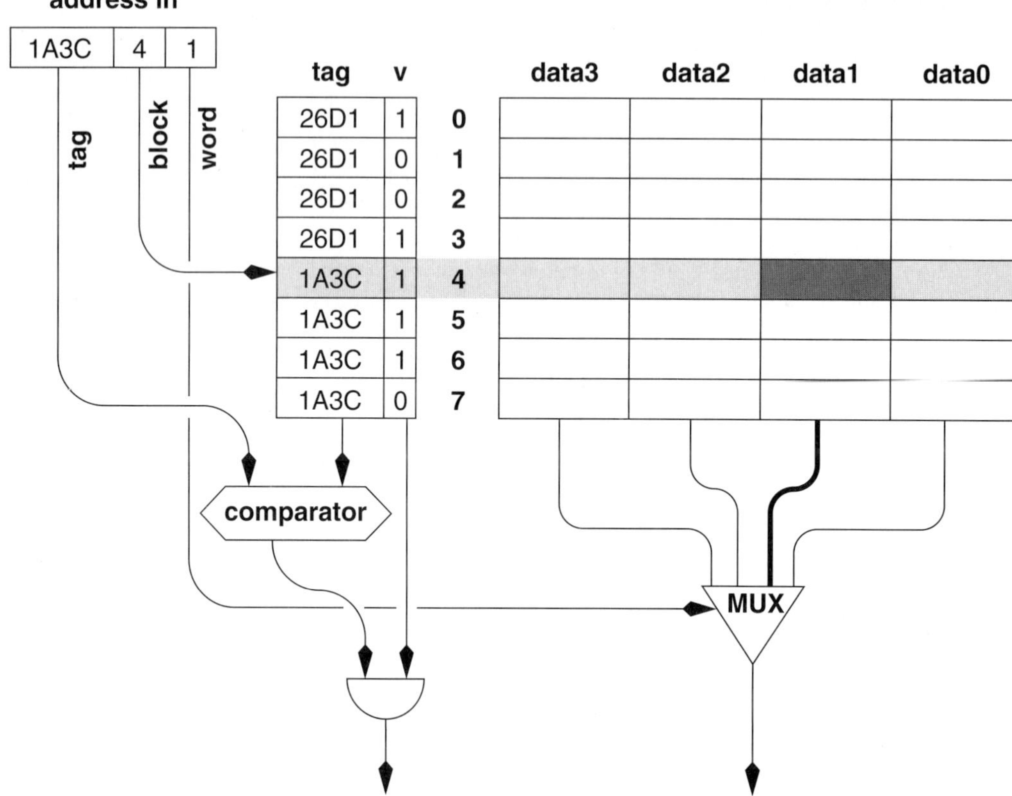

FIGURE 5.2 A direct-mapped cache. The uppermost 27 bits serve as the tag for any address. In the example illustrated, the binary value of the *address in* is

00000000000 0001 1010 0011 1100 | 100 | 01.

The middle field—block—selects row 4. The tag in row 4 is compared with the tag in the address while the data in the row is moved to the MUX. The low-order 2 bits of the address select *data1*. The *hit* line is asserted because the tags match and the *v* (valid) bit is set. Accordingly, the data out is valid.

Using low-order address bits to select the lines optimizes the cache for spatial locality of reference. During a short interval of time addresses will be fairly close together. Their tags will be the same while their lower address bits will be roughly sequential. By using the lower address bits to place words in the cache, we tend to scatter the data uniformly around the available cache locations. If the cache is large enough to contain a loop or hierarchy of loops, the data and instructions will all be able to reside in the cache at once. These data would not be constantly replacing each other.

The method that we just described is *direct-mapped* in the sense that each address maps to only one location. Hardware is simple—both tags and data can use conventional RAMs—and since data fetching and tag comparison can proceed in parallel, the cache can be very fast. For reasonably large caches, direct-mapping proves to be an optimum organization in the sense of giving very good performance at minimal cost. It is widely used. However, not all cache needs are well served by a direct-mapped configuration. In particular, the problem of caching address translations is often best solved by another configuration.

What happens on a miss? In that case, the MMU will have to read the data from the main memory. When the data comes back, the MMU must write it into the data RAMs, put the upper address bits into the tag RAMs, set the valid bit, and deliver the datum requested to the CPU.

Going to main memory entails several somewhat unpredictable delays. First the MMU must contend for the bus with all other devices using the main memory. Once it has won control of the bus, it must send an address and then wait for memory to decode that address and deliver the data. This same up-front cost will be paid whether the MMU interrogates one memory bank or four. If the main memory is interleaved or simply wider than one word, it can deliver several words in just a little more time than it would take for one word. Because of spatial locality and sequentiality, we can reasonably expect that those extra words will be referenced in the near future. The high payoff in getting four-for-the-price-of-one is the reason why we have four words on each line in Figure 5.2. The set of words read together into the cache is called either a *block* or a *line*.

The block diagram shows four banks of RAMs with their outputs multiplexed. If there are operations where whole lines are moved together, such as on a 128-bit-wide bus, this is the fastest organization of the cache RAM. If words are the sole unit of exchange, then a much less expensive implementation would be to use data RAMs four times as large as the tag RAMs, effectively including the multiplexor inside the data RAMs. Thus, the tag RAM would be a 4K memory while the data RAM would be 16K. The 2 word-selector bits would be included with the 12 line-selector bits to form the 14-bit address into the data RAM. Only the datum desired is delivered. As an alternative to building the structure of Figure 5.2, an integrated circuit is available which includes tag memory and comparator in a single package. It has provision for clearing all of the tags to flush the cache. There are 4K $\times$ 4 tag SRAMs available from several companies, with access times from 5 to 25 ns. For a tag plus valid-bit totaling 9 bits, we would require 3 of these to implement the 4K tag store for our 64-KB cache.

While it is always possible to write a program which deliberately trashes any cache strategy, one must ask just how likely it is that a natural program might not work well with a particular design. The problem with the direct-mapped cache, particularly if the cache is small, is that it is not uncommon for programs to jump back and forth between a pair of routines. If those routines happen to map into the same area of the cache, each run of one routine will displace all or part of the other. This is one of several similar memory interactions called *thrashing*. If the cache is small, thrashing is much more likely. If it is large, thrashing will occur with low enough frequency to make us indifferent to it. But what if the cache is or must be small? Our next arrangement will provide better performance.

5.2.4 Set-Associative Cache

Let us consider rearranging the cache of Figure 5.2 to provide some resistance to thrashing. Instead of having a single block in each line in the cache, let us endow each line with room enough for several blocks—a *set* of blocks. Typical arrangements will have set sizes of 2 or 4. Within the set of 2 or 4 on each line, we will do an associative search; any data block may be in any of the 2 or 4 locations. Since there will be only a small number of tags in the set, we will need only a small number of comparators. We still will have a large number of directly addressed lines, but each line will now have 2 or 4 blocks. We will get some of the advantages of a fully associative cache at only a modest increase in complexity over a direct-mapped cache. Such an organization is called a *set-associative* cache. Let us see how this cache is constructed, loaded, searched and flushed.

Figure 5.3 shows the typical arrangement of a two-way set-associative cache. Each main memory address is mapped into a set containing two possible spaces for it. Each line now contains a set of two blocks. The line containing the blocks and the word within each block are still selected by the low-order address bits, just as in the direct-mapped cache. In fact, the direct-mapped cache is the limiting case, a set-associative cache with a set size of 1. A common mistake is to say that the system in Figure 5.3 has two sets, one on the left and one on the right. The *set* is the collection of data on one horizontal line of the figure. The *set size* is 2 blocks; the number of sets in the figure is 8.

- *Structure of the cache.* The data-storage portion and the MUXs of the set-associative cache can still be constructed out of a single block of fast SRAM chips. For our 64-KB or 16-KW example, alternatives for addressing are shown in Figure 5.4. The principal differences between the set-associative cache and the direct-mapped cache are the creation of two parallel tag memories; the column of LRU bits used in the replacement mechanism; and hardware for sorting out if a cache hit has been achieved for any of the blocks in the set selected. The hardware, with some small assistance from the software (principally doing a cache flush on bootup) must assure that there is never more than one hit within the set.
- *Loading data into the cache.* On a cache miss, a block of data is brought in from memory and placed in the appropriate line or set, occupying the block indicated by the LRU bit. If the LRU bit is set, the block goes on the left. Upon loading new data, the valid bit for the block selected is set (it may already be set) and the LRU bit inverted.
- *Searching for a datum in the cache.* The selection of a line and word using the low-order bits of the address is essentially identical to the direct-mapped scheme. If a hit is obtained, the correct bank is selected and the word delivered. Whenever a hit is obtained, the LRU bit for the line selected is set if the hit was on the right side and reset if the hit was on the left side. In this way, the LRU bit points to the *least-recently used block.* Note that if neither valid bit is set, the replacement will be random since the LRU bit will be pointing wherever it was left when there was last valid data in the cache. This fits the model of the purely associative cache where a datum

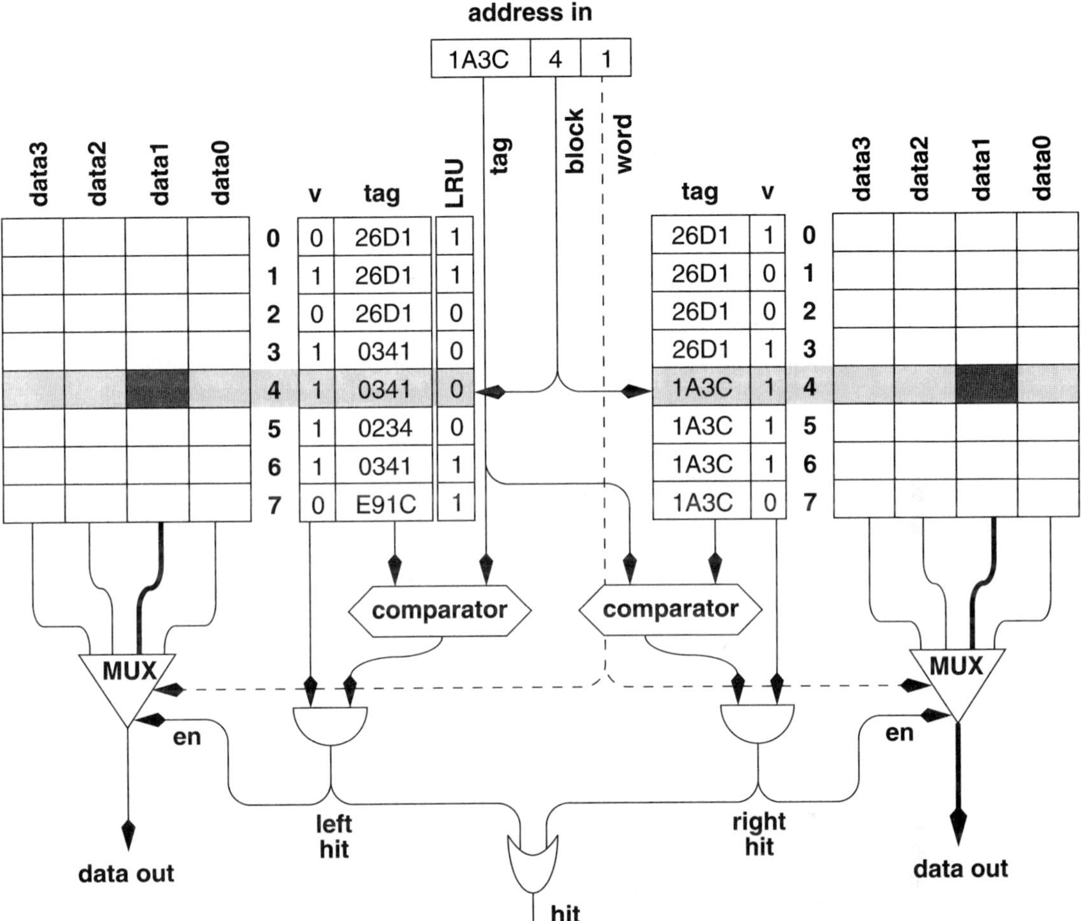

FIGURE 5.3 Organization of a *two-way set-associative cache.* This arrangement is logically a pair of the direct-mapped caches of Figure 5.2 with several additions to ensure that at most one side can respond. These small additions include an OR of the *hit* lines to determine if a hit has been achieved; putting an *enable* or *three-state* on the MUXs to permit the two MUX outputs to be tied together; and the additions of a *least-recently-used* (LRU) bit for each row. The LRU bit is used on a miss to determine which side of the whole line is to be replaced. As discussed in the text, the replacement scheme ensures that there is never a simultaneous hit on both sides.

can go anywhere. However, once loaded, the replacement scheme is deterministic, depending completely on the history of memory references made by the current process.

- *Invalidating the cache.* The cache-flush operation is essentially identical to that employed in the direct-mapped cache. The only addition is having two lines of valid bits to reset rather than one. No modification of the LRU bits is necessary on a cache flush. Since both sides of the cache are always flushed together, the process is indifferent to the placement of the first block in row.

While we have been busily differentiating three different organizations of caches, it is worthwhile to note that the set-associative cache includes both of the other organizations as limiting cases. When the set size is one, we have a direct-mapped cache; when all of the words are in the same set, we have a fully associative cache.

The two addressing schemes of Figure 5.4 present an interesting design issue. The scheme on the left of that figure clearly is more expensive. Doubling the number of chips is expensive in board area, chip cost and power dissipation. That would seem to bias a designer inevitably to choose the single-bank design. Such a choice could come back to haunt the designer who accepted that analysis too quickly. In the scheme on the left, the address for the cache chips is available as soon as the address is available. The decoding for the data can begin simultaneously with the decoding for the stored tags. In the scheme on the right, you have the peculiar problem that the address is not fully developed until the *left-hit* bit has been determined. This prevents the decoding of the

FIGURE 5.4 Two alternative addressing schemes for the data portion of the cache of Figure 5.3. On the right, a single bank of eight 4 ×16K RAMs stores both blocks in the set. The *left-hit* line from Figure 5.3 becomes the third least significant bit in the 14-bit cache address. The *hit* line serves as the enable line for a cache read. In the scheme on the left, two banks of memory chips are used, one for the left block and one for the right. Selection is based on the *left-hit* and *right-hit* lines. With the banks separately selected, only the 13 low-order bits from the memory address are used to address the cache. For both schemes, positive logic is used on the enable lines. In real life, they will almost inevitably be asserted low. The read/write line is not shown.

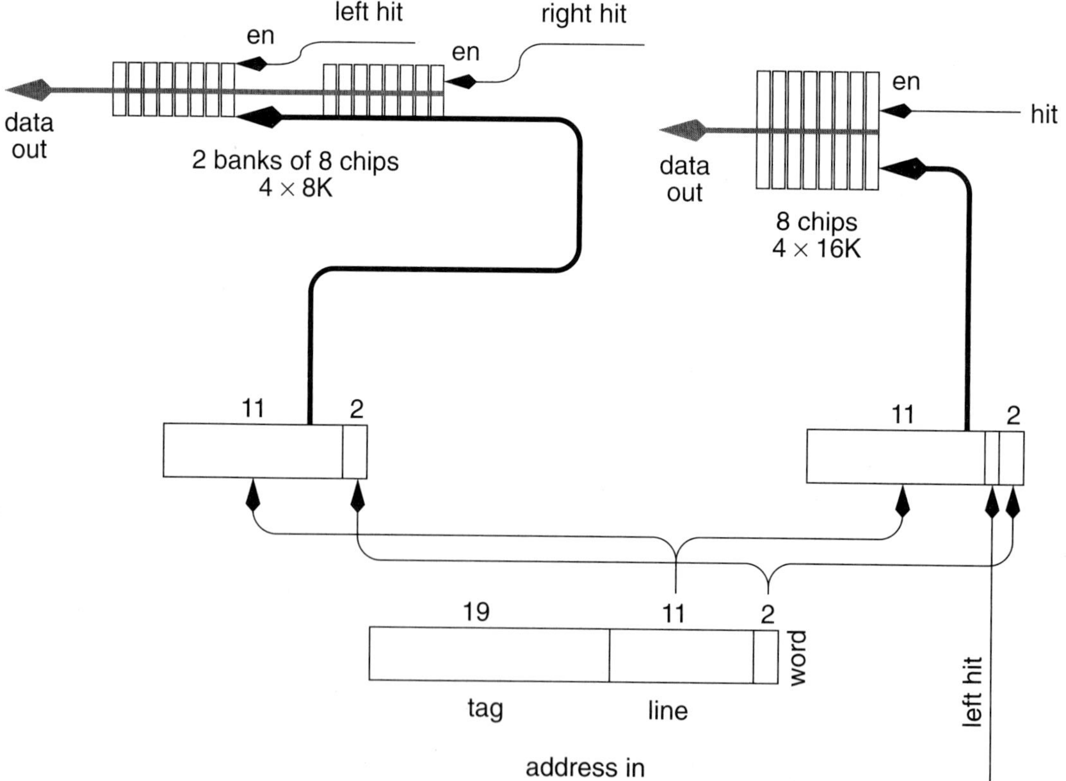

cache address until after the stored tags have been located and the selected tags compared with the address tag field. This serialization of the decodes will require that the decoders on the right be roughly twice as fast as the decoders on the left. The cache must meet very stringent restrictions on response timing. Very fast memory chips tend to be both expensive and hot. Accordingly, without a case-specific analysis of the chips available, you cannot dismiss the faster but bigger organization on the left. Of course, as soon as two banks became the method of choice, chip makers made memory chips with two banks in one chip. That makes the choice very easy.

Economies of integration do come into play both for address decoding and in comparing the direct-mapped with the set-associative organizations. The set-associative scheme requires as many tag stores as it has members of a set. Since all the factors except raw speed favor more bits per chip, the division required for the set-associative tag stores is painful. It is not surprising, then, to discover that as soon as the cache grows large enough that the performance of the direct-mapped cache is not severely impacted by thrashing, designers choose direct mapping. In Section 5.3 we will look at the factors which enter this choice. For the moment, however, let us add a scheme which specifically addresses the issue of minimizing the number of "extra bits" that it takes to store a given amount of data in a cache. This will give as fourth scheme, the *sector-organized* cache.

5.2.5 Sector-Organized Caches

One of the problems with all of the cache organizations we have presented is that a significant amount of storage is required for tags. If memory cells are expensive, either in price or chip area, we would like to be able to use most of them for actual data. Increasing the block size allows us to use a larger fraction of the total cache storage for data, but it turns a block transfer into a major event. In most circumstances, the system cannot permit any single user of the system bus to hold the bus for longer than 1 to 2 μs. That limits the practical size of a single transfer to 16 words or less. (As busses get wider, it would seem that this limit would go up, but generally, as busses get wider—and they are already at 64 and 128 bits—they get wider to get the same data through them in less time. The IBM RS/6000 uses these wider busses and stretches to 32 words in a block.) To get around the blocksize limit, one could load less than a block at a time. That will require more valid bits to keep track of what is valid in each block of the cache, but valid bits are much smaller than tags. This is the principle behind our last cache organization—the sector-organized cache.

The sector-organized cache is not a new idea. In the good old days, bits were expensive. For those rare early machines which had caches, such as the one in the IBM 360/85 [Liptay, 68], *sector organization* reduced the bits needed for tag storage. Interestingly, this type of cache is becoming popular again for on-chip caches, where the area that can be devoted to cache functions is strictly limited. A typical sector-organized cache is illustrated in Figure 5.5.

The operation is not unlike the direct-mapped cache except that there is an extra layer in the addressing hierarchy, now comprising sector, block, and word. The tag is associated with the sector; the valid bit with the block.

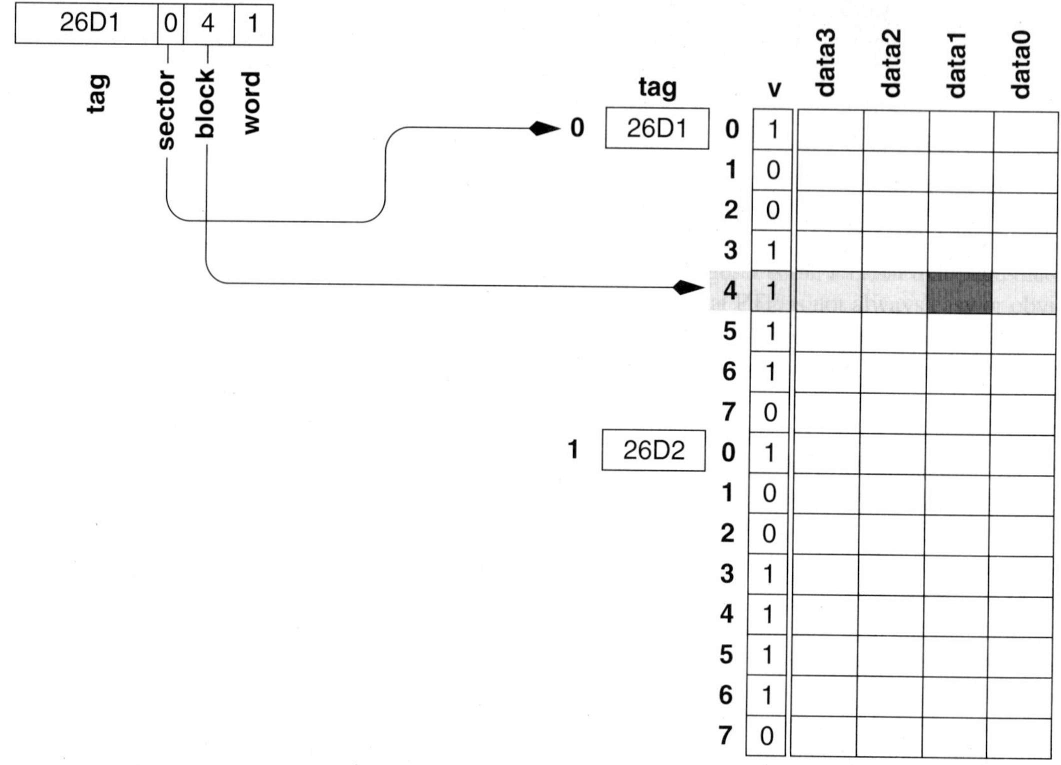

FIGURE 5.5 The sector-organized cache. Compare this to Figure 5.3 where the same number of words (64) requires 16 tags. Note that the valid bits are part of the data line.

This organization reduces the fraction of space required for tags simply by increasing the number of data words associated with each tag. However, it does not increase the delay during misses, because only a single block must be fetched from the main memory, not the entire sector. This saving in tag storage is not entirely free. Upon entering a new sector, an entire sector's worth of cache must be invalidated. This means that a fraction of the data RAMs will be empty, with that fraction being highly dependent on the spatial and temporal locality of the program. In effect we gain efficiency in the tag store at the cost of wasting some of the space in the data RAMs.

The reason that sector organization fell out of favor was that tag storage became cheap. If you could get all of the tags that you wanted in one chip, the cost was *one chip*. That encourages thinking big. As the caches and tags move onto the CPU chip, you are back to the situation of the 1960s where the discrete devices are once again in the designers' hands. While bits are still cheap, there is always such competition for applying those bits to a variety of enhancements that shrinking the number used for tag storage may well pay off in some design factor totally unrelated to caching. Evaluating such issues is complicated and tends to be unique to each specific design. What we can do, however, is develop some tools for evaluating cache performance. With these tools, you can quantify how much better cache performance you will get with design A versus design B.

5.3 EVALUATING CACHE MEMORY PERFORMANCE

Most cache memories are built with one of the organizations described in the previous sections. The entire group comprises variations of the set-associative cache, so we ought to be able to compare performances on a common basis. If all these caches are *set associative*, the parameters normally available to the designer include:

- set size in blocks
- block size
- number of sets
- addressing (physical vs. virtual, process-tagged, etc.)

Since the purpose of a cache is to speed up access to the data and since all design is done with constraints such as cost and heat dissipation, we want to evaluate alternatives in terms of the speed of the cache and the cost. Let us begin with speed.

If the total time to access (read) a word from the cache is T_{acc}, then the average access time of a cache-buffered memory can be expressed in two parts:

$$T_{av} = \text{hit rate} \bullet T_{acc} + \text{miss rate} \bullet T_{fill} \quad \textbf{(5.1)}$$

where T_{fill} is the total time required to detect a miss, read the block from main memory into cache, and return the datum requested to the CPU. Typically T_{fill} is about ten times T_{acc}, so an acceptable average speed will require a high hit rate. To quantify "high," let us put numbers into equation (5.1).

Let us assume a four-word block and a bus that is one word wide. Using modern RAMs, we can take $T_{acc} = 25$ ns, and, using typical dynamic RAM chips, the access time of the main memory system is 120 ns. But the fill time includes more than the direct transaction in seeking one word from main memory. T_{fill} will have to include the 25 ns to detect a miss, 120 ns to read the first word, and the additional time to transfer the other three words in the block. Let the memory be interleaved, or at least wide enough to overlap the four reads. The next three words in the block can be transferred as rapidly as the bus is prepared to handle the transactions. A comfortable rate would return successive words at 30-ns intervals. Then it will take an additional 90 ns to get the other three words back from the main memory. The write to the cache can occur only after each datum is received, so the cache will be updated 25 ns after the last word is transmitted. The total amount of time that the cache is involved in this operation is $25 + 120 + 90 + 25 = 260$ ns $= T_{block}$. This number, which is indeed $10T_{acc}$, still leaves the question of when the CPU received the specific datum that it asked for. It makes sense to design the cache so that it provides the datum to the CPU as soon as it is available, but the datum must still pass through the cache (at least in our design) so that any byte or halfword extraction operation can be performed. That will take a reasonable fraction of the cache cycle—say 20 ns. While one might be tempted to assume that the average delivery would be after the second word, memory accesses are dominated by sequential requests. Accordingly, the average will be closer to one. For lack of a precise specification of what our machine will be doing, let us presume that eight requests would be distributed across the four words as 5,1,1,1. This gives an average of 1.75 words into the four-word sequence and an average delay from request to delivery T_{fill} = 187.5 ns. Based on this value, we can calculate the average access time as a function of hit rate. The results are shown in Table 5.1.

A little bit of caution is required on the meaning of *hit rate*. In a byte-addressed memory, particularly one in which there are no alignment restrictions, one is entitled to view life as a stream of bytes. From that perspective, a request for a word is really four separate requests for sequential bytes and the worst that you can do, allowing for random alignment of the word in the byte stream so that the word sought wraps around the line end, is have two hits and two misses. Such a perspective gives a minimum hit rate for word accesses of 50 percent, but that is not what we mean. We are assuming a word-accessed memory. Even byte or halfword accesses are word accesses as far as cache and memory are concerned. In our machine, the issue of alignment never comes up. The word is in cache or it is not. For sequential accesses, our cache example will give a 75 percent hit rate simply on the basis of the block size of 4. For random accesses, any hit rate is possible. For real code and normal programming with all of the locality of reference and loop repetitions one should expect, we should do considerably better than 75 percent.

From Table 5.1, we can get some idea of how effective a cache with a given hit rate would be. For example, at 40 percent, the average access speed of the

TABLE 5.1 Average access time versus hit rate

Hit rate, %	T_{av}, ns
20	155.0
30	138.8
40	122.5
50	106.3
60	90.0
70	73.8
80	57.5
90	41.3
95	33.1
96	31.5
97	29.9
98	28.3
99	26.6
100	25.0

cache/memory combination will be slower than the access speed of the main memory. We would not want a cache at all! It would slow us down. At a hit rate of 95 percent, we will have a very fast memory system indeed. Having established the importance of achieving a specific hit rate, let us consider next the design parameters which will determine that hit rate: cache size and cache structure.

5.3.1 Cache Size

How large does a cache have to be to produce a particular hit rate? The size of cache can be a critical question because the current direction is to put caches on-chip to minimize the delay in accessing the cache. Cache size will be strictly limited by the other demands for chip turf, so minimizing the size of cache needed to achieve a given level of performance is a discipline worthy of pursuit.

There are two approaches to evaluating cache performance. One is to use an analytical model of the sequence of addresses to estimate the hit rate for different cache sizes and organizations. The other is to use a selection of typical programs to generate a list of typical addresses and then simulate the performance of different caches with this list of addresses. In a moment, we will play with the latter method. A reasonable sampling of the extensive literature on cache simulation includes [Agarwal, 89], [Pohm, 83], [Przybylski, 88], [Przybylski, 90], and [Smith, 82].

In discussing cache optimization, it is very useful to view main memory as being divided up something like a sheet of stamps with, say, 10 rows of 10 stamps. Each stamp, containing some small number of memory entries, comprises a *block*. Let the cache contain 10 stamp positions, although most caches are many orders of magnitude smaller than the address space. Any orderly way of specifying a priori where each stamp in the sheet can be placed in the cache is said to *map* the sheet into the cache. The *direct mapping* is to assign all stamps in the first column to the first position in the cache, and so forth. Thus, 10 blocks are assigned to every slot in the cache. The tag will identify which block, if any, is currently resident in a given slot. A *set-associative* mapping of the same-sized cache pairs the cache positions to make sets and allows any stamp in the first or sixth column to map into either of the first two places, any in the second or seventh in the third or fourth cache positions. Here we would have 20 blocks mapping into each set, but 2 blocks may be coresident in a set. Finally, the *unmapped* case is the *fully associative* cache, where any stamp in the sheet can be put in any position in the cache. While we have called this *unmapped*, in fact, all 100 blocks map into any slot. Obviously, the ratio of available slots to blocks remains constant, but the *mapping* of blocks to slots varies widely.

It is important to begin an analysis of hit rates by asking what causes a miss. Two quite different causes come to mind:

- *First reference*. A block is brought into cache upon the first reference to an element in the block.
- *Mapping conflicts*. One block *interferes* with another in the sense that they are both active at the same time and both map into the same line in the cache. Block size, set size, and cache size interact to determine how the large address space maps

repetitively into the cache space. All three must be considered to determine the hit rate. In the limit of an *unmapped* cache—a fully associative cache—the mapping conflict is simply random replacement in a full cache.

You might think that *first-reference* misses would be unavoidable and outside the designer's purview, but this is not the case. Only the first reference to a block is an unavoidable miss. Using a large block size would minimize the number of such misses in any well-localized data stream. However, a very large block size makes a miss very expensive. Less obvious but equally true, a large block size also causes more misses by making the cache less adaptable to the patterns of addresses in natural programs. Consider, as an extreme, a 256-word cache comprising a single block. Look what havoc a small loop would create if it hung over the edge of a block. A small loop might comprise four or five instructions. If these happened to hang over the end of a block, the memory would be replacing 512 words in the cache every time the loop was traversed. At the other extreme, this same rather absurdly inflexible cache running linear code would have a single miss every 256 requests. That is a hit ratio of 0.996. Not bad for an awful design.

The block size is not a free parameter. It is normally determined within certain memory and memory-bus constraints. The CPU cools its heels while the cache is refilling and no other device can access the memory while the bus is tied up filling or draining the cache. Keeping the block of modest size reduces these penalties and increases cache conformability; making the block larger improves the hit rate for straight-line code. Real best choices range from blocks of one word (4 bytes) to eight words.

Set size can be an important choice, particularly for small caches. Increasing set size requires a significant hardware investment. On the other hand, using a set-associative cache for smaller caches makes a significant difference in hit rate. It might require four times as much memory to obtain the desired hit rate with a direct-mapped cache as it would with a set size of two. Sizes larger than two continue to improve the hit rate, but for caches of typical size, the difference is not very great. Since the number of parts required and the complexity of the replacement algorithm increase rapidly with the set size, it is seldom worthwhile to use set sizes as large as 4. For very large caches, a direct-mapped cache is often the best choice [Hill, 88].

The tradeoffs appear to be different when a cache is incorporated onto the same chip as the CPU. While the chip area set aside for cache size is inevitably quite limited, since standard RAMs are not being used for the memory, the designer is entitled to use any cache organization at all, even a fully associative memory. What limits this apparent freedom of choice, however, is the great benefit of having as big a data capacity as possible in the constrained space. The transistors devoted to address matching displace transistors that store data. Up to a point, data always wins [Eickemeyer, 88].

To develop some insight into the way the several choices of mapping determine the hit rate, let us consider a particularly simple piece of program that was introduced in Table 1.6. This is the SPARC version of `Inner()`, the routine that does an inner product of two matrices. The routine is very regular and predictable, in fact, too regular and predictable to be a very general demonstration. We will use it to see what happens in this routine where all of the behavior is well understood and then discuss how our observations will extrapolate to more realistically general program flows. Since some caches, particularly on-chip caches, are *instruction-only* caches, we consider both an instruction-only cache and a general cache storing all data. The *instruction-only* cache performance is shown in Figure 5.6.

Both expected and unexpected behavior are to be found in Figure 5.6. The data for the figure was obtained by constructing a subroutine which generated the same address stream that the real program would generate. That subroutine tracked a data file which gave rules for selecting the next instruction and, where appropriate, where to get the next data. The subroutine kept track of row and column numbers so that it could compute addresses for both program and data. This stream of addresses was fed to a cache-simulation routine. That routine was perfectly general. It kept track of addresses fed to it, following the rules established for the cache structure chosen. The only arguable point in the simulation is the use of *random replacement* for set sizes greater than 1. We will discuss that issue in a moment. Since the data flow was not at issue, taking the inner product of relatively small matrices gives the same data as very large ones.

FIGURE 5.6 Hit rate versus cache size for an *instruction-only* cache running `Inner()` on the SPARC. Random replacement is used for set sizes greater than 1, giving a perhaps unfair advantage to the set size 1.

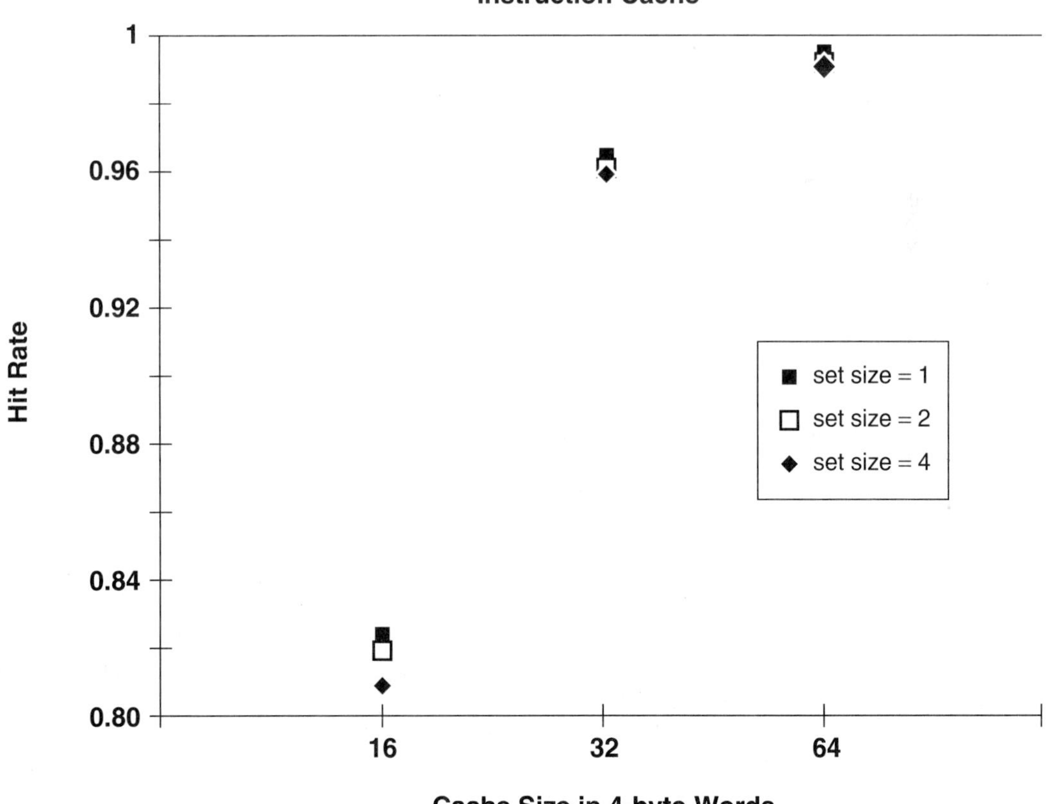

The data shown are for taking the product of a pair of 5 × 5 matrices (with an upper bound set at 100). A total of 2159 memory references results.

The first thing to note is that for this little routine of 51 instructions, a very small cache is highly effective. A cache of only 64 words (256 bytes) gives a hit rate of 0.993 regardless of the organization. Small wonder that the designers of the MC68020 thought it worthwhile to install an on-chip, direct-mapped 256-byte cache!

The one apparently unreasonable surprise in Figure 5.6 is that increasing the set size has a small but negative impact. As we discuss in a moment, this curious result derives from our random replacement policy, where the block to be replaced is chosen essentially by a throw of the dice. Before looking at why that would make the set size of 1 slightly better, consider the general cache—data and instructions—shown in Figure 5.7.

FIGURE 5.7 Hit rate versus cache size for a general cache serving the same program as Figure 5.6. Note that the abscissa is logarithmic. In this case, the inner product is taken for a pair of 20 × 20 matrices. That product requires a total of 190,767 memory references. Random replacement is used for set sizes greater than 1.

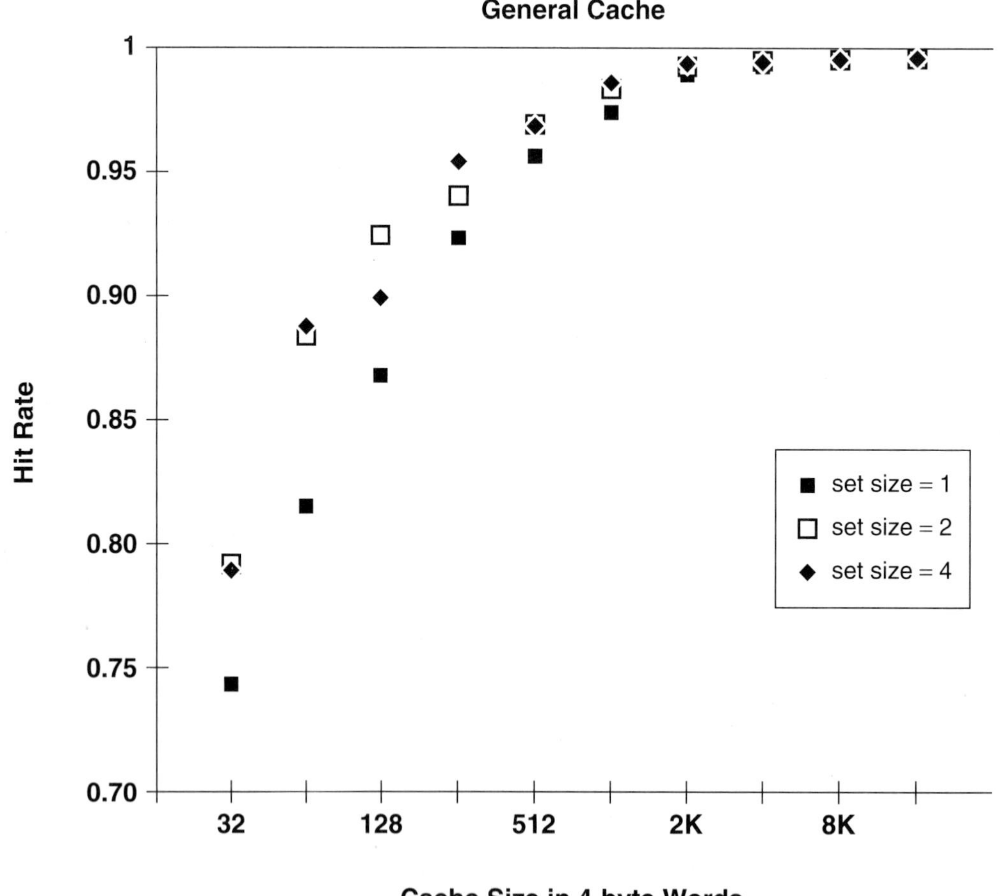

Although we here employ the same replacement algorithm as in Figure 5.6, we are greeted by the opposite result on set size and even some oscillatory behavior on that variable as the cache size increases. Note that good performance now requires a substantially larger cache, 2K versus 64 words in the previous figure. However, put that in proper perspective. The main memory in your typical new Macintosh running in system 7 has got to have 2 to 4 MW of memory to be effective. Accordingly, a very effective cache for this application would be less than 0.1 percent of main memory.

One of the first questions you should raise here is whether these two figures are "typical." Taking inner products certainly does not seem like "Everyman's" arithmetic. But the question should not be answered by pondering the world's need for inner products. What really counts in this section is whether this example represents typical instruction and data flows. The `Inner()` function is certainly unusually repetitive, particularly in the instruction stream. Most programs spend less time in such confined quarters of an instruction stream. This means that our example will have an abnormally small burden of *first-reference* misses. This is indeed observable in the excellent performance of the small instruction caches in Figure 5.6. The data stream is more normal, since row vectors (steps of 8 bytes) are being dotted with column vectors (steps of 800 bytes). The starting points for the two matrices were deliberately offset so that the two streams of data would not be precisely aligned. The excessive regularity in the program is what makes the random replacement algorithm a poor choice for the instruction-only cache. Since the replacement takes no notice of what is useful and what is not, you cannot help but throw away winners even if there is an empty slot just waiting for data. That is why a set size of 1 is optimum for random replacement in the instruction-only cache. In contrast, the data are sufficiently well distributed to restore *random replacement* to its proper place as a reasonably effective replacement policy. The oscillation that you see between set size = 2 and set size = 4 shows that some substantial regularity in the data still persists. Extending to larger or nonsquare data sets changes the oscillation amplitude but data from a $30 \times 20 * 20 \times 40$ case still shows them present.

Lest you feel that "real" data would be remarkably different, we present in Figure 5.8 and Table 5.2 some cache-performance data from address traces taken at Data General. These address traces were obtained from several processors running a wide variety of applications. They represent at least one view of a normal programming load for small and medium-sized minicomputers in the early 1980s. These traces were run through a cache-modeling program similar to the one used in Figure 5.7. There is no doubt that the more typical address stream does have an impact. In particular, the higher incidence of first-reference misses leads to a lower cache performance for all sizes of cache. Figure 5.8 shows the effects of block size, set size, and total cache size on cache performance. While nothing very exceptional shows up, the data show that with respect to cache hit rate, bigger is better:

- A bigger cache is always better, but by diminishing amounts as the set size increases.
- A bigger block size is always better, although set size can compensate for block size.
- A bigger set size gives better performance.

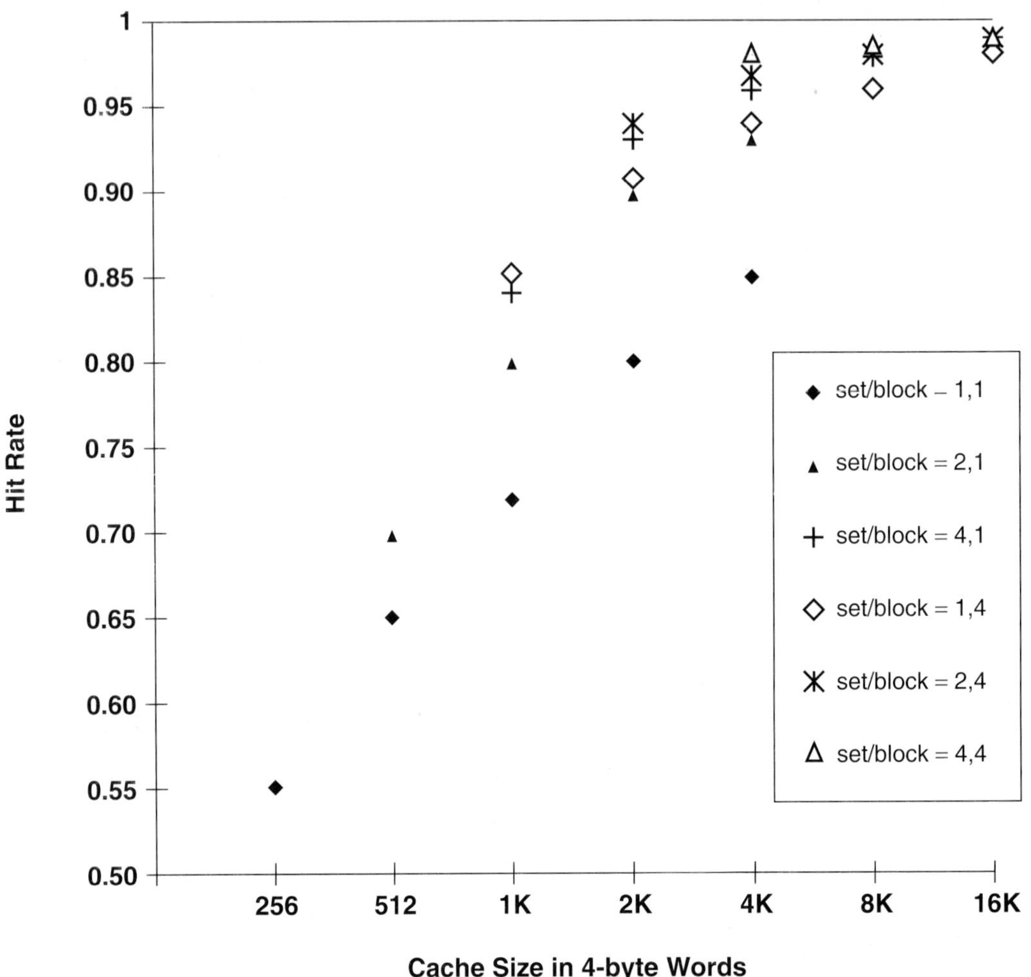

FIGURE 5.8 Hit rate as a function of block size and set size for caches of 256 to 16 KW from address traces taken on minicomputers running a general workload in the early 1980s. The set of data from which this graph was drawn is given in Table 5.2.

In all cases, our data in Figure 5.7 proves to be a bit optimistic, as expected. However, do note that even with the more realistic address model, hit rates in excess of 96 percent are obtained with general caches of quite modest size. To reach the 99 percent level shown for caches of 2 KW and greater in Figure 5.7, the Data General traces require a cache of 16 KW and a set size of at least 2.

One final comment on the three figures presented in this section: Each represents a particular workload. While the data for Figure 5.8 may be more representative of some workdays than those of Figure 5.7, there is no such thing as *the normal workload*. Every machine runs a particular workload. That load tends to change with time. For example, the *typical* workload in the early '80s had a small or negligible graphics component.

TABLE 5.2 Cache dimensions versus hit rate

Set size	Number of sets	Block size, words	Total size, words	Hit rate, %
1	256	1	256	55
1	256	4	1K	85
1	512	1	512	65
1	512	4	2K	91
1	1K	1	1K	72
1	1K	4	4K	94
1	2K	1	2K	80
1	2K	4	8K	96
1	4K	1	4K	85
1	4K	4	16K	98
2	256	1	512	70
2	256	4	2K	94
2	512	1	1K	80
2	512	4	4K	97
2	1K	1	2K	90
2	1K	4	8K	98
2	2K	1	4K	93
2	2K	4	16K	99
4	256	1	1K	84
4	256	4	4K	98
4	512	1	2K	93
4	512	4	8K	98.5
4	1K	1	4K	96
4	1K	4	16K	99.3

That is hardly the case today. PCs and workstations see very different workloads from minicomputers. In most cases, a cache study is done to be sure that an adequate cache is available for most uses. If you want to know how well a particular cache design will perform for a particular customer, you will need an address trace which accurately represents that customer's normal mix of applications or, if a particular application is seen as a problem, then the trace should be for the problem application.

5.3.2 Replacement Algorithms

When a miss occurs in a cache, the incoming data has to replace something already in the cache. As we saw in Section 5.3.1, the choice of which block to replace can affect the hit rate.

With perfect vision, you would replace one which is not going to be used in the near future. Sometimes you can recognize such a block. For example, an invalid block is certainly not going to be used. For special cases, such as stack usage in subroutines, it is possible to know at compilation time what the cache must store. In that case, it is possible to have the software itself control the cache with perfect foresight. Those special cases aside, we normally have to resort to predicting the future addresses from those which have occurred recently. The algorithms for doing this are similar to the algorithms used for virtual memory replacement. However, cache algorithms must be very simple, since they are normally executed in hardware in a short miss interval. Let's examine a few cache replacement algorithms.

One possibility—one that we have just used—is simply to pick at random any one of the blocks within the set. This is a minimalist strategy; we just need some way of producing a small random number. Engineers tend to dislike random algorithms, but this method turns out to work surprisingly well. Hardware to generate random numbers? If one may assume that the mix of addresses causes misses to occur randomly in time, then a random number generator is nothing more than a counter driven by the system clock. No matter what the size of the cache, you need only one such generator. After all, a random number for line 23 will not look different from a random number for line 504.

Random is easy; random is cheap. Still, given our prejudices, let us consider a more systematic approach. We might pick a replacement policy that is popular in virtual memory management. Let us replace the block (within the particular set specified by the address, of course) which has been in the cache for the longest time. That algorithm is first-in first-out, FIFO. It's fairly easy to design the hardware to implement it. If we number the blocks within each set and fill them in sequence, then a simple, circular counter incremented on replacement will always point to the block to be replaced. For a set of 16, about as big as they get, we need only 4 bits per line to implement the FIFO replacement strategy. The bits can be part of the line, so a single adder can serve to increment any counter and a single decoder can serve to identify the block to replace in any line. While we have added a few bits to the cache memory width, there is only a small contribution to cache random logic. We can conclude that FIFO, like *random*, is easy and cheap. The next question is: Is it desirable? The problem with the FIFO algorithm is that a block which was loaded into the cache a long time ago may be getting used more often than one which was loaded more recently. Notice that if this were to occur on a regular basis, FIFO would be far worse than random. In the `Inner()` example in the last section, what you want is to have the code get into cache and stay there. It is used again and again. It would be difficult to design a replacement policy worse than FIFO in that case. Then why did FIFO work in the case of memory management in Chapter 4? The answer is subtle. When a page is replaced in memory, the page being liberated is placed at the end of one of two queues: the *freepage* queue, where it waits reassignment to another process, or the *dirtypage* queue, where it awaits being written out to disk and then being queued onto the freepage queue. In either case, it has substantial dwell time in the queued state before it is zeroed and handed over to another process. Should a mistake have been made in releasing a very useful page, the cost of recovery is only a few table entries to restore the page to its process. The task of finding buffered pages is relegated to the page fault handling software, not all that fast but not all that frequent. In the cache, which handles all its transactions in hardware and at hardware speed, there is no such buffering mechanism. The system must eat its mistakes.

If FIFO threatens to be a pessimal strategy, we can try to get smarter. We can try to replace the block within a line that has had the longest time since it was last used. This leads to a replacement algorithm called *least recently used*, or LRU. To find which block was used least recently we have to keep track of the most recent time that a block is used. If there are a large number of blocks in a set, this can be fairly complex. Consider a set size of 8. LRU could be realized by assigning a 3-bit downcounter to each block. (Note how we have increased the hardware burden!) When the cache is flushed, all counters are reset. The rules are:

- Replace at count 0. (Any 0 will do.)
- Upon a hit (including replacement), set the hit block to 7 and decrement all other counters, but the count cannot go below 0.
- On cache reset, reset all counters as well as the valid bits.

The counter must have the properties that it counts down, stops at 0, and can be set and reset. Presumably, we would do this by having 3 bits for each group in the line. Easy to achieve but we are talking about very fast logic here. You will need still more. There must be some way to pick a 0 counter from the set, which could have 1 to 8 blocks at the 0 level. It is easy to have the counter signal 0, but then, to make a choice, we must use some form of priority encoder. More and more of our cache area is going to management. In a zero-sum game, that is a costly alternative.

If the set size is 2, which is a fairly common case in real cache designs, LRU becomes almost trivial to accomplish. With only two blocks, the one which was not most recently used must be the least recently used. The LRU algorithm for a set size of 2 requires only a single bit for each line. Each time a block is used, the LRU bit for that set is loaded with a 0 or a 1, depending on which of the two blocks in the set was used. When a miss occurs, and one of the blocks must be replaced, we choose the one which was not accessed last. The two-way set-associative memory with LRU replacement was illustrated in Figure 5.3.

For large set sizes (or, particularly, for the limiting case of a fully associative cache) there is an efficient approximation to LRU which actually outperforms what it is modeling. This is Deville's algorithm [Deville, 92], which requires only a shade more than 1 bit per group. This algorithm uses only the valid bit and a single extra bit for the whole line, which we might call *all-valid*. Since we already have a valid bit, this really adds only a single bit, whatever the set size. For LRU with a set size of 32, we would need 5 bits per group, or 160 bits. The Deville algorithm begins each time that the cache is invalidated with all of the valid bits and the *all-valid* bit reset. As long as one element is invalid the individual bits are used as *valid bits*. During this phase of operation, replacement is always at empty (invalid) locations. The critical part of this algorithm is that upon reaching a full set of valid bits (now called *referenced bits*), the referenced bits are all reset and the all-valid bit is set. Now, referenced bits are set when elements are referenced. When the last referenced bit is set, they are all reset, and you begin a new phase of setting referenced bits. Thus there are always unset referenced bits or unset valid bits. Replacement is now at a 0 referenced bit. This system has behavior that is very close to LRU but surprisingly, for real data streams, its performance is just enough not LRU to give even better performance in those few situations where LRU trips itself up. Even more curious, as reported in [Deville, 92], every effort made to "improve" on this very simple algorithm gave poorer performance. At the moment of writing this paragraph, Deville's algorithm is too new to have found application, but we can see no reason why it would not be adopted whenever there is reason to have a set size greater than 2.

Now for the conclusion of conclusions: It turns out that the replacement algorithm does not have very much effect on hit rate in typical cache memories. The choice of algorithm will depend mostly on the amount of hardware required. For set size 1, there is no choice to make. For a set size of 2, use LRU because it's so simple. For larger set sizes, random replacement is good; Deville's scheme seems even better.

5.3.3 Writes with Cache Memories

Quite properly, to this point we have focused entirely on CPU reads from memory. The purpose of the cache was to provide faster reads. Reads certainly dominate. All the instructions must be read; there are roughly three data reads to every data write. Sooner or later, however, the program that is running will want to write something. Now what do we do with the cache? When do we return the new value to memory?

If an old version of the word is already in the cache, we have to do something about that. Either we could replace it with the new word from the CPU, or we could invalidate the block. In either case, we first have to read the tag, to see if the word is in the cache, and we then have to write something into one of the RAMs to invalidate the block. If we are going to have to write to part of the cache, we may as well write the data into the cache.

If we have written the word into the cache, should we also write it into memory? That is a question with a more complicated array of useful answers. The choice is really *return it now* or *return it later*. Any write to memory will take up some of the memory bandwidth. It may cause a delay of considerable duration if it conflicts with the need to read something from memory. While we will have to return written data to memory sooner or later, what a shame to take up bus bandwidth if this write turns out to be something other than the final version of that variable. Programs often send data back and forth dozens of times in the course of running through a repetitive loop. The data may be simply the ephemeral local variables of a subroutine residing in the stack. They would *never* have to reside in memory except for context switches. There is much reason not to write anything back until you have to. As we shall see both here and in Section 5.6 on multiple caches, *have-to*'s come up in more circumstances than just context switches. But there is much to encourage us to try not to write back everything that the program says to write to memory. If each datum is returned to memory every time that the program so indicates, the system is called *writethrough* in the sense that data are written through the cache to memory. If, instead, the data are retained in cache until circumstances demand, then it is called a *writeback* cache. Systems are designed with both writeback and writethrough paradigms. The choice has both dollar and performance implications, so we must consider it rather carefully.

When do we absolutely have to write data back to memory? Four rather different circumstances would certainly demand a write to memory:

- A cache miss which requires that we replace new data stored in cache with another block. The cache contains the only copy of the data that was written into it. We have to write it back to the main memory before we can overwrite the block in cache.
- A context switch requires that an up-to-date image of the task be stored in memory so that pages may be swapped or paged out.
- The datum being written is destined for a memory-mapped I/O device. Picture yourself sending a sequence of control words to an I/O device, where you send several words to the same address with the reasonable assumption that each does its task of controlling the device. A cache that sent only the last such transmission and did it only at the next block replacement or context switch would not serve you well.
- A datum that is shared by a concurrent process running on another CPU sharing the same memory. This is central to the *cache consistency* problem of Section 5.6, but to see the problem, just imagine doing the mutual-exclusion algorithm of Chapter 3 with two caches holding their respective semaphores from each other!

The first two are recognizable events. Responding to them requires only that we keep track of which blocks have new data. These are the ones that must be written back, either as single blocks or all at once. Keeping track of which blocks must be written back is done with another bit for each block, the *modified* or *dirty* bit. When we first load a block into the cache, we clear its dirty bit. Then if we ever write a word into that block, we set the dirty bit. If we need to replace the block or when doing a context switch, we must test the dirty bit, and if it is set, write the block back into the main memory before reading a new block into that space in the cache or clearing the cache.

The third problem with having a data cache is not peculiar to a writeback solution. If we want to use memory-mapped I/O, then there has to be a way to tag blocks or pages as *uncacheable*. The issue is that what you are writing to or reading from is a memory-mapped register in an I/O device. The value in that register may change because of I/O device activity, activity that would certainly not appear in the data in cache. To get the new data, the block must be read from the device and not from cache. Tagging blocks is probably more finesse than needed, so some pages will be set aside for I/O. Page tagging requires dedicating a bit in each pagetable entry to cacheability—not a problem unless there is no free bit. We have a *cache-inhibit* (CI) bit in our PTEs which serves this function (Figure 4.11 on page 188).

Even if a page is tagged as uncacheable, we will not insist that the writeback occur synchronously with the store instruction, only that the order of writes be preserved and that a read-after-write always gets the correct data. Even if we choose the simpler paradigm of writethrough, we will want to buffer the write requests to some depth. The problem is that with several processors competing for the memory (including I/O chips in the nominal *single-CPU* case), the bus may be busy for an extended time—10 to 30 instructions. If the CPU which requested the write has what it needs in cache, it would be a shame to make it sit there until the write was confirmed. This is not unlike the situation we addressed in moving data out to disk in Chapter 3, where we used buffering and system services to accommodate an effective speed difference of 5 to 6 orders of magnitude. While the speed difference here is much less, there is a substantial benefit to be gained by allowing the cache controller to buffer one or more write requests while the CPU continues (if it can). Only when the cache controller cannot accommodate another write would we halt the CPU. When we discuss bus transfers in Chapter 8, you will find that the controller can often make several transactions before it must yield the bus to another device. The time to make a transfer includes both the data movement and the overhead of obtaining access to the bus. By buffering writes until the bus is acquired, the overhead can be spread over several data transfers.

As we ponder buffering writes, whether in writeback or writethrough caches, do not lose track of the obligation to ensure that no read receives stale data from memory because the fresh data was sitting unnoticed in an output buffer queue. Preserving the order of read and write requests will limit the time that data may remain in the output queue.

We must also worry about the loss of timing control for the program. In small machines, particularly those dedicated to real-time control, it is not uncommon to time I/O events by how many instructions separate reads or writes to an I/O device. In bigger and particularly faster machines, such as the one considered here, the more normal paradigm is to use vectored interrupts for handling I/O timing. To see the issue, consider a typical control loop which says

```
*b = 1;          /* sends a byte 0x01 to address b starting some I/O process*/
while (*b);      /* tests the same address repeatedly until a 0 byte is returned */
```

If you have not written such a driver, this two-line routine may seem a bit peculiar. Why it is normal is that many I/O chips use the same address for two purposes, differentiating what is wanted on the basis of *read* or *write*. On the *write*, you are delivering a command; on the *read*, you are getting the chip's status. The *write* would set a *busy bit* in the status register. The sequential series of reads would represent a holding pattern for the CPU. Until a 0 is returned, the chip is busy with the first command. (This classical *spinlock* does tie up the processor, but if the I/O chip finishes its task in a time of the order of a few CPU instructions, the spinlock may be quicker than handling the I/O dialog through an interrupt.)

Fine, but what happens if we buffer writes and just routinely give a preference to reads? Now the read implicit in `while (*b)` could be executed before the write implicit in `*b=1`! Since the chip was not busy before it got the command, almost anything might happen. In one particularly nasty case, if the chip were reading data from an external device, reversing the order of command and test could gully the CPU into reading stale or invalid data under the misapprehension that the chip had acquired a new datum. Bad stuff. Since I/O devices are usually very slow, it is both easier and better to use interrupts to signal I/O events. In effect, you tell the I/O chip: "Tell me when you are done," and go about your business.

While we are going to design a writeback cache, we will limit write buffering in two ways:

- The buffer will hold only a single block.
- A read may precede a write only if the read itself forced the write by causing a cache miss on modified data.

These limitations assure perfect sequentiality at low cost while still providing good isolation on cache line replacement. We are still left with one problem that is particularly grim in a writeback cache—the cache consistency problem. That we reserve to Section 5.6 where we discuss multiple caches.

If writeback is more complex than writethrough, why would we want to use it? Its advantage is that it uses significantly less bus bandwidth. This has been long recognized as particularly important for the case of multiple processors which compete for access to a common main memory [Goodman, 83], but as CPU speeds have outpaced dynamic memory chip speeds, it has become important even for single processor designs. Writeback is good; it is just more complicated and expensive.

So far we've been assuming that the block we are writing to is already in the cache. What if it isn't? We could read it into the cache, just as we would on a miss resulting from a read, and then continue as above. Or we could just write the word into the main memory, and never bother putting it into the cache at all. The process of reading the block into cache when the first access to a line is a write is called *fetch-on-write*. It is usually done by caches which use writeback, since they tend to keep the most up-to-date information in cache. Furthermore, once that data is in cache, subsequent writes stay in the cache, requiring no bus or memory transactions. The simpler writethrough caches normally write the word into main memory, which they would do anyway, and don't bother loading the block into cache. Since the most common places to be writing before reading are in heap and stack and since the data written there is referenced very soon after writing and since one often writes a sequence of values into heap or stack structures, fetch-on-write is a programmatically efficient paradigm.

What do we do with *fetch-on-write* with noncacheable pages? While one might try to perform the *fetch-on-write* operation, ignoring the other data in the block and not caching anything, there may be a problem if we write the whole block back. Recall that one reason for making some pages uncacheable is that those pages contain memory-mapped I/O devices. Who knows what those other data in the line might mean to a device? In other words, the appealing simplicity of always dealing in blocks appears awkward if we want to have the CPU do any direct control of I/O devices. There are (at least) two reasonable ways to sustain the simplicity of block-oriented memory-cache communication. One that is widely used with the similar problem in connecting 32-bit busses and 8- (or 16-) bit I/O devices is simply to have the addresses of the I/O chip's ports separated by units the size of the bus (or in our case, the line). This is a common solution on the VMEbus. (This "separation" is simply a matter of designing your address decoder to respond to every other or every fourth address.) A second approach is to separate out the I/O operations. In other words, install a separate I/O processor with the requisite finesse in handling data of any size. Such a solution has been common in many large multiprocessor systems for some decades. The I/O processor or processors share memory with the CPUs that are not doing direct I/O. To get I/O services, the CPUs queue requests in memory and the I/O processors queue responses. You might still want to render the queues uncacheable, but now you can deal entirely in blocks. Even with this solution, you do not get away clean. There is still the problem of initializing or querying the peripheral chip itself. For that, the direct solution is spaced addresses.

Recall from Chapter 3 that when a process enqueues a request, it first locks the queue. Clearly, the queue must be in uncacheable pages or a writeback must be forced after modifying the queue. In locking the queue, the programmer assumes that the write to memory stores the software lock and that it is safe to proceed. We have already argued in Chapter 3 that no other process may intrude into the read-modify-write operation. To that end, we included the special instruction, LODSET, to accomplish an atomic read-modify-write operation *in memory*. When we discussed LODSET in Chapter 2, we said:

> It is relatively simple to add the READ-MODIFY-WRITE cycle to that board. Accordingly, the instruction looks almost like a normal LOAD with the added proviso that the MMU board will set the LO bit and immediately return the word to the memory (as well as passing the unmodified word to the CPU).

Why should it be easy? In fact, is it easy? The answer is: "Yes, it is relatively easy." What makes it possible to guarantee that this operation is atomic, what makes it *indivisible*, is that a device that is holding the memory bus is not obliged to release it immediately even if requested to do so by another device. The device that is holding the bus is correctly called the *bus master*. It controls who reads and who writes. If we look at the operation of read-modify-write in the context of

- fetch-on-write
- read preference and write queuing
- block operations

a worst-case example would be having, say, two blocks queued for writeback when the LODSET instruction came along. The finite-state machine that comprises the cache/memory-manager controller would normally put the read part of the read-modify-write instruction before the queue of writes. However, read-modify-write must not have any memory operation between the read and the write. That gives us two choices:

1. Write out the queue of writes and then do the read-modify-write.
2. Do the read-modify-write and then proceed as in all other cases.

Both have arguments in their favor. The first assures us that anyone who depends on the previous writes having occurred before the read-modify-write will not be disappointed; the second would allow the cache/memory-manager controller to yield the bus to some other user if asked to do so. This would shorten the maximum time that the controller must hold the bus. If the memory can accept data at the rate of 4 blocks/μs, the worse-case delay is 1 μs. For the second, it would be 0.5 μs. Neither of these seems to pose a problem, so we could choose the first possibility, guaranteeing the user that no writes will be pending at the moment that a queue is locked. In our design we will have at most one line buffered for writing and will always write it out before executing a subsequent read, but some cache designs have writeback queues of greater length and also more elaborate rules on read-before-write.

5.4 TRANSLATION LOOKASIDE BUFFER

In Chapter 4 we developed several schemes for translating virtual addresses to physical addresses. All of the translation mechanisms suitable for large address spaces were hierarchical, requiring multiple memory references to do a single address translation. The burden of such translation was so obviously unacceptable that we had to invoke caching of translations to make virtual memory seem plausible. Now is the time to look at how that caching is accomplished. We will focus on paged memory systems.

Applications generate only virtual addresses. Each VA is passed from CPU to *memory management unit* (MMU). The MMU translates the VA to a PA and passes the PA to the memory. If the MMU used our three-level translation scheme and had no caching, each datum would require a series of four accesses to memory. Memory access time is already and has been forever one of the principal bottlenecks in computation. Quadrupling the traffic would be a disaster. What makes VM practical is the remarkable locality of reference of the *address-translation components*. What is being translated in VA ⇒ PA is the page address, or, more correctly, the *virtual page number* (VPN). Locality of reference suggests that only a few pages will be active at any time and that this small number of translations will be used over and over and over again. What better example of cacheable data could you have? Not only would the cache contain the current pagetable entries but also the hierarchy of PTEs which led to those translations. In our machine, the hierarchy comprises PTEs from the process and system root tables, from midtables, and from pagetables. (See Figures 4.10 and 4.12.) The number of cached PTEs need not be large to be very effective.

While we could and will cache PTEs as data in our D-cache, we do not want to be "doing arithmetic" on entries in the D-cache. We want a hardware solution to a direct translation of VPN to PPN. To this end, we will have a separate, small cache for storing the final result of the three-step translation. The PTE cache is usually called a *translation lookaside buffer* (TLB). Other names are sometimes used, such as *address translation cache* (ATC) and *directory lookaside table* (DLAT). TLB configurations strongly resemble the data caches we have already examined. The input is a VPN; the output is a PTE comprising the physical page number and the protection information. If the requested translation is not in the TLB, we have a TLB miss, and the translation must be obtained by going through the pagetables. For multilevel pageable pagetables, a

TLB miss is potentially more serious than a data cache miss. It may require several successive memory accesses or even page faults to get all the PTEs, but it seldom works out that badly. Over a reasonable interval of computing, the range of most programs is so limited that it is likely that all of the PTEs needed to get the missing PTE will already be in the data cache. Recall that a PTE is simply a word, 1 of n words in the block that the cache would acquire each time that it went to a particular pagetable. Thus, a miss in the TLB will usually result in a single reference to memory. Relatively small translation caches can achieve remarkably good hit rates. Typical TLB sizes are 64 to 1024 entries, and hit rates are usually greater than 99 percent. In the 1980s, many VA machines were built without data caches, but no such machine would ever have been proposed without a TLB. (The alternative of using VAs in the cache to avoid translation altogether we will consider later in this chapter.)

Figure 5.9 is a block diagram of a TLB. This example is a direct-mapped cache and should be compared with Figure 5.2. Set-associative TLBs are perhaps more common, but the direct-mapped TLB diagram emphasizes the differences between a TLB and a data cache. The pagetable entries are the cached data; the format of the PTE in our RISC machine can be gleaned from the figure. The inputs to the cache include the VA and bits indicating READ/WRITE* and PROCESS/SYSTEM*. Results of the

FIGURE 5.9 Layout of a direct-mapped translation lookaside buffer using a hash function for mapping the VPN into the lines of the cache. For an expansion of the protection bits, see Figure 4.11 on page 188. For our machine, the VPN or PPN comprises the high-order 24 bits of the address and the offset the remaining 8 bits.

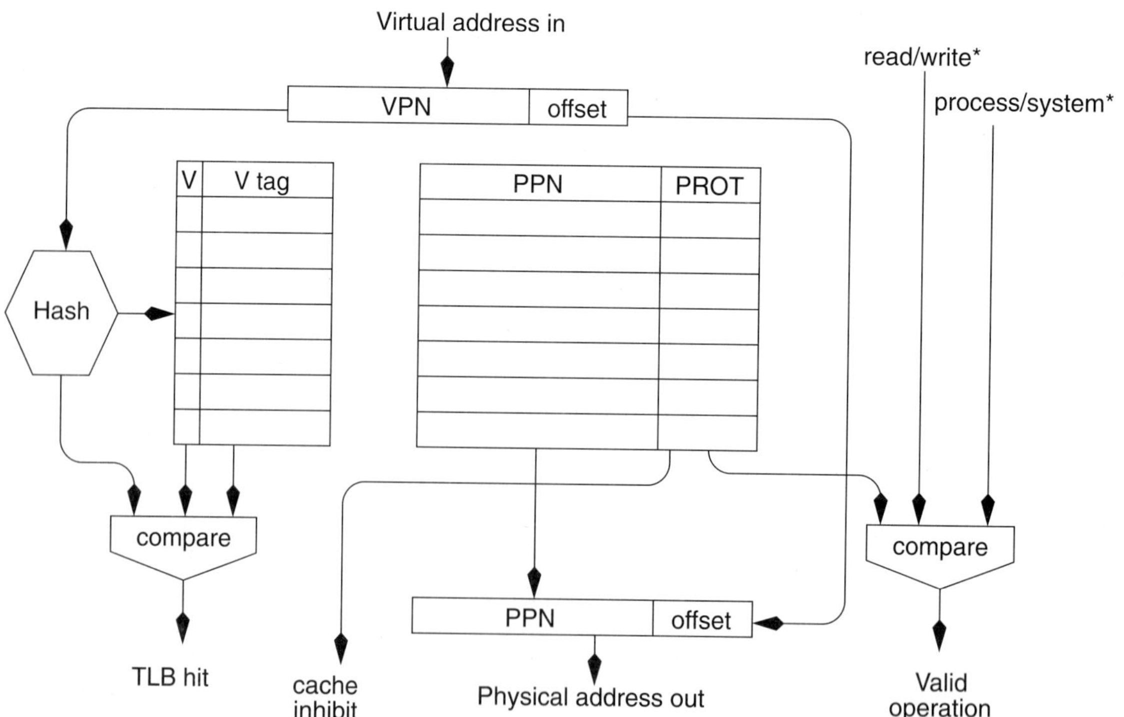

search include the normal test for a hit as well as tests of the protection bits. Should a TLB miss occur, a finite-state machine in the MMU must obtain the missing address from pagetables in main memory or parts thereof in cache and store it in the TLB. The finite-state machine must be capable of mixing and matching, going occasionally to memory but using what is in the data cache to maximum advantage.

If an *invalid operation* is signaled, the reaction must be an *exception*, carrying the application into the operating system. Among the invalid operations are:

- Page faults, which may result in an I/O request and a context switch.
- Attempts to access a page for which the appropriate permission has not been granted. In most circumstances, an illegal access will terminate execution with some minimal notification to the parent of the process.

5.4.1 A Hash Function for Line Selection

The tag store in this TLB example differs somewhat from that of the example data caches. Instead of using the lower bits of the virtual page number to select a block (or a set), and storing the upper bits in the tag store, this TLB uses all of the virtual page bits for both purposes. We introduced the concept of a *hash table* in the *inverted pagetable* (Figure 4.9). Here we will pursue the idea a little further.

There is a problem which arises from the normal and frequently useful tendency to be orderly rather than random in the assignment of regions of virtual addresses. In our system, for example, we define for the process four bins plus heap and stack. In the system itself, we have combined these to make four regions: Absolute, Text, Stack, and Data. Absolute contains bins 0 and 1, Text contains bin 2, Data contains bin 3 and the heap, and Stack contains its namesake. While it would be possible for the *linker* to assess the needs of each bin and to assign contiguous pages up to the bottom of the heap, it is often the case that gaps are left to allow the next region to start on some logical boundary. Let us say that we begin each region on an address with the 15 least significant bits as 0. Such an assignment might lead to the following initial allocations (heap and stack are dynamically allocated during the run):

Segment	Address range	VPN range
Absolute	`0000 0000 to 0000 7FFF`	`000000 to 00007F`
Text	`0000 8000 to 0022 FFFF`	`000080 to 0022FF`
Data	`0023 0000 to 0023 80FF`	`002300 to 002380`
Stack	`00FF FF00 to 00FF FFFF`	`00FFFF to 00FFFF`

(Recall that we are using 24-bit VAs to limit our midtables to a single midtable for each process.) There is nothing amiss with these allocations. It is a good-sized program (8 MB) with modest amounts of Absolute (global constants and variables) and Data (predeclared structures) and with plenty of dynamic growth range for heap and stack (56 MB).

Now let us examine what happens to the TLB with these assignments. The TLB deals only with page numbers. Consider a 256-line cache. If we were to use the lowest bits of the VPN to select the line in the TLB, as we used the lowest bits in the address to select the line in the data cache, we find ourselves with considerable contention in the lower half and almost no use of the upper half of the cache. The low bits of VPNs used by typical programs are not as random as the low bits of addresses. As things start off, only the Text segment extends into both halves (i.e., has a VPN range exceeding 7F). Only if large dynamic allocations occur—something which most applications do not do—would Stack and Data spread out through the TLB.

Three solutions to this problem of line contention present themselves:

- Have the linker start different segments in different parts of the cache (ties the linker to a particular cache size).
- Make the cache shorter and wider by adopting a set-associative cache.
- Adopt a hardware shuffler to achieve a more uniform distribution of line assignments.

The software solution, while simple, is unacceptable as soon as more than one model of TLB is sold for a given family of machines, an event which may well occur on day 1 of a family's life. The second solution is widely adopted, but making the set very wide—essentially moving toward the fully associative cache—quickly becomes prohibitively costly. Few TLBs are more than two-way. If the TLB has more lines than the typical segment has pages, a direct mapping of VPNs to lines will lead to overcontention and poor utilization of the TLB. This is where the *shuffler* solution enters. The objective for the hashing function in Figure 5.9 is to distribute the pages more evenly throughout the TLB.

A hashing function is any easily computable mapping function which tends to scatter the possible input values in some useful way among the possible output values. The hashing function used in a TLB cannot be complex. It must be executed in very fast hardware, typically consisting of a few exclusive-OR gates. Some examples of hash functions used in some actual machines are found in [Smith, 82]. We present one of these, out of the IBM 3033; it accomplishes two goals:

- It spreads out the line assignments.
- It reduces the tag burden on the TLB memory.

The 3033 hashing function simply XORs address bits in selected pairs. Since the tag is used to discriminate between the many pages which map to a given line, and since the XOR function itself already divides in half the four possibilities of 2 bits, we need 1 bit from each pair as a tag to discriminate which PTE is in the line. This 3033 TLB had only 12 bits for its PTE—big page size (4 KB) and modest address space (24 bit). The TLB was a 64-line two-way set-associative cache. The hash function for the 12 page-selector bits, with 0 as the least significant, is shown in Figure 5.10.

By distributing addresses more evenly, hashing should improve the average hit rate of the TLB. Let us consider whether this one does a good job. "Good" will be defined as:

- filling the cache more evenly
- avoiding thrashing in any single group of adjacent pages

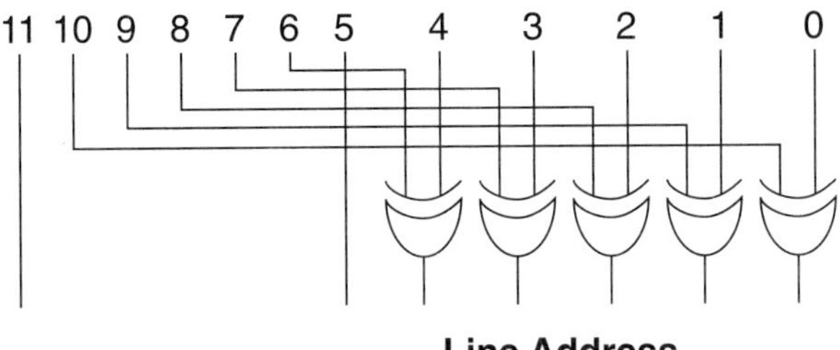

FIGURE 5.10 The hash function for the IBM 3033 64-line TLB. Bit 11 is not used in the hash function, appearing only in the tag.

The thrashing issue arises if there is a *fold* in the mapping. For example, if you go from 0→63 and then 63→0, there is a fold at 63. If you were running a loop between two adjacent pages which happened to map onto this fold, you would constantly trash the previous contents of line 63. (A set-associative cache excuses one such fold, but let us ignore that for the moment.) A first observation is that a straight linear mapping (0→63 followed by 0→63) is best at solving the thrashing problem but at the expense of poor filling for small segments.

A random shuffle will clearly give optimum filling but provides a less perfect protection from thrashing. With a truly random shuffle, there is always a possibility of any two adjacent pages mapping into the same line. The probability of two adjacent pages interfering is 1/64, not entirely trivial at all; worse yet, if your loop happens to stretch over three pages, the probability of any interference is now 3/64 (0.047). That is an unacceptable blow to the TLB hit rate.

The 3033 hash function is clearly not random. In fact, for the first 64 PTEs, the 3033 hash is indistinguishable from the direct linear mapping. On the second set of 64 PTEs, the mapping goes

direct	0→15	16→31	32→47	48→63
hashed	16→31	0→15	48→63	32→47

This is quite a shuffle, yet the folding is such that adjacent pages never map into the same line. All in all, it starts off as a pretty workmanlike hash. To see how a modest-sized pair of segments might fair if they represented pages 0→9 in the direct map, we ran the cross-correlation of the segment starting at page number 0 with those in adjacent sets of 64 pages. The result is shown graphically in Figure 5.11. A direct mapping would give a correlation of 1 in every case.

Remember in looking at Figure 5.11 that the actual 3033 TLB was two-way set-associative. Any two such segments could be completely accommodated, even the one at 1024 with its unity correlation. However, Figure 5.11 certainly confirms the effectiveness of the hashing function chosen, particularly when you consider that 10 pages on the 3033 is a segment of 40 KB and that all of those missing bars represent 0 interference.

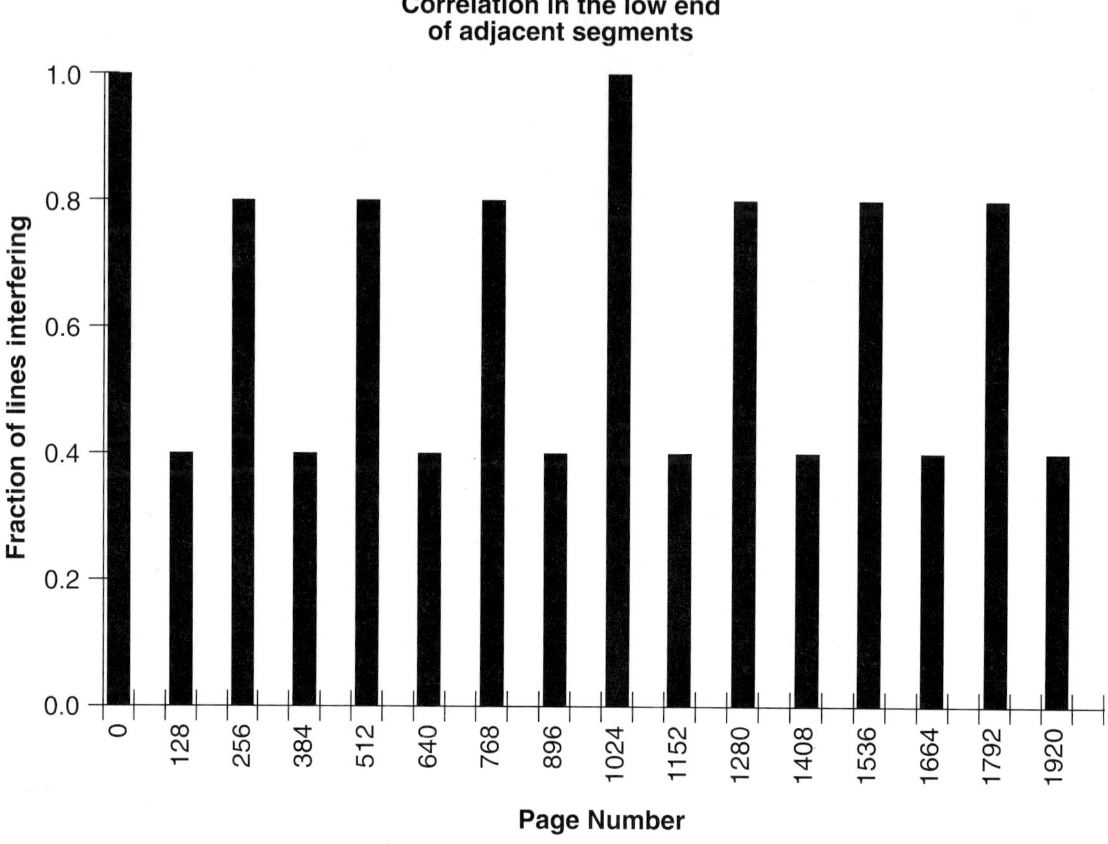

FIGURE 5.11 Cross-correlation between segments of 10 pages in the 3033 TLB using the hash function of Figure 5.10. The missing bars have a correlation of 0. That is, no pages in the two 10-page segments map into the same line.

None at all! Nice job and very typical of the very mathematical approach that has been characteristic of IBM innovation over the years.

5.4.2 Separate TLBs for System and Process

An important issue in TLB design is whether to single out system references from process references. All processes use the same system. When a context switch takes place, replacing one process's VA assignments with another's, the process's TLB entries must be invalidated. But the system is the same system with the same system VAs. Why switch them? There is no reason to, and since the TLB must be aware on each translation whether the address is from system or process space, it would be easy to separate the TLB into two halves and flush only the process data. The VAX is an example of a machine which does this, with split TLBs ranging across the family from 8:8 to 1024:1024. Two-way set-associative caches were used in all but the largest, which employs a linear cache [Levy, 89].

5.5 VIRTUAL OR PHYSICAL ADDRESSING?

If we use only PAs for accessing the data cache, we can be assured that whatever we get from cache corresponds (now or in the future) to some particular datum in some particular place in memory. The cost is that to get a PA, we must read the TLB, which takes approximately as long as reading the data cache itself. We could cut the cache access time roughly in half if we could avoid this sequential reading of TLB and cache. Since the cache is right in the critical timing path, competing with register access, cache access time must be kept very short. Several possibilities present themselves. These include:

- paralleling the TLB and cache searches
- using VAs constrained or constructed to be unique

Both work. Each has its own limitations.

Let us begin with parallelism. How can you search with a PA that you don't yet have in hand? You cannot, of course, but notice that you do have part of the PA—the offset bits—immediately. If the data cache is short enough, those bits can specify the cache line and word even while we are searching the TLB for the PA which must be compared against all tags in the cache for a hit. Figure 5.12 shows a system which does this. It is really a combination of Figure 5.2 and Figure 5.9. As long as the bits required to index into the data cache are not part of the virtual page number, we don't have to wait for the TLB. We can access cache and TLB at the same time, obtaining the physical page number at the same time as the tags which must be compared with it from the data cache.

This mechanism provides fast access, but it limits the height of the data cache. Since our page address is 24 bits, we have only 8 bits of offset. If we have a block size of 4, that leaves us only 6 bits for selecting a line—64 lines. To get a substantial cache, we would have to have a large set size. For example, a set size of 8 would give us only 2 KW (8 KB) of cache. The only way to beat these constrictions is to make the page size larger and thus increase the number of bits in the offset. This is precisely what IBM did in the 3033, whose hashing technique we just looked at. IBM used this parallel-search technique with a set size of 16 and a page size of 4 KB to have a 64-KB cache. A set size of 16 will make the cache more expensive, but it certainly will be fast, as befits this mainframe.

The restriction on the cache height for the scheme depicted in Figure 5.12 arises because we still insisted on using PAs. What was limited was the amount of the PA that is intrinsic to the VA. Why not simply use VAs in the data cache? Then, without restriction on the form factor for the cache, we could access TLB and cache at the same time, with a PA arriving just in time if a data cache miss occurred. VA caches have been built, but they come with two inherent problems:

1. A virtual address is valid only for a particular process. When we switch processes, the same virtual address refers to a different physical address. If the cache is small, we can afford to flush it every time we switch processes, but if it is large and if we can

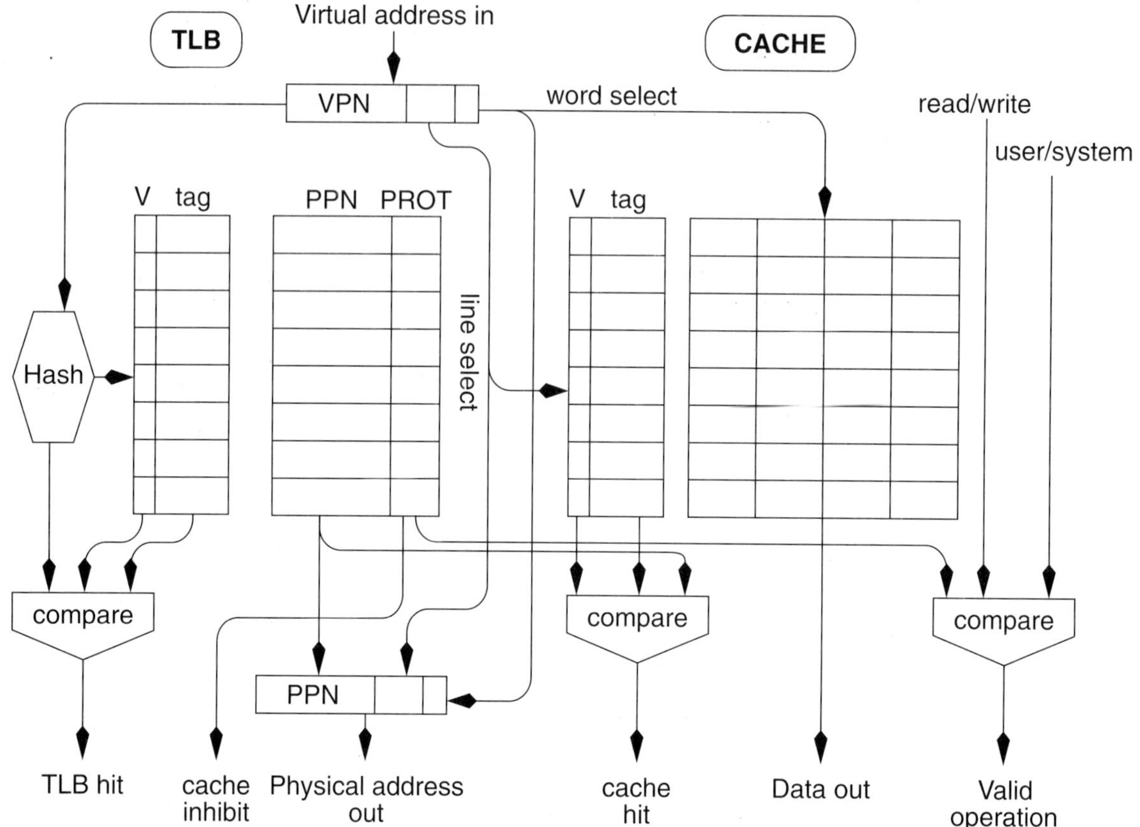

FIGURE 5.12 A combined TLB/cache where the offset bits are sufficient to allow a search of the cache even while the search of the TLB proceeds. All of the TLB outputs in Figure 5.9 are still available along with the cache outputs in Figure 5.2. Such a design would normally use a set-associative cache such as Figure 5.3 to increase cache capacity.

expect some useful data to remain when the first process returns, then flushing is expensive. One solution in that case is to append a process ID number (PID) to the VA. The PID becomes part of the tag, so addresses from different processes can't be confused. The PID should also be hashed into the bits used to index the cache, for essentially the same reasons that hashing is used in TLBs. Different processes tend to use the same ranges of virtual addresses, so they will tend to occupy the same areas of a virtual address cache unless something is done to spread them out. Notice that the TLB itself is a cache which uses virtual addresses, so we must either include a PID in the TLB tag or flush the TLB on context switches. One of the motivations for going to very long VAs—48 bits being popular—is to be able to include the PID in the VA.

2. A more subtle problem involves what are called *synonyms* or *aliases*. These occur when two virtual addresses are mapped to the same physical address. This can occur between two processes if they are sharing memory. It is very common for the operating system and process to address the process's pages with different VAs. Our

own memory management system, described in Chapter 4, does precisely that, as Figure 4.12 on page 191 shows. It is also possible for two virtual addresses within a process to map to the same physical address. Nothing in the definition of our paging mechanism prohibits that.

The problem with aliases in a VA cache is that when data is written to one of the VAs, it goes into the cache block corresponding to that address (and it may also be written to the main memory). Now what happens if the other virtual address is also in the cache, and the program tries to read it? The cache would have no way of knowing that the data should have changed.

This problem can be solved with minimal pain by guaranteeing that any physical address is represented by at most one valid entry in the virtual address cache. To see that this culling of the cache can be done, consider that the only time that aliases can get into the cache is when a miss occurs. When a miss occurs, the TLB obtains the PA to be sent to main memory. During the delay while the data is being read from the memory, the PA is used to look in a *reverse translation buffer* (RTB), which contains the virtual address corresponding to every physical address currently in the data cache. If there is a hit in the RTB, it means that another entry is present in the data cache with the same PA now being fetched from main memory. In that case, we can write back (if necessary) and then invalidate the block in the cache containing this alias. When the data comes back from the main memory, we write it into the data cache at the new VA, and we write its VA into the tag store and the RTB. While you might worry about thrashing between aliases, the alias problem normally arises only in widely separated events, such as having the operating system copy data to or from a process page and then having the process reference that same data but by different VAs. Such a sequence of events almost always means that the old set of VAs will not be used soon again. It is not the access by old VAs whose passing will be mourned but the loss from the cache of the data itself. This represents a moderately large loss in time which you pay infrequently; what you get for that cost is a faster cache. The payoff definitely can be positive. See [Smith, 82] for a more detailed explanation, and [Goodman, 87] for a similar mechanism designed for multiprocessors.

Finally, one subtle but critical VA cache issue: Should a read result in a miss that uncovers an alias, the cache MMU must finish any related writes that are pending before doing the read. Otherwise, stale data may be read into the cache at the new VA. Since a writethrough cache is frequently designed with *read priority*, this is a detail that must be attended to.

One advantage of a virtual address cache is that its speed does not depend on the TLB. In fact, the TLB is used only during a miss, so it can be relatively slow. SPUR [Hill, 86], [Wood, 86] takes advantage of this and, by keeping the translations in the data cache itself, avoids having a separate TLB.

With an instruction-only cache, whether it is the only cache, as in the MC68020, or the second stage in a two-level cache as in Figure 1.1, the alias problem does not arise because most systems do not allow self-modifying code without explicit action to flush the I-cache. In our RISC machine, we will use a relatively small VA cache for instructions, and simply flush it when the process changes.

5.6 MULTIPLE PROCESSORS, SNOOPING, SNARFING, AND INTERVENTION

Having just dismissed the problems of aliases in our I-cache by again casting scorn on those who would write self-modifying code (and providing an out in case they insist), we should pause to consider the complications which can arise when a well-run computer system has more than one cache to handle. That situation is more common than you might suspect. Obviously a multiprocessor will have more than one cache, but even a very simple computer, such as our RISC machine, can benefit by having different caches for different functions. Why, in fact, do we want two caches in Figure 1.1? To execute one instruction in each clock cycle, we must be able to fetch an instruction and do a data *read* or *write* simultaneously. Doing that requires either a *dual-ported* cache memory and separate routes for data and instructions or two caches and those same separate routes. A dual-ported cache is not simply two doors into the same room but two doors into two rooms with the same contents. Since we would have two memories and two routes in any case, we, like most other designers, will use a separate instruction cache and optimize that cache for instruction usage. We also have a TLB, which is yet a third cache. These three caches, however, work together in a way that keeps their contents *synchronized*. While you might have data in the I-cache that is no longer in the D-cache, it had been there and was the latest version when it was brought into I-cache. The translations in the TLB are or at least were those that were used to fetch the data that is in the D-cache. While it is true that the system has the privilege to rewrite pagetables and thus to obsolete its TLB entries, one must presume that it will not do such a thing without flushing the TLB. Accordingly, TLB and I-cache will remain synchronized with the D-cache. However, with parallel rather than hierarchical arrangement of the caches, it is possible to get into some trouble even in a simple uniprocessor system.

5.6.1 In Which Progress Has Unanticipated Results—The MC68040 Writeback Cache

The MC68040, an elegant and speedy member of the MC68000 family, has inadvertently provided us with an important cautionary tail on shooting yourself in the foot with a cache policy. We have several times in this book inveighed against those who would write self-modifying code. Few would disagree that self-modifying code is an invitation to disaster. But a little caution is called for. Just what constitutes code and what data?

There is little doubt that all code was once data—the output of some compiler or assembler and then some linker. "All right," you say, "but it wasn't being executed at that time or in that process." True enough, but let us carry this a bit further. How does code get into the memory to be executed? Easy enough. If you are working within a *development environment*, such as that provided by Think C, the executable program is the output of a compilation and linking that just finished. You are still in the application and can jump into the program with some protective oversight from the environment provided. In truth, your program here is data fresh from the oven. It has every reason to still be in cache. Alternatively, if you made your program into a stand-alone application, it gets read in from disk. What does the reading? Fancy folks, used to nothing but the best, might answer: "A DMA (direct memory access) chip pumps it right into memory." Those used to making do with less expensive stuff might respond: "The CPU reads it in and puts it into memory." Indeed. And what was the state of that stuff *read in* and *put in*? No question about it, it was data. Herein lies an interesting tale.

Consider the Macintosh and its operating system, Multifinder. Unlike UNIX and other preemptive multiprogramming operating systems,[1] in Multifinder, multiple processes share the same processing space through collaborative protocols. Heap and heap management are very important in these protocols. One of the things that can and normally does end up on the heap are certain subroutines. It is proper (and not self-modifying code) to pass pointers to a subroutine in a call to some other routine and also to call subroutines by pointer. C admits this paradigm quite directly; Macintosh Pascals were adapted to allow it. So far, no problem.

One of the protocols which is part of the Macintosh operating system is crunching the heap. The idea is to squeeze the space out of the typical Swiss-cheese allocation pattern in a well-used heap. To accommodate this heap crunch without dislocation, programmers are supposed to use *handles* (pointers to pointers) for the heap rather than direct pointers. The handles point to a table of heap pointers. The table is updated whenever the heap is crunched; the handles remain with the program. Accordingly, even when the heap is compacted, the handles always access the correct parts of the heap. Again, so far no problem.

Now consider an important detail in the MC68000 family of processors. The processors provide an external signal with each memory reference which describes whether a particular reference is *user*, *system*, or *interrupt* (most useful for providing memory protection) and whether the item is *instruction* or *data*. Of course, the machine has no insight into what the programmer thinks this datum is useful for. All that the CPU is indicating is whether the address is coming from the PC (an instruction fetch) or whether the address is associated with a LOAD or STORE operation. Since these operations are rendered distinct even outside the chip, you can manage memory quite effectively from outside the chip. That looks like an advantage when the chip is bare, but there is a hidden pit with snakes at the bottom of it.

In the MC68020, the first fully 32-bit version of this family, Motorola added a small, direct-mapped instruction cache to the chip. In effect, this produced a Harvard architecture in that the instruction stream was at least partially separated from the data stream. If you wrote tight, self-modifying code, you had to flush the I-cache, but everyone knew that. Still no problem.

---

[1] UNIX does not consider itself *preemptive* in the sense that we introduced in Chapter 4 where one process can preempt another, but it is preemptive in the sense that the operating system can, on its own, perform context switches for any one of a variety of reasons. In Multifinder, a process may be switched out only if it agrees to be switched out.

In the MC68030, Motorola added an onboard writethrough data cache. The D-cache danced no fancy read-before-write or write-buffering jigs. If you wrote a datum, it went to memory before anything else happened. The D-cache and the memory always had the same data. If you obeyed the rule about flushing the I-cache, you got what you thought you would get.

Now comes the MC68040. This was to be a really high performance chip with on-board everything. To push the performance to new heights, it was decided to make the D-cache writeback. Reasoning said that the plain-pipe-rack and secondhand folks would not be opting for this high-class chip with onboard everything and that anyone who had spent this much money just for the CPU command center would hardly be doing I/O without a DMA. Probably correct as far as it goes, but what does this do for or to the heap cruncher or program developer who has just bought a top-of-the-line Mac? Yes, that heap cruncher has DMAs for going to disk, but when you crunch the heap, you do it with the CPU. Now you see the evil dragon coming out of its lair. As you crunch the heap, you run "it" through the D-cache. The "it" can contain both code and data. The D-cache writes back only what it cannot hold, so some fraction of that heap crunch is now resident *only* in D-cache.

Now control goes back to the running program. It sooner or later executes an instruction fetch to program on the heap. Since this is an I-fetch, it is referenced to the onboard I-cache which had nothing to do with the data flow in the heap crunch. Since the instruction desired is not in I-cache, the MC68040 goes to memory. Unfortunately, whatever is there in memory has nothing to do with the executing routine; those instructions still reside only in D-cache. Crash!

The short-term cure was quite primitive: turn off the D-cache and give up the performance enhancement it confers. The longer term cure was to flush the D-cache after a crunch or any time that a routine gets written to the heap—inelegant and costly in bus cycles. Here are people who do not write self-modifying code and whose software has stood the test of time and the migration to more sophisticated CPUs being caught by a problem not of their own making which goes under the name of *cache consistency*. Let us turn to that topic.

5.6.2 Coherence and Sequentiality

When multiple D-caches serve multiple CPUs, they introduce not only the cache *coherency* or *consistency* problem but worse yet, they introduce the possibility of breaking causality in that the order of events seen by one processor may not be the same as the order of the same events seen by another. These two issues are important enough to call for precise definitions.

Coherence. We say that two caches are *coherent* or *consistent* if, when data at a particular memory address is present in both caches, that data is identical. We may also say that a cache is *coherent* with memory if the data in cache is identical with its matchmates in memory. If processor A modifies a datum and then B (or A) references that datum in another cache, if the new value is returned, then the caches are coherent. If the CPUs are independent, it is almost inevitable that they will not always see identical values in their caches for identical addresses. Just the delay between a request from the CPU to write something and the actual writing to memory virtually guarantees that A and B will sometimes have inconsistent caches. Certainly in writeback caches but even in writethrough caches, there are periods when caches hold values different from memory and different from each other. While bus latency says that we cannot expect to reduce the duration of inconsistencies to zero, we would like to be able to say that they will persist for *at most* some specified and short time. To that end there is a lovely sentence in the *Alpha Architecture Handbook* under the heading *Timeliness*: ". . . a write by one processor to a given location may not be delayed indefinitely in the access order for that location" [Alpha, 92, p. 5-13].

Sequentiality. By *perfect sequentiality* we mean that the order of operations performed by processor A appears the same if viewed from the perspective of A or any other processor connected to the same memory. One can have perfect sequentiality without maintaining cache coherence and cache coherence obtained at some moment need not imply correct sequentiality. Just as delays in the delivery of data mean that we cannot insist that caches be always coherent, so if we want the CPUs in the multiprocessor to be able to function independently, we must not insist that perfect sequentiality be guaranteed. There are times when we would want to guarantee that all involved observers see the same order of events. We will want to be able to enforce sequentiality when it counts and ignore it when it does not. (Remember that we did vote for sequentiality when we decided that our LODSET instruction would flush the cache WRITE buffer before execution. That takes care of a single processor, but with writeback caches and multiple CPUs, life is much more complicated.)

5.6.3 Updating Data in Multiple Caches

Solving the general cache inconsistency problem entirely in hardware is moderately difficult. It gets more difficult as the system connectivity grows in complexity. With a few CPUs sharing a common bus and a common memory—the situation we have been flirting with in this chapter—we have a situation where every participant can watch every bus transaction. This is King Arthur's Table Round, or at least a small town meeting. Everything public is universally shared. The problem is, not everything is public. With several CPUs all pounding on main memory, the bus will be jammed with traffic unless we are very careful to go to main memory only when absolutely necessary. Such an objective almost inevitably leads one to use a writeback cache. Consider a system with two independent CPUs, *A* and *B*. Let us assume that one application is running on both CPUs. That makes it very clear that *A* and *B* will share data. Say that code running on *A* creates a data structure on the heap and then passes the pointer to that data to *B* by writing it to a global variable. Unfortunately, *B* got a copy of that global the last time that it processed *A* data. *B* is supposed to notice that the pointer has changed, process the new data to create yet another data structure in heap, and respond to *A* by writing the pointer to that structure into another global. This is a neat way to synchronize these two independent processors in a *producer-consumer* operation, but unless we tag this global as uncacheable for both caches, how will *B* ever become aware that *A* has changed the global's value in *A*'s own cache? How, except by going to memory, would *B* become aware that *A* had written it to main memory?

A principal reason for having caches was to limit bus traffic. If three processes share a variable, then if one writes, two must read to stay current. Turning one write into three memory operations seems like a truly pessimal solution to cache inconsistency. However, a little money and a little cleverness make several hardware solutions quite practical. Let us begin with writethrough caches which will guarantee that data gets written to memory not too long after it gets written to local cache. If the three caches watch the address stream on the memory bus, in principle, *A* could discover that *B* or *C*—it matters not who—has just updated something that *A* is holding in cache. Having a cache watch everyone else's writes to memory has earned the sobriquet *snoopy caching*. In order to be able to use a cache while we snoop, we simply duplicate the tag store, so one tag store can be used to check for external writes while the other is being used for normal cache accesses. If an external hit is detected, the snooping machine simply invalidates the datum in its local cache and on the next access, the local cache misses and updates its value from main memory. Snoopy caching is fairly common in multiprocessor systems [Eggers, 89]. To use snoopy caching with virtual address caches, the snoopy tag store uses PAs as well as the VAs—one for snooping and the other for finding the entry in the cache [Goodman, 87]. Snoopy caching solves the problem of how several caches can become aware that a datum they are holding has just been updated. The availability of this information reduces bus traffic since it assures a processor that its cached data is up to date. It does not have to update anything continuously (e.g., render uncacheable) to keep any memory datum current. We will still need uncacheable pages for memory-mapped peripherals, where data can change without traffic on the bus.

Why, you might wonder, if a cache can snoop on addresses, does it not also snoop on data? After all, data and address come down the same pike. Why invalidate data when you can *snarf* it up as it passes by? Snarf? A not unsuggestive word to indicate gobbling something down. We doubt that it has made your dictionary yet, but if you are American-speaking and of the typical age to be reading this book, you probably have heard it or used it. In any case, the young tigers of the computer hardware world have so named caches that snoop on addresses and snatch data from the bus to maintain consistency in common holdings. If the snarfing cache must deal with word or byte writes to memory (rather than block writes), the cache upkeep is much more complicated. But if a lot of data is shared, you save much bus traffic and shorten cache incoherence time substantially by snarfing.

The difficulty with snoopy caches is the obligation to use writethrough caching. If there are many CPUs, writeback caches are almost obligatory. But then how can one cache snoop on the actions in another cache? There are various solutions to this problem, which becomes more severe as the number of processors increases [Agarwal, 88] [Agarwal, 89][Bitar, 86][Dubois, 88]. While pondering such esoterica as snooping and snarfing, we should not ignore a primitive methodology which completely eliminates cache coherence problems: No caching the shared data. Our memory management unit provides a *cache-inhibit bit* for this very purpose. For example, we could set this bit for all pages of bin 1 to force all global variables to reside only in memory. While *uncaching* the globals slows down access to those data and increases bus traffic, the program is always permitted to make a local copy. This copy is a snapshot of the value of the global at some moment. The copy will reside in cache or even in register. It can be changed for local purposes *without affecting the global*. Nor will the local variable ever be changed by snarfing. But if the global is to be used for intercommunication between segments of a program or between two separate applications sharing common data, then the global itself must be used and it must reside only in memory. We have, in effect, moved the responsibility for updating the global right into the hands of the programmer. That sage individual should have the best idea of when synchronization should occur. By making it explicit even in the high-level program—local variable versus global variable—the programmer can know precisely what is being changed and when. Note that this still does not in itself satisfy the needs of mutual exclusion or strict temporal ordering. To achieve those ends, you must, we hope we have convinced you, resort to nothing less than a semaphore methodology (or equivalent) such as that described in Table 3.2. The semaphore itself must come from cache-inhibited memory, but cache inhibition is necessary but not sufficient for achieving strict ordering and exclusion. You still have read-before-write preference on the same CPU and sequential bus sharing with other CPUs.

If a data area is modifiable by more than one CPU or even if it should be read only when in some coherent form, one may use the semaphore methods of Chapter 3 to give to one CPU at a time exclusive access to critical blocks of memory. One may still take advantage of a writeback cache as long as the data is written back before it is opened to others. A good example of a problem that is easily solved by well-timed writeback is maintaining a queue structure. To begin with, that usually requires that exclusive access to the whole queue be accorded to one processor. During the update of the queue, no other processor may even read the queue data. If this exclusive use is a rare event, the spinlock which stops useful processing on another CPU is not a bad burden. Where mutual exclusion is employed, the unit of memory that may be locked for exclusive use is usually limited to a page or less. If you are trying to do that with a writeback cache, the master-to-be must have some hardware means of acquiring the lock. Once acquired, the CPU works its changes, forces a write back, and releases the page. The following example from [Alpha, 92, page 5-8] is typical (and conceptually similar to what the microcode does in the VAX):

```
spin_loop:
    LDQ_L R1, lock_variable   ;load quadword Locked (hardware lock set)[2]
    BLBS  R1, already_set     ;br on LO bit set (test software lock)
    OR    R1, #1, R2          ;(set software lock)
    STQ_C R2, lock_variable   ;Store quadword Conditional (if hardware
                              ;lock set, reset and store. R2 ⇐ lock)
```

[2] DEC's use of *lock* here is confusing. Alpha's "lock" is more of a *telltale* in that it indicates to this CPU whether any other CPU accessed the area. The other CPUs do not detect the presence of the "lock."

```
    BEQ   R2, stq_c_fail      ;(somebody else has reset the lock!)
    MB                        ;memory barrier (synchronize cache/memory)
    <critical section>
    MB
    STQ   R31, lock_variable ;R31=NUL, clears software lock
    ...
already_set:
    <code to block or reschedule or test for too many iterations>
    BR    spin_loop
stq_c_fail:
    <code to test for too many iterations>
    BR    spin_loop
```

Notice that you have a mechanism not only for locking a block of memory but also for some way of assuring that a writeback will be accomplished in full at some particular point in the execution of a program. You might wonder why two memory barrier (MB) instructions are required. The first assures us that the data we are going to use in the critical section was not prefetched before the lock was acquired. The second one assures us that the queue represented in memory is coherent before the lock is released.

In our system, if writeback caching is elected, forcing a writeback is done at program level by a system call. At the system level, any line in the cache can be replaced. If its dirty bit is set, the line is written back. A D-cache miss represents a transaction which should follow the update of main memory. To that end, the MMU will suspend CPU activity (*stall* the CPU) until the writeback is completed. If you wonder why we have put a barrier between processes and synchronization—why we have no simple MB instruction—the answer is that a barrier is required between processes and all access to the MMU. We have memory-mapped all registers and ports in the MMU into pages in system space that are off-base for processes. Then, to provide access to those ports or registers which a process might need, we simply have a trap operation. Traps are very fast on our machine, and the extra burden of the TRAP/RFI pair is small enough.

On the Alpha chip, DEC's 64-bit RISC, two instructions are provided to achieve similar ends. These are MB (*memory barrier*) and IMB (*instruction memory barrier*). The first guarantees that all LOAD/STORE operations performed before the MB will complete before the next instruction executes. It synchronizes the cache and main memory. The second instruction synchronizes the I-cache with main memory. To accomplish that, it first must execute an MB to be sure that no modified code remains exclusively in the D-cache and then flush the I-cache. Note that this is a sequence of operations deriving from a single instruction, something not normally allowed in a RISC. In reality, it is not an instruction at all but a trap into a system routine. A close look at the two instructions reveals an important difference:

> MB is a regular instruction. While the cache may run on for a while with it, the CPU executes MB just as it would any other instruction. IMB, on the other hand, is *PALcode* (Privileged Architecture Library), a subroutine which runs in system mode. In spite of the

name, some PALcode is unprivileged. Those of us in the common masses who write code can call upon it whenever—banish the thought—we choose to write self-modifying code. (While we have been bashing self-modifying code relentlessly, it should be pointed out that anyone who programs in any language and then compiles and links to produce an executable image has *modified code*. Should that code be executed immediately in the same address space, as it can be in some environments, the programmer has, however innocently, created exactly the problem for which an IMB is necessary.)

MB solves the problem for CPU *A* of synchronizing cache *A* with memory. It does nothing about informing cache *B* that things have changed. Snooping and snarfing can help. These are really local facilities built right into the caches that would snoop or snarf. Cache *A* should be blissfully unaware that others are snooping or snarfing. Both detection and update are done simply by "hearing" cache *A* talking to memory. As long as the bus traffic is done in clear and recognized patterns, the comparison of addresses between cache and bus is no different from the normal cache operation of comparing a CPU address or TLB address with cache tags. It is neither more work nor less. It is just the usual amount of work. Snooping precedes snarfing. If the current address scores a hit, the line which follows must be read in and must update the current line in the cache—unless. . . . What would happen if *B* had modified its own value of this common data but had not yet done or finished executing its MB? Whose value is retained? Now you see what the sequentiality issue is. If sequentiality counts, some form of lock is essential.

The nice thing about snarfing is that caches get synchronized without extra bus traffic. The unfortunate thing about snarfing is that, if you use writeback caching, you have to do something like Alpha's MB every time that you need to let other parties know about an update. MB is undoubtedly a bus hog. It moves back to memory every local variable, every counter—anything that could just as well reside in cache and *never* go back to memory. If you do it often enough, it would make writeback look like a rather dyspeptic writethrough. There ought to be a better way, a way of updating only on demand or only on need. Enter *intervention*.

Intervention is a partial solution to this problem of excessive writeback. It is the mirror image of snarfing and is provided for in some modern busses such as Futurebus.

- In **snarfing**, the cache watches for a write to memory of one of its lines by another processor. When it detects the hit, it updates its own data as the other data passes by.
- In **intervention**, the cache watches the system bus for a memory-read reference to one of its dirty lines. When it detects a hit, it intercedes, taking over the bus for the data transmission and sending the updated line from cache instead of permitting stale data from memory being sent. Memory can, of course, snarf to update its own record, allowing *A* to mark its line as clean. Intervention should occur only if the dirty bit is set.

A problem with intervention arises if two or more caches hold updated information. Which of them should respond and what should the others do about the response? Various schemes have been proposed to define a pecking order and proper responses (or, at least, well-defined responses) by all holders of the data. A good example is found in [Papamarcos, 85].

In a writeback cache for our machine, we worried about the cost of a total writeback. The only time you are obligated to write back all dirty lines is at a context switch (to support page swaps and the like). The issue of coherency can be tackled on a line-by-line basis by providing software a way to specify which line to write back. In effect, you say STORE and then you say NOW. The mechanism is simple. One must read another line which will map into that line in the cache. That uses the mechanism already there to force a writeback. The process cannot tell how things map into the cache (unless the cache is using VAs for the mapping) so we will require a method to generate such an address. We will develop one explicitly in Section 5.7.3.2.

Single-line, programmer-specifiable writeback has two very useful advantages. The first we have already cited: less bus traffic. The second is support of information interchange between different processors sharing variables. If the other CPUs' caches are snooping or snarfing, you can feed them by forcing the writeback of only the line containing the shared variable. While this does not do what MB does on the Alpha, where the whole cache is synchronized, it allows the software to synchronize quite specifically while gaining maximum benefit from the writeback cache. A problem at the chapter's end deals with the issue of generating the right address for synchronizing one line in the cache.

5.6.4 Cache Consistency When One Bus Won't Do

It is important at the end of this limited summary of multiple caches to say what we have not done. There is an enormous amount of work going on at this time on *massively parallel* computer structures. These devices have the potential for coupling thousands of processors together. At these levels of connectivity there is no possibility of using a single bus as interconnect. It would be like tying Manhattan together on a single party line. No one could talk. The line would always be busy. There are several interconnecting configurations that are being pursued widely. Some might be considered to be modeled after the telephone system with switchable interconnects (a good example of this approach is the *Butterfly Machine*) while others have each CPU directly connected to some number of nearest-neighbor CPUs with data *diffusing* over longer distances (*Hypercube*). In these massively parallel machines, main memory is mostly an I/O buffer. Each machine is almost an island to itself with its own local memory and one or two caches frequently on the CPU chip itself. Caching is often used on the interconnections themselves just as I/O caches are often used in more conventional systems. With these many layers, local memory coherence and the mechanics of inter- and intra-process communication become the very heart of the design.

One of the biggest problems with these massive machines is to make the overhead scale in sublinear fashion. If it takes a certain amount of work to keep track of which caches have certain data in a machine with 128 processors, then if you need four times as much structure for a machine of 512 processors, the work of searching that list (and many other such tasks) may increase much faster than fourfold. For example, if each shared line got a bit for every cache in which the line was stored, searching that line will require reading 64 bytes rather than 16. You lose much of the advantage of the scale-up in the labor of tracking and moving data.

To address just such issues in a network of collaborating processors, an IEEE group has been working on and recently approved specifications [IEEE, 92] for what is called the *Scalable Coherent Interface* (SCI) [Gustavson, 92]. The basic assumption in this design is that all communications will be point-to-point. That is, each transmitter is hooked to a unique receiver, permitting matched-line transmission, which is limited only by the speed of light and the width of the data path. Why this is fundamentally different from the more usual many-receiver bus structure is a central topic for Chapter 8. What is important here is that all of our just-developed mechanisms of snooping, snarfing, and intervention get blown away when there is no shared bus structure. The SCI clearly had to have another way to deal with shared variables and synchronization, but given their premises of high numbers of caches and no direct route between most caches, that solution was not going to look like any other. The solution depends upon the following observations:

- By an enormous margin, most variables are not shared.
- Most shared variables are shared by only two caches.

What is done is to add node pointers to the information stored in the cache line and to create a small table in memory. The extra storage is used to form a doubly linked list of nodes holding a particular block of shared data. The table in memory is the anchor point for the list. Along with the pointers which can establish a list, status bits are included which support unshared, shared, pairwise shared, and lock-bit sharing of a data structure. The idea of these several modes of sharing is to minimize the traffic necessary to support sharing. For example, unshared data is obtained directly from memory. Pairwise sharing simply requires the pair to inform each other. For lock-bit sharing, the community sharing the resource must be able to resolve conflicts and unambiguously assign one member sole access. Following the acquisition, the data master modifies the data in its own cache and then passes it on to those who are sharing. Ways must be designed for timeouts and recovery if a node which owns a lock goes off the air. It is easy to withdraw from a list of participants by simply informing your nearest neighbors in the community—those whom you point to—to point to each other instead. The organization begins to resemble a town with a telephone system. The town breaks up into small, overlapping groups whose protocols are selected for the activities of the group. Connections are point-to-point. Sometimes message passing is used to spread common data among multiple "processors." There is a problem in carrying this analogy too far because the human processors are highly adaptive and generally slow—rather like executing the protocols in software. If you want things flying about at the speed of light, you have to use fast hardware. That is inevitably limited in its perspective and adaptability. Hence precise and rigid set of protocols must be adopted. Interestingly, the committee has chosen to make the protocol description *executable*, having written it in C. In that way, hardware designers can test their behavioral models directly against the standard.

5.6.5 Ideas about a Reverse Translation Buffer

Our machine's clock rate is now glaringly slow so we will be able to use PAs in our cache with no difficulty. Were we to zoom up to the heights of chips such as DEC's Alpha processor (200 MHz), there would be no way that we could get through the TLB and then the cache in a time short enough to make the cache results useful. We would have to resort to a writeback cache indexed directly through VAs. With a VA-indexed cache, the VA is delivered simultaneously to TLB and data cache. Data is being delivered even while the PA is coming out and the tags, valid bits, and access rights are being checked. Data from the data cache is presumed good unless proven to be otherwise. It will be good more than 95 percent of the time. When it is not, the system takes the loss of time associated with hurrying down the wrong path, but that loss is not a large fraction of the memory cycle in any case. The only problem which must be solved is the elimination of multiple copies of data from the same physical page.

One obvious place such multiple copies will arise—not *might* but *will*—is in the adding of a new page to heap or stack. The system adds the page and then zeroes the page to assure that no one else's data gets delivered. In zeroing the page, the kernel will use either the SVA = PA addresses or, optionally, the SVA of the form 10xxxxxx shown in Figure 4.12 on page 191. In either case, these addresses will not be the same ones that the process would use to access the same page. Since the addition of a stack page inevitably follows an attempt to write to that page, as soon as the kernel returns control to the process, the process will write, using a different VA, to that very same page. Since this is a writeback cache, the zero that the process is attempting to overwrite in the page probably has not been written back to memory. It exists in cache only and in a line that has no relationship to the line to be written by the process. Somehow, we have to get that line of zeroes back to memory. Enter the RTB.

RTBs can be constructed in many forms [Wang, 89][Goodman, 87], but let us limit ourselves to our own machine and a specific example. Let us say that we had a 16-KW cache in a direct-mapped arrangement with 4 KL of 4 words/line. With our 32-bit address, this says that a VA or PA can be parsed as shown in Figure 5.13.

First, let us dispose in the cheapest manner possible of the kernel/process problem of having two virtual addresses pointing to the same PA. If the only problem were the one we just described of having the kernel deliver a zeroed page to the process, we need only insist that the kernel use the 10xxxxxx address form for zeroing the page. With reference to Figure 4.12, if we use that form of addressing, the SVA and PVA will differ only in the uppermost byte. Thus, the cache index will be the same for both addresses and the data will be in the same line in cache. The zeroed page will be dirty, so when the tags do not match—they differ in the upper 8 bits—the writeback cache will simply write the data back and then, unwittingly, read it in again. Thus, the direct-mapped writeback cache would expunge any duplicate VA addressing *as long as we enforce a rule of having a common index*. This is cheap and easy. It covers a big piece of the problem. If the only sharing is between the kernel and individual processes, we are done. If we want to allow interprocess sharing or if we want to snoop or snarf, we have not begun. So how do we do a RTB?

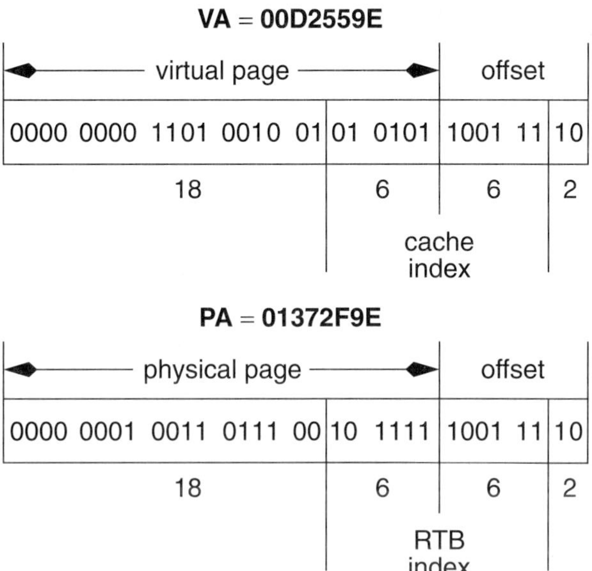

FIGURE 5.13 Parsing of the VA and its associated PA to show the 12-bit cache and RTB indices. The low-order 6 bits are common; the high-order 6 bits generally different. The upper 18 bits form the tag in each case.

The answer begins with Figure 5.13. Notice that for the specific cache that we defined for that figure, the PA and VA share the lowest 6 bits of their indices. Since the upper 6 bits are now allowed to be freely assigned, there are 63 other lines which could reference this same PA. How would we recognize such a collision? The basic solution would be to construct an RTB of 4K entries, one for every line in our data cache. Each 24-bit entry is the PA tag associated with that line. Once we have the low-order 6 bits of the RTB index, we compare all 64 lines to see if there is a match. There can be at most one, because we will always expunge the older reference from the cache. The address of the match in the RTB identifies the line in the cache. An example is in order.

Let us say that the VA is 00D2559E and that the TLB (or system bus) delivers a PA of 01372F9E. As advertised, the last 8 bits match. The VA-indexed cache will go to line 567 (hex) and, by assumption, will find a mismatch in tags. Accordingly, the MMU must fetch a new line from memory into cache. With the last 2 bits truncated, that block of 4 words will come from the PA 01372F9C. The question that the RTB must answer is: Is that same PA line referenced by another VA on some other line in the cache? The RTB is searched on all 64 entries whose last 6 RTB-index bits are 100111. These comprise the set 027, 067, 0A7, 0E7, 127, . . . , FE7. If the RTB returned a hit on 0A7, it would indicate that line 0A7 had a reference to this specific physical address. By hypothesis, we have assumed that we had already had a cache miss, so we know that this could not be the same VA we started with. In other words, we have already searched line 567 and found something else there. Whatever is in line

0A7, its presence is incompatible with this VA. It should be written out (if dirty) and invalidated.

A hit identifies the right line. If you are snarfing, just pick those words from the system bus and plant them in the cache. The method is complete. The only thing that should look a little alarming is the idea of doing 64 compares. You might well contend that the data would have long since passed you by while you were still stepping through the RTB. It need not be that bad.

VLSI and a few dollars will bring the search time down to any reasonable standard. There is no reason why you could not arrange to have all 64 tags come down at once. With a modern CMOS technology, the 64 comparisons could be accomplished on chip in under 5 ns. The whole memory is still only 4K × 25 (we have included a valid bit with each tag). It is just that we have arranged the entries in 64 memories of 64 × 25. While it might be hard to buy that as a ready-made chip, it would not be a difficult design in VLSI.

Alternatively, in a method suggested by [Goodman, 87], we could use direct addressing using the whole RTB index. Stored at that location is an 18-bit PA tag and the upper six bits of the VA cache index. Those six bits enable us to identify the line in the cache while the 18 bits are sufficient to identify the PA of that line. As soon as we have a PA, we can go directly to the correct entry in the RTB. If the PAs match and the cache line that we find is *different* from the one we are going to replace, we must flush it to avoid having two lines referencing one PA. While this certainly simplifies the design of the RTB, it has the undesirable effect of mapping many PAs into the same RTB entry. Thus, rather than having an RTB entry tied to a line in the cache, it will be tied to a family of PAs which share a common RTB index. If you have a conflict here, Goodman suggests that you flush the line in question to open up the RTB slot for the new entry. He is paying for his simplicity of RTB searching by having both empty lines in cache and extra bus traffic.

We are not going to include an RTB, since we have cycle time to burn, but were we really in the race to be *fastest CPU on the block*, we would be obliged to adopt a VA cache and an RTB. From what we have presented, you should be convinced that you could put one in and that it would not break the silicon budget.

5.7 DESIGNING A DATA CACHE FOR OUR RISC MACHINE

5.7.1 Design Choices—Size and Mapping

To complete this chapter, let us design a data cache for our machine. The data cache system will include the data cache itself, the TLB, the interface to a VMEbus or Futurebus (one of which will be the system bus), and one or more state machines for control. While our on-chip instruction cache will be somewhat limited by chip area, the data cache will not be on-chip, so we can make it much larger and choose any reasonable organization. Before we can begin the design by drawing a block diagram, we have to make some decisions about the organization and sizes of the caches:

- PAs or VAs?
- Direct-mapped or set-associative?
- Cache size? Set size?
- Block size? Possibly sector size?
- Writethrough or writeback?
- Fetch-on-write misses?
- Direct-mapped, set-associative, or fully associative TLB?
- TLB size? TLB set size?

How do we start? First, examine Table 5.1. The table is based on the speed ratio of the main memory and cache chips that we expect to buy. The initial rapid improvement in performance with cache size suggests that we want a hit rate above 95 percent. Beyond that point, each hit-rate percentage point improves the average access time by about 1.5 ns.

Now we can look at Figure 5.8 and Table 5.2 to see how big the cache should be. These data are a better choice for this purpose than Figure 5.7 because they were based on a far more general workload. Still more accurate estimates would be based on simulations of our specific machine with programs typical of our expected customers, but the table will suffice for now. Figure 5.8 strongly suggests a block size greater than one. Bus and memory performance will be better as well since the overhead of acquiring mastery of the bus and decoding the address is distributed over more data. Table 5.2 strongly suggests a cache size of at least 4096 words (16 KB), preferably more. A compelling reason for making any choice is the ready availability of suitable components. For example, fast 16K $\times$ 4 RAM chips are widely available. They would permit building an inexpensive 16-KW direct-mapped cache using 8 of them and 5 tag RAMs of 4K $\times$ 4 chips.

As a first cut at picking a design, let us try the organization of Figure 5.12. That was an excellent cache design for the IBM 3033. Unfortunately, our page size is 1 KB versus 4 KB in the 3033. With that page size, the total size of our cache would be 1 KB times the set size. Since we want a 4-KW cache, we would need a 16-way set-associative cache. Using a large set size involves too much extra hardware. The alternative of limiting the total size to a few kilobytes will not achieve a reasonable hit rate. That option is eliminated, but if our page size were larger, we might consider it. Notice that a choice of page size, which was based on the system considerations in Chapter 3, is a determining factor in specifying cache hardware. The design choices are anything but orthogonal.

Second cut would be a set-associative cache. We noted in Section 5.3 that set-associative caches gave better hit rates per kilobyte than direct caches. Better performance should not be based on hit rate at constant kilobytes but on effective memory speed per dollar. If the same dollar buys more performance in a direct cache because the direct cache has more kilobytes, then direct caching should be our choice. Table 5.2 does not encourage us to use a set-associative cache. By the time you are operating above 95 percent, the gain in hit rate would produce only a few nanoseconds improvement in the average access time. To get those few nanoseconds, we will have to spend some money. The obvious questions are:

- How much?
- Are the few nanoseconds worth that much?

The second question is a curious one. We are not talking about a go–no-go decision. If you have a cache, you are going to get some cache misses. What we are talking about is having a few less or few more of them. Notice how different these few nanoseconds are from those of the cache chips themselves. If the cache chip must respond in 24 ns, a 20-ns chip will work and a 25-ns chip will not. Those "few nanoseconds" are worth the price. On the other hand, will the customer buy your machine over your competitors' if it runs his/her application 1 percent faster? Will they buy your machine if it is 1 percent more expensive for its 1 percent faster speed? Legitimate questions on which we have no expertise. We suspect that 1 percent variations in speed and price are in the noise.

The first question is more easily plumbed. If we used conventional RAMs, we would need more than twice as many RAM chips simply to divide the memory into two banks. The biggest expense in a board-level product is board space, which translates directly to chip count. A specific comparison can be obtained from Table 5.3. A direct cache of 64 KW built of 15-ns chips can be compared to a two-way set-associative cache of the same size and speed. We assume that you need to access only one word at a time, not a whole line. This allows us to use a data memory that is 32 bits wide and use the built-in word selector in the memory chip as our "MUX" for selecting the appropriate word in the line as well as the line itself. The calculations of chip cost are constructed as shown:

Direct. 64 KW in blocks of 4 W gives 16 KL. Then 16 KL implies a line selector of 14 bits, which leaves 18 bits for tag. Add to that 1 bit each for *valid* and *dirty* bits, you end up with a line being 148 bits wide. (See Figure 5.2 for the configuration.) From Table 5.3, we can select an array of chips comprising:

two 64K $\times$ 16 chips @ $75 (64 KW of data)
one 16K $\times$ 4 chip @ $15 and one 16K $\times$ 16 chip @ $35
total chip count of four at a chip cost of $200

Set-associative. We still have 64 KW in blocks of 4 W but now we have only 8 KL with two blocks in each. (See Figure 5.3 for the configuration.) Now the line selector is 13 bits, leaving 21 bits for the tag and valid and dirty bits. Each side now needs 149 bits, so we must go to a width of 152. Presuming that no one makes an 8K $\times$ 16 chip, we find that the two sides require:

six 8K $\times$ 8 chips @ $15
two 32K $\times$ 32 chips @ $75
total chip count of eight at a chip cost of $240

TABLE 5.3 **Static RAM sizes, speeds, and prices (1992) for 1-Mb, 256-Kb, and 64-Kb RAMs.** These are typical sizes and prices (in 100's or 1000's) for ordinary static RAMs with TTL-level outputs. Faster, smaller RAMs are available with ECL outputs. Many other sizes and special features are available, usually for higher prices. For example, RAMs optimized for particular microprocessors, RAMs with built-in address counters for burst access, RAMs with address and/or data latches on the chip, and dual-bank RAMs for caches with a set size of 2.

Size	8 ns	10 ns	12 ns	15 ns	20 ns	25 ns	35 ns
256K × 4 128K × 8 64K × 16 32K × 32				$75	$50		$25
64K × 4 32K × 8 16K × 16		$120	$85	$35	$25		
16K × 4 8K × 8	$44	$20		$15		$12	

To this must be added not only the cost of circuit board and assembly but the cost for additional power to drive the chips and the cooling to take that power away. The set-associative configuration will be somewhat more expensive because of the higher chip count.

The MUXs shown in the defining figures for these units are part of the memory. Right or left bank is simply *chip-enable*. Selection of the word from the group of four is a normal memory word-select function. Special RAMs are made with the tag comparators built in (see Table 5.4). This eliminates another chip or chip pair. Even though the cost difference is not enormous, the conclusion seems to be that as soon as cache sizes become moderately large, a direct-mapped cache is the best choice [Hill, 88].

TABLE 5.4 **Typical tag store RAM sizes, speeds, and prices (1992)**

Size	10 ns	12 ns	15 ns
16K × 4 8K × 8 4K × 18	$75	$50	$30
4K × 4	$55	$45	

Note: Time delay is from address-in to match-out.

If the cache were on-chip, however, you would be reasonably indifferent to the organization of the memory blocks, but concerned with the cache size. You might ask: Why this dichotomy in perspectives? On-chip, memories tend to be made up of a hierarchy of decoders feeding a set of independent memory blocks. As Table 5.3 suggests, a 16K memory can be organized to select one of 16 blocks of $1K \times 1$ to yield a $16K \times 1$ chip or to select 4 blocks of $1K \times 1$ in parallel to make a $4K \times 4$ chip. The 10-bit decode of the address for each block is identical. Thus, it is a small change for a chip manufacturer to partition a 16-Kb memory into a $16K \times 1$ or a $2 \times (2K \times 4)$ chip suitable for a two-way set-associative cache. The issue here becomes getting enough chip area for the cache. As chips grow to include as many as 2 million transistors and more (Intel's Pentium is has 3.1 million [Alpert, 93]), substantial on-chip caches are included. The advantage is that on-chip circuits are inherently faster than off-chip circuits. This observation is countered by the obvious fact that off-chip caches can grow almost without bound. The 1-Mb static RAMs shown in Table 5.3 show that designers today are enabled to design quite substantial caches of very fast response times.

The issue of chip count looms very large in any design. Both to reduce chip count and to provide the fastest possible response, special tag-store RAMs are available with the address comparator on the chip. Lower production volumes tend to make these chips more expensive per unit storage, but the lower chip count can make this higher price worth it.

5.7.2 Design Choices—Writeback

Let us consider a writeback cache to see what that entails. While writethrough is conceptually simpler, writeback will give better bus performance, particularly in the multiprocessor applications in which most modern high-performance processors must be competitive.

In Chapter 2, we selected word addressing as our memory address paradigm. Halfwords and bytes were subdivisions of words with a CPU signal to the MMU to specify which part to extract. This gave us a bigger address space and made the most common memory operation the basic building block. Many benefits derive from doing all memory transactions in blocks. In particular, it simplifies the design of all the interfaces to the bus and it distributes the overhead of a memory reference over more data. This leads to a *fetch-on-write-miss* strategy with subunit operations only in cache. One of the hidden benefits of this scheme is that memory never has to work with subunits of its basic storage element. If error-correcting codes (ECCs) are used in byte-oriented machines, the memory unit must do five steps to accomplish the insertion of a subunit:

1. read-before-write to bring down the unit (say a 4-byte word)
2. check of the word to make sure that the original is correct
3. insertion of the new subunit
4. regeneration of the error code
5. storing of the new unit

Since our system will always read a block (e.g., 4 words), we could take advantage of the greater length by running the ECC over the full length of the block. That will give us a substantial saving in chips since it takes 7 bits to do single-error-correction–double-error-detection on 32 bits and only 9 bits for 128-bit lines. The saving is 9 versus 28 bits of ECC per line. Also, if all writes on the bus are 128 bits, the memory need do nothing but the last two steps in the list above. As soon as you start thinking of doing everything in 128-bit lines, you start thinking of busses with 64- or even 128-bit widths. Wider busses are becoming the norm in high-performance workstations and servers. The IBM RS/6000 series provides backplane busses of 64 and 128 bits. Both Futurebus+ and VMEbus now accommodate these sizes.

In general, the bus retains the ability to do operations from a byte all the way up to its full breadth and with multiple sequential data cycles for a single initial address. The question that we are raising here is whether to select the simplicity and speed of a single data size or the versatility to deliver any unit to any node on the bus. At this juncture, we will opt for simplicity and speed.

What all of this adds up to in cache design is that we must arrange to do all subunit extraction and insertion in the cache. This means that we have to have subunit addressing and a pair of little "switchyards" for right-justifying halfwords and bytes and for properly aligning them for reads and writes. Since our addressing scheme does not admit the possibility of "unaligned" reads or writes—no halfwords in the middle or crossing word boundaries—the switchyard is reasonably simple. The sign extension is done by the CPU, so the cache is freed of that burden.

Figure 5.14 shows the MUXing arrangement to move both words and subunits between the cache and CPU. The unit selection is derived from three control lines from the CPU. Table 5.5 is the truth table for selection based on these three lines. For insertion, we take advantage of the fact that the 32-bit-wide cache data memory provides byte control. The correctly aligned new bytes, in the form of a byte, a halfword, or a word, replace the old ones. Notice in the figure that the "line" is really four successive words in the cache data memory. This arrangement brings with it the very critical ability to select the word of choice as well as subunit storage without having to do *read-modify-write*.

TABLE 5.5 Truth table for subunit selection signals

Byte	A	B	Select
0	0	x	word
0	1	0	right halfword
0	1	1	left halfword
1	0	0	byte 0
1	0	1	byte 1
1	1	1	byte 3
1	1	0	byte 2

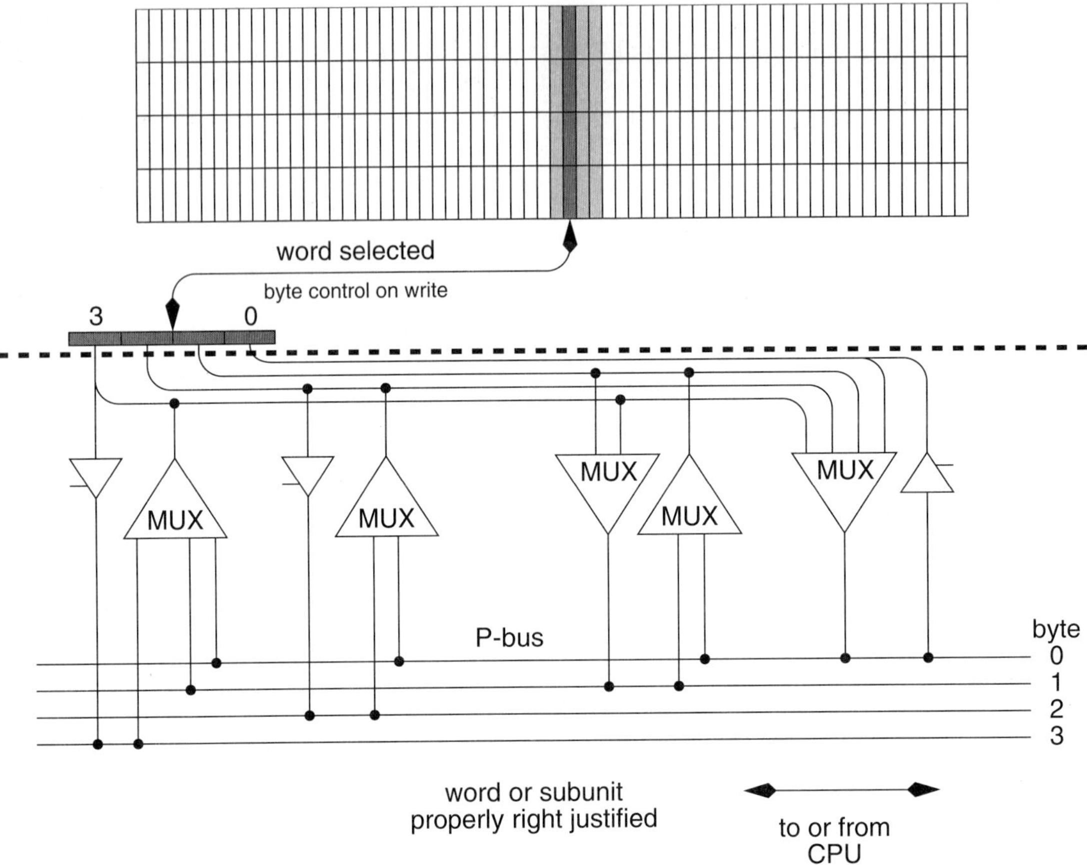

FIGURE 5.14 The MUX arrangement to move words or properly right-justified bytes or halfwords between the cache and the CPU. The cache always delivers a full word to the CPU, but since the CPU will sign-extend subunits to the full width, the upper bytes will be ignored. On write, the 32-bit wide memory chip provides byte control. The dashed line defines the edge of the memory chip.

We are definitely planning to take advantage of the speed of static RAM. The critical direction is *out* from cache. The 15-ns RAM will allow us to get the word out and through the MUXs with plenty of time for setup before the data must be read. The RAM is quite adequate to the clock speeds we are planning.

Next in line is the choice between virtual and physical addressing. Since our small page size prevents our overlapping the TLB and data cache access, using VAs would give us a faster cache. If we use simple VAs, we will have to invalidate the cache on every context switch, but our cache is large enough that we would find that expensive. To separate one context's VAs from another's, our virtual address tags would have to include the process ID. That is not too expensive but we would also need to solve the alias problem—a nasty but reasonably rare possibility, which would require a fair amount of silicon to solve. It would cost us a reverse TLB, as detailed in Section 5.5.

Two factors inhibit us from proceeding in this direction. To begin with, we can make our cache fast enough using PAs. That gives us freedom to focus on the second reason: not having an RTB is noticeably cheaper than having one.

The choices we will make for the TLB are similar to those we have made for the data cache. If we were going to include the TLB on the CPU chip, we would consider a small, fully associative cache. Since we will be building the TLB with standard memory chips, a large direct-mapped cache is much easier to build. The TLB can be smaller than the data cache and still have very high hit rates, since the number of pages referenced by a program is far smaller than the number of words. We will choose a direct-mapped TLB with 1024 entries, which allows us to use standard $1K \times 4$ RAMs for tags and PTEs. One bit of the 10 select lines for this direct cache will be derived from the interrupt level, allowing us to split our cache between system and process levels. Process is IL0. Everything else is system. An interesting observation is that, within reason, it is width, not height, that determines a *board-level* cache's cost. The reason is that the principal cost is printed-circuit boards and the number of chips. A 512-entry TLB would not be materially less expensive than our 1024 entry design.

To summarize, we have chosen to use:

- PAs in the data cache
- direct-mapped data cache
- 4096 blocks of four words each
- writeback
- fetch-on-write misses
- direct-mapped TLB
- 1024 entries in the TLB, split half and half between system and process

Having decided on the fundamental features of our caches, we can begin the detailed design with a block diagram. Figure 5.15 provides a simplified first look at our D-cache/MMU system. Control aspects are not shown in the diagram. Several important features of the design stand out clearly. To accommodate the transition from the CPU chip's multiplexed address/data bus, it is necessary to latch the address (either VA or PA) before the start of the data phase. The choice to latch the VA derives from the need to retain it in the case of a TLB miss or invalid operation. A TLB miss requires the MMU to generate and utilize the sequence of addresses needed to acquire the missing PTE. These derive from the VA. Page faults and other invalid operations can intrude. In the sense that addresses are data, Figure 5.15 really shows data paths and a few control signals. What we must now do is develop the control structure which makes all of these pieces work together.

5.7.3 Design of a Simplified Cache Controller

Walk through Figure 5.15 to see how the MMU/cache system will do its tasks. Two examples will show most of the hardware. Consider first the normal cache cycle. The CPU issues an address and control signals indicating the size of the datum, whether the

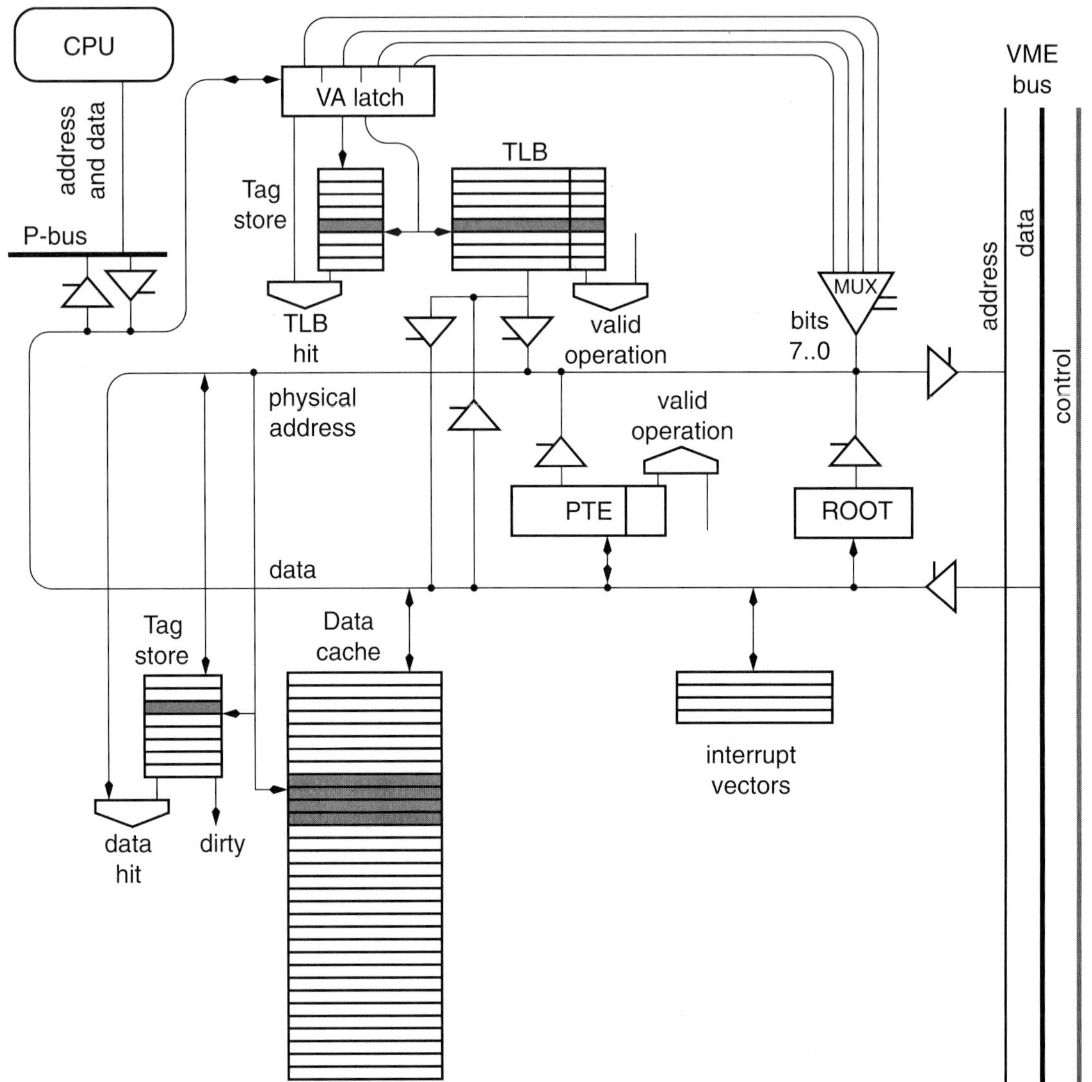

FIGURE 5.15 Layout of a simplified cache memory system. The bus on the right is shown in VME form (separate data and address lines). The diagram includes necessary paths and storage devices but neither the control engine nor control lines are shown. The interrupt vector memory, loaded at boot time, is used to handle faults and other irregularities which occur during MMU operations.

operation is at system or process level, and the direction in which the datum should move. The VA will be latched and delivered in pieces to the TLB and to the physical address bus according to:

- bits 7:0 ⇒ low-order byte of PA
- bits 16:8 ⇒ select line in TLB
- bits 31:17 ⇒ TLB tag comparator

Presuming a hit and a valid operation, the PA will then be formed from the upper 24 bits of PTE appended to the lowest 8 bits of the VA. The PA is delivered to the D-cache in the following way:

- bits 1:0 ⇒ select word from line
- bits 13:2 ⇒ select line in D-cache
- bits 31:14 ⇒ D-cache tag comparator

Once again, presuming a hit, the datum is moved between CPU and cache over the internal data bus.

Now consider a TLB miss with all intermediate PTEs in cache but the datum itself in memory and let the operation be a *write*. Let us begin with the VA latched but a TLB miss. Our hierarchy of address decoding requires that we walk down through the root and midtables to reach the pagetable from which the PTE will be obtained. In other words, the MMU must generate three successive PAs to get the PTE with the translation that is needed. The first PA comprises:

- bits 7:0 ⇐ bits 31:24 of the VA
- bits 31:8 ⇐ bits 31:8 of the root address (only these 24 bits are stored)

This PA scores a hit in the D-cache. The word selected is loaded into the PTE register to form the basis for the next PA. This new PTE must be checked for validity. While illegal addresses may cause a trap, the principal issue is the possibility of a page fault. Only the root table is guaranteed to be in memory. Presuming that there is no page fault, the next PA—the PA of the midtable—is constructed as:

- bits 7:0 ⇐ bits 23:16 of the VA
- bits 31:8 ⇐ bits 31:8 of the PTE

By assumption, this hits in the D-cache and the datum delivered is loaded into the PTE register. This is the PTE for the pagetable. Note that we replace the previous PTE in the PTE register. Once again, we form a PA from the PTE and VA as:

- bits 7:0 ⇐ bits 15:8 of the VA
- bits 31:8 ⇐ bits 31:8 of the PTE

Once again, this hits in the D-cache but this time, the datum delivered is loaded into the line in the TLB indicated by the VA, replacing the value that was there. At the same time, bits 31:17 of the VA are written into the TLB tag store and the valid bit in that line is set. Now the MMU is ready to try the D-cache for the datum that the CPU originally requested. By presumption, this misses. The MMU must execute a bus operation. We have shown a VMEbus, so that defines the conventions which must be followed. If memory admits a burst-mode operation, the MMU would send one address and then strobe in or out four data. Let us presume that that will happen. First the MMU checks the current dirty bit. If set, the MMU's first task is to write out the dirty line. (We will add a buffer in a moment.) To obtain the dirty line's PA, the MMU replaces PA 31:14 with the same bits from the D-cache tag store. It drives that address onto the VMEbus and handshakes the four words from the D-cache to memory. Now it is ready to load the new line of data.

The MMU asserts[3] the PA of the data line that it wants. When the MMU sends the PA to the VMEbus, it also loads the D-cache tag store with the new tag, resets the dirty bit, and sets the valid bit. As the data arrive, one word at a time, they are loaded into their appropriate slots in the D-cache. When the word that is wanted by the CPU arrives, the CPU is allowed to proceed.

Ah, yes, the CPU. What has it been doing all this time? As it turns out, nothing, nothing at all. The MMU controls CPU cycles by delivering the clock cycles to the CPU. To suspend CPU activity, it simply stops sending clock cycles. (This is called *stalling* the CPU. Hardware may require that we limit the stall duration, but the upper limit is well beyond any delay that would arise from the transactions that we are considering here. Long-duration events such as page faults are handled by the CPU, not the MMU.)

What these two examples illustrate is that the hardware is in place in Figure 5.15 to perform the principal D-cache/MMU functions. To control all of this hardware in proper sequence for each of the transactions that we expect from the MMU, we will use one or more state machines. Let us start with the single state machine shown in Figure 5.16. It is drawn as a *Moore machine*; that is, its outputs are strictly a function of the state. This provides the advantage that the outputs can be made glitch-free. In Figure 5.16, they correspond to individual register bits. The Moore machine has the disadvantage that outputs can change only after the CLK edge, implying a longer delay from inputs to outputs than in a *Mealy machine*, where the outputs are a function of both the state and the input variables. Where a considerable setup time is needed, the earlier availability of Mealy signals can be a considerable advantage. The best choice may be a combination—signals which must be glitch-free, such as strobes, should come directly from the state register, while other signals can be generated more quickly by combining some of the inputs with some of the state bits.

In Figure 5.16, the details of the control circuit are in the PROM or PLA, which determines the sequence of states. Most of our design effort will be devoted to the construction of flow diagrams which can be transcribed into the contents of the PROM or PLA. We begin the design by restricting ourselves to the most important events which occur in the cache:

- Read with TLB hit, valid operation, and D-Cache Hit
- Read with TLB hit, valid operation, and D-Cache Miss
- Write with TLB hit, valid operation, and D-Cache Hit
- Write with TLB hit, valid operation, and D-Cache Miss
- Read or Write with TLB hit but invalid operation
- Read or Write with TLB Miss

---

[3] "Assert" here means "to drive a bus with a particular signal." It is a reasonable usage in the sense that a tristate driver is essentially an open circuit when unasserted and either a 0 or 1 when asserted.

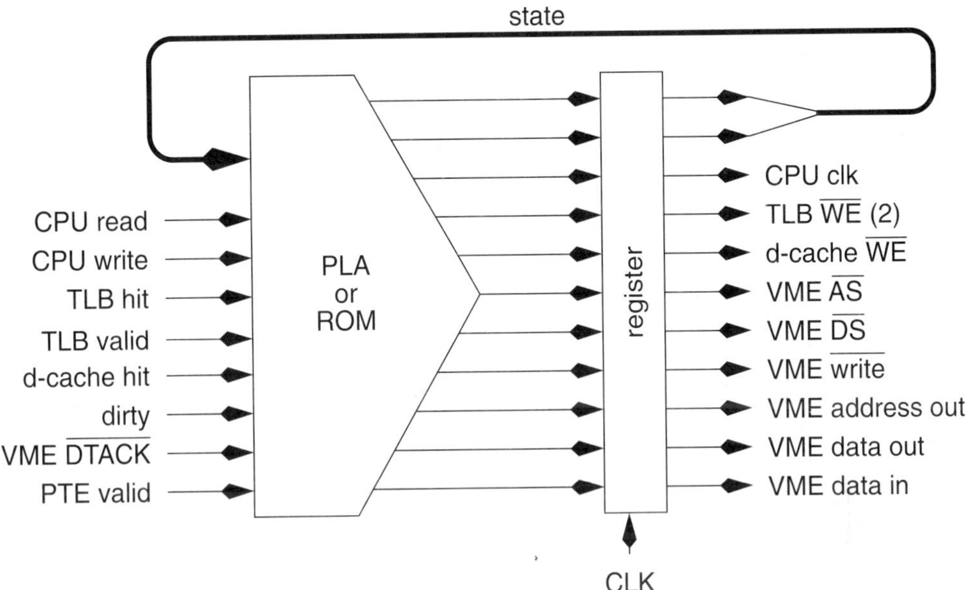

FIGURE 5.16 The simple cache controller state machine. Many of the outputs are not shown. For example, the MUX of Figure 5.15 requires two control lines, ROOT requires read and write enables, the P-bus transceiver needs two control lines, the data tag store requires both read and write signals, and the TLB requires a read signal. The outputs shown are mostly those which receive special attention in the text.

In this section, we will make some simplifying assumptions to avoid discussing other state machines and less critical data paths. We will assume that the CPU will wait for the completion of all operations. We will assume that the data cache system is always the master of the VMEbus. We will also ignore such things as bus errors, protection faults, cache inhibit, LODSET, and the dirty bit. All of these restrictions will be removed when we complete the design of the cache controller in the next section.

Much of the simplicity of our first-pass design derives from the assumption that the CPU will wait for the completion of any operation being performed by the cache. This CPU stall is accomplished by stopping the CPU clock signal while the cache controller executes a cache or VMEbus operation. To provide control of the CPU clock, the state machine will use a clock (CLK) running at twice the CPU clock frequency, and it will produce the CPU clock by counting (÷2). That is, the normal input to the CPU-clock bit in the register is simply the complement of the current output of the CPU-clock bit, but when a stall is required, that input is set equal to the output. The P-bus is a synchronous, multiplexed Address/Data bus, which contains a virtual address when the CPU clock is high and data when the CPU clock is low. The cache controller will simply latch the address at the end of the clock-high phase and then extend the clock-low phase as long as necessary to accept or produce the data. During the interim, the MMU data bus will be disconnected from the P-bus.

Cache operations may involve one or more VMEbus transfers. A detailed exposition of the VMEbus will be presented in Chapter 8, but we will have to deal with some of the VME signals here. A transfer on the VMEbus starts with the bus master placing an address on the VME address bus. After a delay of at least 35 ns to allow the address to set up, the master asserts the Address Strobe $\overline{\mathrm{AS}}$ signal to indicate that the address is valid.[4] The signals $\overline{\mathrm{DS0}}$, $\overline{\mathrm{DS1}}$, $\overline{\mathrm{A1}}$, and $\overline{\mathrm{LWORD}}$ are used in various combinations to transfer 1-, 2-, 3-, and 4-byte pieces of data with various alignments. Since we are transmitting only whole lines of four words (longwords in VMEspeak), A1 and $\overline{\mathrm{LWORD}}$ are always low, and $\overline{\mathrm{DS0}}$ and $\overline{\mathrm{DS1}}$ are asserted together. If the transfer is a write, the bus master pulls the signal $\overline{\mathrm{WRITE}}$ low, places the data on the VME data bus, then waits at least 35 ns before asserting the Data Strobe signals ($\overline{\mathrm{DS0}}$ and $\overline{\mathrm{DS1}}$). The master must then wait until some slave device (e.g., memory) responds by asserting Data Acknowledge, $\overline{\mathrm{DTACK}}$. When the master sees $\overline{\mathrm{DTACK}}$ asserted, it can release $\overline{\mathrm{DS0}}$ and $\overline{\mathrm{DS1}}$ and stop asserting the data.

To perform a read operation, the bus master leaves $\overline{\mathrm{WRITE}}$ high (*unasserted*), asserts $\overline{\mathrm{DS0}}$ and $\overline{\mathrm{DS1}}$, requesting 32 bits of data from the address, and then waits for a slave to respond. In this case, the $\overline{\mathrm{DTACK}}$ signal indicates that the slave is placing the data on the VME data bus. However, because of possible *skew* between the bus signals, the master may see DTACK as much as 25 ns before the data is valid. When the master has waited for this delay and taken the data, it can release $\overline{\mathrm{DS0}}$ and $\overline{\mathrm{DS1}}$, ending the transfer.

The use of separate address and data strobes makes the address and data transfers somewhat independent. The slave should latch the address when $\overline{\mathrm{AS}}$ is asserted to allow *address pipelining*. That is, the master can begin sending an address for a new transfer before the data has been taken from the previous transfer. It is also possible to transfer more than one word based on a single address. A *block transfer*—the form that we will use exclusively whenever the cache/MMU is operating—is done simply by keeping $\overline{\mathrm{AS}}$ asserted and using multiple Data Strobes to transfer successive words of data. The other multiple-transfer operation which we will be using is a *Read/Modify/Write* operation (though not the conventional VMEbus version). To get one block read and then written back, we will use a standard VME operation to hold onto the bus while we treat the read and the write as two separate block operations. As with a block transfer, the master keeps Address Strobe asserted during each transfer. However, after the read of 4 words has been completed, the master continues to assert $\overline{\mathbf{DS}}$ while it releases and reasserts $\overline{\mathbf{AS}}$. This holds the bus and starts the second data cycle. $\overline{\mathbf{DS}}$ is deasserted and the master then asserts the WRITE signal and new data, and then asserts the $\overline{\mathbf{DS}}$ again. This same sort of transaction allows for pipelining or reads or writes. If we pipeline addresses, the $\overline{\mathbf{AS}}$ line will be released and reasserted only during a data phase when the $\overline{\mathbf{DS}}$ pair is asserted. As long as one or the other is asserted, the MMU continues to own the bus. All of the sequences that we have described are included in the VME protocol. Any fully compatible VME product should be comfortable with the protocols.

5.7.3.1 READS WITHOUT WRITEBACK. With a hit rate in excess of 95 percent, the most important cache operation is a read with hits in both the TLB and the D-cache. The timing for such a read is shown in Figure 5.17, and the states involved are shown

---

[4] An overbar, such as $\overline{\mathrm{AS}}$, indicates that the signal is asserted by driving the voltage toward nominal "0." On busses, this most frequently means essentially grounding the bus line.

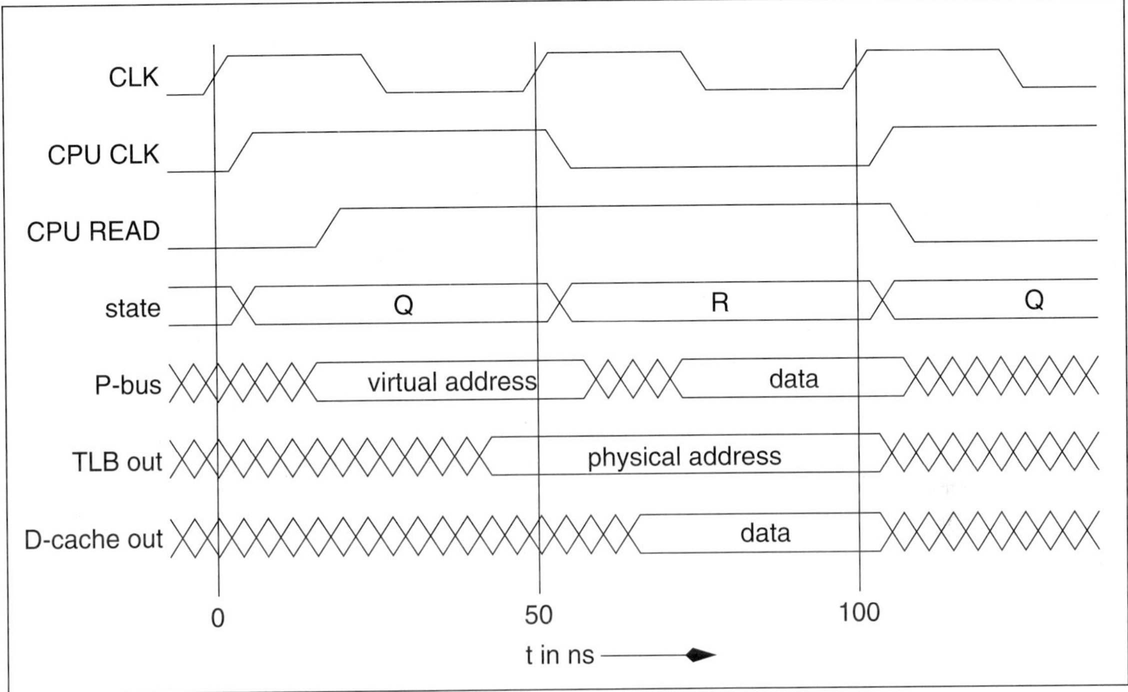

FIGURE 5.17 Timing diagram for a CPU read with TLB and D-cache hits. Crosshatching indicates *undefined* state (meaningless data). The valid time for data on the P-bus always ends after the state transition because of the delay in the bus transceiver (Figure 5.15). This positive skew assures the reader of the data that the data is valid on the clock edge.

in Figure 5.18. State **Q** is a quiescent state for the cache controller. It provides a high level on the CPU clock, opens the virtual address latch, and waits for the CPU to begin a read or write operation. If the CPU does not assert READ or WRITE by the end of the period, the next state will be **N**, which is a no-op for the cache controller. State **N** simply keeps the CPU clock low for one period and then returns to state **Q**.

FIGURE 5.18 The very simple state diagram for a successful cache read.

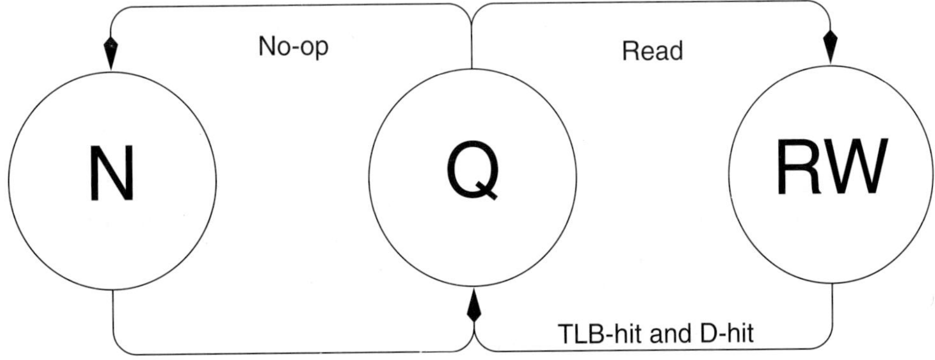

The period of the cache controller clock has been set to 50 ns, which implies a period of 100 ns for the CPU clock. We will assume that the CPU chip can provide each of its signals at its output pins no later than 25 ns after the rising CPU-clock edge. Similarly, we will provide inputs to the CPU at least 25 ns before the next rising CPU-clock edge. Thus we have 50 ns to get through the address latch, the TLB, the data cache, and any other delays we may have to include. In order to accomplish this, we will use cache RAM chips with access times of approximately 15 ns.

When the CPU requests a READ operation, it must place the virtual address on the P-bus in the middle of state **Q** and also assert READ. The virtual address latch is open during state **Q**. It closes at the end of that state before the address is removed, latching the virtual address. At the start of the next clock cycle, the state machine goes into state **RW** because of the READ request. About the same time, presuming a TLB hit, the physical address becomes available at the output of the TLB. By the middle of state **RW**, assuming a D-cache hit, the data becomes available and is placed on the CPU bus. The combination of TLB-HIT, no protection faults, and D-HIT allows the state machine to return to state **Q**, which raises the CPU clock again, signaling the CPU to take the data.

Of course, other things can happen. Within the MMU, one will see page faults and various types of access errors as well as misses in either TLB or D-cache. External problems under the general classification of *bus faults* can abort an access to memory and all of the interface devices can signal their need for service by posting interrupts. All of these will be treated in due course, but we are beginning here with the simplest operation. For the successful cache read, **N**, **Q**, and **RW** will do.

Now let's consider a read in which the D-cache misses. This raises the ante considerably. The MMU must load a line of four words into the D-cache. If the line to be replaced is dirty, it must be written out before the line that replaces it can be written in. Buffering would clearly help. In a maximum-performance cache, we would want to deliver the desired word or fraction thereof as soon as it was available, but in our design exercise here, we want to keep things as simple and orderly as possible. To that end, we will start with the case of the dirty bit reset (no writeback) and design a state machine which first loads all four words and only then delivers what was requested. The CPU will simply have to wait (though at 97 or 98 percent hit rates, it won't wait often!). The timing for such a read is shown in Figure 5.19, and the states involved are shown in Figure 5.20.

The first cycle is identical to the previous case, since the CPU issues a READ request, and the TLB hits. Now in state **RW**, the data cache tag store reports a miss. Having presumed that the cache controller is the master of the VMEbus, the physical address can be driven onto the VMEbus immediately. However, *immediately* is a Mealy machine response. For a Moore machine, the fact that the MMU *owns* the bus (i.e., is master of the bus at that moment) must define a new state, which in turn results in driving the address onto the bus. This state is **AD**. The VME spec [VME, 87] requires that the address be driven onto the address lines at least 35 ns before the address strobe is asserted. By asserting $\overline{\textbf{AS}}$ as the controller goes to state **0A**, we ensure a delay of 50 ns. At this point, we are beginning the four memory cycles which will deliver a block of four words to our cache. $\overline{\textbf{AS}}$ and the PA will be asserted continuously from **0A** through **3C**. Each cycle of reading comprises the handshake of:

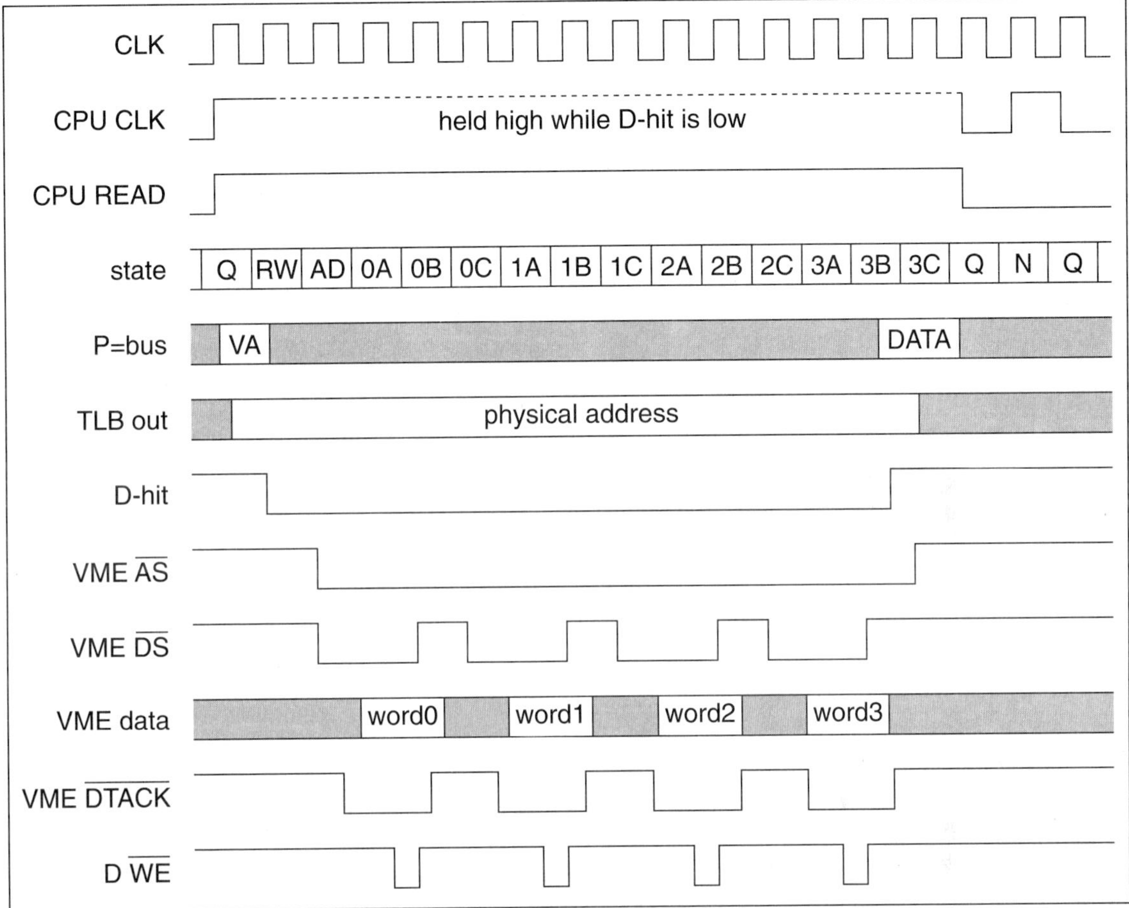

FIGURE 5.19 Timing diagram for the cache-fill operation. Note how long a delay there is between the issuance of the VA and the receipt of data.

- $\overline{\textbf{DS}}$ is asserted by the master ($\overline{\textbf{DS}}$ is the pair of data strobes driven together)
  The slave drives data onto the bus and asserts $\overline{\text{DTACK}}$
- Master logs data in by asserting **D-$\overline{\textbf{WE}}$** and deasserts $\overline{\textbf{DS}}$
  The slave releases $\overline{\text{DTACK}}$ and data lines

Figure 5.20 details the repetitive execution of this pair of handshakes through the first two cycles. They continue in essentially identical fashion through state **3C**. The only thing that is changing as the MMU steps through the four cycles is the specification of the word in the block. This specification is occurring at both the memory and the cache. One is reading; the other is writing. One way to do this addressing, and certainly the way that is most obvious, is have the MMU spell out the last two bits of the word address for both memory and cache. However, as we mentioned in Section 5.7.3, there are considerable benefits to be achieved by dealing only in blocks and doing all subunit

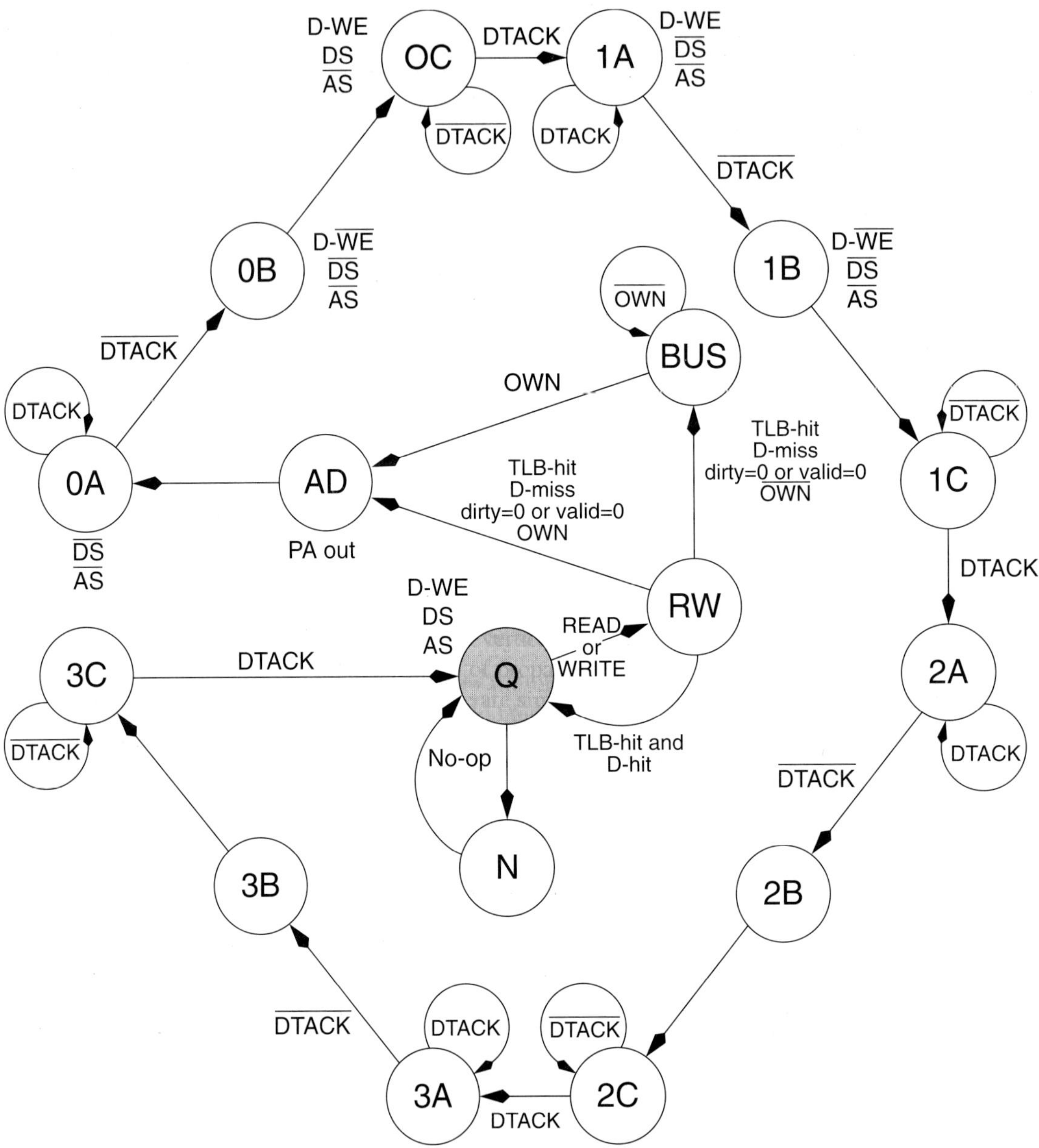

FIGURE 5.20 State diagram for the read operation for the MMU/D-cache of Figure 5.15. The boldface labels next to the states indicate the signals asserted or deasserted in that state. PA-out is asserted until $\overline{\textbf{AS}}$ is deasserted (**Q**).

operations on board the cache. For one thing, this will allow easy scaling to the progressively more popular 64- and 128-bit data paths. For this design example, though, we are using a 32-bit VMEbus.

Having decided that the memory unit will always return a whole block, we must assign the tasks of generating the word-selection bits at both ends of the data path. Our choice is to have each end generate its own selection bits. They will be set to zero before word 0 is sent and step progressively to 3 as the data strobe, $\overline{\mathbf{DS}}$, is deasserted. (This would require extra hardware—*glue*—for most standard VME products.)

Since the VMEbus spec allows $\overline{\text{DTACK}}$ to be asserted up to 25 ns before the data, as seen by the bus master, state **0B** is essentially a unit time delay (50 ns) to be certain that the data is valid when it is read into cache. As the data is being written into the data RAMs for word 0, bits 14:31 of the physical address are written into the D-cache tag store, the dirty bit is reset, and the valid bit is set.

When the memory releases $\overline{\text{DTACK}}$ for the fourth time, the controller returns to state **Q**. That raises the CPU clock and allows the CPU to take the data. As we announced at the beginning of this exercise, no attempt is made to retrieve the desired word before the entire block is read in. With a more elaborate controller, it would be possible either to deliver the requested word first or simply to deliver the word as soon as it arrives in normal sequence. Given the predominance of linear progress in memory addresses, there should be little difference in performance between these two strategies, and either would be a considerable improvement over the long wait for the fourth word. The step up in complexity is not trivial, however, since the only purpose in earlier delivery is to free the CPU to continue. Unfortunately the CPU wants cache assistance frequently, so the only way to get much advantage from early delivery is to provide for nearly independent action at both the CPU and bus sides of the cache. The two sides cannot be entirely independent, so some accommodations must be made to allow the two controllers to snake through each other's territory. For example, you could improve the decoupling by creating a one-block read buffer and a PA-latch for the address of the first read. If, for example, the first word read yields the requested datum, the CPU can proceed while the next three words are read into the buffer. Then the entire block could be transferred in a single cycle.

This wave of the hand gives little idea of how many different things could happen while your fancy cache was reading its block. For example, the CPU could ask next for the second word in the line. It could be in the buffer, not here yet or in cache. The more enterprising programmer might modify that first word and write it out to cache before the line was transferred to memory! Now how do you handle that? There are several ways, but our purpose here was not to solve all the problems but to show that the complexity of the cache can grow very rapidly as you add functionality. This section concludes with the observation that we have not yet dealt with the TLB miss. We will in a moment, but first let us consider shipping back some of what we have just gotten in.

5.7.3.2 WRITES AND WRITEBACKS. In a writeback cache, write operations with a hit in the cache are little different from a read-with-hit operation. The principal differences are the data direction, timing of the write pulse, and the setting of the dirty bit.[5] Similarly, for a miss in the D-cache with the dirty bit reset or the line invalid, the write must go

[5] Setting the *dirty bit* is easily accomplished. In Figure 5.21, note that if we have a hit, the data at the input of the tag store matches what is currently there. The tag store may be directed to load "it" where "it" includes not only the tag but the dirty bit, $dirty = dirty \cup write$. Little setup time is required.

through all of the steps in Figure 5.20 to fetch the block and then write in the new word *in cache*. Figure 5.20 has all the states for executing either CPU $\Rightarrow$ cache or cache $\Rightarrow$ CPU with the necessary line being fetched from memory. What is missing from Figure 5.20 is the action to be taken on a write miss if the line is both valid and dirty.

When a valid dirty bit is set, things get considerably more interesting for a cache miss on either read or write. Conceptually, the operation is to return the dirty line and then proceed as before. Unfortunately, that will essentially double the delay in getting the CPU going again. While the high hit ratio says that that will not happen very often, we can avoid it almost completely if we buffer writebacks and execute the read before the write on a cache miss. A single-line buffer fills the need. If we were to opt for a deeper buffer, we would have to provide the buffer with the monitoring and extraction capability to provide a buffered line that was rereferenced before it was written out. In effect, the data buffer would become yet another cache and we would be endowing it with the ability to intercede.

Figure 5.21 shows the additions that will be needed to buffer a single writeback. When a writeback is executed, the cache transfers the line being written back to the FIFO output buffer. At the same time, the address buffer copies the line's PA with the lowest bits coming from the *physical address bus* and the higher bits from the tag store. The act of loading the output buffer starts the writeback state machine (WBSM), which writes out the line as soon as the read is completed and it can get the bus again. The WBSM will be asynchronous with the cache state machine (CSM), but we need a handshake between them to assure that we get

read before write but write before next read.

The WBSM will issue a signal $\overline{\text{WBSY}}$ whenever it is in the process of transmitting a line. If $\overline{\text{WBSY}}$ is asserted when CSM enters the **RW** state in Figure 5.20, the CSM must not proceed. Similarly, to keep the WBSM waiting while that first read is accomplished, CSM will issue a signal $\overline{\text{RBSY}}$ when it is in any state from **BUS** to **3C**.

Both the WBSM and CSM must be able to request the bus. In Figure 5.20, the state **BUS** signals the bus acquisition state machine (BAQSM) that it wants the bus. BAQSM simply follows the VMEbus (or other bus) protocol for acquiring the system bus. BAQSM signals successful acquisition with signal OWN. If another user requests the bus, BAQSM releases OWN and the bus itself will be released when both $\overline{\textbf{AS}}$ and $\overline{\textbf{DS}}$ are released at the end of the block.

This brings us back to forcing a writeback. How will that be accomplished in our machine? We laid out the principle of selective writebacks in Section 5.6.3. With a trap operation, the program may ask for any specific line to be written back (if dirty). The program sees only VAs. The lines are specified in the cache by PA. Unless we decide to use VAs in our cache, we are stuck with the requirement to employ a TLB. Let us presume that the operation of forcing a writeback is reserved to the system and that it is infrequent. With that proviso, we need not make the process efficient.

From the process's point of view, the writeback request is a system call—a trap—with two parameters, the beginning and ending word addresses. From the system point of view, we need only read "something" into the lines in question. If we bring in a new

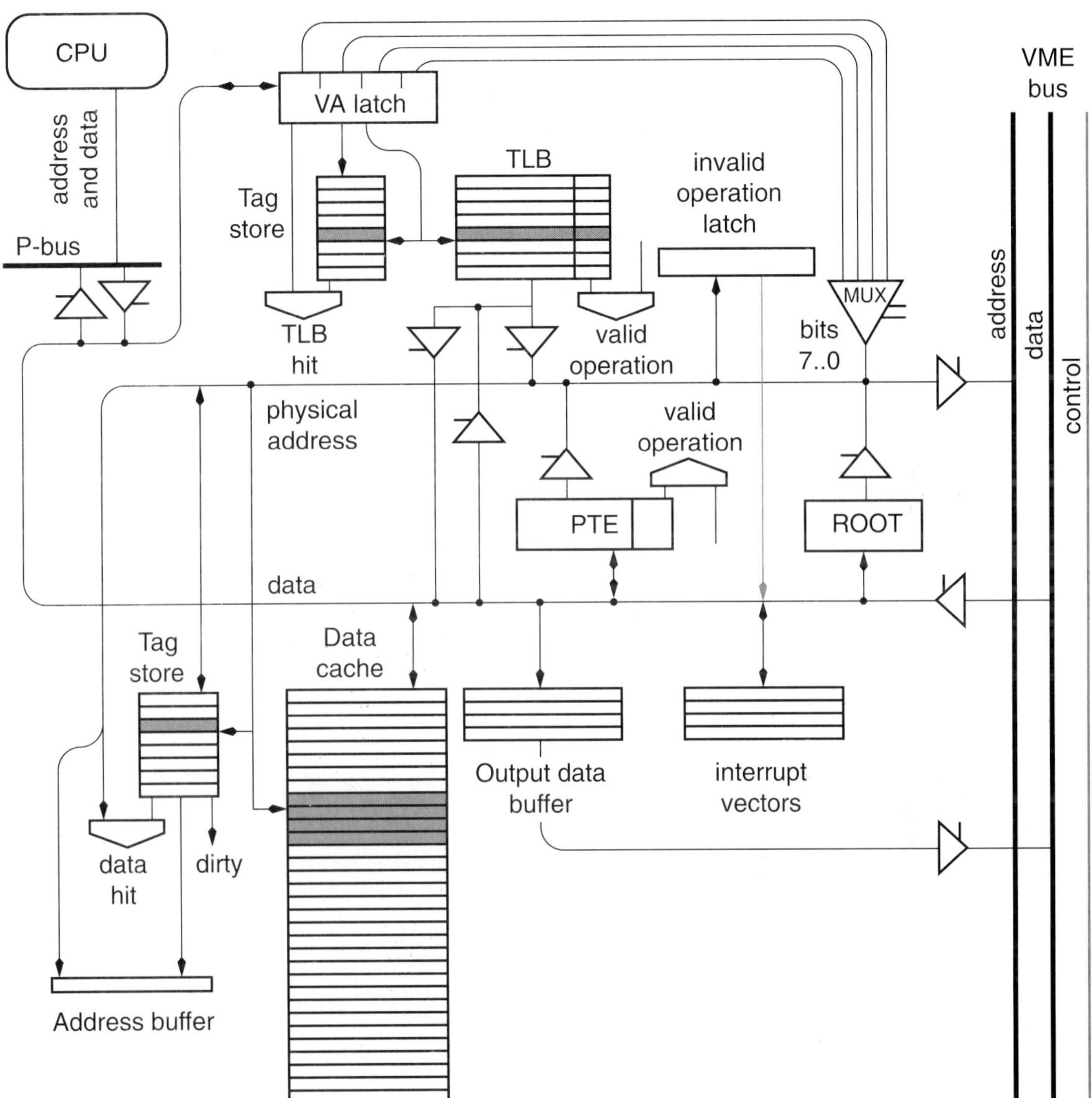

FIGURE 5.21 The MMU/D-cache of Figure 5.15 updated by the addition of a writeback buffer and an invalid operation latch. The buffer comprises storage for a single line of data as well as an address buffer (lower left) which holds the PA of that line of data.

line, the old one will be written back *if dirty*. No hardware is required, yet it is far less costly than a full cache flush.

Let us assume that we have the pagetable hierarchy of Figure 4.12. The process has provided the starting PVA. Let it be 001A2B3D. We may obtain the associated PTE by reading the data at SVA 20001A2B (see the figure). Replacing the protection bits with the last byte in the VA provides the PA of the word specified. Let us say that that PA happened to be 0018E43D.

We may presume that the system will know the size and layout of the D-cache, data it would acquire at boot time. From that, it knows that, for example, the cache is direct-mapped, that it has 4 KL, and that each line contains four words. That data establishes which bits in the address specify the line. In our particular example, it would be bits 13:2. All that the system must do to flush that line in cache is to find another line to replace it. If it replaces any of the bits 31:14 and does a read, it will have achieved that goal. To avoid having something silly such as an invalid address pop up, the system should use an address it knows is valid. That is easy. *Invalid* in a PA means an address for which there is no physical memory. If the VA could be translated, it yields a valid PA. We simply flip bit 14 in the PA. Unless there are fewer than 8 KL in the memory—an absurdly small number—the resulting PA will be both different and valid. The line in cache will be changed. If it was dirty, it will be written back. For the case in question, that address would be 0018A43D. Line 90F will be replaced. One final note. If we were to use a set-associative cache of set-size N with an LRU replacement policy, we would have to replace each line N times to guarantee that we had forced a writeback on the desired data.

The system routine writes out the lines by running a loop which sends the line address, adds 4 to the PA and VA, tests for exceeding the last address (a VA), and repeats until done. If the sequence of addresses goes onto another page, the routine would require another full translation, but that is a small expense. In fact, the whole cost of this is pretty small. There will be one read to obtain the PTE from which the PA can be constructed. It is likely that this will cause a TLB miss but that the PTE will be in memory. After that, the first READ will be likely to cause a TLB miss and then everything is in place unless and until the string of selective writebacks walks over a page boundary. This is not costly for a rare but important operation. One last caution, should you ever be charged with writing this writeback trap handler: Be sure that *every* VA which the process passes to the trap handler gives a valid translation. It is your code, not the TLB, which is checking. If invalid, terminate the process *with prejudice*.

What we just described is the selective writeback. It is an efficient mechanism when a small, well-defined block of data must be written to memory. There is also a need for a general cache flush. We could do it with a state machine, but since a complete synchronization of the cache generally occurs programmatically at a break in computation—either a program call for complete synchronization or a context switch—there seemed little reason not to use precisely the same mechanism and do the full cache synchronization as a system operation. The CPU can easily outpace the bus transactions, and the CPU has nothing else to do.

5.7.3.3 TLB-INVALID RESPONSES. A TLB miss requires another song and dance from our MMU. We gave a brief example of the transactions which follow a TLB miss in Section 5.7.3. What we wish to do here is define our system's reactions to all of the outcomes of the attempt to acquire a PTE to satisfy the request from the CPU. In Section 5.7.3, the happy scenario was presented. What we want to do here is consider what happens if either the pages are not in memory or the process (or, heaven help us, the system) has attempted to access data for which permission has not been granted.

An invalid operation cannot go forward. The MMU must force an *exception* or *synchronous interrupt*. Details of the interrupt from the perspective of the CPU are fully developed in Section 6.3. Here we need to know that the MMU must signal the interrupt during the address phase and halt normal CPU processing by stopping the regular CPU clock, CLK_A, while still in this address phase. A second clock, CLK_B, continues to pump the CPU through its interrupt steps but no normal CPU processing is occurring. The interrupt vector comprises a total of 15 bits. The low-order 12 bits are an offset from an *interrupt base vector* which resides in a register on the MMU. The upper 3 bits of the vector specify the interrupt level (IL) at which the CPU is to respond to this interrupt. The lower 12 bits of the interrupt vector are combined with the interrupt base vector to form the PA of the first instruction of the interrupt handler. The MMU can get vectors from external devices on either the P-bus or system bus sides, but for TLB-invalid responses and any other MMU function failure, it gets the vectors from its own set of stored interrupt vectors.

With reference to Figure 6.12 on page 349, the MMU must assert $\overline{\text{IACK}}$ to the CPU to indicate that an interrupt is being handled. At the same time, it places the new IL on the CPU control lines. As CLK_B makes its downward transition, the CPU switches to the registers appropriate to the new (higher) interrupt level. As the CPU enters that level, there will be two NOP instructions in the pipeline. The interrupt vector is then used to provide the address of the next instruction to be fetched. This is done by having the MMU resolve the double indirection of the first address, to wit:

base_address + vector ⇒ PA of system VA of first instruction

This double indirection is a bit strange in that the first address is a PA while the second is a VA. However, a moment's reflection will show that this is the only reasonable pairing. The base address points to a block of unpaged system memory. The position of the table is established at boot time before the system gets to the point of using VAs. Creating a VA for this PA could be done, of course, and that would be needed if modifying the interrupt table were considered, but it would serve no purpose for handling the interrupt itself. The second address, on the other hand, is used by the CPU as the address of its next instruction. The CPU uses only VAs so the second address is, perforce, a VA.

The MMU treats (base_address + vector) the same as a PA coming from the TLB with a READ request. If the word indicated by the PA is in the cache, it is returned to the CPU (still running under CLK_B); if it is not in the cache, a line must be read from main memory. Note that what is delivered to the CPU is the *address* of the first instruction in the interrupt handler. This address is placed in the program counter of the CPU during the data phase. As the clock goes back to the address phase, $\overline{\text{IACK}}$ is deasserted and CLK_A is back in control. In the address phase, the CPU fetches its next instruction—the very instruction whose address was just deposited in the program counter. From there, everything proceeds in normal fashion, except that the machine is running the exception handler rather than program which caused the problem.

Now, how does the interrupt handler know what the problem is? It gets a first clue from the very fact that it was called. That is, this handler is called only if a certain class of problems has arisen. Different faults will be made to select different vectors. Thus, if there were a page fault, the page-fault handler would be called. If the program attempted an illegal access, a different vector is specified, and unless the system has stored the same value at both vectors or the same address where the two vectors point, the CPU will be running a different handler for each different vector.

However, knowing that you are the *page-fault handler* does not give you the data to handle the page fault; knowing that you are the *illegal-address handler* does not give you many clues on the nature of the illegality. That data must be provided by the MMU. A look at Figure 5.21 will show several sources of necessary data. To begin with, the VA-latch contains the program address which started this problem. This will enable the handler to print a message in the error file: "Illegal access attempted at address. . . ." Page faults should not be so answered and in fact not all out-of-range accesses are necessarily evil. The handler needs more. In the upper right quarter of Figure 5.21 is a register called the *invalid operation latch.* This register latches the output of the TLB. If the operation is invalid, all 32 bits from the TLB are written to the PA bus rather than just the page address. In this way, the handler gets all of the data that was used in establishing a fault. It can reconstruct the fault, and, using data retained in the CPU chip itself, it can see which instruction caused the fault. This can be necessary to establish, for example, whether the faulting address was an offset from the stack pointer. If so, it *may* indicate a request for more stack space rather than a brazen assault on forbidden territory. In a chapter on the MMU/D-cache, it is not appropriate for us to probe into all of the possibilities which the operating system must be able to handle, but it is incumbent upon us to be sure that all of the data that is necessary is where the system can retrieve it with minimum pain. Once again, all of these data registers that you see in Figure 5.21 can be accessed by using the appropriate addresses in the block reserved for the MMU.

Are these MMU addresses VAs or PAs? The answer is unequivocally: "Yes." The MMU chip will decode all of the addresses coming down the PA bus in Figure 5.21 and react directly to those that apply to itself. These are part of the hardware. In the *bare state*—the situation which obtains when the system is booting and address translation is turned off—the addresses from the CPU go directly to the PA bus. When the system is bare, there is no protection. During boot up, the system will use this direct access to load critical registers such as the interrupt table and base register in Figure 5.21. Later, when the system is up and running in normal fashion, we want to prevent unauthorized access to the MMU. This requires the hardware protection function that resides in the TLB. Thus, the address is now treated as a VA and translated. Once again, the PA is monitored by the MMU to see if it is "one of its own." If it is, the MMU responds by moving the desired information to or from one of its registers.

That the address could be first a PA and later a VA is not really so strange from a hardware perspective. The address decoder/monitor is watching the PA bus in Figure 5.21. All that is being switched to go from bare operation to protected operation is the source of the PA. In the bare case, the source is the address directly from the CPU; in the protected case, that CPU address gets translated by the TLB and gets its protection checked at the same time. How is protection turned on? The MMU will have a status register. One of the bits in that status register is the protection bit. The CPU can turn it on or off by writing to the status register. A reset of the MMU will turn it off so that the system always boots with a bare MMU.

The software side of the switch from bare to protected operation is part of the boot process. The boot software is obliged to build the system pagetables as part of the startup. Those tables will include access to the I/O structures, as you can see in Figure 4.12 on page 191. The "peripherals" in that figure include all of the hardware mapped into the address space. When the table structure has been created, the boot program can simply invalidate the TLB (at that point, using the PA of the port which causes the TLB invalidation) and flip to protected mode. The next reference to memory will miss in the initially empty TLB, so the MMU will go out and start fetching pagetable lines which it needs to decode that first request. Should the system now wish to invalidate the TLB, it would have to use the appropriate VA. The MMU would check that the IL of the current process had permission to access MMU registers.

5.7.3.4 CACHE-INHIBIT PAGES. Our PTE (Figure 4.11) includes a *cache-inhibit (CI) bit*. Two common reasons for avoiding the cache are:

- to force the MMU to access all I/O device registers at the horse's mouth rather than writing to the cache or using cached images of stale data
- to provide a method to force shared data structures to remain in the common memory

Since the CI bit is in the PTE, it will be available at the output of the TLB at the same time as the physical address. If CI is set, the CSM treats a read as if there were a D-cache miss and a write as if it were a D-cache miss that displaced itself into the write buffer. That is, when the CSM is in state **RW**, it cannot go back to **Q** but instead proceeds as if this were a normal read or write with a cache miss. If CI is set, we always get a fresh copy. If the operation is a write, the MMU will do a fetch-on-write and follow that by putting the written data into the write buffer. It will get out before any other read and usually in the same bus ownership period.

Those who are familiar with I/O chips may question both the read-before-write and the use of lines rather than bytes, halfwords or words. Typical I/O chips have byte, halfword or word registers spaced tightly together. Some chips, particularly the older ones designed for 8-bit microprocessors, have side effects to a read such as resetting bits in the byte just read. How then can we write to the target of choice without messing up the neighbors? This problem is hardly new. While it is possible to use enough glue to make our line-oriented memory cycle compatible with all possible I/O chips, it is generally easier and less expensive to use ready-mades that already fit. Our design clearly favors the use of I/O chips designed for a 32-bit bus environment and free of side effects on a read. Undoubtedly, we would design DMA interfaces which would be compatible with our line mode for memory access, but we might well want to talk directly with chips whose internal registers are an array of words. If we want to use word-addressed chips on our system, with all transfers still being 128-bit lines, we must glue the 32-bit chip to the 128-bit environment. In transfers between D-cache and memory, we send one address and then pump four consecutive words in the appropriate direction. For a write with cache inhibit, we would read four, modify one, and write back all four. In gluing the 32-bit peripheral adapter to this line oriented world, we can simply map the chip's packed registers into the rightmost word of consecutive lines. Knowing that there are always 4 words being transferred, the glue, whether in the chip or adjacent to it, must enable the data transfer on the first handshake but provide only the requisite handshake on the next three requests. (See Figures 5.19 and 5.20.) With the read-modify-write operation of the cache-inhibit cycle, data is transferred on the first and fifth handshakes. Finally, as with all the memory operations, only address bits 31:2—the line address—are used. Figure 5.22 shows the memory-space view of the peripheral's register set. While the meaningless data are dutifully read in and written out of the cache during the cache-inhibit cycle, they are never used or recorded by either party to the transfer.

5.7.3.5 READ-AND-SET OPERATION. The Read-and-Set operation that is elicited by the instruction LODSET (Section 2.4) is a bit peculiar in that it will involve reading in and writing back a whole line with the specific rule that it must complete the whole operation without releasing the bus. As long as memory is *single-ported*, holding the bus guarantees an atomic operation. This 8-word transfer will not be difficult to obtain

FIGURE 5.22 Gluing a 32-bit peripheral into our line-oriented memory system would have the program stepping by 4's. The peripheral is shown as having 16 registers. The chip sees these as adjacent; the program sees them as separated by 4 words. In the illustration, register 0 is mapped into the first word in a page. Only the top 30 bits of the address get sent on the bus. The bottom 4 bits of that 30 will be used by the chip for selecting the register. The glue will be responsible for selecting the correct data strobe to transfer data.

			internal chip address	physical address
			0	xxxxxx00
			1	xxxxxx04
			2	xxxxxx08
			3	xxxxxx0C
			4	xxxxxx10
			5	xxxxxx14
			6	xxxxxx18
			7	xxxxxx1C
			8	xxxxxx20
			9	xxxxxx24
			A	xxxxxx28
			B	xxxxxx2C
			C	xxxxxx30
			D	xxxxxx34
			E	xxxxxx38
			F	xxxxxx3C
handshakes only			data and handshake	

with small modifications to the state machines we already have considered. The VME-bus (and most others that we would consider) is quite suitable and well designed for this operation. The steps are:

1. CPU signals LODSET, which is treated as if it were a CI reference regardless of the setting of the CI bit for this line in the TLB.
2. Read in the line.
3. Send the desired word to the CPU.
4. Send the line to the write buffer, *setting the LO bit in the word specified.*
5. Write out the line.

Line 4 shows that LODSET is similar to writing to cache-inhibited data: What is returned is modified. What differentiates the two operations is holding the bus throughout the transaction. The Read-and-Set operation uses what is more generally called Read-Modify-Write. While it is often described as a separate bus function, what is really happening is:

1. An address is sent to memory and $\overline{\mathbf{AS}}$ and **R** asserted.
2. The $\overline{\mathbf{DS}}$ is pumped four times with handshakes from $\overline{\text{DTACK}}$ to bring in the desired line.
3. The word selected is passed to the CPU while switching the **R/**$\overline{\mathbf{W}}$ line (or line pair, on other busses) from R to $\overline{\text{W}}$. The memory has counted around back to count-0 and this change to $\overline{\text{W}}$ simply sets the data direction in the memory chips. The line is passed to the output buffer with the LO bit of the word selected set (ORed with 1).
4. Four more pumps of the data strobe carry the line back.

It sums up to: Pump one line in; change R to $\overline{\text{W}}$ and set LO bit; pump one line out.

In our case, the operation requires that the memory module be able to take back the whole line rather than just a word. This is easy to arrange. At the memory end of things, you can think of the operation as:

1. (Latch and) decode the address to select the rows and activate the column read drivers.
2. Check the ECC bits and load the 128 data bits into a buffer.
3. Transfer the 4 words in the buffer, one per data strobe, replying with $\overline{\text{DTACK}}$.
4. As the count reaches word 3, the buffer pointer moves cyclically to word 0.
5. The MMU asserts $\overline{\text{W}}$ and sends the 4 words back with appropriate pumps of $\overline{\mathbf{DS}}$.
6. When the fourth word is in place, the memory unit appends the ECC and stores the line in memory.
7. The MMU releases all strobes including $\overline{\text{AS}}$, terminating the operation. Another master can now take control of the bus.

All of this fits rather neatly into what we have been doing. It adds a bit of detail to the operations but does not change or introduce any fundamental operation.

5.7.3.6 MAINTAINING THE PAGETABLE REFERENCED AND MODIFIED BITS. Figure 4.11 shows that a PTE contains *referenced* (RF) and *modified* (MD) bits. The virtual memory routines in the operating system use these bits to determine which pages should be kept in memory, and whether a page being freed up must first be copied to disk. Since all of the real action with PTEs takes place in the MMU/D-cache, a good question is: How are these referenced and modified bits maintained in memory? Setting those bits is clearly a responsibility of the MMU. Clearing them is to be done by operating system software followed by a flush of the TLB. Keep in mind through this discussion that whenever your program references a page, it is the PTE of that page that is to be modified, not the data in the page. Grabbing that PTE is not always easy or obvious.

The RF bit in the PTE is to be set when a page is first referenced; the MD bit gets set only if the page is modified. These could be at the same time or at different times. There are only two times when the cache must modify a PTE: during a walk down the hierarchy of page tables or when writing to a page whose PTE is already in the TLB. Let us presume that the PTEs are all in the cache, since getting them in from memory is an ordinary memory read. Let us first consider a table walk.

root table read: The first PTE obtained contains the page address of the midtable. This PTE is placed in the PTE register (Figure 5.21). We know that both the RF and MD bits should be set, because the pagetable will be modified at least by having this PTE's RF bit set. Accordingly, if the two bits are not already set, the data in the PTE register is written back to D-cache with those two bits set. Those two output bits can be wired high. Since this writeback is needed quite infrequently, we would simply use one extra cache cycle to write back this modified datum.

midtable read: The second PTE, read from midtable using the current entry in the PTE register, points to the required pagetable. The pagetable will be modified at least by having one PTE RF bit set, so here too, the first time that we access the pagetable, we want to set both RF and MD in the midtable PTE. This new PTE replaces the value in the PTE register. If the two bits are not already set, it is written back to the D-cache in exactly the same fashion as the previous PTE.

pagetable read: The third and last PTE on this table walk comes from the pagetable and points to the page. It goes to the TLB. It too should be written back with its RF bit set. Its MD bit should be set only if the next operation is a write and MD is not already set. What happens if a write occurs later? This turns out to be quite a different problem, because we have no guarantee that the PTE is still in the D-cache. We will treat this special case in a moment.

If you look at Figure 5.21, you will see that the hardware is in place. While this table walk looks a bit slow, TLB misses are rare so the net cost is negligible.

Let us consider the MD bit with a write after a read to the same page. The PTE would then reside in the TLB and we no longer have its PA in hand. How then will we get a handle on the PTE? It is awkward to go from a PTE to the address that contains the PTE. (See Problem 5.9.) One reasonable way to get there is to treat the first write reference to a page as a TLB miss. That is, if a write occurs to a page whose PTE is in the TLB but whose MD bit is reset, then the TLB declares a miss. Upon walking the steps to bring in a new PTE, the MMU will find it either in cache or in memory. Having acquired the PTE anew, we have the MMU set both RF and MD in the word going into the TLB. Then we write the word back into the D-cache. We propose this somewhat awkward-looking method on the basis of the following observations:

- Writes are much less frequent than reads.
- Only a tiny fraction of the writes will be preceded by reads in the same page. For example, the most commonly written pages will be stack pages or heap pages. They are almost always written before they are read. There is nothing there until something is written.
- The cost of the occasional extra table walk is small when distributed over all writes.

5.7.3.7 BUS ERRORS. Generally, the address space of a machine vastly exceeds the sum of all the connected addresses. Should a program manage to issue a PA which does not correspond to installed memory, no conventional response comes back. For example, on the VMEbus, you might get no $\overline{\text{DTACK}}$. If nothing is done to recover, the absence of a $\overline{\text{DTACK}}$ would hang the system. It would just sit there inserting wait states forever. An unresponsive address can arise from a programming error or it can simply be a device that was there but has since gone off the air. Generally, busses provide a way to signal such a problem and system designers put in bad address detectors and/or bus timeout circuits. Since the MMU is a bus user, it must be able to respond to such a finding by causing an exception to be taken and by indicating what caused the problem.

On the VMEbus, the error is signaled by asserting $\overline{\text{BERR}}$, rather than $\overline{\text{DTACK}}$. To allow for that possibility, all of the state diagrams which wait for $\overline{\text{DTACK}}$ should be modified to test also for $\overline{\text{BERR}}$. The nature of the error should be recorded in the MMU status register so that the handler can determine the proper response. For example, a bus error on a table walk is probably symptomatic of an unrecoverable system failure while a bus error on writing to a peripheral may indicate only that someone turned off the printer.

Clearly, this just adds detail to the picture we have already painted. We think that by this point, both structure and form have been developed in full measure. That being the case, it is time to sum up.

CHAPTER SUMMARY

This chapter has dealt with the design of an MMU/D-cache board. It is the companion to Chapter 4 since two of the important topics dealt with are the efficient translation of VAs to PAs and the efficient transfer of data from and to memory. The first half of the chapter addressed the following issues:

- cache structures and cache replacement policies
- how to fetch data into the cache

- how to arrange access to the data in cache (addressing)
- how to or whether to deal with virtual addresses
- how to keep cached data consistent with memory data

We began by looking at possible cache structures. In all cases, the cache considered was much smaller than main memory. The structures were classified according to the methodology of mapping data into the cache. We began with an essentially random mapping and moved toward mappings of greater and greater complexity. This gave us four types of cache:

- *A fully associative cache*, in which any block from memory can reside in any block in the cache. Determining whether a particular datum is in the cache is done by comparing the address for the desired data block with those of each data block in the cache. These block addresses are called *tags*. All tags are compared in parallel with the target tag. In most cases, the design of any cache must ensure that never more than one copy of a given block exists in a cache at one time.
- *A direct-mapped cache*, in which each block in memory maps into a specific line in cache. Since multiple blocks in memory map into the same block in cache, we once again found ourselves using tags to determine if the target block is in cache. However, in contrast to the fully associative cache, only one tag need be scanned since each block in memory maps into a unique block in cache. The direct mapping could be cyclic, based on the low-order bits in the block address, or all of the block address bits could be hashed to provide a more even distribution of adjacent blocks through the cache.
- *A set-associative cache*, in which each line or set in the cache contains 2, 4, . . . , 32 blocks. Within the line or set, the mapping is random and the search is similar to the fully associative cache. Any block in memory will have a direct mapping into a particular line but a random distribution within the line.
- *A sectored cache*, where large segments are mapped into the cache, either randomly or directly, and then the individual blocks within a particular segment are directly mapped into the segment in cache. If a block is present, its valid bit is set. The advantage of this method is the limited number of tags which must be stored and searched—one per segment. The liability is that if a segment must be replaced, all of the blocks within the segment must be invalidated.

We turned next to evaluating cache performance and developed some tools for determining both the average time to access memory for a particular hit rate and the hit rate for a particular program and cache structure. Our most important result was that for typical cache and memory cycle times, a hit rate in excess of 95 percent was needed to make our machine run at roughly the raw clock rate. In fact, if the cache hit rate is too low, the cache actually impedes data transfers. We also saw that for a given capacity set-associative caches gave better hit rates than direct-mapped caches, but that difference was small for capacities in excess of 8 KB.

Two types of misses can be identified and they are reduced by different design parameters. The first of these is the miss which occurs on the first reference to a data block. These are reduced by bringing in larger blocks on each miss, but since the granularity of a program and of most data structures is modest, this cure saturates at block lengths in the range of 16 to 64 bytes. The other type of miss occurs because of mapping conflicts. Set-associative structures and hashing functions are good structural elements to reduce mapping conflicts. The other cure to mapping conflicts is a large cache size. When caches are made quite large, direct mapping is often the most cost-effective design.

Some cache structures admit only one form of replacement; others give the designer a choice in replacement policy. The portion of the cache which is direct leads to a simple, inflexible choice for replacement; the portion which is associative is open to any form for replacement. Those that we considered include:

- *Random*, using some easily generated number such as a time count to select the block in the set to replace. This proved to be cheap and reasonably efficient.
- *FIFO*, using orderly insertion and a counter to identify the most recent addition, makes it easy to identify the oldest member in the set. However, there is no reason to assume that the oldest is least useful. It is not too surprising to find that a bald FIFO strategy is not especially efficient.
- *LRU*, using a counter for every block in the set. For a set size of 2, the method is trivial and widely used. For larger set sizes, the method is considerably more expensive. In many cases, the added cost does not produce a commensurate improvement over random replacement.
- *Deville's algorithm*, giving a very good approximation of LRU with almost no additional hardware. It employs the valid bit in a dual but not conflicting role and adds but 1 bit to the whole line. In some circumstances, Deville's algorithm outperforms even LRU.

Writes required a lengthy discussion. The principal algorithms are called writethrough and writeback. Writethrough does approximately what the programmer pictures with data going back to memory with at most a short delay. Writeback keeps modifications in cache until forced to return them either by a replacement of a modified line in the cache or a command from the system to write back a line. If writeback is adopted, the question of how to do a write on a miss is not obvious. We adopted the conventional method of *fetch-on-write*, where the whole line is fetched for caching and the modified word substituted in the cache. In such a scheme, the data does not get back to memory until forced by a writeback. This delay between data written by the CPU and data appearing in memory can lead to breakdowns in sequentiality and even to such non sequiturs as writing new data and then reading back the old. To avoid such potential potholes, we created a design with a single-line writeback buffer and adopted the rule that a read which forces a writeback is completed before the writeback but a subsequent read cannot be started until the first writeback is completed.

After considering why I/O devices must lie in an uncacheable address space, we pondered how fetch-on-write would work and the variation on that theme which led to the *read-modify-write* cycle that our LODSET instruction demanded. We treated this concept in general and then later for our design with a single-line writeback buffer.

The other form of cache that would be on our MMU board is the *translation lookaside buffer* (TLB). This cache stores translations of VAs to PAs. You search it with the VA and get out the PA and the protection bits—in other words, the PTE. We used this example to explore the details of a hashing function to assure uniform spreading of the addresses over the cache.

Having introduced the translation methodology, we then could choose to use VAs or PAs for searching the D-cache. The advantage of VAs is speed. The delay in getting the PA from the VA will slow the cache response for data that is in the cache, the result expected in greater than 95 percent of the cases. An important disadvantage of using VAs is the problem of aliases. While one can use a *reverse translation buffer* (RTB) to identify and invalidate aliases, this adds considerably to the cost of the MMU/D-cache. Another problem with VAs is that they are not unique. All processes share the same virtual address space. This too can be solved by throwing money at it. One can flush the cache on a context switch (expensive for large caches) or add the process ID to the VA to make them unique (expensive in cache memory widths).

Our final preparatory subject was the problem of sharing data among multiple independent caches sharing a common bus structure. This topic introduced the issue of cache synchronization and the methodologies which have been developed for maintaining synchronism without excess bus traffic. These methods include:

- *Snooping* simply has each cache watch the system bus, comparing each PA that accompanies a write with the tags in its D-cache (actually a copy of the tags in its D-cache). Upon a hit, the line is invalidated in cache, forcing the MMU to go to memory the next time that this line is accessed.
- *Snarfing* takes snooping one step further. If the line is identified as being in its own cache, the snarfer simply copies the data into its own cache as it passes by. This is really a free update in the sense that the data was going by anyway. However, the snarfing cache is complicated by having to service its own processor at very high speed while this asynchronous bus transaction is delivering new data. Both snooping and snarfing are particularly effective with writethrough caches, but unfortunately, the need for snooping and snarfing arises only in the same sort of circumstance that calls for minimizing bus traffic. Writethrough caches generate much more bus traffic than writeback caches.
- *Intervention* is a method for assuring that the most up-to-date data is sent when a cache asks for it. When a cache asks for data that has been modified but not written back from another cache, instead of having the memory respond, the holder of the new data intercedes, temporarily taking the active slave's position and responding to the request by sending the newest data. Only some busses allow intervention. VMEbus does not; Futurebus does.

Finally, we turned to the design of our own MMU/D-cache. Using data we had from the first half of the chapter, we arrived at a set of specifications for this design. These specifications included:

- PAs in the data cache
- direct-mapped data cache
- 4096 blocks of 4 words each
- writeback
- fetch-on-write misses
- direct-mapped TLB
- 1024 entries in the TLB split between system and process

Another choice that we made, which was somewhat outside the cache design but important in it, was to use nothing but blocks in all memory operations. This simplified memory design, particularly with respect to error correction, and made the bus transactions very efficient for the most common bus operations. With these choices, we could lay out the basic working structure of our cache (Figure 5.15) and set about designing a controller for it. We considered the most common transactions, which included:

- Read with TLB hit, valid operation, and D-Cache Hit
- Read with TLB hit, valid operation, and D-Cache Miss
- Write with TLB hit, valid operation, and D-Cache Hit
- Write with TLB hit, valid operation, and D-Cache Miss
- Read or Write with TLB hit but invalid operation
- Read or Write with TLB Miss

The remainder of the chapter was focused on designing state machines which would perform the several tasks assigned to the MMU/D-cache. The build began from the simplest of the operations:

- Read with TLB hit, valid operation, and D-Cache Hit

The simple but powerful state machine of Figure 5.16 was combined with the timing diagram of Figure 5.17 to travel the state diagram of Figure 5.18. This combination showed how timing was controlled and how the MMU and CPU worked together. With the CPU clock derived from the MMU clock and controlled by the MMU state machine, the concept of stalling the CPU was introduced to allow synchronous transactions on both hits and misses of several different durations. The simple read-with-hit was completely resolved with this simple model.

We next introduced the added complexity of going through the VMEbus to memory. This required compliance with VMEbus standards as well as dealing with our own choice of working only with full lines. The timing diagram of Figure 5.19 and the more complex state diagram of Figure 5.20 resulted. This Moore machine included Figure 5.18 and incorporated the write transaction as well. Figure 5.20 showed how the state machine provided the delays required by the VMEbus specification and how the bus would be acquired, how 4 words would be cranked in. (*In* is the only direction for this state machine since writeback is run by another state machine.)

Writeback was the next operation considered. A writeback buffer of 1 line was added to the working structure (along with several other components for exception handling) in Figure 5.21. Writebacks could result either if a dirty line was displaced from the D-cache or if the CPU wrote to a memory-mapped block.

The response of the MMU to a TLB-invalid response brought home the mechanics of our pagetable mechanism. This was first discussed in Section 5.7.3, where we walked down through the pagetables to get the PTE needed into the TLB. We returned to this subject in Section 5.7.3.3 to consider all of the other problems which the TLB could report and which would result in an exception. These exceptions included page faults and illegal accesses such as out-of-range or writing to read-only memory. The concept of an interrupt vector was viewed from the perspective of the interrupter, with hardware added to the structure of Figure 5.21 to hold the interrupt vectors themselves and to save state data which would enable the interrupt routine to determine the detailed cause of the interrupt.

We concluded the chapter by considering some of the details and specific cases which the MMU must handle. These included:

- cache-inhibit pages
- LODSET
- setting the MD and RF bits
- bus errors

In some sense, we have moved inward in Figure 1.1 from software up to the gates of the CPU itself. This is the topic of the next and in some ways central chapter of this text.

PROBLEMS

5.1. Assume that it takes six transistors to store a bit in the static memory typical of cache. Determine the number of transistors that it will take to store the bits of an 8-KW cache. Then compute percentage increase in the number of transistors that it will take to store tags and valid bits for:

(a) a direct-mapped cache

(b) a two-way set-associative cache (include LRU)

(c) an eight-way set-associative cache (include LRU)

5.2. Consider a writeback cache scheme with a read-preference writeback queue of 2 blocks. Let it be a two-way set-associative cache with blocks of 4 words and 2K of lines. Assume that the queue will store the physical block addresses and have valid bits to indicate a block to be written. Design a state diagram which handles the case of a read to either of the blocks in the queue. If such a read occurs, the data in the queue should be restored to cache, the queue updated, and the datum returned *as a cache hit.*

5.3. The IBM 3033 TLB of Section 5.4.1 utilized a hashing function for a 64-line cache with a page of 4 KB and an address space of 24 bits. In our machine, we also plan to use effectively 24-bit VAs, but these are word addresses and our page size is 256 words. That leaves 16 bits for the page number. Design a hash function for a 128-line TLB for our machine and obtain the cross-correlation function for 10-page segments starting at the same direct-mapped line in the cache. The line chosen need not be 0. Comment on whether your design is a good one.

5.4. In Section 5.6.3 we introduced the idea of using software to force a one-line writeback. The problem is how to generate the correct address for that line. Let us say that you are to put the first address in r0 and the last address in r1 and then TRAP 511 to get the system to do the force the writeback. See also Section 5.7.3.2.

(a) If you had just exercised the instruction ISTORE r9, (r10,r3), write the code to force the writeback of this datum.

(b) Now let us say you had done STOREB r8, (r7,r2). Write the code to force the writeback of this datum.

See Problem 5.7 for the OS side of this transaction.

5.5. The time to bring in a block is an important determinant in deciding what hit rate is necessary in a cache. Figures 5.19 and 5.20 show the transactions necessary to accomplish a read with a cache miss. Determine the total time for execution of a CPU read request if the memory can set up to return all four words and give the first $\overline{\text{DTACK}}$ in 80 ns.

5.6. Modify the state diagram of Figure 5.20 to include the possibility of a dirty line with a cache miss. Assume that the writeback buffer of Figure 5.21 is in place and that the writeback itself will be handled by a separate state machine.

5.7. Write a program in C to handle the cache flush for PVAs *X* to *Y*. Assume that the process requesting this action pushed these two addresses onto the process stack before doing the trap and that the process SP can be accessed as a variable named USP. Do not forget that the address in the USP is a PVA, not a SVA. Appropriate translation is required. (See Figure 4.12 on page 191 for clues on translation.)

5.8. Design the state machine which handles a TLB miss. Since the cache will fetch lines from the pagetable, you should find it helpful to use large parts of Figure 5.20. By defining a state bit, **TM**, to signal a TLB miss, you can have the CSM do different things when it is responding to a TLB miss than when it is handling a cache miss. Include the setting of RF and MD bits.

5.9. In Section 5.7.3.6, it is stated that "It is awkward to go from a PTE to the address that contains the PTE." Show that you can use the VA to find the address of the PTE.

REFERENCES

[Agarwal, 88] Agarwal, A., R. Simoni, J. Hennessy, and M. Horowitz, *An Evaluation of Directory Schemes for Cache Coherence*, **Proceeding of 15th International Symposium on Computer Architecture**, 280–289 (1988).

[Agarwal, 89] Agarwal, A., *Analysis of Cache Performance for Operating Systems and Multi-programming*, Kluwer (1989). This book studies the performance of various types of caches in realistic situations. Most of the results are based on address traces, but analytical models are also included.

[Alpert, 93] Alpert, Donald, and Dror Avnon, *Architecture of the Pentium Microprocessor*, **IEEE Micro 13**(3), 11-21 (1993).

[Alpha, 92] *Alpha Architecture Reference Manual*, Edited by Richard L. Sikes, DB–ISBN 1–55558–098, Digital Press [1992].

[Black, 89] Black, D.L., et al., *Translation Lookaside Buffer Consistency: A Software Approach*, **Proceedings of the Third International Conference on Architectural Support for Programming Languages and Operating Systems (ASPLOS–III)**, 113–122 (1989). The method used by MACH.

[Bitar, 86] Bitar, P., and A.M. Despain, *Multiprocessor Cache Synchronization, Issues, Innovations, Evolution*, **Proceeding of the 13th International Symposium on Computer Architecture**, 424–433 (1986).

[Bloom, 62] Bloom, L., M. Cohen, and S. Porter, *Considerations in the Design of a Computer with High Logic to Memory Speed Ratio*, **Proceedings Gigacycle Computing Systems** (1962), **AIEE Special Publication 2–136**, 53–63 (1962).

[Cheriton, 86] Cheriton, D.R., G.A. Slavenburg, and P.D. Boyle, *Software–Controlled Caches in the VMP Multiprocessor*, **Proceeding of 13th International Symposium on Computer Architecture**, 366–374 (1986). Virtual address caches with both misses and coherency handled by software.

[Chi, 89] Chi, C.H., and H. Dietz, *Unified Management of Registers and Cache Using Liveness and Cache Bypass*, **SIGPLAN 89 Conference on Programming Design and Implementation**, 344–355 (1989). The compiler specifies with each reference whether it should be cached.

[Conti, 69] Conti, C.J., *Concepts for Buffer Storage*, **Computer Group News 2**, 9 (1969).

[Deville, 92] Deville, Y., and J. Gobert, *A Class of Replacement Policies for Medium and High-Associativity Structures*, **Computer Architecture News 20**(1), 55–61 (1992).

[Ditzel, 82] Ditzel, D.R., and H.R. McLellan, *Register Allocation for Free: The C Machine Stack Cache*, **Proceedings of the International Conference on Architectural Support for Programming Languages and Operating Systems (ASPLOS)**, 48–56 (1982).

[Ditzel, 87a] Ditzel, D.R., H.R. McLellan, and A.D. Berenbaum, *The Hardware Architecture of the CRISP Microprocessor*, **Proceeding of 14th International Symposium on Computer Architecture**, 309–319 (1987).

[Ditzel, 87b] Ditzel, D.R., H.R. McLellan, and A.D. Berenbaum, *Design Tradeoffs to Support the C Programming Language in the CRISP Microprocessor*, **Proceedings of the Second International Conference on Architectural Support for Programming Languages and Operating Systems (ASPLOS–II)**, 158–163 (1987). CRISP contains a 32–entry stack cache.

[Dubois, 88] Dubois, M., C. Scheurich, and F. Briggs, *Synchronization, Coherence, and Event Ordering in Multiprocessors*, **IEEE Computer 21**(2), 9 (1988).

[Eggers, 89] Eggers, S.J., and R.H. Katz, *Evaluating the Performance of Four Snooping Cache Coherency Protocols*, **Proceeding of 16th International Symposium on Computer Architecture**, 2–15 (1989).

[Eickemeyer, 88] Eickemeyer, R. J. , and J.H. Patel, *Performance Evaluation of On-Chip Register and Cache Organizations*, **Proceeding of 15th International Symposium on Computer Architecture**, 64–72 (1988).

[Goodman, 83] Goodman, J.R., *Using Cache Memory to Reduce Processor-Memory Traffic*, **Proceeding of 10th International Symposium on Computer Architecture**, 124–131 (1983).

[Goodman, 87] Goodman, J.R., *Coherency for Multiprocessor Virtual Address Caches*, **Proceedings of the Second International Conference on Architectural Support for Programming Languages and Operating Systems (ASPLOS–II)**, 72–81 (1987). This cache uses a virtual tag store for CPU access and a physical tag store for external access.

[Gustavson, 92] Gustavson, D. B., *The Scalable Coherent Interface and Related Standards Projects*, **IEEE Micro**, 10–22 (1992).

[Hill, 86] Hill, M.D., et al., *Design Decisions in SPUR*, **IEEE Computer 19**(11), 8–22 (1986).

[Hill, 88] Hill, M.D., *A Case for Direct-Mapped Caches*, **IEEE Computer 21**(12), 25 (1988). Direct-mapped caches are cheaper and have better performance than set–associative caches when the total size is large.

[IEEE, 92] *SCI—Scalable Coherent Interface*, **IEEE Standard 1596** (1992).

[Kessler, 89] Kessler, R.E., R. Jooss, A. Lebeck, M.D. Hill, *Inexpensive Implementations of Set-Associativity*, **Proceedings of 16th International Symposium on Computer Architecture**, 131–139 (1989). Uses multiple accesses to one RAM, instead of parallel accesses.

[Lee, 84] Lee, J., and A.J. Smith, *Branch Prediction Strategies and Branch Target Buffer Design*, **IEEE Computer 17**(1), 6 (1984). A branch target buffer is a cache used to speed up conditional branches.

[Levy, 89] Levy, H. M., and R. H. Eckhouse, Jr., *Computer Programming and Architecture, The Vax,* 2nd edition, 344–347, Digital Press (1989).

[Liptay, 68] Liptay, J.S., *Structural Aspects of the System/360 Model 85, Part II: The Cache*, **IBM Systems Journal 7**(1), 15 (1968). The first computer to use a cache.

[Papamarcos, 85] Papamarcos, M., and J. Patel, *A Low Overhead Coherence Solution for Multiprocessors with Private Memory Caches*, **Proceedings of the 11th International Symposium on Computer Architecture**, 348–354 (1985).

[Pohm, 83] Pohm, A.V., and O.P. Agrawal, *High-Speed Memory Systems*, Reston (1983). Most of this book is devoted to cache memories. It includes analytical models of their performance and descriptions of the caches in various commercial computers.

[Przybylski, 88] Przybylski, S. A., M. Horowitz, and J. Hennessy, *Performance Tradeoffs in Cache Design*, **Proceeding of 15th International Symposium on Computer Architecture**, 290–298 (1988).

[Przybylski, 90] Przybylski, S.A., **Cache and Memory Hierarchy Design: A Performance-Directed Approach**, Morgan Kaufmann (1990).

[Pugh, 91] Pugh, E.W., L.R. Johnson, and J.H. Palmer, **IBM's 360 and Early 370 Systems**, MIT Press (1991).

[Radin, 83] Radin, G., *The 801 Minicomputer*, **IBM Journal of Research and Development 27**(3), 237 (1983). The 801 includes instructions for explicit control of cache entries. (also presented at ASPLOS (1982).

[Smith, 78] Smith, A.J., *Sequential Program Prefetching in Memory Hierarchies*, **IEEE Computer 11**(12), 7 (1978). The effect of fetching blocks before they are needed.

[Smith, 82] Smith, A.J., *Cache Memories*, **Computing Surveys 14**(3), 473 (1982). This is a good overview of various types of cache memory and the factors which affect their performance.

[Smith, 86] Smith, A.J., *Bibliography and Readings on CPU Cache Memories and Related Topics,* **Computer Architecture News 14**(1), 22 (1986).

[Smith, 91] Smith, A.J., *Second Bibliography on Cache Memories,* **Computer Architecture News 19**(4), 154–182 (1991).

[Stanley, 87] Stanley, T.J., and R.G. Wedig, *A Performance Analysis of Automatically Managed Top of Stack Buffers*, **Proceeding of 14th International Symposium on Computer Architecture**, 272–281 (1987).

[Steenkiste, 89] Steenkiste, P., *The Impact of Code Density on Instruction Cache Performance*, **Proceeding of 16th International Symposium on Computer Architecture**, 252–259 (1989). Code density affects memory traffic more than it does execution time.

[VME, 87] *IEEE Standard for a Versatile Backplane Bus: VMEBUS*, **ANSI/IEEE Standard 1014–1987** (1987).

[Wang, 89] Wang, Wen-Hann, Jean-Loup Baer, and Henry M. Levy, *Organization and Performance of a Two-Level Virtual-Real Cache Hierarchy*, **Proceedings of the 16th Annual International Symposium on Computer Architecture**, 140–148 (1989).

[Wood, 86] Wood, D.A., et al., *An In-Cache Address Translation Mechanism*, **Proceedings of the 13th International Symposium on Computer Architecture**, 358–365 (1986). SPUR uses virtual address caches to hold PTEs, eliminating the need for a TLB.

[Wood, 89] Wood, D.A., and R. Katz, *Supporting Reference and Dirty Bits in SPUR's Virtual Address Cache*, **Proceedings of the 16th International Symposium on Computer Architecture**, 122–130 (1989).

CHAPTER 6

THE PROCESSOR CHIP

IN WHICH WE LAY OUT THE COMPUTER'S "FACTORY FLOOR"

6.1 AN OVERVIEW OF THE CPU IN ITS CONTEXT

By now you can see that, on the one hand, the *central processing unit* (CPU) is a relatively insignificant fraction of the total computer hardware, while, on the other hand, it is the very center of a basically hub-and-spoke organization. The large resources that are devoted to primary and secondary memory and to the central bus which connects the memories to each other and to the processing section all exist to serve the processor. The objective of the design is a computer which executes some class of programs at very high speed. To that end, we must design a CPU which can execute a useful set of instructions at very high speed and a memory and bus system which can both feed this hungry CPU with a steady supply of instructions and data and take back the processed data. With that description, we have delineated two of the particular architectural concerns of the CPU designer: speed of execution and speed of communication. The third area which must be addressed is the somewhat diverse area of *special cases*—interrupts, exceptions, and the like. In some *real-time* applications, interrupts are a major component of everyday operation for the processor; in others, interrupts are relatively rare. Where interrupts are frequent, efficient handling of interrupts must be carefully factored into the architecture; where they are rare, one is simply bound to see that they always work correctly.

Within this chapter, we want to complete the architecture of our own CPU and compare that design with other options which we could have exercised. We will begin with a look at what our instruction set requires for data flow through the system. This will quickly establish a large fraction of the CPU chip. In essence, these components will make the instructions function. Then we will turn to a theme that has been a central target of the overall streamlined design: *getting one instruction executed per clock*. In attempting to achieve that goal, we will examine the general topic of *pipelining*—an idea that follows directly from Henry Ford's development of the assembly line in the first decade of this century—and have a close look at the instruction cache. Finally, we consider the interrupt issue and install the hardware necessary to handle nested interrupts with reasonable efficiency.

6.2 DATA FLOW IN THE CPU

Consider a typical simple arithmetic statement in a HLL program, say,

```
A = A+B;
```

If we assume that both *A* and *B* were initially in memory, then in a VAX we could translate that line quite literally as

```
ADDL3 A,B,A
```

where *A* and *B* are assumed to be labels. The assembler will translate the labels to what we have been calling base-displacement format, using the PC as the base. To be specific, that instruction becomes

```
ADDL3 disp_A(PC), disp_B(PC), disp_A(PC)
```

The displacements are all 4 bytes long;[1] the opcode and each of the mode-register specifiers are 1 byte long. The whole instruction, then, is 16 bytes long.

To execute this instruction, the VAX CPU must do precisely what our RISC machine will do—fetch two operands to CPU latches, add them and collect the result in another latch or register,[2] and put it back in memory. The principal programmatic

[1] Since the PC changes as the VAX scans the variable-length instruction, the displacements must be calculated from the current position of the PC—that is, at the byte just after the displacement itself. That means that the first *disp_A* differs from the second *disp_A* by 10 bytes, the PC change in fetching the first and second. In the VAX system, the linker, which "knows" all label references, computes the displacement and inserts it in the program.

[2] A *latch* has two states: *open*, where the input ⇒ memory element ⇒ output, and *closed* or *latched*, where the input is disconnected and memory element ⇒ output. In the *open* state, the latch is said to be *transparent*. For a register, data is *clocked* from input to output; there is never a direct connection. The difference, while subtle, is critical. For a latch to change value, the input and output must be the same for some period; for a register, the value at the input at t_1 is passed to the output at t_2 . . . . While t_2 can approach t_1 so closely that the transfer can be said to occur at a particular moment, the input is latched in before it appears at the output. There is never a period when both must be the same. In this way, it is possible for one register to be receiving data for a new value while it is transferring its current data to another register.

differences in the RISC case are that the registers are explicitly in the hands of the programmer (be that human or a compiler), and, at least in our case, we are likely to use a static data-area base in one of our regular registers rather than the PC. Consider that code:

```
DLOAD disp_A(r8), r0                ;fetch first operand
DLOAD disp_B(r8), r1                ;fetch second operand
NOP                                 ;waiting for r1 to be loaded
ADDc r0, r1, r0                     ;add them and set condition flags
DSTORE r0, disp_A(r8)               ;store the sum
```

Note that this small block of code is 25 percent longer than the single VAX instruction and that it does the same things. It is reasonable to view this as rather typical of what a CPU will do, whatever its flavor. Accordingly, let us look at what set of small tasks must be accomplished:

- Each of the first two instructions requires taking the sum of two numbers—one from a register and one from the instruction itself—to form the address of a datum. That address must be presented to the cache or memory and the datum returned must be put into an appropriate register.
- The fourth instruction has two data moving to an adder, whose output is then returned to the destination register.
- The last instruction forms an address just like the first two and then provides the cache with the address and the data to be returned.

We have above a list of basic tasks for which we must provide the following hardware:

- an adder or *arithmetic and logic unit* (ALU)
- a register set
- busses to carry data to and from the registers
- a path to and from the D-cache

If we were minimalists, we could make do with one of each, but if three people must tighten screws, it is a pity to have but one screwdriver. While it was not always so, today gates are cheap. We need not skimp. Our eye should be first on productivity and only second on minimization of gate count. Busses, on the other hand, use up chip area at a ferocious rate and cross each other only with difficulty. Each time that we add a bus, we are proposing 32 more lines. We should be careful not to be too expansive, but at the same time, it would be a mistake to create a traffic jam by being too cheap. The real test will come when we start worrying about pipelining. If we cannot meet our goal of one instruction per clock, we may have to add more busses to allow for parallel activity.

6.2.1 Register-Register Instructions

All of our arithmetic and logical instructions deliver two operands and get one result back. Since the ALU itself is all combinational logic, one could easily accomplish any such operation in a single half-cycle if we had three busses, as in Figure 6.1. On the upstroke of the clock, data would be put onto the source busses, *A* and *B*. It would propagate through the network of ALU gates and the shifter, form the result specified by the OP bits in the instruction, finally reaching the destination bus, *D*, and stabilizing there. Then, on the downstroke of the clock pulse, that data would be logged into the destination register.

Figure 6.1 has a slew of little details worthy of note. The first item to observe is that the system permits a single register to provide source data to both busses simultaneously and to sink the result. In other words, one may do

```
SUB r3, r3, r3
```

to clear R3. Not only that, the operation works as fast as any other way to clear the register and uses no hardware that would not be there already. The only excuse for having a separate CLR Rx instruction is that the instruction can be *shorter*. However, we hold that the streamlining one obtains by having instructions of constant width far outweighs

FIGURE 6.1 A three-bus arrangement of the ALU to allow direct propagation of the result from input to output in a single half clock. The breaks in the conductors with the bars over them indicate *pass switches* or *tristates*. A pass switch would be connected, when enabled, when the clock was high. The ALU is assumed to contain the shifters specified in MUL and DIV in Chapter 2.

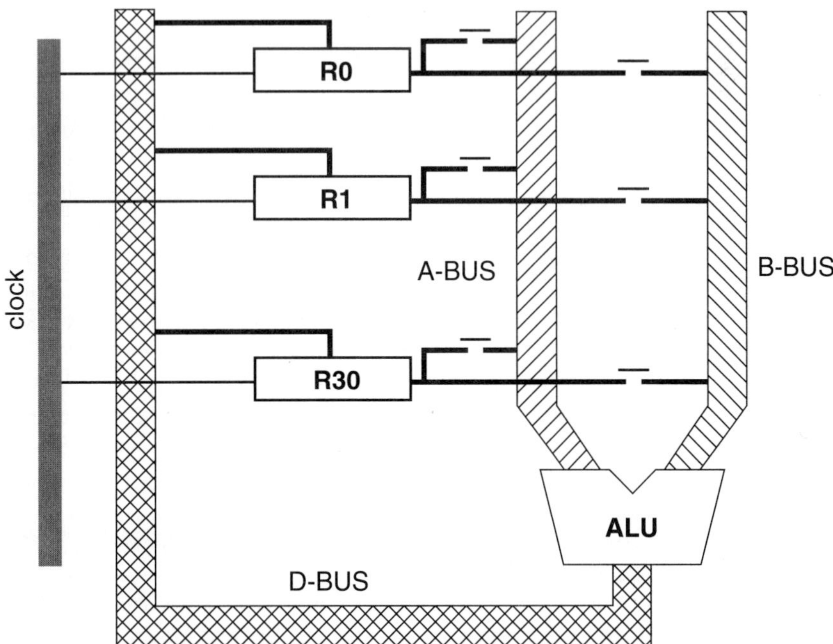

the disadvantage of some wasted space in the instruction stream. (If it pleases you or your customers, the assembler can translate CLR Rx into SUBx Rx, Rx, Rx. The assembler for the SPARC does many such translations.)

In thinking about clock strokes, remember that the data in the register is always available at its output, but new data is logged into the register—that is, it overwrites whatever is in there—on a particular edge of the clock signal. In Figure 6.1 we have chosen the falling edge for that data transition. To prepare new data for reading, the upstroke is used to close the pass transistors enabled by the current instruction. The dwell time between upstroke and downstroke must be long enough for the signal to propagate from input to output and stabilize.

Notice that each bus has at least 32 loads to be driven. For example, if the pass transistor which connects R3 to the A-bus is turned on, it must pull with it the capacitance not only of the line itself but of all the other 31 pass transistors as well. Charging all of those capacitances, which happens almost every cycle, is not only a major component of the energy load for this chip but a principal cause of delay in executing instructions. In these days, as clock speeds for PC computer chips race from 30 MHz to 200 MHz, one should ask just how long it must be between the upstroke and downstroke in the half-cycle we are considering. Four delays *in series* determine the minimum time: the delay in driving the source busses; the delay in propagation through the ALU/Shifter gate network; the delay in having the ALU/Shifter gates drive the destination bus; and the delay to get properly into the register input circuitry (register setup time). How long would all of that take? A very fast 32-bit adder/subtracter executed in CMOS today should be able to propagate its data from input to output in less than 15 ns. If we allow 5 ns for bus drive and setup time, the total is 20 ns. If that is half a clock, we are talking about an upper limit of 25 MHz on the chip. Before being disappointed in that number, note that that is the time to do a whole instruction. CISCs inherently use multiple clocks per instruction for many instructions. A 25-MHz CISC does not do 25 million instructions per second (MIPS). However, it is really too early for a realistic comparison. We are not done yet with our timing analysis. On our way to pipelining later in this chapter, we will find it advisable to break the operations into somewhat smaller pieces. Doing less per half-clock means that the half-clock can be briefer; 20 ns is not the final figure.

A quick glance at Figure 6.1 shows no signs of R31. Since the PC/NUL register has a variety of uses and meanings, you might wonder at its absence. It was left out precisely because inserting it called for a bit of discussion. Let us first consider the NUL usage. As a destination, *not being there* is precisely what we had in mind. The ALU/shifter will write to the D-bus, but nothing will be enabled to record the result. As a source, however, the NUL reference is supposed to provide a 0. This is done by *hard-wiring* a 0 to pass transistors as shown in Figure 6.2. Notice that to the logic which decodes the instructions, R31 is no different from any other register. Let us leave the other meanings of R31 to a little further on in the discussion where we handle addressing and branching.

Finishing up this section, let us consider the consequences of reducing the number of busses. Obviously, if the A- or B-bus must serve as both a source and destination bus, we must provide latches for holding one kind of data while the bus is conveying the other type. Furthermore, more half-clocks must pass to get the whole task done.

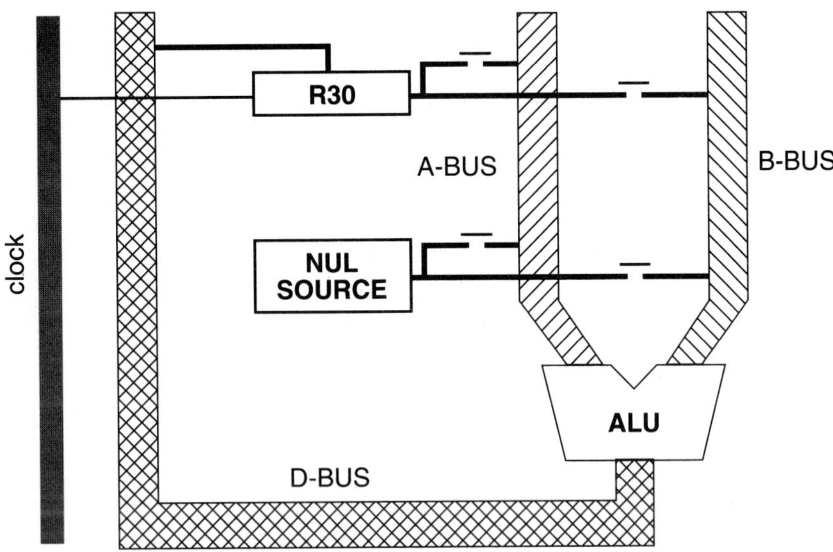

FIGURE 6.2 The connection of a hardwired zero (i.e., a connection to the ground bus) through pass transistors to realize the NUL function for R31.

While that might seem to imply a slowdown, pipelining and shorter clock cycles may allow us to maintain or even increase our speed of processing. Let us look at the two-bus scheme, which is the one we will implement. It is shown in Figure 6.3.

Figure 6.3 shows the register file and ALU of Figure 6.1 plus latches A, B, and C and the mechanism for getting literals out of the instruction. Looking ahead to the pipelining problem, we provide C with the capability of writing to either A-bus or B-bus. This is necessary to allow sequences like

```
SUB r3, r4, r7
ADD r7, r7, r7
```

without requiring that we always put back the last result *before* loading operands for the next operation. The sequence of half-clock steps would be something like

1. $A \Leftarrow r3$, $B \Leftarrow r4$
2. $C \Leftarrow A - B$
3. $A \Leftarrow C$, $B \Leftarrow C$
4. $C \Leftarrow A + B$, $r7 \Leftarrow C$;note that $A - B$ is going to R7
5. $r7 \Leftarrow C$;here $A + B$ is going to R7

The hardware must recognize that C contains the value needed in step 3 when the instruction actually asks for r7, but that is easy to do. Such a controller is called an *interlock*.

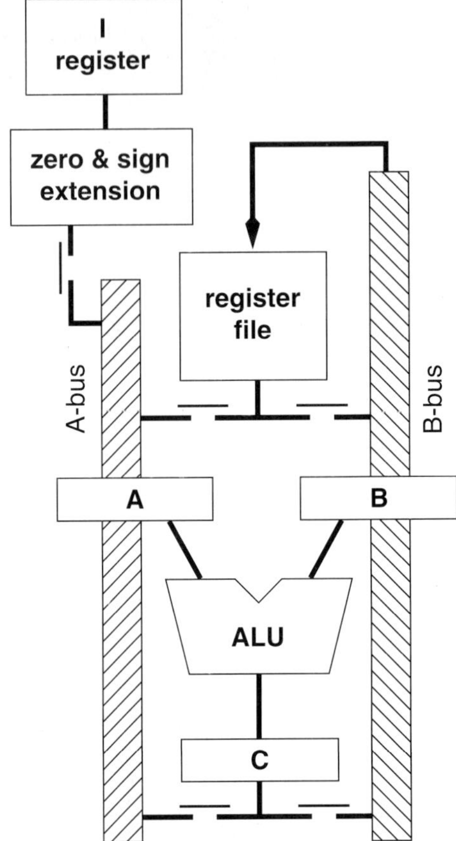

FIGURE 6.3 A fully developed two-bus scheme for handling register-register instructions. The register file contains R0… R30 and the NUL equivalent. Pass switches provide operand access to the A- and B-busses. Data from the C latch can be applied to either the A- or B-bus (or both). Data can be read into any of the registers from the B-bus. Literals can be obtained from the I (instruction) register and put on the A-bus.

Were we now ready to do a timing analysis, you could look at the sequence of operations above and notice that sometimes we have pure bus operations and sometimes we have ALU operations. One might be tempted to use some nonsymmetric split of the clock to minimize wasted time. While this may be possible (and is done on some machines), we are not yet at the point where we can see all of the cycles which must be handled. To do that, we must proceed through our complete instruction set. The next big block of instructions are the LOADs and STOREs. Let us turn to them.

6.2.2 Laying Out LOAD and STORE

In either a LOAD or STORE instruction, regardless of type, an address must be formed and a datum moved between D-cache and register file. Address formation is either a zero-extension of the 22-bit field of the instruction or the sum of two numbers from the register file and I register. Given the availability of NUL, we can consider any of the address operations as a sum. In a machine that was pipelined but not as regular and streamlined as a typical RISC, there might be a need to put in a separate adder to generate addresses. In that way, you can make the timing of the generation of addresses much more independent of the processing of data. In the RISC style of design, however, and particularly in this machine, the ALU will always have one calculation per clock. That can yield an address or a datum. We will never need both in one clock, so the single ALU will serve. A fast 32-bit adder is a nontrivial piece of silicon, so having only one on the chip is a pleasant result of the RISC design paradigm. On the other hand, if a second adder would have improved performance significantly, we would have devoted space to it.[3]

With this introduction, let us consider the steps performed in a LOAD. As an example, let us take

DLOAD 1223(r17), r3	00110	00011	10001	0 0000 0100 1100 0111
	DLOAD	r3	r17	1223_d

The array logic which interprets the instruction will use the two rightmost fields for the source operands. Accordingly, I<16:0> will be sign-extended and loaded into A, while the contents of R17 will be loaded into B. Our steps then become

1. operands to A and B
2. $C \Leftarrow A + B$
3. $C \Rightarrow$ P-bus $\Rightarrow$ D-cache
4. D-cache $\Rightarrow$ P-bus $\Rightarrow$ B-bus $\Rightarrow$ destination

From steps 3 and 4 one can see that register C must write to the P-bus and that B-bus must read from the P-bus. For STOREs, register data must be written to the P-bus. We will use the B-bus for that transfer. Looking ahead, we connect the I-register to the B-bus (so that CP instructions can be passed to the coprocessor). Furthermore, we must be able to write out an address in latch C while a new datum is moving from the register file to the B latch. In Figure 6.4, these are added to the structure we have already created.

Note what the additions really comprise, not another bus but rather a MUX and a bidirectional bus buffer with tristates. While we delay a thorough discussion of bus connections and use to Chapter 8, the appearance of our first specific interconnect calls for at least a little explanation. At some point, we must go off-chip to make connection to the outside world. The connection is made through some robust physical connector—we indicate *pins* in the diagram—but that does not indicate what is demanded of the chip at that point. There are two main approaches to driving an external bus. In one, the bus floats, and any user must pull it up or down to write a 0 or 1. This approach, which is the norm for internal (on-chip) busses, has all sorts of problems for external busses both in terminations of the bus (as a transmission line) and in dealing with the possibility that two noncooperating chips may pull in opposite directions at the same time. Why wouldn't they cooperate? Well, it is probably not a shock to discover that

[3] There will be a second adder, but it will be only 6 bits wide. It will be used to compute the sum of the static and dynamic portions of a shift.

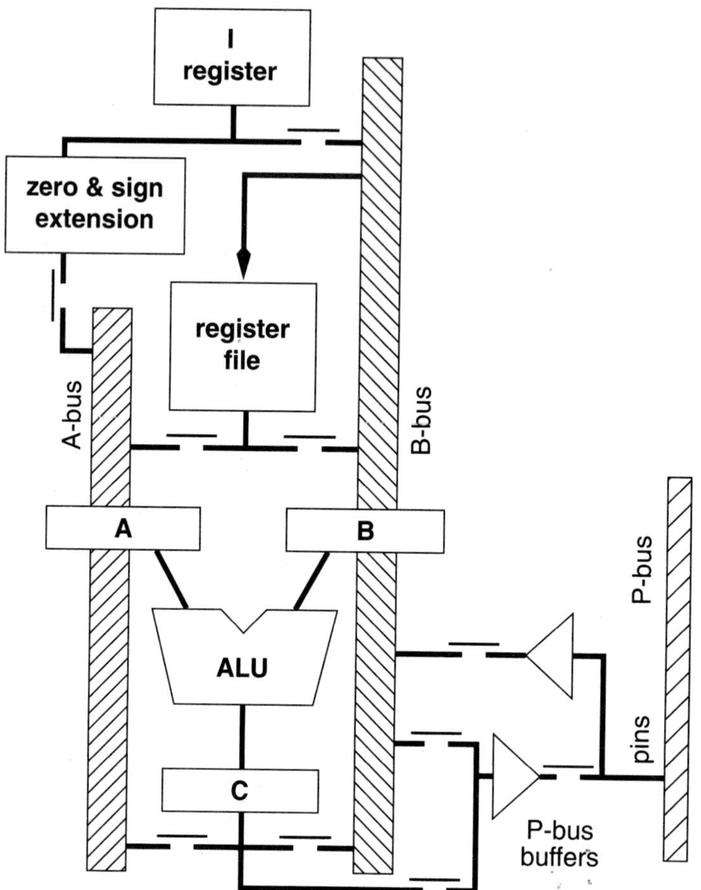

FIGURE 6.4 The circuit of Figure 6.3 modified to include a two-way connection to the P-bus. The connection is through tristated bus buffers. The tristates must be at the outputs of the buffers. The contents of the B-bus or register C can be written to the P-bus. The P-bus can drive the B-bus.

some *other people* make programming errors. Also, chips just plain fail. You would not want the failure of man or silicon to cause other chips within the system to self-destruct. Simultaneous writing of 1 and 0 on a line is the same as shorting + to – on a battery. Chips are not constructed to withstand sustained shorts.

The alternative approach is to use the drivers to pull *down* and to have resistive terminations which pull *up*. The circuit for a single line is shown in Figure 6.5. Three drivers are shown connected to the one line with pullup resistors at each end. The resistors serve both to properly terminate the bus to reduce or eliminate reflections as well as to act as passive pullups. Note that if any or all of the pulldowns are active, the line is low; if none of them are active, the line is high. A failure or misprogramming of one of the drivers may render the system inoperative, but it will not cause another chip to fail.

The drivers themselves, which are little more than the pass switches shown, must be robust enough to supply a solid, low-inductance path to ground. They are obliged

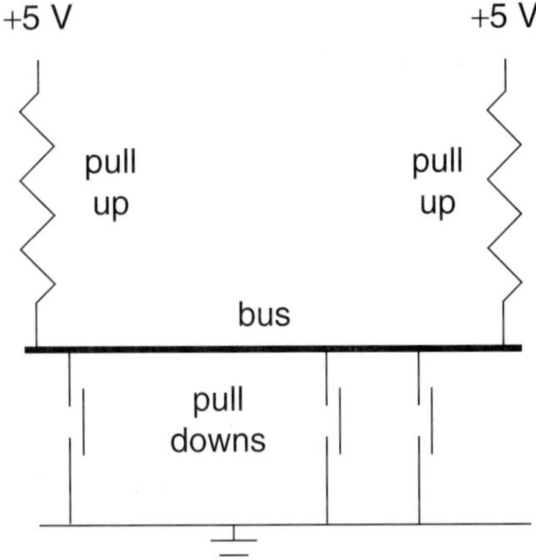

FIGURE 6.5 A typical passive pullup–active pulldown bus arrangement with terminating resistors at each end.

not only to sink the full current coming from the terminating resistors but to discharge the line capacity on top of that current in a time that is short compared to a half clock cycle. First, that requires that the switches be reasonably large, that they really represent an *amplified* response to the logical value; second, it obliges us to give serious heed to the transmission-line characteristics of a bus. Chapter 8 does transmission lines with some enthusiasm.

After accounting for a proper physical connection, we must turn to timing. Each of the steps listed above is to take one half-clock or *phase* to accomplish. The data required is *written* to the appropriate bus shortly after the leading edge of the phase and the received data is logged in on the trailing edge. Thus, the four steps become (see Figure 6.4):

1. *operands to A and B*
   Operands specified in the instruction enable the appropriate tristates (I register or register file, or, if an operand was the result of the preceding instruction, register C) on the rising edge of the pulse. Displacements are sign-extensions of I<16:0> while absolute addresses are zero extensions of I<21:0>. With absolute addresses, NUL is the "other" operand. On the downstroke, data on the A- and B-busses are logged into latches A and B.

2. $C \Leftarrow A + B$
   Whatever is in A and B propagates through the ALU. The instruction code is "interpreted" through a PLA to make the ALU operation addition.[4] On the upstroke, register C latches the data coming out of the ALU.

---

[4] The ALU is "programmed" by having the correct control bits arrive at its logical control lines. These control bits are obtained either from a PLA (or equivalent) that is doing a *hardwired* interpretation of the instruction or from a ROM if the machine uses microcode.

3. *C ⇒ P-bus ⇒ D-cache*
On the upstroke, the contents of C are driven onto the P-bus. The instruction interpretation is continued with the read/write control line being driven as appropriate for the operation. The D-cache determines first if the address is "good" then if the datum is cached. A page-fault or illegal access, which will be discovered in the TLB, will cause an exception, halting the clock in phase-A and switching into the kernel. If the address hits, the cache prepares to deliver or receive the datum and moves into phase-B. If a cache-miss occurs, the CPU clock is stopped until the cache is ready to continue. When the cache is ready, the CPU clock does its downstroke.

4. *D-cache ⇒ P-bus ⇒ B-bus ⇒ destination* **LOAD**
Source ⇒ B-bus ⇒ P-bus ⇒ D-cache **STORE**
In a LOAD operation, after the clock downstroke data from the D-cache is put on the P-bus, from which it is driven onto the B-bus by the bus buffer. In the case of a byte operation, the D-cache extracts the desired byte and sign-extends it. The PLA that interprets the instruction enables the destination register for a load. On the upstroke, the enabled register logs in the data from the B-bus.

In a STORE operation, on the clock downstroke the source register is connected to the B-bus and the B-bus data driven onto the P-bus. On the upstroke, the D-cache accepts the data.

We are now almost home on all of the standard data operations. To handle MUL and DIV, we need to include the prescribed shift and bit test operations (see Appendix I and Section 2.2.5). Remember that a portion of those changes relate to the special MQ register (r28) and that the rest require a preshifter on the A data. Many students think of a shifter as a *shift register*, a clocked, sequential circuit. Such devices certainly abound, but that is not what we mean here. In our case, as we detail in the next section, a shifter is nothing more than a "switch yard," a set of lines and switches which select which input bit gets to which output bit. They are both simple and purely combinational. The MQ register, on the other hand, is a *shift register* with both left and right shift capability. It is unusual in that it shifts left by 1 bit but right by 2. In both cases, the bits shifted in come from the ALU.

The only "normal" data operation that we have not included is the SHIFTyz operation. This we now proceed to rectify.

6.2.3 The SHIFT Operation

To do MUL and DIV we need pre- and postshifters surrounding the ALU. The SHIFT operation will use these same shifters. All data passing through the ALU passes through the shifters. In most cases, the specific shift is set to 0, so in that sense, the shifter network is set for *straight through*. Just as the ALU itself must be "programmable" in order to specify a particular operation, such as ADD or AND, the shifter must be programmable to specify the shift desired. Whether that program step is ultimately derived from an explicit SHIFTyz instruction or is simply an intrinsic part of another operation, it is one of the architect's obligations to see to it that the control bits get to the shifter on each instruction execution to specify what must be accomplished. Let us begin by arranging our shifter to accommodate the SHIFTyz instruction and then see what must be done to get the correct shift (usually but not always 0) for the other instructions.

Our SHIFTyz instruction places four tasks upon us:

1. A static and a dynamic shift index must be combined—an ADD operation.
2. The operand itself must be passed to the ALU or around it.
3. A shift of 0 to ±31 bits must be accomplished in one phase.
4. If the status bits are to be set, *V* must be set if the sign *ever* changed during a multiple-bit shift and the carry bit must reflect the last bit shifted out.

We clearly have a time/resource conflict here. We must pass three data in the one instruction time: the number to be shifted and two shift indices. We have but two busses. One way or another, we need some additional resources.

The first thing to note is that the indices are only 6 bits wide—enough for signed numbers up to ±31. Both indices could fit on one bus. We put them both on A-bus since that is the bus with a connection to the literal field of the I register. The additional resource here would be the switches or muxes to make multiple connections to some of the lines on A-bus. Alternatively, we could simply run six more lines from the I register to the adder for the shift index. Which we would do in practice would depend on chip economics. On B-bus is the datum to be shifted. The remaining resource problem is generating the combined shift index while passing the datum through or around the ALU.

"Through or around" is simply a speed issue. It is cheaper to put the ALU and the shifter in series. However, both of these circuits have considerable delays. The question which must be answered is: Is the total propagation time too long? This is one of those places where a less expensive version of the same architecture might be willing to sacrifice speed for cost. In our current design, we will parallel most stages of the shifter and the ALU. We will incorporate the postshifter and the B preshifter into the barrel shifter to save two layers of effectively duplicate circuitry. Look at Figure I.3 on page 549 for the specifics of the pre- and postshifters. Since timing is the essence of the design problem here, these layout decisions are normally made only after detailed gate- or SPICE-level simulation.

To get the shift index in place, we will need a second adder. Why not use the now dormant ALU? Because both index operands come simultaneously from A-bus (on 12 of the bus's 32 lines) and the result of the add must be stable well prior to the actual shift. That is, the index essentially programs the shifter itself. Note that our index adder is a simple and very fast 6-bit adder. An index latch is not needed since the source data for the adder is latched in A. As is usual with a combinational circuit, the index adder is always active. Since the shift index is most often static and will normally come from the instruction itself (and most often be 0), a MUX controlled by the I register selects either the 6-bit result from the index adder or the equivalent field from the I register. In this way, the index can be set for MUL, DIV, SHIFT, and all other ALU operations (0). That seems to satisfy all of our needs but the shifter itself. Let us see how that will work.

To specify the shifter, we construct Figure 6.6, which is a map of the shift operations. To build a shift of N places ($-31 \leq N \leq +31$), we run the B data through five sequential shifters, each providing a three-way choice of shifts of $\pm 2^k$ or 0 bits, where $0 \leq k \leq 4$. Thus, there is a 16-bit shifter, an 8-bit shifter, a 4-bit shifter, and so forth. Consider the choices open to each shifter in the following hierarchical order:

1. no shift
2. a left shift of *n* bits right-filling with 0's
3. a right shift of *n* bits left-filling with either 0's or replicating bit 31

As the number passes through a stage in the shifter, the C and V status bits must be amended as appropriate. For example, on a 0-bit shift, C and V simply propagate unchanged from input to output, while on a left shift, the V bit must be set if the input V bit was set *or* there was a change, however transient, in the sign bit. If this begins to sound like the start of an undergraduate exercise in minimizing the gate count in a combinational circuit, you are right on the mark. What we must do is specify the transformations that we want and then look at optimizing—not necessarily minimizing—the gate and switching array which will give us that transformation. The map of Figure 6.6 is the first step in that effort.

What that figure requires in terms of circuitry should be split into horizontal and vertical components. In the vertical direction, we must worry about the decline of signal strength and the speed of propagation as the signal goes through the five layers. In the horizontal direction, we are simply executing the switching called for in each layer.

The attenuation/delay issue derives from the fact that a series of pass switches constitutes an RC delay line. The capacitance of each successive switch and line must charge through all of those that precede it. This leads to delays which grow exponentially with depth. The alternative to the pass switches are gates. They have delays, but the inherent nonlinearity of gates—they *snap* into the 1 or 0 state—means that the signal is restored to full value at each stage and that the delays grow only linearly with depth. Using gates for the switching function is simply inserting an inverter pair (two layers plus the switch) between the driving section and the isolating switch.[5] Alternatively, if the pass switches are serving a MUX function, one may construct a conventional MUX out of gates. Generally, the circuit designer must simulate the circuit (or use a rule of thumb derived from simulation) to see how often simple pass switches must be boosted or replaced by gates.

The horizontal layout at each stage of the shifter is the circuit to do what the map of Figure 6.6 describes. Each bit at the output of a given stage must be connectable to three or four input bits or to constants. The connections and the controls for the

---

[5] The term *pass gate* is used in CMOS to describe a complementary pass switch—a PMOS and NMOS pair tied together at source and drain but having complementary drive to the two gates. This device is nicely symmetric for the passing of a 1 or a 0, whereas a single transistor is not. However, neither pass gate nor pass transistor restores the signal or provides drive or power gain. An inverter pair does.

switches can be read right off the map. For example, Figure 6.7 shows two of the bits (30 and 4) from the shift-by-8 stage. To do the same circuit using gates rather than pass switches, one combines the control and the bit controlled in a NAND gate and then combines the outputs of the three or four NANDs in another NAND. The output of the second NAND is the output bit desired. This, of course, is the MUX function.

Take a moment to consider what VLSI technology is doing for us here. If one did this purely with pass switches, and if there were about 3.5 switches per bit per stage,

FIGURE 6.6 Switching map for three stages of the five-stage shifter, with the sequence from 1 to 16. The first stage (1) is the preshifter on the B side of the ALU. All bits except for those that are underlined ($\underline{b}$) reference the input data for that stage. The underlined bits reference output data from the stage. V_{16}, which represents the *cumulative* overflow of the entire shifter set, becomes the overflow bit (assuming that flag-setting is enabled in the instruction). The C bit is obtained by selecting the $\mathbf{X_i}$ from the highest shifter level selected (e.g., *priority* selection). The control bits derive from two sources: the s/u bits come from bit 11 of the instruction (see Figure 2.9); the G_i bits, which act as the select bits for the several stages, and the +/– bit, which selects right or left shift in each stage, are the bits of the shift-length sum in signed-magnitude form.

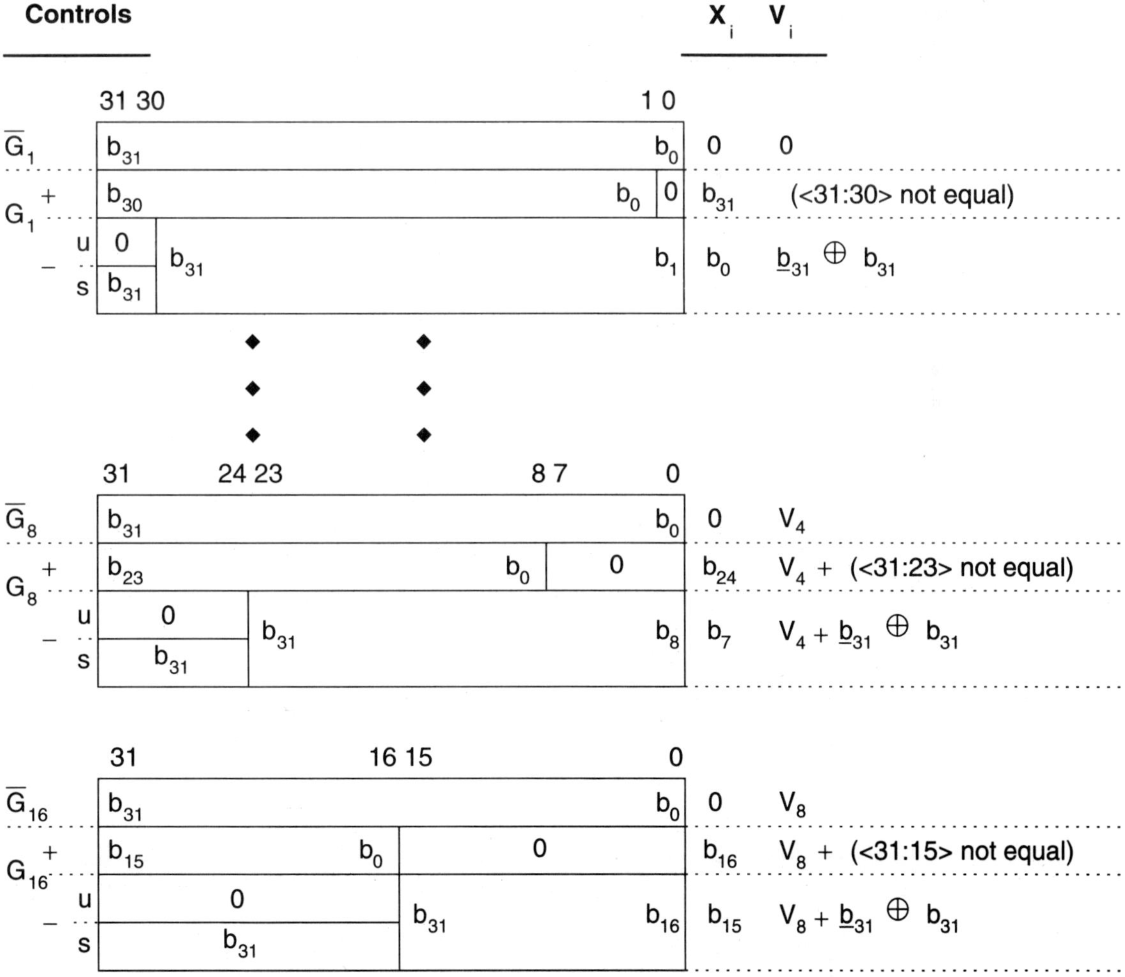

Controls

Controls	31 30 … 1 0	X_i	V_i
$\overline{G}_1$	b_{31} … b_0	0	0
G_1 +	b_{30} … b_0 | 0	b_{31}	(<31:30> not equal)
G_1 – (u / s)	u: 0; s: b_{31} | b_{31} … b_1	b_0	$\underline{b}_{31} \oplus b_{31}$

◆ ◆

◆ ◆

◆ ◆

Controls	31 … 24 23 … 8 7 … 0	X_i	V_i
$\overline{G}_8$	b_{31} … b_0	0	V_4
G_8 +	b_{23} … b_0 | 0	b_{24}	V_4 + (<31:23> not equal)
G_8 – (u / s)	u: 0; s: b_{31} | b_{31} … b_8	b_7	$V_4 + \underline{b}_{31} \oplus b_{31}$

Controls	31 … 16 15 … 0	X_i	V_i
$\overline{G}_{16}$	b_{31} … b_0	0	V_8
G_{16} +	b_{15} … b_0 | 0	b_{16}	V_8 + (<31:15> not equal)
G_{16} – (u / s)	u: 0; s: b_{31} | b_{31} … b_{16}	b_{15}	$V_8 + \underline{b}_{31} \oplus b_{31}$

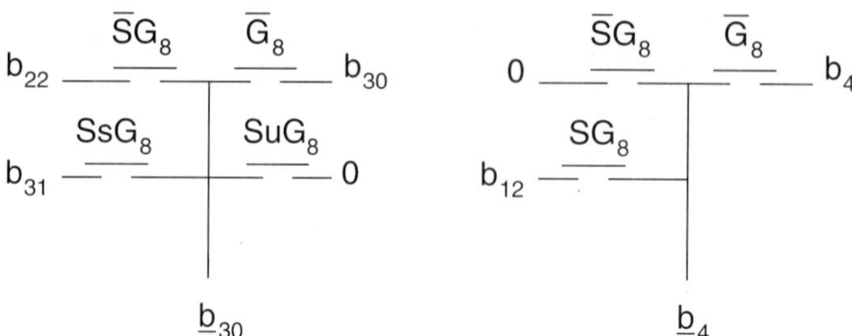

FIGURE 6.7 Switching diagram for 2 bits in the 8-bit shifter level, following Figure 6.6. Output bits are underlined (b). G_8 is the fourth bit in the signed-magnitude form of the shift sum; S is the sign bit in that representation; s/u is bit 11 from the I register in a SHIFTyz instruction or a bit from the control logic in other cases. When the logic condition under the switch is met, it closes.

you can see that this shifter function is going to take $3.5 \times 32 \times 5 = 520$ switches. With inverters and/or gate stages, the number of transistors for this one function alone will exceed 1000. That is only 1 percent or less of a typical VLSI chip, but if you were doing this circuit with SSI chips, such a shifter would be dear indeed.

6.2.4 CP

The CP instruction increases the CPU chip's connectivity to the nearby environment. CP calls for the CPU simply to pass an instruction to one of the adjacent coprocessors. The CPU does nothing more than hand it on. Each instruction moves through stages of the pipeline. At the point when the P-bus becomes available for output from this instruction, the instruction is in the LAST-I register. A connection from register LAST-I to the B-bus is provided for this transfer. Control lines are used to indicate the selected coprocessor (1 of 4). The remaining 25 bits are simply written to the P-bus, where they are picked up by the coprocessor selected. No additional hardware other than the control-bit connections is required.

This completes our discussion of the hardware for all of the "everyday" instructions but CALL and JUMP. These are so intimately tied up with the design of the pipeline that we will defer them briefly while we "set up" for the pipeline. The last two instructions, TRAP and RFI, are part of the interrupt operation, so these too are deferred until later in the chapter. Let us turn now to the issue of instruction flow in normal programs and a bit of history of efforts to speed up instruction processing.

6.3 TOWARD ONE INSTRUCTION PER CLOCK

6.3.1 Choices and Directions

It is clear from our discussion in this chapter that an instruction will take more than one clock to execute. Not only is "an instruction" a sequence of clocked events which must proceed in orderly fashion from instruction fetch to data delivery, but our program must frequently go to memory for data. How then can we hope or expect to process one instruction per clock as we have been advertising from Chapter 1 onward? The answer is that we plan to run an assembly line and that *one instruction per clock* is a goal our line can approach only asymptotically. Just as it takes an automobile days to proceed from loose parts to a finished car, so it will take our instructions three full clocks to execute. The length of time in the pipeline is not what one measures in determining the production rate; product coming out the end is the observable we want. To the extent that we can avoid cache misses—part shortages which stall the assembly line—we will be able to sustain a rate of one instruction per clock. It will also help to cheat a little in how we count instructions.

The analogy to a classical assembly line is a strong one. The ideal, easily optimized assembly line does one thing and one thing only. It leads to Henry Ford's famous color chart: *Any color as long as it's black*. As soon as variations are allowed, design of the line becomes more difficult. If changes can be inserted at irregular and unpredictable times, it can become very difficult to avoid *bubbles*—periods of reorganization in which no productive work is accomplished. Even worse, if a real digression in the normal production is permitted, it can be very difficult to restore normal production without damage to the product that was in the pipeline at the time of the interruption. The classical saw about avoiding cars completed on Monday is a reflection of the problem of restarting a line that has been interrupted for a weekend.

You might think that it would be possible to organize a well-disciplined computer pipeline that would avoid *unexpected interruptions*. It would see an interruption coming, complete its processing, and only then accept the interrupt. Nice idea, but it won't fly. The interruption can be caused by the currently executing instructions rather than some externality. What, for example, can the processor do if the current instruction attempts to load from or store to a page that is not there—your everyday *page fault*. The processor finds itself standing there holding an address which cannot currently be translated. The solution, as you now know, is to have the *system* fetch the page. Ah. But the system runs on this same processor. What is needed is for the kernel to queue a request for the needed page and then perform a *context switch* from the current process to the process designated as *next to run*. There must be, then, three immediate consequences of the page fault:

1. an orderly retreat to a safe restarting position in the current process as in Figure 3.4 on page 136
2. posting of request for a page
3. an orderly context switch or other recovery

Items 1 and 3 are strongly connected to processor and instruction structure. Consider, for example, the VAX instruction

`PUSHL r4` or its equivalent `MOVL r4, -(SP)`

which decrements the stack pointer and then stores the contents of R4 at the location indicated by SP. The processor would already have decremented the SP before it would find out whether the new SP points at a page currently assigned to the process. It is the use of the computed address which triggers an error response. On getting an *address translation error*, how can the processor let go of the current instruction to take up handling the problem?

Our choices are two (with shades of gray). We can have our machine back up to a legitimate state just before the instruction was run—that is, change all modified registers and restore the PC—or we can save the current state of the half-executed instruction and pick up where we left off. Look at the pipeline as you ponder the choice. Some other instruction(s) preceded this current problematic one; one or more successors have already started as the problem is detected. Back-up or save-it-as-it-is, our processor's state is suddenly more complicated to behold. We will develop reasonably direct interrupt handling for our processor in this chapter.

Along with interruptions to the normal flow of instructions through the pipeline, computer architects must also deal with another classical production-line problem: the delivery of raw materials where and when they are needed for "production." In the CPU, the delivery problem is the von Neumann bottleneck. Both instructions and data ultimately derive from central memory and are delivered over a common bus. Numerous solutions to the bottleneck have been tried and many of the better ones are very much in common use. In our own case, we employ two levels of caching, memory interleaving and a form of passive look-ahead in that we cache a whole line of words when we fetch any element in the line.

From the production-line perspective, the caches are warehouses. Really clever assembly lines do little warehousing, depending instead on production and delivery of source material at approximately the rate it is consumed. However, for irregular production management, which certainly describes most computational tasks (but not all, by any means), warehousing is an essential part of resource management. Since the mid-1960s, when IBM introduced the cache [Lipstay, 68] for the storage of both data and instructions adjacent to the CPU on the 360 series of computers, it has been clear that the local warehousing of these source materials provides a substantial benefit in computer speed. In recent years, there has been something of a trend toward having separate data and instruction caches. Ours is such a design, with the large D-cache residing off-chip and the I-cache on-chip. In fact, the I-cache is *in series* with the D-cache. Why would one want caches upon caches?

The answer derives from the fact that most of our instructions use either no data or data that already resides in our big register set. Only the LOADs and STOREs have potential conflicts with instruction fetches from the D-cache. The rather high prevalence of those instructions, however, suggests that a method of minimizing the conflicts in access to the D-cache be investigated.

The first recognition that instruction buffering could present substantial benefit seems to have been Seymour Cray's in the early '60s when he was chief architect at CDC. Note that Cray was considering this before *caching* had been invented and the word coined by IBM. He observed the rather remarkable frequency of small loops in normal programming and thought about a way to avoid fetching the same instruction multiple times in a single loop. His solution, variously named the *look-backward buffer* or the *instruction stack* [Thornton, 64], stored the last eight 60-bit instructions that had been fetched *in linear fashion*. That last phrase means that a branch outside the buffer automatically invalidated the buffer. Since instructions were either 30 or 60 bits in length, the buffer would hold 8 to 16 instructions. While the addressing scheme for this little instruction cache would look clumsy today, by storing a starting and ending address for the valid string of sequential instructions in the buffer, the 6600 was able to save refetching instructions on most of the little loops which are so common in normal programming. This saving helped to make the CDC 6600 the number-crunching wonder of its day (1964).

With similar objectives, though with a more modern structure, we choose to put our instruction cache right on the processor chip. Its structure and relationship to the pipeline are developed below. What it will do for us is to permit the processor to tick along doing one instruction per clock even if LOADs or STOREs are part of a loop. When processing *new* instructions, the CPU must stall when it requires a simultaneous access—data for the LOAD/STORE and an instruction for the second successor to the LOAD/ STORE—from the D-cache, but since a very large number of such data fetches do occur in loops, the I-cache provides a worthwhile addition.

Another way of speeding up processing in an assembly line is to parallel nonsequential tasks. Today, almost anyone's general-purpose machine does this to some extent. Ours is no exception. As detailed in Chapter 8, we will have completely independent processors handling many I/O tasks, communicating with the operating system through message passing in central memory. However, our focus here is paralleling tasks in processing of the instructions of a single program. At its simplest, this might mean having separate adders for address generation and data operations. As mentioned above, our streamlined instruction set and its associated pipeline would not benefit from that addition, but in the big machines of the '60s, parallel, interlocked execution units were the rage. The CDC 6600 was highly paralleled;[6] the IBM 360/370 had multiple processors with stacks of interlocked instructions lined up at each one.

The multiple-processor idea has since taken off in several directions. We are following a common route of offloading special functions to coprocessors. These special-purpose processors are slaves to the CPU, though they have the ability to stall the CPU by being *busy* and unable to accept another instruction. This is a rudimentary scheduling technique but functional for many kinds of processing. If coprocessor speed itself is process-limiting, one may solve it either by building very fast coprocessors or by having multiple coprocessors and moving the coordination out to the compiler. In the extreme, where huge numbers of identical operations are done, one may get enormous speedups by designing a system with many parallel paths all doing the same operation. This becomes the *vector processor*, a specialized but extremely valuable device for solving the huge matrix problems which arise in such fields as fluid flow (e.g., weather prediction, plasma dynamics, airfoil design), animation, and simulation in theoretical physics and chemistry. Finally, one can move to arrays of processors, each with its own

---

[6] Its influence is still to be found in the execution units of the Fairchild Clipper and Motorola's RISC chip, the MC88000.

cache, either working in concert (*single-instruction multiple-data*, or SIMD, as in a vector processor) or only weakly linked (*multiple-instruction multiple-data*, or MIMD). There is a rule called *Amdahl's law* [Amdahl, 67] which states that, in general programs, there always exist software bottlenecks which severely restrict how much leverage one can get by paralleling processors. One must emphasize *general*. Some problems can be broken down into pieces which can proceed with communications only between nearest neighbor pieces and for which Amdahl's law [Gustavson, 88] is not valid. For these special cases, MIMD machines arranged in multiply interconnected networks can sometimes speed a program up by factors approaching the number of processors. With low-cost, powerful processor chips now in such abundance, these arrays of processors present opportunities for inexpensive solutions to very complex computational tasks.

Our focus, of course, is a general-purpose, streamlined machine well suited to multiprocessing. In pursuit of that goal, we have set out to execute approximately one instruction per clock—and to make that clock fast. Our next question is: How do we lay out our assembly line?

6.3.2 Designing a Pipeline

In its simplest terms, the design of an assembly line requires that the designer break up the task into subtasks of approximately equal duration, τ. Recognizing that these tasks are ordered, one then attempts to pack them in such a way that the overall length is as short as possible (maximum parallelism). In the simplest of situations, the pure serial case, one simply puts the ducks in line and starts work proceeding through the stages of the line. If there are n stations in the line, then after n units of work have entered the line, the first unit emerges from the output. After that point, one should have a single unit of work per unit of time, τ. Thus, the pipelined unit runs n times as fast as the non-pipelined unit.

Life is seldom that simple. Get a line going making left-handed widgets to a fare-thee-well and the business will immediately need to intermix right- and left-handed widget making on the same line. Supply rates and demand rates will vary for both products. There will be equipment slowdowns, employee illnesses, and holidays to work into the schedule. The greater the number of stages, the more versatile and rapid will the line be, but it will also be more complex to design and harder to manage. The consequences of changes and problems in production will also grow with complexity.

One of the design objectives in the RISC philosophy is to push for the regularity which makes pipelines simpler to design and more robust against perturbations in the production schedule. For example, we have specified a fixed instruction length—one word. That means that the instruction fetch is a simple operation—fetch the word that the PC is pointing to. Contrast that to the VAX in which the length of the instruction is unknown until the last operand is accounted for. The VAX also fetches its instructions in chunks of 32 bits, but such a chunk could contain four instructions, or less than 10 percent of one instruction. In fact, the VAX fetch is far too complex to put into the pipeline design directly. Instead, the machine code of the VAX is interpreted by *microcode*, and the microcode is what runs through the pipeline. One may argue that the VAX is run by a RISC-like computer inside. That computer does do one microinstruction per clock, with the pipeline stages being designed to serve the needs of the microcode computing engine. Even so, the VAX pipeline is substantially more complex than ours need be. By moving the lowest level of code out to the compiler, we will enable the compiler to foresee and eliminate irregularities that we would otherwise have to handle by more complex hardware. Furthermore, at least according to the early RISC philosophers, we can have the optimizer on the compiler speed up the processing by packing instructions in a way that makes optimum use of each time slot on the pipeline. This is extremely difficult to do dynamically even if one is willing to spend the money on such complexity in the hardware. Only the biggest and most expensive machines—the *mainframes*—attempt dynamic allocation and optimization of the processor's resources. Quite obviously, dynamic optimization must have a very small worldview, whereas optimization at compile time can see, at least in principle, the entire program.

A caveat is in order on the very appealing RISC notion of moving small-scale program optimization out to the compiler. Optimization by instruction ordering is done with specific knowledge of the design of the pipeline. This locks into applications a particular hardware design and works against the establishment of an instruction architecture which remains stable while performance is improved by incorporating ever better hardware designs. "Owning the architecture" is the route to long-term success [Ferguson, 93], so we do not want to preclude success by myopic optimization of the first model. For academic reasons, we are going to adopt a direct and simple approach that will lead to a simple hardware design quite typical of the early RISCs. Then, we will compare it with a modern RISC and ask why the differences.

With our relatively simple instruction set, what pieces must we fit together? We are now looking at the machine primitives. Once we have designated the units and assigned expected times to complete each unit, we can line up the units in appropriate order and we will have a first cut at our pipeline.

Take another look at Figure 6.4. The units of our pipeline must come from there. They should represent atomic operations or small groupings of atomic operations. Consider the data in Table 6.1, which is a basic list of operations with conservative time estimates appropriate to the technology of early 1991.

We could further break down the transactions with the caches into an address transfer followed by a data transfer. Equally well, if it suited our needs or our fancy, we could subdivide the ALU into layers of combinatorial logic separated by registers. In that case, each such layer would have a minimum safe propagation time. Such times would be less than the 30 ns we have indicated because fewer layers of gates would have to be traversed. For example, if the ALU were divided into an adder/subtracter and a shifter, both layers could be built to function in under 25 ns. The obligation to transfer data from input to output in each of the register layers would add a bit of time—several nanoseconds—but the individual stages would still be less than 25 ns. In the steady state, it is the length of time per stage that determines the throughput, so there would seem to be a definite advantage to subdividing as much as possible.

The liability in excessive subdivision comes to the forefront in cases where nonequilibrium obtains, such as filling an empty pipeline or storing or draining a line to meet exigencies. Don't get the idea that we are talking about context switches or interrupts when we speak of *pipeline exigencies*. The pipeline designer must deal with

TABLE 6.1 **Unit operations for the processor of Figure 6.4 with time estimates based on CMOS construction circa 1991 and some rough approximations of loading and fanout.** The D-cache operations could be broken down into two pieces; send an address and send/receive data. Each would be about 50 ns. As VLSI technology advances, these numbers shrink by about 25 percent per year. Some of that speedup results from increased device speeds; the other major contribution comes from moving components from on-board to on-chip.

Operation	Time required, ns
ALU operation	30
read I-cache	50
register transfer	25
read D-cache to register	100
write register to D-cache	100
read D-cache to I-cache	100

such everyday changes as branches which get taken sometimes and passed over another times. If the pipeline is filled in the expectation of going back and your program goes forward instead, the successor instructions in the pipeline must be dumped. If they have side effects which occurred before the dump, then those side effects must be undone. As pipelines become longer and more complex in an effort to wring the most possible speed out of the maximum subdivision, the problem of dealing effectively with a pipeline flush becomes ever more severe. Let us consider an example.

If the designer decided to subdivide ALU operations so that each stage required less than 25 ns, then a pipeline can be built on units of 25 ns. In the steady state, that will give a potential for doing 1 instruction per 25 ns or 40 MIPS. That would have been very competitive in 1991. However, notice that a *read* or *write* operation requires four such units while an ALU operation looks as if it would require three. Neither of those estimates includes time for the instruction fetch, but presumably that time will be constant. Immediately we have the classical assembly-line problem of ordered operations of different durations. In a sense, we are processing (at least) two different products in some prescribed order. The solutions to keeping things in step include:

- Break out the line into two lines and use some form of interlock to assure that operations which require synchronization cannot get out of order.
- Insert *bubbles* (null operations) in the line to extend the shorter operations enough to assure synchronization.
- Provide some form of intermediate "warehousing" to store instructions until the data which they require becomes available.

All of these are used in one or another machine, and all have the effect of adding complexity and, by slowing the transient response of the pipeline, slowing the average rate at which instructions come out of the machine.

Consider the important case of the branch. Let us here take the simple approach of doing no planning for the branch. We will take it as it comes through the pipeline. In the following section, we will apply greater intelligence to this issue, but for the moment we simply want an illustration of subdivision of the pipeline. Making maximum division of the operations listed in Table 6.1, a not unreasonable pipeline length might be ten stages as illustrated in Figure 6.8. Each stage is allotted 25 ns and each cache access or operation is divided into its atomic parts.

Figure 6.8 shows the resulting pipeline. Assigning time slots is only the beginning of the design effort. A larger problem is making sure that there are enough hardware resources for each stage to do its assigned task without colliding with any other stage's activities. For example, acquiring an instruction gets broken into three stages—PC to I-cache, instruction from I-cache, and decode (a time to propagate through the decode logic). Consider the resource issue. On each clock, an address goes out and the predecessor instruction comes in. Clearly, that requires separate paths and some latches to hold onto addresses, instructions and data as they move from stage to stage. The conflict between the 100 ns D-cache cycle—remember that we chose to use PAs so there are two sequential searches in accessing the D-cache—and the 25 ns cycle time is particularly imposing. Without too much difficulty, the 100 ns can be broken into four stages, each requiring only 25 ns. If we devote the hardware resources, this pipeline could deliver an instruction every 25 ns. That is a 40 MIP machine versus the 10 MIP machine that we are going to design with the same basic technology. Subdivision costs hardware, but it delivers speed. DEC's Alpha chip has a 7-stage pipeline and ticks along at 200 MHz.

Is there a down side to subdivision? Consider the problem of a JUMP instruction. Table 1.1 shows that branches and jumps are very common instructions. A JUMP cycle begins like all others with fetch and decode stages. Register operands are then moved to the ALU to compute the jump address. Only then can the fetch for JUMP's successor be done. Notice where this instruction would now be in the pipeline—at the sixth stage. That means that five other instructions have been lined up and started before the

FIGURE 6.8 A highly divided pipeline example for our machine. No single step takes any longer than 25 ns.

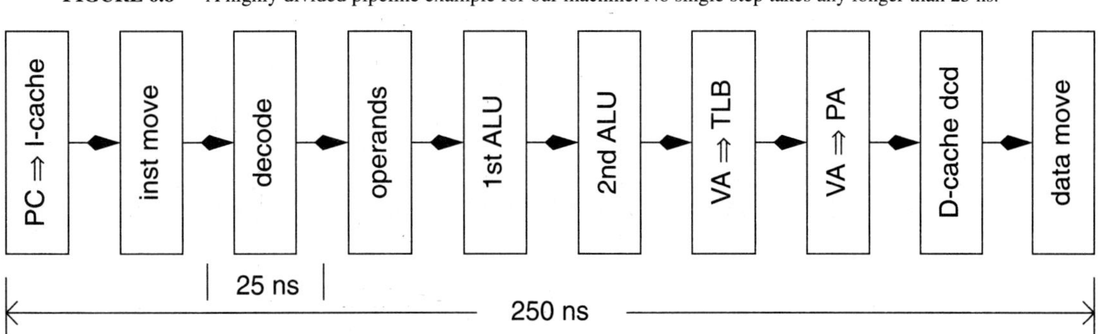

machine can reasonably determine what comes next. Sure, one can look ahead and try to be clever about handling JUMPs. Several clever methods are discussed below. But just looking at the pipeline itself, note that the minimum *hit*, if we simply dump the now useless instructions, is five instructions. Since these JUMPs occur with great frequency in most normal programs, one immediate consequence is that the long pipeline will be slowed by frequent dumps. If we apply no foresight whatsoever, we would be guessing that no branch is ever taken. If we include calls and unconditional branches, far more than 50 percent of branches get taken. If all forms of branch constitute 15 percent of the instruction stream and if, say, 60 percent of them are taken and thus cost six slots, the actual time per useful instruction is:

$$(0.15 \times 0.6 \times 6 + 0.85) \times 25 = 34.75 \text{ ns}$$

That is a 39 percent increase in the effective cycle time. Clearly, something better than blindly charging straight ahead will be called for.

A second problem will occur with I-cache misses. With our setup, there could be four different operations going on in the D-cache/MMU in any one clock. The I-cache miss in our arrangement requires going to the D-cache to get the missing instruction. We must stall the pipeline in place, grab the missing instruction from the D-cache (by inserting two cache clocks independent of the pipeline), and then restart the pipeline. Clearly, we will need a parallel path for this transaction so that the work in progress can be held while the D-cache is queried for the needed instruction. An alternative to parallel routes to the D-cache is to have parallel D- and I-caches, each with its own access to the next layer out in the memory hierarchy. Such an arrangement is particularly appealing if both caches use VAs, but the caution about cache incoherency which we related about the MC68040 is worth keeping in mind.

Finally, on a context switch, all of this work-in-progress must be retained in the PCB. That saving and restoring operation is a burden both in execution time and in the hardware it requires to make all of these intermediate data available to the kernel.

We hope that we have made the point that complexity enters the design equation at a rate much higher than linear. This brings us to the crux of this chapter: combining I-cache and pipeline to meet our speed goal. While pursuing that noble quest, we must make it possible to do a sensible interrupt after any step in the pipeline.

6.3.3 Pipeline Breaks

A *pipeline* is not simply a piece of hardware any more than an assembly line is. It is really the organization or plan of how each workpiece will move from initiation through completion. There certainly will be hardware choices to make and hardware restrictions to live with, but organization is the crux of the issue. In the design stage, there is much back and forth between the instruction set and the pipeline. It is hard to recreate that in a text, but it is worth noting that the instruction set of Chapter 2 was modified several times in the designing of the pipeline we are about to present. Such modifications come about not because of the regular, predictable instructions. Those are a snap. You can define what you want and then deal with the consequences.

For example, if we had wanted to include a full 32-bit multiply in a single instruction, we would have either to invest heavily in array-multiplier hardware or abandon the hope of doing any and all instructions in one clock. High-speed integer multiplication was not one of our important goals, as we defined them in Chapter 1; maximum speeds on LOAD and ADD were. Accordingly, we planned from the beginning to do one instruction per clock and limited our expectations on MUL and DIV to the primitives that we have defined.

The problems do not arise with the arithmetic or logic instructions nor with the LOADs and STOREs. The problems occur with JUMPs and CALLs. Consider JUMP. It comes in three flavors:

- JUMP *always*
- JUMP *sometimes*
- JUMP *never*

While the last is our NOP, the instruction is, in fact, a JUMP and will be so interpreted. Now consider the simplest of three-stage pipelines, one that is very close to what we will use. At any one time, there is an instruction in each stage. On each clock, they will advance one stage. The stages comprise

- Fetch an instruction.
- Execute the instruction (e.g., form an address, do arithmetic, etc.).
- Store the results of the instruction (e.g., a sum from latch C or a datum from memory in a register or a datum from a register in memory).

Now let us watch a JUMP propagate through this pipeline, as shown in Figure 6.9. The fetch simply brings in the JUMP instruction. While that is happening, the two predecessor instructions are *executing* and *storing* results respectively. At the next clock, the ALU will calculate the jump address. Finally, at clock 2, that address may or may not be loaded into the PC. The question that faces us: What do we fetch for instructions post_1 and post_2 in the figure? If we know that we are *not* going to jump, no problem. We will simply continue happily on our way, incrementing the PC as we go.

If we *are* going to jump or if we *may* decide to jump, we have a problem. Even if we know we are going to jump? Indeed! The problem is, *post_1* has to be loaded before

clock	fetch	execute	store
0	JUMP	pred_1	pred_2
1	post_1	JUMP	pred_1
2	post_2	post_1	JUMP

FIGURE 6.9 Progress of a JUMP instruction through the simple three-stage pipeline.

the address in the JUMP instruction is computed. So what do you load? There are numerous answers, almost none immediately obvious.

By the time that we get to *post_2*, things have improved . . . slightly. Based on the *TEST* field in the instruction (see Table 2.2, on page 70), we would fetch the correct second instruction from the address we had calculated the clock before. However, getting the right second instruction still leaves post_1 in the pipeline. Let us look at how we might best use that slot.

6.3.4 Bubbles, Guesses, and NOPs

Our problem is that we must select a *next* instruction before we have its address. During the *fetch cycle* in Figure 6.9, the CPU does not know that it has a JUMP. By the end of the fetch and interpret cycle, the CPU would know that it might need to branch, but the only address available—unless we have some preprocessing done—is the address of the successor to the JUMP itself.

Would the CPU, at this moment, be able to determine whether the jump will be taken? Yes, but just barely. If the predecessor instruction, which was just being executed, affects the flags, those flags will not be set until the end of the cycle. Thus, just as the CPU must select its next instruction, it could find out that it did not have the correct address. The JUMP address will be available only after the next clock. This inability to calculate the address of the next instruction by the time that the CPU needs it is rather fundamental. How then can we deal with it?

The jump problem is almost as old as computers and certainly as old as pipelined CPUs. Computer architects have been wrestling with these *pipeline breaks* since the late 1950s [Bucholz, 62]. The principal methods which have been developed for dealing with such breaks include:

Pipeline flushing. In this mode, the CPU always loads NEXT. All instructions carry a valid bit with them. If it then turns out that NEXT is not the right instruction to execute, all the "wrong" instructions are invalidated ("flushed"). This method is particularly wasteful for all branch-backs. The pipeline is flushed on each such branch in the loop. Since a branch-back is part of DO . . . WHILE, WHILE, and FOR paradigms of a HLL loop, simply flushing the pipeline is our worst-case scenario.

Dual pipeline. This is the "equivocation" mode. Both possibilities in the branch are developed in separate pipelines. If any branches can use general addressing modes, such a scheme may require fairly elaborate interlocked lookahead in order to calculate the address for the branch without having stale data used for the address. The idea is simply to switch pipelines without missing a beat if the branch is taken. Note that if the instruction set permits instruction side effects such as predecrementing registers, the side effects on the two branches may be different.[7] Accordingly, they must be buffered until the correct path is chosen. Consider what a mess this would be to either back up or

---

[7] This occurs in the IBM 370/168 and 3033 [Lee, 84].

save if an exception came along in the middle. It could get worse. Since it is not only possible but not uncommon to have a succession of branches (*If X then ... else if Y then ... else ...*) one is not off the hook in this design with just two pipelines. At least the initial stages of three or four might be necessary to be able to sort out all of the possibilities which might exist within a pipeline of a given length.

Branch prediction. This method attempts to obtain most of the benefits of a dual pipeline with only one pipeline's worth of hardware. The branch instruction itself carries a bit which indicates whether the branch is *likely* to be taken.[8] The expected address is then used. If the other address proves later to be chosen, then the pipeline is flushed. This method also may require interlocked lookahead to calculate the address and may require some delay if the data for the address is itself being calculated by the previous instruction. However, it certainly is far better than the first scheme since it assures correct branching on all JUMP *always* and pretty good statistics where the branching is dominantly one way. One way to avoid delays in address calculation is to enforce sufficient *spreading* between instructions which generate dynamic parts of a jump address and the branch itself. In this way, the pipeline can always calculate the address in time for its application. The penalty for doing this *branch spreading* is the requirement to stick in occasional NOPs to do the spreading. Branch spreading may also be used to separate flag-setting from the branch itself to assure that the flag to be tested in a conditional test is correctly set when the JUMP enters the pipeline. This is discussed under branch folding below.

Alpha uses very simple static conditional branch prediction. Forward branches are assumed to fall through and backward branches are assumed to be taken. This static and simple rule is improved upon by having a *branch history* for each instruction in the I-cache. It stores the last branch decision for a particular branch. On the next execution of the branch, the guess is that the branch will do the same thing that it did the last time. While not spectacularly effective in reducing branch misses, the Alpha branching rules scale well to multiple instruction issue and to multiprocessor designs.

Delayed branching. This is simply an explicit way to accommodate the time that it takes to calculate a branch address. The idea is always to do one or more instructions following the branch instruction and only then do the actual branch. It is a method which dates all the way back to the MANIAC at Los Alamos in 1952. We will use a single-instruction delay. If possible, that "extra" instruction is one you want to have done in any case—for example, part of the loop itself. You might think of this as simply making good use of the time while the branch address is being calculated. Then, with both addresses available, either the branch is taken or the program goes right on. If you cannot make good use of the time, then a NOP is inserted. Only if a NOP is used is

---

[8] What is described is *static branch prediction*. It may also be done, either statically or dynamically, by hardware. In *dynamic* branch prediction, the hardware "remembers" the last branch direction and "predicts" a repeat of the same. See [Gustavson, 88]. In the AMD29000, dynamic prediction is carried dramatically forward by caching not a prediction bit but the last destination address. Fetches are based on the cached address, with a pipeline flush only when the actual destination fails to match the cached destination.

there effectively a bubble. Note that this synchronization is moved out to the program generator, be that compiler or programmer. To be able to make good use of the delay, it is necessary to have a little maneuvering room—a few instructions with which to play. You cannot put the condition-generating instruction after the branch which will test the instruction. Other similar constraints limit your placement freedom. Accordingly, to be effective, the code that is natural to the machine in question must generate typical loops with four or five instructions between start and branch. When such a synergy exits, delayed branching is both simple and effective. Patterson [Patterson, 85] reports that their optimizing compiler achieves a 90 percent effective utilization of a single branch-delay slot in the Berkeley RISC.

Branch folding. This is a pretty complicated system developed by Bell Laboratories in the CRISP microprocessor [Ditzel, 87a]. The problem in the CRISP was that the instruction set produced loops too short to make delayed branching efficient. Too often one would have to use a NOP for spacing. To reduce branch times Bell Labs developed the ultimate lookahead system, in which instructions are *preprocessed* as they enter the CPU. The preprocessor expands and caches the instruction, producing something reminiscent of microcoding in which a NEXT address is stored directly with the instruction. Notice that this means that each and every instruction is an unconditional branch. Thus all unconditional branches get *folded* into their predecessor instruction. Notice that this elimination of unconditional branches is done by the preprocessor. The instruction stream in memory looks normal. What has just been done here is remarkable: All of these now missing branch instructions execute in *zero* time. It will be hard to beat that for speed.

This description still leaves two critical questions unanswered:

- How does the preprocessor handle addresses calculated at run time?
- How does the system handle conditional branches?

In the CRISP, branch instructions cannot use completely general addressing modes. Those allowed include PC-relative, absolute, and indirect-SP-relative. If programming rules forbid changing the SP within the loop—quite reasonable if a static-SP algorithm is employed in each subroutine—then all of the parameters needed for address calculation are available to the preprocessor.

Conditional branches require two addresses. Accordingly, spaces for NEXT and ALTERNATE-NEXT are provided in the expanded internal form created by the preprocessor. By this time, the internal instruction width has grown to an awesome 192 bits. However, this is only for the small group of expanded instructions dwelling within the instruction cache between the preprocessor and main execution unit. In memory, instructions range from 16 to 48 bits. One bit in the instruction is used for static prediction. This is set by the compiler and used by the processor to determine which of the two addresses is NEXT.

If one assumes that the prediction algorithm is efficient, most often NEXT is exactly what your program wants. Again, with this folded branching scheme, choosing NEXT requires 0 cycles because the branch itself has vanished into its predecessor. What happens if NEXT is not the right address? Your program takes a hit from a pipeline flush. That hit can be as much as 3 clocks, but given that it is infrequent and that the preprocessor eliminates most of the rather frequent unconditional branch instructions by folding them into their predecessors, your program's net profit from this unusual pipeline could be large indeed. In simulations of realistic programs, Ditzel and McLellan found that they averaged 0.90 clocks per branch with *branch prediction* plus branch folding [Ditzel, 87b]. If they forced the compiler to spread the COMPARE which set the flags away from the BRANCH which tested the flags, thus permitting the smart pipeline to always pick the right path, they found that the average time dropped to 0.74 clocks. Why didn't it drop to 0 if the pipeline never broke? Because *spreading* must sometimes be done by inserting NOPs. All in all, this branch-folding paradigm, however complex, is impressively fast.

Which method are we going to employ and why? While branch folding with branch spreading is noticeably faster, delayed branching is so much simpler that it is compelling in any but the most hell-bent-for-leather designs. RISC machines with their LOAD/STORE paradigm have typical small loops of four to five instructions, leading to efficient use of a single delay slot. For the 90 percent figure quoted by Patterson, if we attribute the necessary NOPs to the branch, the average branch will take 1.11 clocks. Only if we were to go all the way to branch folding are we likely to do better. Measuring time in "ticks of a clock," simplicity recommends delayed branching.

Before we leave this discussion, it would not do to ignore entirely "hell-bent-for-leather" designs. To speed up the clock with a given semiconductor technology, one makes a long pipeline. There is no way around it. As soon as the pipe gets deep enough that one gets two or three bubbles, delayed branching is a loser. Furthermore, to make the machine even faster, one uses multiple parallel pipelines to allow different flavors of instruction to proceed in parallel. This allows multiple instructions to be issued in a single clock, producing what is called a *superscalar* design. For a discussion of superscalar processors, see [Johnson, 91] and or section 3.5.5 in [Stone, 92]. Superscalar designs are basically incompatible with delayed branching. Accordingly, the Alpha team chose branch prediction.

Not obvious in branch prediction is how to get rid of the bubble that is inherent in calculating the branch address. How can Alpha avoid loading something while calculating the address? The answer is that by restricting branching to something that can be precalculated, the correct fetch can be made. Alpha restricts the programmer to PC-relative addressing on branches and to register-indirect addresses on jumps and calls. Both of these forms are completely predictable and can be available when the CPU must choose which instruction to fetch. Whether the branch is to be taken may not yet be determined, but the address for the predicted direction will be available for the fetch.

So why are we choosing an unscalable single-bubble branch mechanism? We have two motivations. The first is processor simplicity. Dealing with the details of recovery in the break of a long pipeline would add much complication to the design and distract from the development of a good overview. Second, many of the first and second generation RISC computers use the single-bubble branch, making that a paradigm whose consequences are worth pursuing. With that as our motivation and the appropriate caveat on the consequences of pushing a hardware decision into the architecture, let us see how our pipeline will work.

6.3.5 Structure of the Pipeline

As described above, we divide each clock into two phases in order to have enough timing edges to move data through sequential circuits. Our objective is one instruction completed per clock and we expect to process each instruction in a 3-clock-long pipeline. Thus, we end up with six phases of 50 ns each in which to accomplish the atomic (i.e., indivisible) steps which comprise a machine instruction. Organizing the pipeline involves keeping tabs on two immutables: propagation times and physical resources. For the former, you cannot use data until they both arrive and settle down; for the latter, you cannot spend what you don't have. That sounds fair enough. Let us see how it works in practice.

With six edges and changing our perspective to clocks rather than cycles, our pipeline of Figure 6.9 will look like Figure 6.10. Each horizontal line represents a single instruction. The situation at any given moment is given by a column. The full complement of bus activity is visible between clocks 2 and 3. Bus usage is listed below the two fully developed phases. Note that every bus but A is used in every phase. The *I-bus* carries instructions and instruction addresses. It is discussed immediately below.

The proper way to proceed through Figure 6.10 is to step some single instructions through a row and then to look at competition for resources by following down two complete phases. We will use three instructions which show the bus usage and data switching, say LSUB followed by DJUMP followed by ISTORE. These might nicely represent the end of a DO {. . .} WHILE loop. Note the order: ISTORE is the filler for the *delayed branch*. In the programmatic sense, ISTORE is part of the loop and not what follows the loop.

Table 6.2 takes you through the actions for these three instructions. Each phase represents a vertical slice through Figure 6.10. The first thing you may note is the

FIGURE 6.10 The pipeline plan fully developed to include the two phases. The instructions spanning the top minor rows are discussed in Table 6.2 and the text. The second minor rows show where the decoded instruction from minor row 1 is currently stored. The third minor rows specify the action being taken on that instruction in that phase.

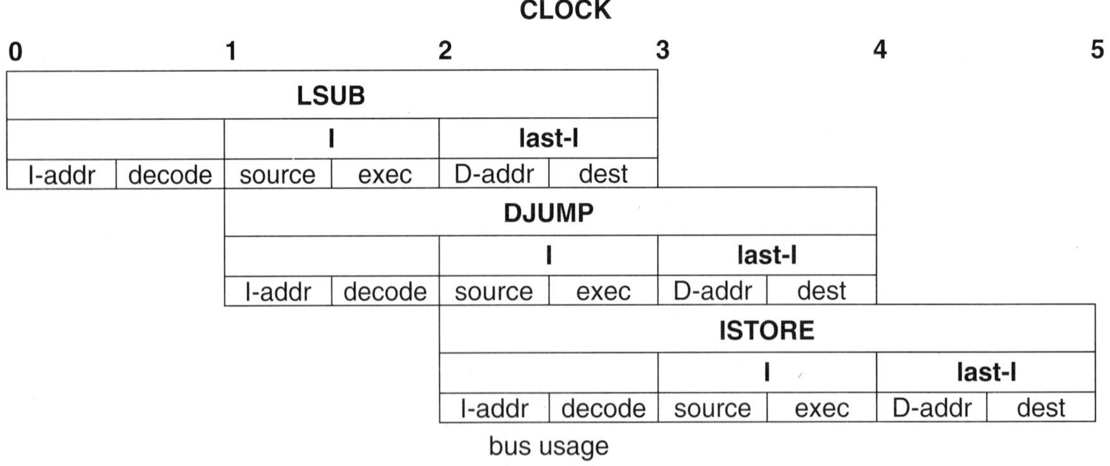

TABLE 6.2 Steps taken by each of three instructions in the pipeline according to the clock times shown in Figure 6.10.

Instruction	Clock	Phase	Action
LSUB	0	a	PC ⇒ I-bus ⇒ I-cache; PC ⇒ LAST-PC; PC + 1 ⇒ PC
	0	b	instruction from I-cache ⇒ I-bus ⇒ I. Note that the instruction is decoded in the sense that it passes through combinational logic on its way to the I register. This logic adds those bits which will enable the registers, switches, and ALU to carry out the instruction.
LSUB	1	a	sign-extended rightmost 16 bits of I ⇒ A-bus ⇒ A register specified in I ⇒ B-bus ⇒ B
DJUMP			PC ⇒ I-bus ⇒ I-cache; PC ⇒ LAST-PC; PC + 1 ⇒ PC
LSUB	1	b	A − B ⇒ C with flags set if specified; I ⇒ LAST − I
DJUMP			instruction from I-cache ⇒ I-bus ⇒ I
LSUB	2	a	nothing
DJUMP			sign-extended rightmost 17 bits of I ⇒ A-bus ⇒ A register specified in I ⇒ B-bus ⇒ B
ISTORE			PC ⇒ I-bus ⇒ I-cache; PC ⇒ LAST-PC; PC + 1 ⇒ PC
LSUB	2	b	C ⇒ B-bus ⇒ R specified in LAST-I
DJUMP			A + B ⇒ C, no flags set; I ⇒ LAST-I
ISTORE			instruction from I-cache ⇒ I-bus ⇒ I
DJUMP	3	a	If (condition specified in LAST-I) {C ⇒ I-bus ⇒ I-cache; PC ⇒ LAST-PC; C + 1 ⇒ PC;} ELSE {PC ⇒ I-bus ⇒ I-cache; PC ⇒ I-bus ⇒ I-cache; PC ⇒ LAST-PC; PC + 1 ⇒ PC;}
ISTORE			register specified in I ⇒ A-bus ⇒ A register specified in I ⇒ B-bus ⇒ B
DJUMP	3	b	nothing
ISTORE			A + B ⇒ C (opcode from I) I ⇒ LAST-I
ISTORE	4	a	C ⇒ P-bus ⇒ D-cache
	4	b	R specified in LAST-I ⇒ P-bus ⇒ D-cache

mention of some new hardware—the register LAST-I. This is the first element explicitly there for serving the pipeline. Obviously, if an instruction is processed at three different stages in the pipeline, it must be present in some form or another at each of those stages. Let us consider this flow of information immediately since it should give a better feeling for the motion of instruction information through the pipeline. Several new items have been added to our CPU to accommodate both the pipeline activities and interrupt handling. An essentially complete version of the CPU is provided in Figure 6.11.

In phase-a of the first clock—stage 1 of the pipeline—an address is provided for the I-cache. An on-chip I-cache will easily provide the needed datum in less than the

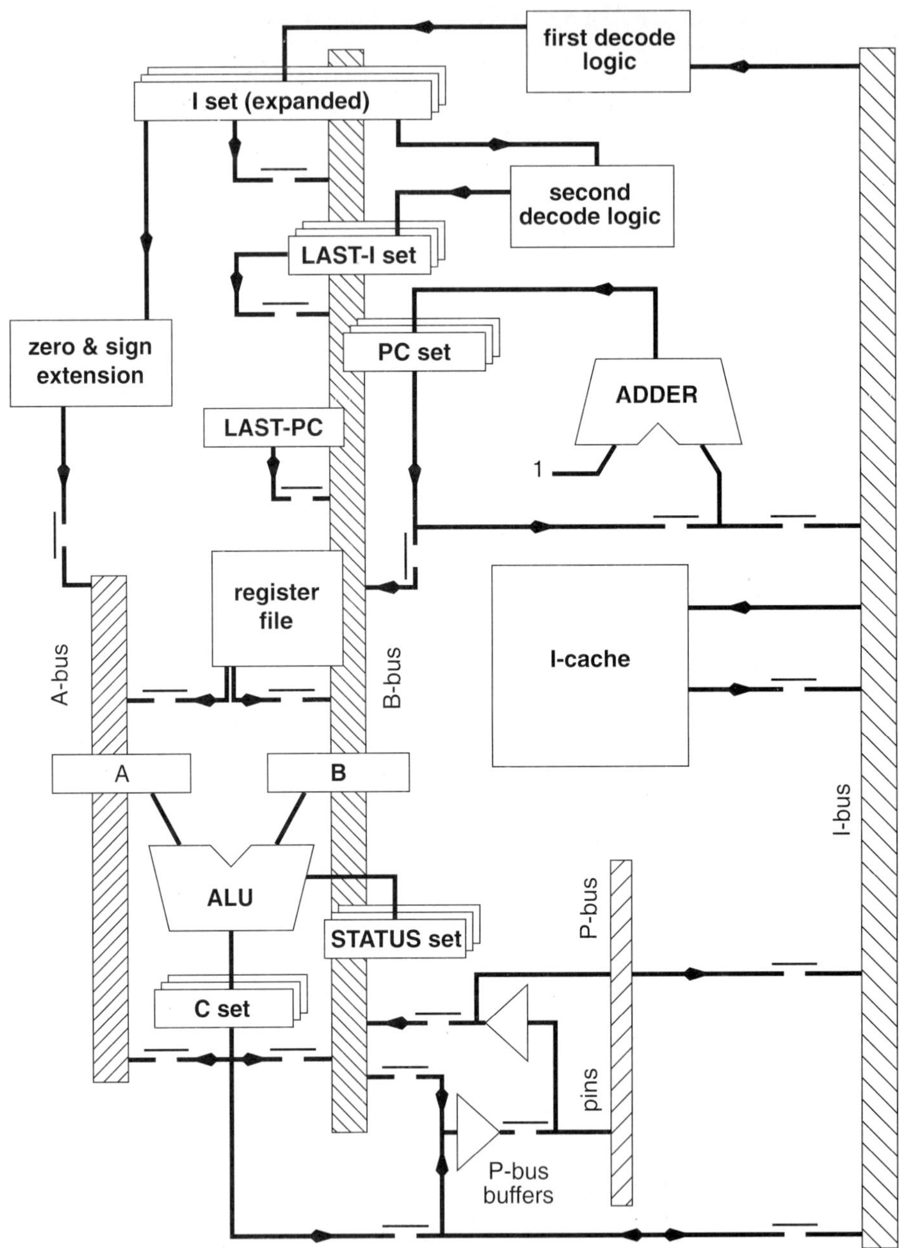

FIGURE 6.11 Layout of the CPU with all of the parts needed for the pipeline and for interrupt handling. Blocks marked *set* represent a group of registers. The register file includes a single copy of r0…r29 plus three copies of r30 (SP). The other sets include eight copies of the register named in the block. The active copy (in front) in each case is the one specified by the current interrupt level. Registers which overlay a bus may read from that bus. *Unselected* registers in a set may be activated by the D-cache to read from or write to the B-bus as if they were data words in the D-cache. LAST-PC is a debugging aid used only with IL0. Its purpose is to retain the previous PC so that an exception taken on the instruction following a JUMP or CALL can be attributed to the correct instruction.

phase width of 50 ns. (We will consider a cache miss below.) In the b-phase of this cycle, the 32-bit machine instruction is written to the I-bus. Note that this is marked as the DECODE phase. *Decoding* in this usage is a mixture of logical recognition and expansion. The idea is to expand from 32 bits to whatever number of bits is necessary to actually control the hardware. Whether one chooses to go *fully horizontal*, in the sense that all of the decoding takes place right here, or still have some *vertical* code which will be decoded later is a matter of where you want to or have to put your silicon. For example, if the register tristates were to have their drive bits fully decoded here, there would be three blocks of 32 bits, one for the A-bus and one for the B-bus in the SOURCE phase and one for the B-bus in the DEST phase. At most there would be 1 bit active in any of these fields. Alternatively, instead of expanding to 96 bits, we can leave the register specifications in 5-bit encoded form and do the decoding of this field at the point of use. The decision would be based on chip layout and timing considerations with one modestly important constraint imposed by our 32-bit word size.

This constraint comes about as a direct consequence of our decision to do interrupt handling by switching registers. On a context switch, the OS will have to save all of these registers. Since context switches take place from IL2 (see Figure 3.4 on page 136) we must save all registers from IL0 and 1. This means that every bit of width that we add to the expanded instruction register becomes 2 bits—one for each level—and that for every 32 bits of width, we will have another 2 words to save. Since each save/restore requires a LOAD and a STORE, each extra block of 2 words that we must save costs us at least four instructions. Big deal? Well, a typical time-slice is of the order of 10 ms, so you are going to see at least 100 context switches a second. That brings the cost of that one extra word to 0.004 percent of the total computing power of the machine. Small, yes, but you only get to spend performance once. An alternative is to have both decode and encode hardware on the I registers, with the encode gates used for compressing the expanded fields on storage. An equivalent alternative is vertical encoding in the I register, which can then be made horizontal through logic that requires neither replication nor storing and reloading.

We have chosen to expand in the I register to 64 bits. The only thing that would force us to go to 96 would be a finding that we could not meet some time constraint on propagation through the vertical-to-horizontal expansion logic. With our rather leisurely clock rate, that is most unlikely to occur.

After the machine instruction passes through the combinational logic which does the decode, there is a value in each field for control of each and every part of the ALU, the register set, and the busses. As the now expanded instruction passes through the pipeline, each piece of hardware's control specification is ready for immediate use.

Having expanded the machine instruction in phase-b, we latch it into the I register. Thus, at the start of clock-1/phase-a, enabling bits are available from I to put the correct registers on bus-A and bus-B and then, in phase-b, control bits are available to specify the ALU and shift operations. Since a new instruction will be ready to move into I, the necessary parts of the current contents of I are moved into LAST-I. Many of the fields in the expanded instruction apply only to the second stage of the pipeline. These are not copied into LAST-I, so I is much wider than LAST-I. Fields from the remaining part of the expanded instruction in LAST-I provide controls for B-, I-, and

P-busses and for enabling writes back to the register set. We can, of course, expand fields from I into LAST-I. That could save precious space in I without imposing a delay penalty in LAST-I. As long as LAST-I does not go over 32 bits, there would be no reason not to expand to more horizontal code in the transition. This is shown as the *second decode* in Figure 6.11.

Another issue is well raised with this example set of instructions. DJUMP is usually a PC-relative branch. In other words, the base register for the address is PC. Back in Figure 6.2, we showed that PC as a source field would invoke the NUL or 0 response. That is hardly what is meant in DJUMPyz x(PC). You should consider which PC value is called for here; it must be specified in order to compute the displacement. One could use the PC value extant either before or after fetching the DJUMP. In most computers, *after* is more convenient because, at the moment when the machine is ready to use the PC as the base register, the PC has been incremented to point to the next instruction. Thus, if we wanted to jump back to the LSUB instruction above the DJUMP, the displacement should be -2. That is the displacement from what will be in PC at the moment that we would want to put it on bus-B. Fine, but how do we arrange to get PC and not NUL on bus-B? The instructions for which NUL is NOT the proper interpretation of R31 are the LOADs, STOREs, JUMPs, and CALLs. These comprise the instructions whose first 2 bits are either 00 or 10. Bit 30 selects PC or NUL.

Consider how r31 must be connected to accommodate all of its several incarnations. NUL resides in the *register file* and can be invoked in any register field. Thus, 0 may be written to either A-bus or B-bus. PC may be used only as a base register (r31 would be NUL as an index), so it requires connection to B-bus. In its incarnation as the address of the next instruction, it requires connection to the I-bus, where it connects to the I-cache as well as being able to receive a jump address from C.

One final programming limitation is evident from Figure 6.10. The data from a LOAD is placed on B-bus (and thus made available) only in phase-b of the third clock. Register data for the instruction following the LOAD must be available in phase-a of that clock. Accordingly, an instruction which does not depend on this new data must follow the LOAD. As was pointed out in Section 2.2.2, this is another bubble-filling operation, and if all efforts to fill it usefully fail, the programmer/compiler must insert a NOP.

After you have followed Figure 6.10 and Table 6.2 to the bitter end, you should be convinced that we can indeed put out one instruction per clock as long as the caches can keep feeding our hungry pipeline. We mentioned *cheating* in doing the counting. By that we mean that we count the NOPs that are necessary when we cannot otherwise fill a bubble from a delayed branch or LOAD. If we count those—and we do—our pipeline will tick along quite contentedly, munching 10 MIPS.

What about when the caches *don't* keep up with demand, when we inevitably find ourselves going off to central memory for another helping of data or instructions or when the I-cache needs a refill from the D-cache at the same time that data is going to or coming from the D-cache? Well, we will still get one instruction per clock but not 10 MIPS. When a cache fault or conflict is detected, the CPU clock is halted until the required data is obtained. Such a pause in processing is called a *stall* or a *wait state*. Depending on whether this is a fetch from central memory with possible delays for bus contention or error correction or simply a cache-to-cache transfer, this delay can range from 1 to 10 clocks. However, with a high cache hit ratio in each cache, these delays cause only a modest reduction in the system performance.

If one loads a single instruction at a time into the I-cache—an issue we consider later in the chapter—there is the possibility of not even missing a beat. As long as the P-bus is free for that clock, it would be possible to simultaneously search the D- and I-caches. If the I-cache faulted and the D-cache hit, the instruction could be logged in from P-bus to I-bus rather than from I-cache to I-bus. It would simultaneously be entered into the cache and be expanded into I during phase-b.

A clear conflict arises when there is an I-cache fault in the same clock as a datum transfer. Both want to use the P-bus. Precedence must go to the instruction fetch, so the I-cache miss must cause the D-cache to stall the CPU and the CPU to release the P-bus. The D-cache runs the CPU briefly through its control lines, first getting the VA which caused the cache fault and then returning the desired instruction to the I-cache. These two transfers use the P-bus. The transfer accomplished, the CPU is started again when phase-a goes high. Minimum delay, corresponding to a cache hit for the instruction in D-cache, is 1.5 clocks. This delay comprises the lost phase-a of the conflict, followed by another phase-a and then -b for the instruction fetch.

Ah, but what happens if the desired data is in memory or even out in the great beyond? Well, it is obvious that the CPU is not left hanging there while the operator scrambles around looking for the tape he forgot to mount or even for a hard disk to transfer a page to central memory. A D-cache miss simply extends the delay until the new line is fetched; a page fault causes an interrupt. The interrupt routine saves the current process in restartable form, initiates page-fetching for the needed page, puts the faulting process into the *waiting-for-input* queue, and then initiates a context switch (a trap-driven event) to bring in the next process in the highest priority *ready-to-run* queue. This, of course, leads to the question: But how do you pick up all of these loose marbles rolling around in the CPU? That is a worthy question with an interesting set of answers which we are finally in a position to provide. Let us consider the details of how our machine will handle interrupts.

6.4 INTERRUPTS AND EXCEPTIONS, RETURN FROM INTERRUPTS, TRAPS, AND RECOVERIES

6.4.1 Interrupts and Exceptions

An interrupt is a break in the normal processing of instructions in response to an *external* request for service; an exception is a similar break in normal processing in response to a problem in that processing. *Exception* should be read in the sense of the processor saying: "I take exception to that." These two are often combined under the sobriquet of *interrupt*, but they differ in two very important respects. Since the interrupts arise from external events, they are both asynchronous with the normal processing stream and quite independent of it. An exception, on the other hand, is a pothole in the way of progress and must be acted upon before processing can proceed. Accordingly, interrupts can be handled in some hierarchical order and responses may be reasonably delayed while a sequence of instructions is pursued to do something else "more immediately important." An exception, on the other hand, indicates a problem which prevents continuation and must be handled at once. Apart from these differences in execution ordering and immediacy, exceptions and interrupts are essentially the same. Let us begin by treating them as if they were all interrupts and then bring out the subtle but important differences between them.

In a pipelined machine, making the transition from process program to interrupt program and back without losing anything but time will require preserving all of the data which constitutes *the state of the machine*. An interrupt is an unanticipated branch to instructions that are outside the current process space. The switch has the software implications of a CALL, particularly saving and later restoring any registers that are used, including PC and SR. Interrupts can also involve a transition to (and then from) a more privileged state. Since exceptions arise from the processor's inability to complete an instruction (e.g., a page fault or a divide-by-zero error), the exception handler must have access to the current process including such data as which instruction caused the interrupt, the address which generated the fault, and the contents of the register set. Uses for this information include error identification, debugging, running virtual machines, and context switching.

There is considerable motivation to design efficient interrupt handling. Interrupts are not all that infrequent, and if the cost of handling one is high, they will have a noticeable negative impact on processor throughput. The transition to the interrupt state must be able to provide both a route back to normal processing as well as a reasonably direct method of tracing what the state of the machine was at the time of the interrupt. In a pipelined machine, the PC references an instruction which may be several instructions after the one that caused the interruption. You could have a page fault on an instruction fetch or, at the other extreme, on a load operation. In our machine, these would represent instructions at the beginning or end of the pipeline. Many machines save the information that must be retrievable on the stack. This requires lots of memory traffic and a rather substantial amount of time at both ends of the interrupt. A much more rapid but not inexpensive alternative is to save the information on-chip by providing some separate registers for the interrupt to use. We have adopted that alternative.

In general, an interrupt begins by having the interrupter indicate that it has an interrupt which needs service at a particular IL. Only the highest-IL requester will receive a response. Upon receiving the interrupt acknowledgment, the interrupter asserts its *interrupt vector*. With the vector, the interrupt state machine can obtain the starting address of the interrupt handler, pass it to the PC, and set the new IL in the SR of the CPU. The CPU is then off and running in the interrupt handler.

Where can interrupts and exceptions come from? Here is a partial list:

- *Externalities*. These are the true interrupts. They come in, typically, from I/O devices which have completed a task, have run out of some needed resource, or have run into some problem such as an attempt to write to a write-inhibited disk. Included in the list of externalities will be the interrupt clock(s) which announce that it is time to switch tasks (contexts). Extremities such as loss of power or overheating provide rare but critical events heralded by interrupts at the highest level. Each interrupter provides its own vector to lead the processor to the correct service routine. No hardware internal to the interrupt state machine or CPU is necessary to determine why this type of interrupt was invoked.

- *Page faults*. As discussed in some length in Chapter 4, running under virtual memory implies that many parts of a program will reside on disk. References to those disk-resident pages cannot be answered in reasonable time, so the MMU will signal a fault which calls for a context switch to a task that can make use of the CPU while the missing page or pages are brought in from disk. A page fault can also arise from accesses to unfulfilled stack and/or heap addresses. In those cases, a free page can be supplied almost immediately and no context switch need be invoked. It is up to the page-fault service routine to determine whether a given page fault is a request for an extant page of data or simply an empty free page. To accomplish this task, the fault-handling software must have access to data from the MMU (faulting address) and the faulting program's C, SP, and PC registers. Since the heap may be unfulfilled, then access to the *top-of-heap pointer* is also required.
- *Address translation errors*. These comprise the other sort of access errors which the MMU would detect such as trying to write to *read-only memory* or do any operation in a space that is not open to the running program. It is particularly important to be able to tell the user which address caused the fault and where it came from. The faulting address is retained in the MMU and with C, PC, SP, and SR, the fault service routine can sort out the precise source of the problem.
- *Illegal instruction fault*. This classification includes undefined opcodes (we have but two) and instructions reserved for higher levels of privilege. (We have only RFI. Instructions such as HALT in the VAX or ILLEGAL and RESET in the MC68000 can be invoked only at privileged levels.)[9] Here it is desirable to get hold of both the instruction and the address of the instruction. The instruction, in expanded form, will be found in I. The address of the next instruction in line (which will be the adjacent successor to the offending one) will be found in PC.
- *Arithmetic errors*. This class includes *divide-by-zero* and word and halfword *overflow*. Similar errors on the coprocessors can trigger exceptions (see Chapter 9). These exceptions have mask bits in the SR which permit the software to enable and disable exceptions.
- *Bus faults*. This curious name covers the range of misadventures which can befall a data transaction once it goes from the MMU to any of the memory-mapped devices that are (or are not) out there on the system bus. The data might fall into a black hole

[9] DEC makes special use of HALT as a trap for evil programs. HALT has 00 as its opcode, probably the most common byte in the machine. If you are inclined to let your machine wander off to start running random bytes in the memory space, you will sooner or later try executing a 00. That will immediately cause a fatal interrupt, which tells you that you have used a reserved opcode. Presumably, you will find the fact that you were executing *anything* in this location to be pretty bizarre, and while you are pondering this finding, the VAX will be off working on more productive fare.

either because the device it was intended for just went off the air or because the address that was used is not fulfilled—nothing is there. Generally, some sort of bus timer is out there checking on every bus transaction. If there is no "I've got it" handshake within the specified period, the watchdog timer signals with a bus timeout interrupt. Recovering the origins of the failing address here is quite problematical. In a machine such as ours in which even uncacheable writes are buffered by the D-cache, such an interrupt could derive from an instruction that has already completed. The MMU agreed that the address was legal, the instruction was allowed to "complete" by passing the data to the D-cache, and the D-cache buffered it while contending for the bus and then attempting the fetch-on-write. While this off-chip activity was going on, the CPU could be happily processing away. The failure is recognized only after a timeout interval. It could well be 20 instructions or more away from the STORE when the transaction actually fails. By the time of the error, it may be difficult to completely reconstruct what transpired. At best, we might have the physical address associated with the failed execution and the cause of the failure. Whether recovery is possible is a software issue; for example, a timeout on a test to see if a device was alive and alert would tell the program: "No one at this address." The program which made the request may simply cross that device off the list of devices available. In other circumstances, such an interrupt may indicate an unrecoverable system crash.

Clearly, interrupt data—what happened to cause the interrupt—has to be made available to the interrupt routine. The source or cause of the interrupt will be indicated by the interrupt vector used, but this may not be enough by itself. In general, the vector tells the system where to look, not what it will find there. This means that these internal registers from wherever the interrupt may arise must be available to properly privileged software. Let us move into the details of the interrupt response in our machine and then ask how one might access the registers. Meanwhile, note in Figure 6.11 that the register sets all have input and output lines accessible from the B- or I-bus. The question, to be answered in stages, is: How will we make these registers accessible to our skinny instruction set? Let us begin with the details of handling the interrupt.

In our machine, the interrupt will be taken up *prior to the start of phase-b*. Look at that moment in Figure 6.10. Phase-b is when the following sorts of transitions can take place:

- PC $\Leftarrow$ PC + 1 or PC $\Leftarrow$ Jump destination + 1
- instruction from I-cache $\Rightarrow$ I-bus $\Rightarrow$ I
- A op B $\Rightarrow$ C (opcode from I)
- C $\Rightarrow$ B-bus $\Rightarrow$ R specified in LAST-I
- R specified in LAST-I $\Rightarrow$ P-bus $\Rightarrow$ D-cache
- D-cache $\Rightarrow$ P-bus $\Rightarrow$ R specified in LAST-I

In other words, all of the register changes, events overwritten, get done in phase-b. By interrupting during phase-a before any changes take place, we assure ourselves that no results of a failed instruction—at least none that is detected synchronously—get carried out. If we preserve the current state of the registers at the moment of accepting the interrupt, we can rerun the same instruction when things get fixed or report to the user or operator where the program was when the unrepairable programming bomb went off. Of course, most interrupts have nothing to do with the current process. They are simply wake-up calls to the system to take care of some externality. However, even for those, the system may need to initiate a context switch, so the data necessary to preserve a context must be available to any and all interrupts.

If you recall our initial discussion of interrupts in Chapter 2, we proposed having eight levels of interrupt and multiple versions (not copies) of necessary registers. The registers, most of which are unique for each interrupt level, that define what we are doing at any instant include:

PC	for the next fetch
status	defines state of current level
I	the decoded instruction for the middle pipeline stage
LAST-I	the decoded instruction for the last pipeline stage
register C	for the data for the last pipeline stage
SP	defines current top of stack (USER, SYSTEM, or INTERRUPT)

At any one moment, one register in each group of registers (e.g., PC0...PC7 or SP0...SP2) is enabled. The enabling is determined by status register (SR). While there are eight SRs, they all share the same upper 8 bits. These bits are set whenever their particular interrupt level is active. Recall that level 0 is the user and levels 1...7 are the kernel. Thus, the bit for level 0 is always set while those for levels 1...7 will be set only by their associated interrupts, traps, or exceptions and reset by the RFI instruction. Here we must identify one important functional difference between an interrupt and either TRAP or an exception. The latter two increment IL while an interrupt specifies an IL.

Our interrupt cycle must accomplish the following tasks:

1. recognize (in the sense of acknowledge) the highest pending interrupt and halt the operation of the CPU during phase-a
2. change the registers selected to those for the new interrupt level (if, at system startup and every time an RFI is executed, the I and LAST-I registers are left with expanded NOPs in them, then the pipeline is always properly primed at each level)
3. acquire the vector and use it to place the address specified into the PC to initiate the fetch of the interrupt service routine
4. restart the CPU at the start of phase-a

The system interrupt interface resides on the MMU/D-cache board (or chip). This is a logical placement both because it is the interface to the system bus and because the base address for the array of addresses referenced by an interrupt vector resides there and is used by the MMU. The MMU is also an important source of exceptions since page faults and address translation errors arise there. Control lines are part of any inteface including those between the system bus and D-cache and between D-cache and CPU. Seven of the control lines between MMU and CPU are used for specifying interrupts:

- IN2...IN0 *bidirectional* lines specify the current or next interrupt level.
- EXN is a pulldown line used by the CPU and coprocessors to indicate an exception. EXN must be negated upon receipt of IACK.
- TRQ is used by the CPU to indicate a TRAP request.
- IACK is driven by the D-cache to indicate that it is acknowledging the exception or external interrupt. This line is daisy-chained through the CPU to the several coprocessors, so each of those chips must provide a pair of pins, IACK_IN and IACK_-OUT. (See discussion of daisy chaining in Section 8.3.2 on page 425, particularly Figure 8.11.) An equivalent line is provided to interrupt sources, but it is asserted only if EXN is not asserted. Thus exception handling is started before an interrupt is handled. This is necessary to get the CPU or coprocessor back to a normal state before starting on an interrupt. The exception will take the CPU up one IL, but if a higher level interrupt is waiting, it can be serviced on the next instruction.
- TACK is driven by the D-cache to acknowledge the CPU request for TRAP service. Interrupts and exceptions take precedence, so only when all pending interrupts clear will the TACK line be asserted.

There are also two clock lines, C_CLK and B_CLK, controlled by the D-cache, which provide sequencing for the interrupt transaction. In the absence of a pending interrupt or exception, IACK is negated. The three IL lines are driven by the CPU to indicate the interrupt level (IL) currently operating. The D-cache compares this level to any pending interrupts. If IL is less than a pending interrupt level and C_CLK is high (phase-a), the D-cache asserts the IACK line and stops C_CLK. In response, the CPU stops driving the IL lines. With the stall of the CPU clock, processing stops, suspended in phase-a. The D-cache board is now in charge. To accomplish the other tasks in the interrupt, we proceed through a sequence of steps timed by the B_CLK line (see Figure 6.12):

1. The D-cache asserts the IACK line and the chosen respondent replies with its interrupt vector. The D-cache board writes the new IL onto the IL lines. The upstroke of B_CLK provides a timing edge to turn on the SR bit indicated by the IL lines and for reading the vector. A priority encoder enables the specified level in all of the register sets in the CPU.
2. The MMU gets the datum at the physical address (interrupt vector + interrupt base vector). This datum is the virtual starting address for the interrupt service routine. In general, the address and the routine itself must be in memory and could be in cache. Once the address is available, the D-cache puts it on the P-bus. On the upstroke of B_CLK, the new address is logged into the current PC.
3. The C_CLK is reenabled. Processing recommences with NOPs in I and LAST-I and the address of the first instruction in the interrupt service routine in PC.

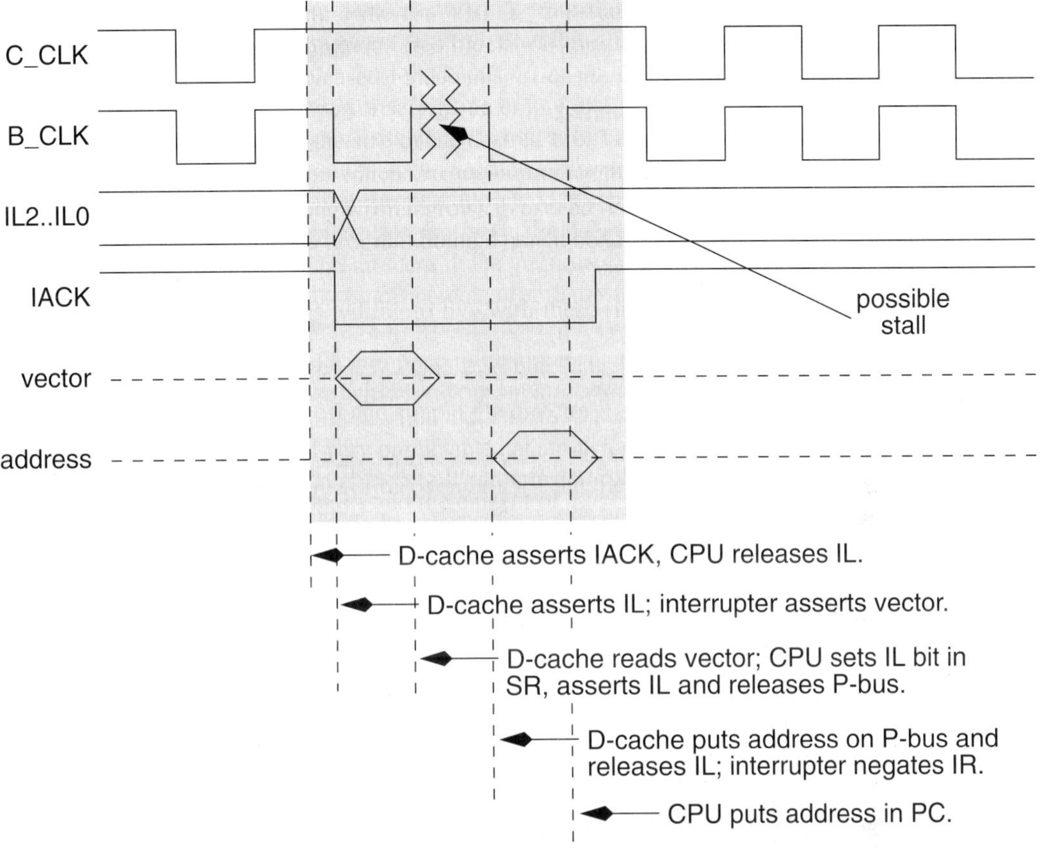

FIGURE 6.12 Timing diagram on interrupt handling. The shaded area represents the full span of the interrupt cycle. If the address of the interrupt handler is available in the D-cache, the interrupt transition is over in an exceptionally short 2 clock cycles. The request to which IACK is responding is not shown. It could be an external interrupt request, EXN, or an internal exception such as a pagefault or address translation error.

If the starting address is in cache, the whole switch should be done in two full clocks. Otherwise, it should take the two clocks plus one memory cycle. Note that all interrupt routines must reside in memory. It would never do to have an interrupt elicit a page fault. However, Saying “Never!” does not really preclude the event. Should the TLB signal a PF with IL>1, the MMU responds not with the PF vector but with an *unanswerable page-fault* exception. Were this to elicit yet another page fault, the computer is certifiably brain-dead. Processing is suspended until the system is reset.

The issue of which interrupt gets attention and how the vector gets there in the first place is important to understand. Interrupts are queued according to their level (IL) and, at a given level, according to their “distance” from the host. The IL is programmed into the interrupter either by software or by hardware. The concept of distance-from-the-host is a little artificial. What is done is to take the IACK line and string it in an ordered way through all potential interrupters at one level. (See Figure 8.11.) The resulting single file is referred to as a *daisy chain*. Each element along the chain has a switch through which the chain passes. If that element is asserting the interrupt request line, it opens the switch. Accordingly, any element that is "further away" on the chain cannot receive an acknowledgment until all of its predecessors get satisfied. (In Chapter 8, some schemes are presented to overlay a measure of *fairness* on such preemption schemes.)

An example of daisy chaining here would be CPU first and FP coprocessor second. Note that exceptions are responded to first since the D-cache will not acknowledge an interrupt until the EXN line is negated. Should the unlikely event of two essentially simultaneous exceptions arise—an overflow in the CPU and the FPU, for example—the CPU will be driven through two interrupt sequences, raising the IL by 2. The handler for the FPU would be the first to start running. If there were a higher priority interrupt waiting out there, it would receive its response as the CPU started into the first instruction of the FPU handler. Thus, a *full* response to each of these exigencies would go in the order

high-order interrupt handler ⇒ FPU handler ⇒ CPU handler

For exceptions, the vectors are preassigned and may even be hard-wired. For interrupts, the vectors are installed by software as part of the initialization of the machine, although nothing prevents reassignment later. Each process may have its own trap table, though most will default to a standard table. Each possible interrupter must have an internal storage location for every vector it is expected to own. Many devices will require several vectors to request different responses from the host. These may be at different ILs or they may share a single level. These device vector registers, as with all device registers in this machine, are mapped into the memory space; the host merely writes in each of them whatever vector belongs there. Generally, it is the custom to assign a specific vector to the value of *unassigned* and to see to it that upon reset, all vectors are set to that value. At bootup, a proper pointer is assigned in the vector table to the *unassigned* vector. Then, if the software fails to set a meaningful vector or if a chip resets, the error shows up and is handled in a useful way. In the MC68000 microprocessor series, for example, *uninitialized* is vector 15.

The CPU and its coprocessors work their exceptions in much the same way as the external interrupts with the exceptions of using the P-bus to communicate their vectors and getting an automatic upgrade of 1 on the IL.

6.4.2 Return from Interrupt

The process that we just described is easily reversible. The interrupt service routine need only load the two NOPs into I and LAST-I and then reset the highest-order bit that is set in the status word (by doing RFI, NOP, NOP). Automatically, that enables the next lower interrupt that was running, with the pipeline at that level still filled with what it had just been doing. Accomplished at the end of phase-b, the CPU will properly execute from the point of interruption, repeating only the transactions which take place in phase-a.

Note that our interrupt scheme requires that we enforce the rule that RFI is *always* followed by two NOPs. Then, as RFI propagates through the pipeline, the

NOPs are naturally loaded behind it. How does one "enforce" such a rule after the computer has left the factory? Well, in general, computers do not get sold free of basic software. Those who create the software can make it generate two NOPs after an RFI. Notice that there is an essential difference between a JUMP and an RFI. With JUMP the delay is only one instruction; in the case of RFI, we seem to be putting two fillers in there. The difference is real because our objectives are different in the two cases. Consider each of these instructions entering the pipeline in clock 0 (Figure 6.10). For JUMP, the jump address moves to latch C in phase-b of clock 1 and is available *at the start* of phase-a of clock 2 to serve both as the source for that next fetch and to be incremented and loaded into the PC. Thus, if the JUMP is to be taken, it is taken in phase-a of clock 2. There is only the instruction fetched in clock 1 as a bubble to be filled.

The case of RFI is different because we want to be able to specify that *both* I and LAST-I have NOPs in them. When we next enter this interrupt level, whatever is in LAST-I will do whatever it is designed to do in the third stage of the pipeline. Since we want it to do *nothing*, we must leave a NOP there. To that end, we make the RFI instruction reset the bit in the status register in phase-b of clock 2. In other words, RFI does nothing until the third stage of the pipeline. At the same time that that bit is resetting, the second NOP is moving into I and the first into LAST-I at the current IL. On the next cycle—clock 3—the CPU is at the lower IL, using different I and LAST-I registers and fetching from the new PC.

What would happen if something other than two NOPs were inserted? That is a good and unanswerable question. It would depend on what got left there. On entering the pipeline at that IL, that "leftover" would be in the pipeline and could do whatever it would normally do at that point in the pipeline. That certainly could work mischief and would be a very devil of a bug to find. The conclusion is obvious: Don't do it.

For completeness, let us step RFI through the pipeline. In stage 1, it loads. In stage 2, it does nothing. In stage 3, during phase-b the highest bit set in the SR is reset. This operation applies to all of the top 7 bits (IL 1...7) but not IL0. That bit is permanently 1, being the bottom possible level (USER). An RFI at IL0 causes an exception. It is our only forbidden instruction and essential to running a virtual machine. All other protection is done by address and that is definitely IL-specific. (While not exactly "forbidden," we do have unassigned opcodes. If they appear in an instruction stream, an exception will be taken.)

6.4.3 Traps

The TRAP instruction provides vectored access to trap handlers and increases the IL by one. Trap vectors are in a separate block of interrupt-vector addresses. TRAP's action, from the programmer's perspective, is very much like a CALL to an external library routine. Since the TRAP instruction raises the IL, in guarded fashion it opens access to anything the machine can do.

The mechanics of the TRAP instruction are reasonably simple, once the interrupt mechanism has been discussed. The 12 low-order bits of the I register have a high-order 1 appended and are then zero-extended into the C register. In phase-a of the third stage, instead of signaling READ or WRITE as it puts its "address" onto the P-bus, the

CPU signals TRAP. This signal causes the D-cache to do a slightly abnormal interrupt routine in phase-a by asserting TACK. The timing is shown in Figure 6.13. An IL one higher than the current IL is asserted by the MMU. Using B_CLK as in regular interrupts, these data are clocked in and the system is prepared to go on with the trap handler at the new IL. RFI gets the machine back to the trap-calling program.

Note that bit 12 in the vector is 1, so the TRAP vectors reference a different array than the interrupt vectors, even though both use the same base address. These two blocks of 4096 words must be unswappable and located in a contiguous area of physical memory.

FIGURE 6.13 Timing diagram on TRAP handling. The shaded area represents the full span of thc interrupt cycle. The principal difference with Figure 6.12 is the timing on IL, since IL is derived from the address rather than from the interrupter.

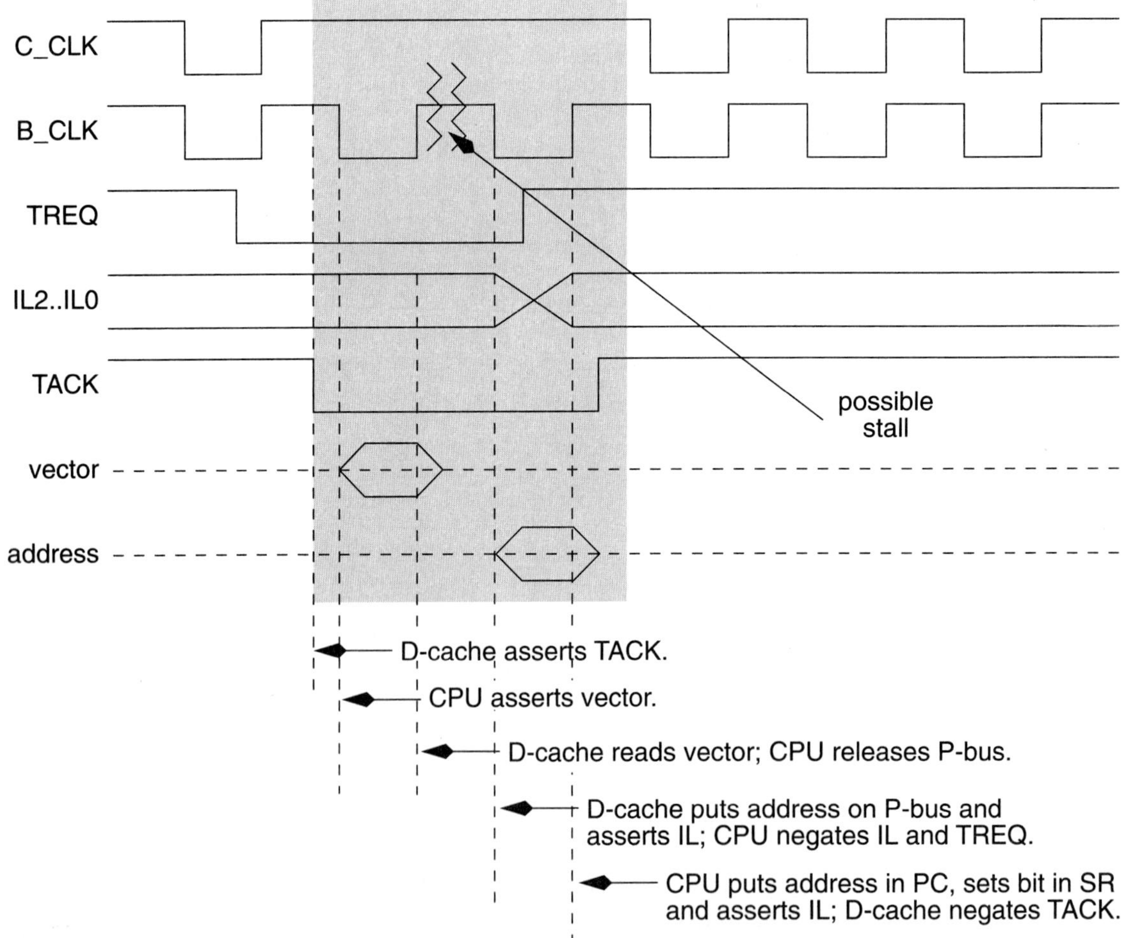

Since TRAP is "just an instruction," what do we do about deliberate or accidental misuse of a trap vector? The burden for checking both the circumstances and validity of the TRAP falls on the handler. Generally, trap routines expect to find particular data at particular locations. If the trap routine detects some flaw in the data, it forces a context switch with an error message rather than proceeding as if nothing were amiss. It is this sort of checking and filtering that we referred to in Chapter 2 when we talked about the ogre at the gate. Since traps result in a change in IL, protection and system security must be preserved across a trap operation. A vigilant ogre at the gate is necessary for system security.

A critical capability in a well-rounded ogre is the ability to look at all aspects of any process that comes knocking at the door. How can the ogre or the handler which stands behind him access the data which defines the caller? Access to data that is neither in memory nor in active registers is both necessary and certainly not obvious. Let us consider that next.

6.4.4 Hidden Data, Context Switching, and Memory Mapping

Memory space is normally much larger than any single block of memory, where the block is defined by the size of the memory chips. For example, the largest chip currently being sold is 16 Mb. A row of 32 such chips would comprise a very large block (16 MW) but a minute fraction of the total memory space of 4 GW. Thus, installed memory will comprise one or more blocks of realized addresses, each of which covers a small part of the available address space. To know if it is being addressed, each block must recognize that part of the address which specifies the block.

Recognition of an address is simple enough. For example, if you set up a memory using 4-Mb chips, then each chip's internal addressing will examine the least significant 22 bits. By decoding the remaining 10 bits of an address, one identifies which block of a possible 1024 is being specified. The output of the decoder can be used to enable the chips in the correct block to respond to this particular READ or WRITE.

It is a simple step from this to use this same decode scheme to enable data transfers between devices other than what we conventionally call *memory*. For example, one can use the decoded lines to enable READs and WRITEs to registers in a peripheral chip. When things other than RAM or ROM are included in the address space, we say that they are *memory-mapped*. Anything that can be enabled for a READ or WRITE can be memory-mapped. "Anything" certainly includes registers. By providing a set of seven address lines as control lines between MMU and CPU, we could specify any of 128 words stored in the CPU. Let us say that we had defined the addresses of the top 128 words of memory to be assigned to the CPU. Then the base address would be FFFF FF80. Let us say that we make the assignments shown in Table 6.3. Then the following code loads PC0 into R3:

```
.dseg
.hex
.gc CPU_base:    0FFFFFF80
```

```
.pseg
    LOAD CPU_base, rl         ;put base address into Rl
    DLOAD 28(rl), r3          ;note that HEX still applies
```

Probably the best problem to use as an illustration here is the context switch. Recall from Chapter 3 that a context includes as its most fundamental component a block of data which has a complete description of the machine state at the moment it was last switched out. In that *context descriptor block* is an *image* of everything that the system would require to restart the context. This image would include the contents of all of the changed registers from the CPU and the coprocessor(s), the three PTE's for the kernel root and absolute tables and the process root table, the starting address of the interrupt address block, and process identification data.

When we do a swap of contexts, it is done at IL2. All the registers from IL3 up have no useful data (except for their NOPs). From that state, what we do is:

1. Copy out all of the context data into the context descriptor block of the current context.
2. Invalidate the TLB to remove all translations for the old context.
3. Copy in the context data from the next context to run.
4. Invalidate the I-cache and execute an RFI.

This task is neither extremely lengthy nor difficult to program. For data exchanges in the hidden registers, the little swatch of code above can be extended at will. Fine. Programmatically, no problem. But how do we physically get the rabbit out of the hat?

Consider what happens on a LOAD. (For STORE just reverse the direction of data flow.) An address gets calculated in the CPU in phase-b of the second stage of the pipeline. In the following phase-a, the address is passed to the D-cache. The D-cache would normally find the word requested in cache, but if not, it stalls the CPU until the line arrives from central memory. Then, in phase-b, data is transferred from D-cache to P-bus to B-bus and parked in the register specified. What we want to do with our rabbit is to make it seem to be coming from D-cache. In that sense, the registers would look like data stored in D-cache. If we can get that data on the B-bus at the right time, we have one rabbit delivered on schedule.

TABLE 6.3 Memory mapping of internal CPU registers

Offset	0	. . .	7	8	. . .	F	10	11	. . .	1E	1F	20	. . .	27
Register	S0	. . .	S7	C0	. . .	C7	I0a	I0b	. . .	I7a	I7b	Last_I0	. . .	Last_I7

Offset	28	. . .	2F	30	. . .	32
Register	PC_0	. . .	PC_7	SP0	. . .	SP2

What is the hardware doing? Look at Figure 6.11. We know that the regular registers r0…r29 aren't at issue here; the instruction set handles them explicitly. Each of the other register sets is shown with multiple layers. Only one layer is currently active, but the back layers can be connected as inputs to the B-bus. Similarly, all of the inactive layers can receive data from the B-bus. B-bus can be connected to the output-driver to the P-bus. If we can control the switches, LOAD is in hand. The programmer sees himself or herself doing DLOAD 28(r1), r3. In inner-sanctum reality, 28(r1) or FFFFFFA8 is recognized by the MMU as a special address. The address 28 is sent over control lines between D-cache and the CPU. We would need an enable line and an "address" for the register (eight lines total). The CPU is fully aware of whether the operation is read or write. When read is signaled, the data in PC0 would be placed on the B-bus and stored in R3 just as if it came from the D-cache. Rabbit in and rabbit out.

Rabbit out all right, but all is not peaches and cream (or even lettuce and celery). If you stare at bus-B spanning Figure 6.11, you cannot but be struck by the number of connections to that bus. This *fanout* means an enormous load on the bus. Heavily loaded busses are slow, and in any high-traffic area they are energy gobblers. Bus-b can be counted on to switch data in *every phase*. It is undoubtedly our busiest bus. Making that bus work and work well will be a major task for the chip designers.

In reality, the drawing of Figure 6.11 is not a final representation of layout, only of connectivity. A central task for the chip designer would be to segment the B-bus. To reduce dissipation, only those segments active in a particular transaction should be driven. However, working against excessive segmentation is the need to move data from any segment to any other. Whatever the division of the B-bus, there will still be a lot of turf to be devoted to the connections shown. Before this chip got through design, there is no doubt that there would be much argument between the architects and the layout engineers about whether all of these connections are really necessary.

6.5 THE I-CACHE

6.5.1 Harvard versus Princeton

We have defended having the separate I-cache on the grounds that it greatly reduces the traffic between the D-cache and the CPU and thus makes possible almost one instruction execution per clock. The idea of separating instruction flow and data flow is hardly a new one. It bears the name *Harvard architecture* and derives from the early work in computational engines that Howard Aiken was doing at Harvard University during World War II. The alternative of storing instructions and data in one memory—in fact, making instructions just another flavor of data—is often misattributed to John von Neumann. In fact, the stored-program idea goes all the way back to Babbage and was certainly central to Turing's concepts of computer organization.Von Neumann gets credit for it because of a report that he wrote after visiting with Eckert and Mauchly at the University of Pennsylvania where they were building the ENIAC (not a stored-program machine) and designing the EDVAC. Von Neumann, who dwelt in Princeton's Institute for Advanced Study, was pursuing better methods for doing the massive calculations needed for the Manhattan project. EDVAC represented an enormous leap forward and greatly excited von Neumann. He wrote an informal but seminal report about the design of the EDVAC computer at the University of Pennsylvania in which he discussed (without credit) many of the ideas that Presper Eckert had proposed for EDVAC [von Neumann, 45]. To be fair to von Neumann, many concepts in the report were his own, and he certainly described the whole problem of digital computation with remarkable insight and clarity. Included among the many ideas was Presper Eckert's concept of storing the program as "data" which he had disclosed in a patent memo on January 29, 1944 [Metropolis, 80]. The report was widely disseminated by Herman Goldstine and its impact established "once and forever" that being able to treat instructions as data had enormous advantages. Having but one memory was central to the design Burks, von Neumann, and Goldstine developed at the Institute for Advanced Study, a design that became known as the *Princeton* or *von Neumann* architecture [Burks, 46]. Chief among its virtues were:

- One memory instead of two. Von Neumann wanted parallel access to the bits, proposing one CRT memory unit for each bit in the word.
- The instruction stream itself could be modified by events during the execution of the program.
- The memory could be reconfigured at any time to accommodate whatever changing need there was for program space and data space.

One has to remember the enormous cost of memory in those days. Furthermore, the programming paradigms that we take for granted today—stacks, subroutine calls supported directly by the instruction sets, indirect addressing, and even elementary programming aids such as assemblers—had yet to be invented. With tiny memories, reconfigurability is critical. Without decent instruction primitives, self-modifying code is essential to be able to create the equivalent operations. For example, if you have nothing but absolute addressing as a machine primitive, you *have to* be able to change the address field in all sorts of instructions. If you are doing such things, then you must be able to treat instructions as if they are data. The Harvard architecture isolated instructions from data memory and did not permit modification of a running program.

If you have a machine which has a truly fixed program, the Harvard architecture is usable. The issue of reconfigurability still hangs there unanswered, but if the machine has a rather fixed set of chores to do, then the program size can be known and the separation of memory into program and data is workable. One class of computing engine is frequently applied in such situations. It is called a *controller* or *industrial controller* rather than a computer. For such machines, the program is frequently stored in an EPROM and is quite immutable. (In von Neumann's day, the "program" might well be stored on a patch panel called a *plug board*. This was the case with ENIAC, which brought von Neumann to Philadelphia.) A separate RAM is attached to the system for storing variable data. Instruction books for using installed controllers often refer to "programming the machine," which means changing certain stored constants in RAM. They even retain their ancient relay origins in using *ladder logic* for this pseudo program. With such configurations, you will often find a 2-memory Harvard architecture rather than a single-memory von Neumann design.

With the versatility of the general-purpose computer, the growing sophistication in computer control, and the remarkable and steady decline in the price per computation cycle, industrial controllers as a separate architecture have almost vanished. ROMs and RAMs routinely occupy the same address space, and programmability and versatility have won the day in central memory design. For many years, industrial versions of the MC68000 family had a very large part of this controller market. Now, with RISC machines delivering so much bang for the buck, Advanced Micro Devices's 29000 family has become the dominant player in the high-end market for embedded computers.

The issue of bus traffic, though, has never vanished from the computer architect's field of view. As memories and CPUs get ever faster, that umbilical cord between them remains fixed as the limit to processing speed—the von Neumann bottleneck. Ever since the concepts of cache and look-backward buffers were invented in the '60s, designers have been aware that programs tended to be full of loops and that caching instructions on the CPU side of the bus could lead to much faster system throughput. In some such configurations, the instruction cache could be accessed at the same moment that the central memory was delivering data. This parallelism is supported by having two physical ports through which data can flow. With multiple ports into the CPU, throughput was much enhanced. In effect, the Harvard architecture was adopted for the local storage paradigm while the von Neumann architecture was retained for central memory.

Putting the instruction cache on-chip in even a modest-sized microprocessor has become increasingly popular. For example, the MC68020 has a direct-mapped instruction cache on-chip that gets queried every fetch cycle. Even at a diminutive 256 bytes, it is dramatically effective in reducing memory cycles.

Our putting the I-cache on-chip is thus nothing new. What we wish to look at are the issues of size, organization, and addressing. Our objective is to get an efficient cache in the sense that we approach as closely as possible our goal of one instruction per clock period. We have to say "clock period" because we always achieve one instruction per CPU clock. However, we get that perfect rate by stalling the CPU clock whenever an instruction cannot be serviced with the data at hand. If our clock rate were 10 MHz, our goal is to approach 10 MIPS. We cannot get there, of course, but we can get pretty close with typical cache hit ratios.

6.5.2 Caching on a Limited Budget

What limits the I-cache? Being on-chip now turns from advantage to constraint. Every bit that we must store in static RAM will require about six transistors. Say that we limit the chip to about 100,000 transistors—a student project today! Then, if we did nothing but I-cache, we would be able to store 16 Kb. That is only 512 32-bit words! And we have left no room for tags, valid bits, or protection (or CPU, for that matter.) Obviously, a huge cache we will not have. Possibly 64 words. The problem set considers a variety of cache configurations and even the possibility of using dynamic RAM. Here we should consider what must be in the cache, regardless of configuration.

The I-cache is intrinsically different from the D-cache in at least four important ways:

- I-cache is *read only* in the sense that a program can never write to the I-cache.
- The I-cache is tiny.
- The cache contains only instructions, so there is no reason to deal with anything but words. Words may be grouped into lines to reduce the number of overhead bits per word.
- Instruction sequences are inherently very linear.

Since our objective in designing the I-cache clearly must be to get the most possible data into a constrained total number of bits, we should try to reduce *overhead bits* to the fewest that we can get away with. Overhead bits include protection, address translation, and validity. What may we extract from the special properties of the I-cache?

The first item in the list permits using *virtual addresses* rather than physical addresses. This will eliminate the need for an address-translation buffer. When an instruction first moves into the I-cache, the D-cache does a normal translation of VA to PA as well as a full protection check. All of the worries about different processes using the same VAs for different code can be swept away by observing that it is cheap to flush a tiny cache. Similarly, since a higher IL loads code that a lower IL should not be able to access, we need only tie an automatic cache flush to RFI to assure that there is no wormhole into system space. It is a little less obvious what to do going the other direction. If dynamic linking were used, process and kernel could share library routines. Should we worry about this sharing? Even a small kernel routine is going to use a good portion of 64 words. That both process and kernel could be using the same library routine at the same instance seems most unlikely. Accordingly, any switch of IL up or down will effectively flush the cache by replacement. Why then not flush it automatically to avoid rare but evil conflicts in the use of VAs? With this decision, the only time that a program need flush the I-cache is if self-modifying code is employed.

The inherent linearity of code would suggest that we should read in very long lines of instructions. The reading mechanism in our hierarchical cache system says otherwise. The whole motivation for the I-cache was to reduce conflicts for the P-bus. contention for the P-bus occurs only on LOAD, STORE and CP operations. The data quoted in Chapter 1 show that these represent 30 percent or less of typical code. This means that 70 percent of the time, one can fetch an instruction from D-cache without conflict for the bus. In that time, you can fetch one word, but not two. We can still have long lines; we will just load them one word at a time. A long line saves bits by having fewer tags. Loading one word at a time uses bits by requiring one valid bit per word. Given the size of a tag, the advantage of long lines as a bit saver is clear. What is much less clear is what line length is the best choice for performance.

Were code randomly organized, long lines would be very costly. Every time that an address missed, the cache would have to dump four or eight words. But code is not random; it is quite orderly. In a study of just this problem of constant-area on-chip instruction caches, Alpert and Flynn [Alpert, 88] found that there seems to be a best performance in several senses—traffic, hit ratio and utilization of cache area—if the line size is between four and eight words.

The Alpert and Flynn paper is interesting in a variety of ways. For example, they show that it is relatively cheap to arrange the cache as a fully associative cache; that is, the comparison hardware is not particularly costly. What is not so clear from their paper is how they plan to do a full LRU replacement algorithm. That is certainly neither cheap nor usually practical for any large number of lines. The fully-associative cache eliminates the *index* field, since all tags are searched in parallel. Indexing in itself is no problem, but one can get into a thrashing problem where two small loops trash each other because they share indices. With relatively few rows to index, this collision of indices could be a problem for some programs. A solution which is less difficult to do neatly than the LRU algorithm is to put two (or more) lines at each index and do the associative search only on the tags at that index. This, of course, is nothing other than the set-associative design discussed in Chapter 5. With a 2-member set, a local LRU algorithm can be accomplished with a single bit that flips whenever a hit occurs in a line or a new word is loaded.

CHAPTER SUMMARY

The CPU has been laid out in great detail. A three-bus structure was developed to permit two data and one instruction to move simultaneously. The ALU was equipped with pre- and postshifters. The shifter, which is a full 31-bit bidirectional shifter, was fully developed to include the functionality needed for MUL and SHIFT, including, for the latter, the setting of the V and C flags.

The design was developed around a simple three-stage pipeline with much of the effort directed toward accommodating breaks in the simple flow of instructions through that pipeline. The diversions from normal flow can be programmatic (JUMP, CALL, or TRAP), external interrupts, or simply the delays—stalls—that arise when data or code must be fetched from memory. After considering a variety of techniques to minimize unproductive bubbles in the pipeline, we selected *delayed branching* to handle JUMP and CALL and *delayed utilization* to handle LOAD. This choice pushes the problem of minimizing bubbles (NOPs) onto the compiler. One may criticize this decision on the grounds that it makes delayed branching part of the architecture. Since delayed branching is most appropriate to short pipelines and since longer pipelines can enhance speed, making the easy decision now could be disadvantageous later. To maximize the compiler's or programmer's flexibility in arranging instructions for delayed branches, flag-setting instructions all contain a bit to inhibit flag changes.

The interrupt concept and the idea of interrupt levels were introduced as early as Chapter 2 and much use of them was made in Chapter 3. In this chapter, we fleshed out the hardware that would make the concept work. Interrupts can be requested from devices which reside on the central bus, from the MMU, or even from within the CPU itself. Programmatic interrupts are obtained through the TRAP instruction. All of these interrupts are handled by a single *finite-state machine* located in the MMU. All interrupts are executed in phase-a prior to the transfer of any results to registers or memory. Accordingly, nothing need be stepped back or undone. The interrupt engine sets the appropriate IL in the SR which switches internal CPU registers (including PC and possibly r30). Only the registers used by the interrupt service routine from the common register file need be saved and then restored prior to the RFI. The RFI instruction simply resets the highest IL bit in the status register, which automatically switches operation to the next lower active bit and flushes the I-cache. In order to preset the interrupt level for its next use, all interrupt service routines should end with two NOPs. These get stored in I and LAST-I. Then, the next time that the level becomes active, the CPU can begin by fetching the proper first instruction of the specified interrupt service routine without fear of unexpected actions from remnants left in the pipeline.

The last topic concerned the I-cache. Its inclusion on-chip allows the CPU to both fetch an instruction and do a load or store operation in the same clock. However, with the limited turf available on-chip, the I-cache is a tiny memory. In order to minimize the fraction of the cache devoted to overhead, we eliminated the look-aside translation buffer, choosing instead to obtain both index and tag from the VA. Having eliminated any memory protection in the I-cache, we found it advisable to have the hardware flush the I-cache on any change in IL. Should programmers choose to write self-modifying code, they must force an I-cache flush before trying to use the modified code.

We turned to finding a "best scheme" for laying out the tag and valid bits. Since tags are so large, we wanted to use as few tags as possible. A line of four to eight words proves best, but we do not wish to load it more rapidly than one word at a time. This is because for roughly 70 percent of the time, one can fetch a single instruction from D-cache with no stall. With a reasonable I-cache hit rate, we will get very close to one instruction per clock fetching them one at a time. Were we to fetch more per request, a stall would be inevitable and our production rate would suffer.

PROBLEMS

6.1. Design the combinatorial circuit which properly sets the C and V bits for the five shifters. Remember to take care of the special case of MUL, where the C bit is set according to Figure I.3 on page 549.

6.2. Consider that the blocks of registers, such as LAST-I, have adjacent addresses in our memory-mapping scheme, that I is 64 bits wide, and that the principal task in doing a context switch is swapping registers. Include a single floating-point coprocessor in the swap. (All eight data registers in this coprocessor are two words wide. There is also a CP status register.) Just on the basis of the register count plus ID, process status, kernel pagetable entries, and interrupt-address table base, what is the minimum size context descriptor block? Make liberal use of Figure 6.11 and remember that context switches take place from IL2.

6.3. With the context descriptor block of the previous problem, design an efficient scheme for storing and transferring the block. Then determine the time to accomplish the switch. Assume that time slicing alone will result in 100 context switches per second. On that basis, calculate the fraction of total computer time devoted to context switching.

6.4. In the discussion of the I-cache, we came to the conclusion that VAs were usable. Issues which were raised before we accepted that conclusion included *instructions only* and *read only*. We cannot use VAs in the D-cache without resorting to heroic measures such as inverse pagetables. Explain why.

6.5. After reading and considering Problem 6.4, must a context switch invalidate the D-cache? Since all processes utilize the same operating system, we really would like to leave those parts of the OS which survive in cache right there for the next use thereof. Remember that the D-cache has a data/instruction repository as well as a set of recently referenced page-translation tables (*look-aside buffer*). State what must be invalidated on a context switch and support flushing or retaining as you see fit. Finally, try designing a scheme which would allow a selective flush of the look-aside buffers, leaving system references intact.

6.6. Consider the I-cache. Let's think small and say that we will store 64 instructions in the I-cache. We could arrange the cache in a number of patterns. Let us consider two of them. Let one be a 64-line direct-mapped cache with 1 tag and 1 valid bit per line; let the other be an 8-line set-associative cache (set size 2) with 1 tag and 4 valid bits on each side on each line. Consider the specific address 00A7B296 and describe for each case what the cache must do to determine if the instruction at that address is in the I-cache.

6.7. For 64 words stored, the designer must supply room for 64*32 = 2048 bits of storage, regardless of the arrangement. The two arrangements above, however, do not have the same burden of "extra" bits—tags and valid bits. Compare the two schemes given for the burden of extra bits.

6.8. At startup, the system must write a NOP properly decoded into every IL's I and LAST-I register. Using Table 6.3, on page 354, write an appropriate C or assembly program to accomplish this task. You may use any three numbers you wish to represent the expanded code in the respective registers.

REFERENCES

[Alpert, 88] Alpert, Donald B. and Michael J. Flynn, *Performance Tradeoffs for Microprocessor Cache Memories*, **IEEE Micro 8**(4), 44–54 (1988).

[Amdahl, 67] Amdahl, G., *Validity of the single-processor approach to achieving large-scale computer capabilities*, **AFIPS Conference Proceedings 30**, 483–5 (1967).

[Aspray, 87] Aspray, W. and A. Burks, ed., *Papers of John von Neumann on computing and computer theory*, Charles Babbage Institute reprint series for the history of computing, MIT Press, Tomash Publishers (1987).

[Bucholz, 62] Werner Bucholz, editor, *Planning a Computer System: Project Stretch*, 238–9, McGraw-Hill (1962).

[Burks, 46] Burks, A. W., H.H. Goldstine, and J. von Neumann, *Preliminary Discussion of the Logical Design of an Electronic Computing Instrument*, report to the U.S. Army Ordinance Department, 1946. A description of the IAS machine, the original *Princeton architecture*. Reprinted in [Randell, 82] and [Aspray, 87].

[Ditzel, 87a] Ditzel, D.R., H.R. McLellan, and A.D. Berenbaum, *The Hardware Architecture of the CRISP Microprocessor*, **Proceedings of the 14th International Symposium on Computer Architecture**, 309–313 (1987).

[Ditzel, 87b] Ditzel,D.R. and H.R. McLellan, *Branch Folding in the CRISP Microprocessor: Reducing Branch Delay to Zero*, **Proceedings of the 14th International Symposium on Computer Architecture**, 2–9 (1987).

[Ferguson, 93] Ferguson, Charles H. and Charles R. Morris, *Computer Wars*, Times Books (1993).

[Gustavson, 88] Gustafson, J., G. Montry, and R. Brenner, *Development of parallel methods for a 1024-processor hypercube*, **SIAM Journal of Scientific and Statistical Computing 9**(4), 1–32 (1988).

[Johnson, 91] Johnson, Michael, **Superscalar Microprocessor Design**, Prentice-Hall, 1991.

[Lee, 84] Lee, J.K.F. and A.J. Smith, *Branch Prediction Strategies and Branch Target Buffer Design*, **IEEE Computer 17**(1), 6–22 (1984).

[Lipstay, 68] Lipstay, J.S., *Structural Aspects of the System/360 model 85, Part II: The Cache*, **IBM Systems Journal, 7**(1), 15–21 (1968).

[Metropolis, 80] Metropolis, N., J. Howlett, and G. Rota, *A History of Computing in the Twentieth Century*, Academic Press, 1980. Papers presented at a conference on the history of computing in 1976 by many of the people involved, including Backus, Knuth, Burks, Stibitz, Wilkes, Eckert, Mauchly, Dijkstra, and Zuse. Includes Eckert's "Disclosure of a Magnetic Calculating Machine," describing the stored-program concept.

[Patterson, 85] Patterson, D.D., *Reduced Instruction Set Computers*, **Communications of the ACM 28**(1), 8–21 (1985).

[Randell, 82] Randell, Brian, *The Origins of Digital Computers: Selected Papers*, 3rd edition, Springer-Verlag, 1982. Excerpts of papers including: Babbage on his analytical engine, Zuze's 1936 patent application, Aiken and Hopper on ASCC, Atanasoff on ABC, Mauchly on ENIAC, [von Neumann, 45] and [Burks, 46].

[Stone, 92] Stone, Harold S., *High-Performance Computer Architecture*, 3rd edition, Addison Wesley (1992).

[Thornton, 64] Thornton, James E., *Parallel Operation in the Control Data 6600*, **AFIPS Proceedings Fall Joint Computer Conference 26**, part 2, 33–40 (1964); also, *Design of Computer Systems, the Control Data 6600*, Scott Foresman (1970).

[von Neumann, 45] Von Neumann, John, *First Draft of a Report on the EDVAC*, 1945. Reprinted in [Randell, 82] and [Aspray, 87].

CHAPTER 7

FILE SYSTEMS AND I/O OPERATIONS

ON FINDING TREES IN A FOREST

7.1 EXPLORING I/O LIMITS TO PROCESSOR THROUGHPUT

Chapters 7 and 8 focus on input/output operations. It is probably safe to state that most computer processes are more I/O-limited than computation-limited. To get some sense of why, it is necessary first to get an overview and then to get down into the hardware itself to see what the limitations on I/O speed really are. I/O is a pervasive subject. If one generalizes I/O to mean data transfers between storage systems of greatly different size and speed, then we have dealt already with one important level of I/O in Chapter 5. That chapter covered transfers of data between main memory and cache and between cache and CPU. It is now time to move from that innermost circle and to look at interactions between processes and the really massive data storage on disk.

In many ways, this chapter picks up themes from Chapters 3, 4, and 5. While you could skip this chapter and its successor and still have a good understanding of the CPU and its environment, what you would miss is one of the central themes in real computer system design. It does little good to have a CPU which can devour 300 MIPS if you cannot feed the beast. Keeping the feed trough full is what Chapters 7 and 8 are about. It is a topic much ignored in most architecture textbooks. We commend it to you.

At the cache–central memory interface, transactions are both quick and generally quite small. At the central memory–disk storage interface, transactions tend to be quite long and quite large. A different set of paradigms has been developed to serve these differences, though in both cases maximum throughput and minimum overhead have been the central objectives.

A rather different set of optimizations is involved with what has been a traditionally slow data interface—terminal I/O. While terminal I/O is becoming a critical problem in sustaining and supporting video output on workstations, for most character-oriented terminal operations the data rate oscillates between almost none and none. What makes this laid-back data stream quite different is the need to interface it with a human operator's needs, a subject interesting enough that we have included it in this chapter. In fact, we will begin with that and then turn to the more pressing problem of disk I/O.

7.2 INPUT/OUTPUT

Except for real-time systems, direct input/output operations are the sole domain of the operating system. There are four compelling arguments for relegating I/O to the sacrosanct preserve of kernel space:

- I/O functions are generally very low level, very full of detail, and too easy to mess up.
- In general, many processes share individual devices—hard disks and printers, for example—but the operations requested must be isolated one from another (e.g., the printer must finish one job before starting the next).
- Since all programs share the principal I/O devices, a large saving in memory usage can be obtained by having only one copy of the I/O routines.
- In multiprogramming environments, it is essential that no process can read, erase, or modify any file to which it has not been granted access.

HLLs generally provide a hierarchy of I/O calls. As you get closer to the realities of I/O, even languages which attempt to be "above all that"—in fact, particularly those languages—tend to get complex. Consider this quote from Tiberghien on files in Pascal:

> The association between Pascal files and files managed by the operating system can only be made through additional parameters in the procedures used to open and close the files. [Tiberghien, 81] p. 112.

In other words, "At this point the language runs out and the operating system intrudes."

In C you normally specify an output operation by calling the function `fprintf()`, `fputc()`, or `fputs()`, which are library routines that manipulate the data in convenient ways and then call the extremely primitive `write()`. In UNIX and C, files are streams of bytes and `read()` and `write()` are system calls to read or write bytes in that stream. Typical of C, the buffer for the stream is directly available to the program. As a user, you can avoid worrying about the buffer by invoking one of the higher order library routines or you can handle the buffer yourself. However, you cannot move that data to a device. For that, your program or the library routine you have called upon must issue a `write()`. The parameters of `write()` are instructive:

```
write(int fileDescriptor, char *buffer, int n)
```

`fileDescriptor` is the number assigned by the system when an `fopen()` command is issued. For example, the three automatically-open files, `stdin`, `stdout`, and `stderr`, are assigned file descriptors 0, 1, and 2 respectively. Anything you opened deliberately will have a higher number. Most systems limit the number of simultaneously open files to a small number such as 16. The second parameter simply points to the start of the buffer, and the last variable says how many bytes to move. While in a sense C lets you play with all the knobs and levers as far as your program is concerned, you don't get near the real hardware—at least, not unless you are writing code that will run in the kernel. You can set up the whole operation, but when you want it *really* to happen, a TRAP is your only recourse.

Since any good hacker wants access to everything, let us consider why operating systems insist on being *pilot in command* even when you own the resource you wish to write to. Let us presume that the `write()` is directed to file 1 (stdout). The characters will be sent to your terminal. But terminals are slow devices that can accept only one character at a time. Since the kernel has the obligation of keeping the CPU busy, it would never let you sit there, putting out characters at a snail's pace. Instead, the kernel will copy the characters onto the end of a queue of characters going to your terminal. The characters will be transferred to the terminal one at a time, usually through a chip called a UART (universal asynchronous receiver transmitter). Since each character takes a relatively long time to send (about 1 ms at 9600 baud; 4 ms at 2400), the processor must give a character to the UART and then wait until it is ready to accept another one. Rather than wait uselessly (we are talking about wasting 10,000 to 40,000 instruction times!), the kernel leaves itself a pointer to the next character and returns control to your program or does a `wait()`, the choice differing from one operating system to another. Nothing but the UART is watching the character transfer.

Generally, the kernel does not come back to look at the UART. It can but it does not. Instead, the UART completes its transfer and then issues a call for its next character by interrupting the host. That interrupt will usually come in while someone else's process is running, but the operating system is the same for all processes. The interrupt is *vectored* to the proper operating-system routine and that routine will simply deliver the next character in its buffer and then return to the current user. The interruption is but a few microseconds per character.

Generally, an output buffer is of fixed and modest size. While its output buffer is not full, a process can put out characters at processor speed and without pause. Should the buffer fill, however, the process is temporarily stuck. The system has two choices:

- provide expandable buffering (a list or queue of buffers)
- block the process until the buffer opens or empties

Expandable buffering using queues of small buffers is a very efficient way of equitably dividing by need the limited memory space devoted to buffering among a set of independent processes, but it does not completely eliminate the need to block a process in the midst of output. Just as a buffer can fill, the queue of empty buffers can be emptied. In that case, you must block the process.

One problem that is not solved by buffering is a program's (or programmer's) expectation that when the program executes instructions which follow an I/O request, the I/O request has completed. In other words, if you write:

```
scanf("%d",&x);
if (x>9) {...
```

you have every reason to assume that **x** will be on hand before you compare it to 9.

A more subtle problem concerning output occurs if a program sends a sector's worth of data out to disk, and then, after further computation, sends an *updated* version of some subset of that same sector to the same place on disk. Since all writes to disk are in units of a whole sector (see Appendix III), the partial rewrite of a sector is a read-modify write operation. If the first write has not completed, the second must not begin. On the other hand, if the transfer has not yet begun—that is, if the earlier transmission is still sitting in a buffer waiting its turn—rereading or rewriting directly into the buffer is not only possible but desirable. In a busy multiprogramming environment, there can be very substantial delays between queuing an I/O request and its execution. Operating systems solve the strict sequentiality problem in various ways. If a process is blocked until each I/O request completes, the kernel is said to use *synchronous I/O*. It is synchronous in the sense that each I/O request is fully answered before the next program line is executed. If the kernel simply buffers the I/O operation and returns control immediately, it is using *asynchronous I/O*. This sounds a bit more absolute than it is in practice. In UNIX, and many other operating systems, an I/O request has completed when the data is in buffer, regardless of the direction the data is traveling. If there are enough buffers, the transfer of output is essentially immediate. If not, the process will be blocked until the buffer supply is replenished. For input, on the other hand, synchronous operation will require blocking the process until the data is in. Rather than being blocked, a process with sufficient foresight could ask for the input long before it needs it and then go off and do something useful. The question is: How would the system then prevent the process from trying to read the data before it is there? In other words, how will synchronism be maintained in an asynchronous I/O system? An intermediate approach to asynchronism is to pass the burden to the user. Such systems require that there be a user-programmable test for completion of an I/O operation. Then it becomes the programmer's burden to recognize potential conflicts and to test for completion. The benefit gained from this added responsibility is that, at relatively low cost, your program can do something else while I/O operations complete. A distinctly possible liability is that files can be left in a damaged state because an unwary programmer failed to anticipate a conflict. UNIX uses synchronous I/O; VMS permits asynchronous operations. Both achieve good file security but at very different costs. Note that in both systems the *physical I/O* is asynchronous. The process itself fills buffers for output and empties buffers on input. Emptying buffers on output and filling buffers on input are handled entirely by the system. Thus, even in a synchronous I/O system, the low-level I/O operations are asynchronous.

To accommodate the slip inherent in asynchronous operations, the routines (usually called *drivers*) which communicate directly with the I/O devices often are divided into upper and lower halves. The upper half comprises the procedures which deal with user programs, while the lower half deals directly with devices. The only connection between the two halves is that they share certain data structures. In the previous example, `write()` calls the upper half of the device driver. The upper half copies the data specified into a buffer of bytes and queues the buffer for the lower half. If the lower half is not active, it is told that there is output in the queue. What the lower half does is very device-dependent. Some hardware devices are prepared to handle pages; others, such as terminals, deal in individual characters. If we were dealing with a terminal, for example, the lower half sends the first character and returns control. Each subsequent interrupt from the UART results in a call to the lower half of the terminal driver. It need only take a character from the queue, send it to the UART, and return control. When the last character has been transmitted (or an error has occurred), the lower half enters the success or error code into a table for the upper half. When the process next runs, it picks up in the upper half of the driver where it was when it went to sleep. Lo and behold, the response is there in the table. If something evil happened, such as the terminal dropping off line, the system can respond appropriately. Otherwise, the lower half just waits for the next activation.

The whole loop of terminal I/O reveals some more details of the operating-system services. Let us walk that circuit at least once.

7.2.1 Terminal I/O

The typical university multiprogramming machine will have dozens of active terminals, each "connected" to one or more concurrent processes. Several terminals may have a character to send at any one instance and many—sometimes all—of them may be receiving data concurrently. Not only must there be a method to sort these data streams so that they arrive where they belong, but there must also be adequate buffering in the system to accommodate the asynchronism between events in the process, events on the keyboard, and events on the screen. For example, on input:

- You can "type ahead," writing characters that the program is not yet looking for. What happens to characters that are typed ahead?
- How does the operating system know which program should receive the characters that you type?
- When should the characters be echoed?

On output:

- When a program writes characters to `stdout`, how does the operating system decide which terminal to send them to?
- Characters are produced by an application at processor speed—some characters per microsecond. They are delivered to the screen at rates of the order of $^{1}/_{1000}$ of processor speed and generally at times when the generating process is not the current process. How are the different rates and asynchronism accommodated?

Let's begin with the "connection" between a terminal and a process. When you log in at a terminal, the login process spawns a shell process, which executes your commands. That shell or command-line interpreter is "connected" to your terminal. "Connected" here has context equivalent to or literally that of a phone connection. The physical arrangement of the interconnect is shown in Figure 7.1. One simple and rather old-fashioned model of that link is a phone line terminated at each end by a *modem* (modulator/demodulator), which, at the sending end, turns a stream of level-determined digital signals into a sequence of tones (audio signals) suitable for transmission over a telephone link. At the receiving end, the process is reversed. By preventing echoes (echo cancellation), simultaneous transmission is possible in both directions over one line pair. The stream of bits emerging from or directed to the modem is handled by a UART chip or its equivalent. This device accepts bytes to be transmitted and delivers the bits serially at the proper baud rate, properly bracketed with start, stop, and parity bits. Alternatively, it receives the properly bracketed stream of bits and delivers bytes to the host. A simple organization for a multiprogramming machine is to have numerous modems, each individually connectable to incoming phone lines on one side and each individually addressable by the host on the other side. This completes the physical link. Beyond that, the kernel has a table connecting each process's `stdin`, `stdout`, and `stderr` to the correct UART. These data will also be stored in the PCB of each process.

Since each UART is talking to a very slow device, it can accommodate a character no more often than about once per millisecond (9600 baud = 960 cps with 10 bits/char). Whenever it has new data from the outside or has finished sending a current byte, it signals availability by interrupting the host. The host responds to the interrupt and gets a vector which is directed to the proper handler. The handler will either know

FIGURE 7.1 Physical links between two terminals and a multiprogramming host. The two unconnected modems are waiting for a callin. Phone lines connect the modems. The CPU will query the UARTs by address, with each UART receiving a unique block of addresses.

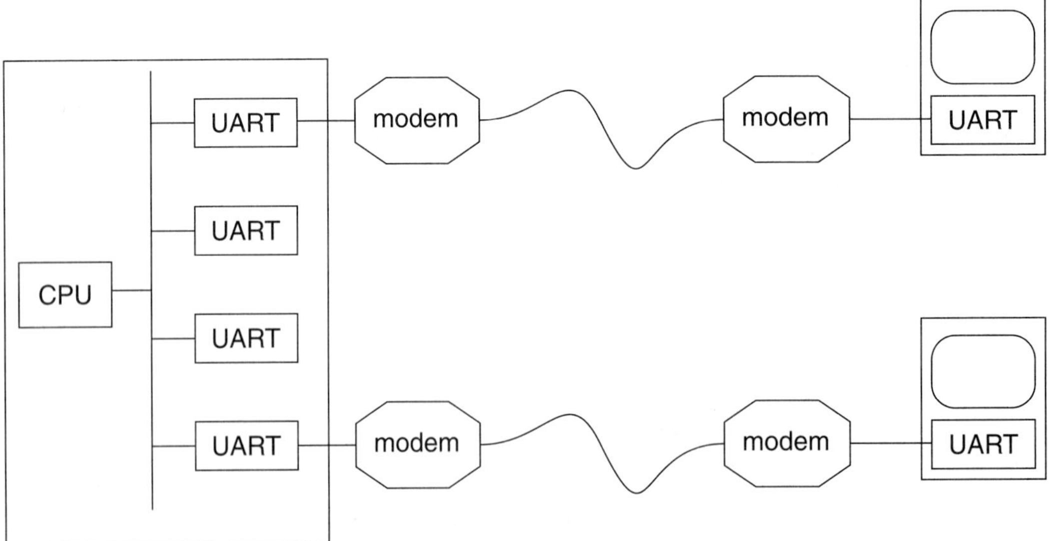

where the interrupt came from on the basis of the vector or alternatively, if one vector fits all, then the handler must poll status registers in the UARTs which identify the UART(s) that hold data for reception or are ready to accept another byte for transmission. The handler uses its table to select the correct buffer of input or output data and moves the byte into or out of its queue. When many terminals are to be handled, the interrupt rate becomes unacceptable. To make better use of both the CPU and the central bus, the function of handling some number of modem channels is moved out to an I/O concentrator called a LAT (local area translator) in DECspeak and a Telnet server in UNIX systems. This device will handle data streams for 8 to 32 terminals, vastly reducing the interrupt rate to the host. Included in this handling is the first-order data filtering, which would otherwise become yet another burden for the host. Since a process can change the input "filter" to suit its needs, the table which describes the input processing rules for each process must be visible to both the host CPU and the concentrator. While it would be possible to download tables to the concentrator every time they changed, a far less expensive method is to share that structure along with all of the I/O queues in the host's primary memory. Here is yet one more example of shared data in simultaneous multiprocessing. Whenever changeable data is shared, there is always the problem of preventing simultaneous users from getting or creating scrambled data. This is the *synchronization* problem discussed in Section 3.4 on page 142.

The description of the connection sounds very much like a conventional phone call. I dial, you pick up, we talk. Things need not remain quite this neat. Your shell spawns processes. Most shell commands do precisely that. Some of these processes may spawn still others. Unless the command that you type otherwise redirects input or output, by default these child processes will use that same terminal. Were you to create multiple processes which run concurrently, the output from all of them would appear on your terminal (possibly with a block of characters from one process followed by a block of characters from another). You have probably seen this happen if you receive mail (one process) while editing (another process). Given your ability to sort out the sense of such interleaved messages, no great harm and some benefit results from this sharing of the output screen. Input is entirely different. If all those processes connect to one terminal, they would all be capable of taking the input characters that you type. The characters are lined up in a single queue, ready to be taken first come, first serve. There is no way to tell which of your processes would take which characters. Since all of them are sharing the same `stdin`, the next to run will get whatever it chooses to read. Disaster awaits. There has to be some way to make things more predictable. Three choices present themselves:

- The simplest solution is to let the little kids go first. Most often, processes which create other processes simply suspend themselves until the child process has finished. While sitting in the *wait* queue, they take no input and generate no output.
- The second choice is to redirect the child process to take its input from some other source. Obviously, to do that, suitable file input must exist, so redirection is not always possible.
- A last, considerably more complex, and increasingly popular option is to use some kind of windowing program (e.g., Macintosh or X-windows), which allows the

terminal to act like two or more virtual terminals, one of which is connected to each process *which chooses to appear as an independent interactive application.* For programs which so choose, program input and output are directed to the correct window-dependent destination while keyboard input goes to the *current* (user-selected) window, of which at any moment there is only one.

The absence of a direct connection between your terminal and your current process(es) mirrors playing telephone tag with both parties talking to answering machines and responding to necessarily dated messages left thereon. Both you and your process communicate by stashing your outputs in system buffers. As your terminal becomes ready to take another character, the system delivers one to it; as your process gets ready to accept input, the system provides it from the buffer. This buffering certainly has some very desirable features from both perspectives. It provides a comfortable and resilient link between transactions going on at very different rates. But it means that the routine which deals with the terminals (the lower half of the driver) is only weakly coupled to the routine which deals with the user processes (the upper half of the driver). Sometimes the two routines must synchronize their actions, a general, nontrivial problem which we addressed in Section 3.4. Let us continue with protocols and choices in handling terminal I/O. Figure 7.2 is a simplified diagram of the UNIX terminal routines.

The first question that we must address is when to echo characters. While many users think of themselves as "typing to the screen," what actually appears on the screen is the host's echo of what it received or, sometimes, its response to that input. Should characters be echoed upon receipt as shown in Figure 7.2, or should the echo originate in the *terminal read routines* and appear on screen as the process actually uses the characters? Different operating systems have different answers to this question. Immediate echo allows the user to see what he or she is typing, but it means that the image on the screen may be a confusing mixture of input characters and output characters. Echoing when the program accepts the characters produces a better final result on the screen but requires the user who types ahead to be able to type without seeing the results. UNIX generally echoes characters as they are typed; VAX/VMS generally echoes them as they are used. Both sometimes do not echo them. Let us consider some reasons not to echo what is typed.

In most applications, characters are not transferred to a user process until a <CR> has been typed on the terminal. This allows the user to make changes in the line before giving it to the program, and it frees the program from dealing with the common line-editing functions. However, that means that the keyboard routine must recognize and respond to special characters. For example, if the character is a *delete*, the keyboard routine removes the previous character from its buffer and typically inserts the three characters *backspace-space-backspace* into the output buffer to erase the previous character on the screen. Each time the keyboard routine takes a character from the UART, it checks to see if the character has some special meaning. If not, it simply inserts the character into a buffer, and also (in UNIX) inserts it into an output buffer to be echoed.

For terminal I/O, it is usually the case that the input and output are streams of lines, where a line is a stream of bytes terminated with <CR><LF>. It is natural to set

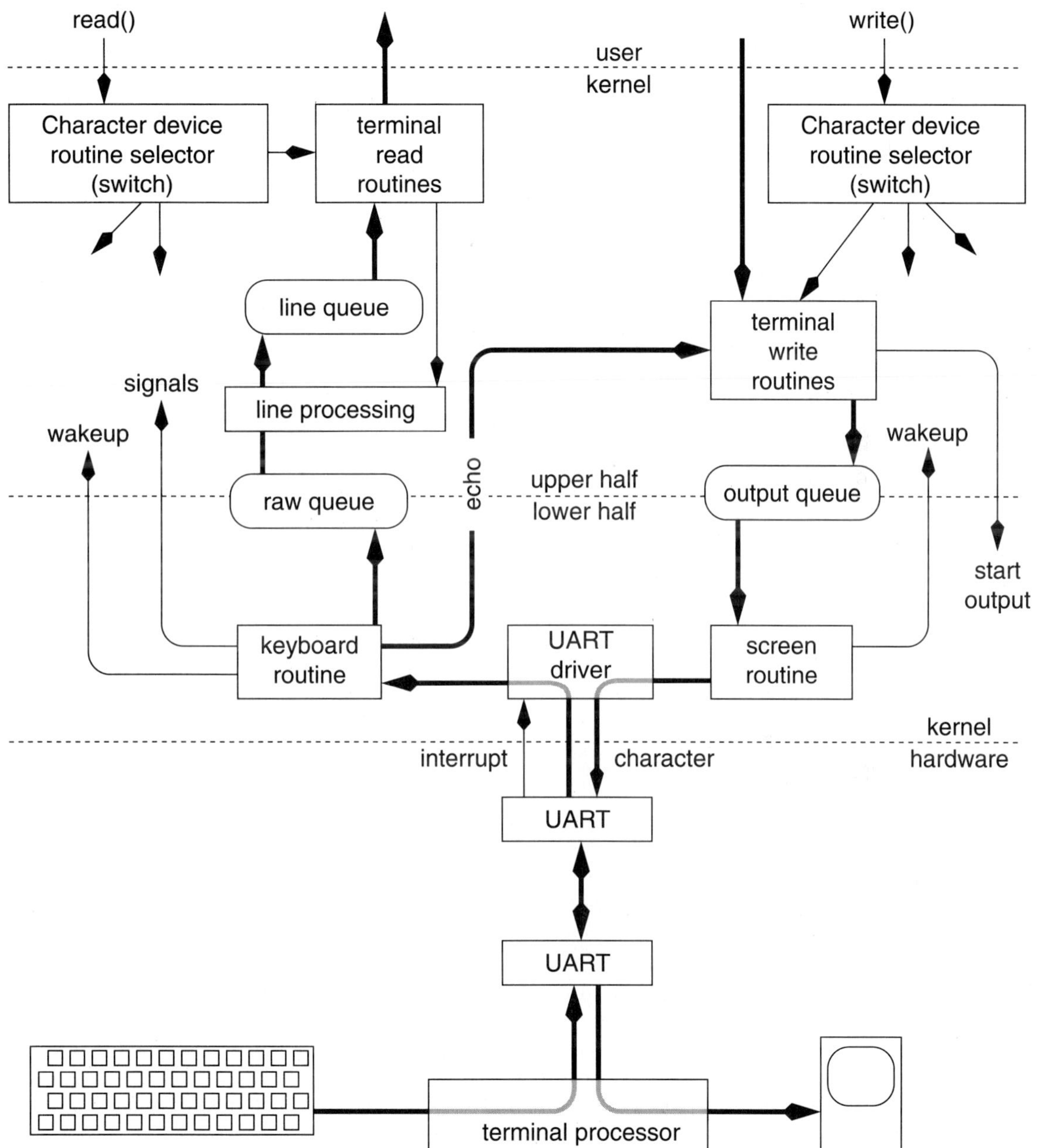

FIGURE 7.2 Flow of characters through the UNIX terminal I/O routines. The bold lines show the flow of characters. Lines of lighter strength show the flow of other signals.

up the input queues to handle such line oriented data. With many terminals delivering streams of data rather lethargically to a variety of applications, a reasonable structure for the buffers is a linked list of line buffers reminiscent of Figure 3.6. In UNIX, the length of each buffer is 64 bytes, but the buffers can be linked to make lines of any size. Some other operating systems, such as VAX/VMS, set limits on any single line. At the start of a line, the data receiver acquires a buffer from a system freelist. When the buffer is filled (or the line is finished), the buffer is requeued, this time on the appropriate transmission queue. The rules for input (which can be changed by the application) usually specify that the buffer is not queued until it holds a line. For output, that would be unsatisfactory. Users want to see the characters that they are typing as fast as they are typing them. Since typing more than 2 char/s is rather exceptional speed, it is not much of a burden to meet that requirement. However, to do it requires that the terminal write routines must enqueue any partially full output buffer only a fraction of a second after its first character is entered. This would seem to eat up buffers at a furious rate, but a buffer that is queued on the output queue will very shortly be emptied and put back on the freelist. By sharing many small buffers among all interactive programs, a reasonably efficient allocation of a small piece of memory is obtained.

When a process uses the `read()` system call to obtain characters from the terminal, it can specify the number of characters it wants, but it will not be given more than a line at a time, and they won't be transferred until the user has typed *newline* (i.e., carriage return) to end the line. If the line is already in the line buffer when the `read()` call occurs, the terminal read routine in the kernel will simply take characters from the line buffer until it has enough. If it empties the buffer, it will call for more from the *raw queue* and if necessary suspend the process until they arrive. The `read()` concludes when all of the characters requested have been copied into the user's buffer (which was specified in the system call). Control is returned to the user program.

The keyboard interrupt routine scans for certain other special characters in addition to *delete* and *newline*. Operating systems almost always define one or more characters to stop a process—a panic button. For example, in UNIX ^C and ^\ are generally so recognized; in VMS ^Y achieves the same end.[1] Should the system detect either of them, the keyboard interrupt routine sends a *signal* to all processes in the group of processes that are children of the shell associated with that terminal. A *signal* has the connotation of an interrupt, but it is implemented in software. It will interrupt only the process it is sent to. Since that process may not be active at the time, signals are sent simply by making an entry in a table. Then when the scheduler decides to run the process, it notices the signal entry, and it simulates an interrupt. This will usually cause the process to be terminated, unless the process has arranged to "catch" the signal and call some special routine of its own.

All of the special characters and most of the actions described above can be modified by the process if it wants to use the terminal in some other way. A modification frequently used by screen editor programs is called *raw mode*. This changes the operation of the keyboard interrupt routine to pass the characters directly from the UART

[1] The circumflex character, ^, implies simultaneous pressing of *control* and the character which follows. These pairs generate the first 32 (nonprinting) ASCII characters by transposing characters 40 to 5F into 00 to 1F on a one-to-one basis.

into buffers on the input queue. It ignores special characters and does not echo anything. The process itself must echo the characters using a write system call. The application also changes the behavior of the terminal read routine so that each character is queued as it is typed.

The terminal output routines are somewhat simpler than the input routines. The terminal write routine transfers characters from the user's buffer to buffers on the output queue. If necessary, it activates the screen routine to start transmission. The lower half sends off a character and returns control. Interrupts from the UART trigger subsequent character transmission until the last character has been sent and the last buffer returned to the freelist. Even here, life is not completely simple. The user program could be trying to write a very large number of characters and consume all of the buffers on the freelist. The terminal write routine must stop transferring characters to the queue and block the process. As characters are sent by the UART, buffers will be freed up and returned to the freelist. Once the freelist becomes long enough, the interrupt routine will wake up the blocked process, and it can then continue transferring characters.

We have skipped over many of the complexities of UNIX. UNIX terminal I/O routines recognize many more special characters and have many more options and additional queues. For the details see [Bach, 86] and [Leffler, 89]. Our objective is to illustrate how the upper routines communicate with the lower routines. In most cases, the only communication is through changes to data structures in the kernel. The upper and lower routines are asynchronous. Neither can tell exactly when the other will execute, and neither cares. However, both count on the coherence of the queues. It is quite possible for an interrupt to occur while one of the terminal routines is modifying a queue. Guaranteeing that all users of a common queue always find it coherent is a critical hardware-dependent problem which must be solved. We wrestled with that important subject in Section 3.3.5 on page 137.

Now we should look at the other principal I/O scenario, disk I/O.

7.2.2 Disk I/O

Terminal and printer I/O are inherently rather simple. Apart from a smattering of special characters which induce other well-defined transactions, delivery of individual bytes from a known source to a known destination constitutes the activity. The user is generally in the loop so that there is an excellent opportunity to pick up and correct erroneous transmissions. Disk I/O is inherently more complex and, in opportunities to destroy data, far more dangerous. Disks are file systems—large numbers of files with a complex hierarchy of indices into the system. Files range in length from a few bytes to many millions of bytes, a range of 6 or 7 orders of magnitude. Disk files are supposed to be accessible in quasi-random fashion with rapid access and extremely high reliability and security. What you wrote to disk is there and will be there when you read it next week. These expectations are to be met using a data-recording mechanism that is inherently noisy and of modest reliability driven by a system which occasionally crashes, trashing data that was supposed to be sent out to disk. Tough problem. Not entirely solved yet, though great progress has been made and is continuing to be made. In Chapter 8, we delve into the issues of speed and reliability. Here we wish to look briefly at the system services which support disk transactions. In the next subsection, we will open a few of the mysteries of the file system to see how to go from a program's system request for bytes n to n + m from file *filereference* to having those bytes in the proper place in memory.

Having carried on for a whole paragraph about how different terminal I/O is from disk I/O, we must confess that UNIX (and VMS for that matter) treat both of them as "files." Whatever a file is, terminals and disks are represented to the user as files. UNIX makes it so easy to redirect `stdin` and `stdout` from a terminal to a disk file that the user might well conclude that there is nothing to it. They are of course different. You cannot read what you wrote to the terminal but you certainly can recover what you wrote to disk. But at the upper level, the level a user sees, files are streams of bytes that can be handled by a simple and small vocabulary of commands. What differentiates the terminal from the disk file can be found mostly in the lower halves of their respective drivers.

What commands are in the "simple and small vocabulary"? Seven in all:

- open   Opens a file for Read, Write, or Read & Write
- creat   Empties old file (length = 0) or opens a new one for R, W, or R&W
- close   Disconnects a file from the program
- read   Reads N bytes from an open file starting at the current position
- write   Writes N bytes into an open file starting at the current position
- unlink   Removes a file from the current directory (file vanishes if last link)
- lseek   Moves the current position to any valid position within an open file

C's libraries include many function calls which provide higher level access to files, but these are the essential commands from which they are built. To the extent that the file device can respond to these commands—*creat*, *unlink*, and *lseek* would be inapplicable to the terminal—all the devices can be approached with this set of commands. Only those who write the lower half of a particular device driver need be concerned directly with device mechanics and interfaces.

While these seven commands serve to manipulate files, they do not satisfy all needs. For example, in shared database systems, one user must be able to lock files to prevent simultaneous modification or the acquisition of incoherent data by other users. This is another of the "synchronization" problems that abound in shared systems. In large shared-data systems, the processes which share the data may be distributed over several hosts and the disk drives on which the data lies may reside on yet other hosts. Since hosts occasionally crash or go off the air, managing a lock on such a multihost system is an *interesting* design problem. See in particular [Snaman, 87]. Some very different solutions have emerged.

It is worthwhile in our present context to look at what happens to a process when it attempts a lock and finds it busy. In UNIX, one uses the function `lockf()` to ask for exclusive access to a file or part thereof. This is an I/O request and true to its basic principles, UNIX does synchronous I/O. Accordingly, a process gets the lock or it gets blocked. As you can infer from Figure 3.4, in our machine, this will require the `lockf()` function to trap into the kernel at IL1 and if the lock is not granted, it will call the SLEEP function in the kernel, trapping into IL2, where a context switch will be executed. When the lock is returned, the process is awakened and finds itself holding the lock. Since file transactions tend to be very slow in busy systems—a modest access may have a latency of as much as a second—the nap may be a long one in computer cycles.

UNIX and VMS both hide the device structure from the user. While the user has every reason to think of a file according to its HLL data structure, in UNIX, the underlying structure is always just a string of bytes. A long file is a long string of bytes. The low-level commands work with byte strings; the high-level library functions, such as `fscanf()`, take that stream, chop it up according to a format specification, and then deliver it to the indicated program variables (storage space). When the file is resident on disk, it is not organized either as bytes or data types. A disk could be considered to be simply an orderly arrangement of *blocks*. A block is an integer number, often 1, of the disk's basic unit—a sector. (See Appendix III.) Blocks are physically contiguous groupings of sectors. They are set up when the disk is formatted and remain immutable until the disk is reformatted. Single disk drives, comprising any number of platters, may be divided into logically isolated, contiguous groupings of blocks called *partitions*. The block sizes of the different partitions need not be the same. No file on disk is shorter than a block. Longer files will be distributed over several or many blocks; in most systems these blocks are scattered in somewhat haphazard fashion around the disk.

As you can see by the commands above, none of this is recognized by HLL commands, or even the low-level HLL commands. A program can `lseek` to any byte in the entire file and then execute a `read` or `write` of any length. In fact, it can `lseek` to bytes that are not yet within the file and start to write there. The system must accommodate this disparity in views of a file. First, there must be some way for the `lseek` command to locate the correct sector in the file's assortment of sectors. Then the `read` or `write` must be able to track from there to other sectors as necessary, or, in the case of a `write`, it must be able to add sectors at the end of the file to accommodate file extension. Because disk data is encoded for error correction over a whole sector, all underlying transfers must be by whole sector. If blocks are bigger than a sector, the system generally requires all actual transfers to be by block. Since there is no obligation on the user to deal in blocks—generally, the program is blissfully unaware of such structure—the system must provide a buffering mechanism. If the user does a `read()` system call, the kernel reads one or more blocks from the disk into its own buffers, and then copies the requested number of bytes, starting from the current file pointer, into the user's memory space. Writes are similarly unaligned. The byte stream to be written is contained within blocks currently in the system buffer. There is no reason for the data in buffer to align with the block structure on disk. To do a write, the blocks spanning the data in buffer first must be read into system memory, modified, and only then copied out.

This sounds inefficient, but it is not only necessary, it can be turned to advantage. Buffering gives the system a chance to run a *buffer cache*. The buffers are, as usual, a general system resource. They are inevitably an integral number of blocks long, usually 1. The kernel can keep a fairly large number of these buffers in its memory area, and it remembers which disk blocks they contain. Whenever a disk block is requested, the kernel first looks in this buffer cache, and if it finds the block there, there is no need to read from the disk. Since the UNIX file system tends to read certain disk blocks over and over again (the directories and the file block indexes), this buffer cache can significantly increase performance. In addition, the kernel sometimes guesses which block will be needed next and reads it into the buffer cache. Since there is usually a lot of coherence to a single file, reading an extra block or two is almost free. It is likely to lie physically right next to the block just read and the read head is there already. If the system guesses correctly, the program will get its data immediately. If not, the data in the buffer will eventually be replaced with something else, the dwell time being determined by the rate at which the running processes develop demand for free buffers. Both UNIX and VMS arrange for some disk caching. Some new disk servers provide additional caching in their own private memories, a form of *ramdisk*. While the data cached in this private memory still must be copied into the central memory to carry out the disk request, it eliminates the mechanical delays (tens of milliseconds) that are such a large fraction of I/O latency. On a busy disk, the server disk cache can yield rather remarkable gains in performance.

Even though I/O appears to be synchronous to the user process, it is actually asynchronous in the kernel. On a `read()`, the process will be blocked while the several transactions which comprise a read are carried out. In another view of asynchronism, you can think of asynchronism as having your reads being carried out during someone else's run time. In the case of writing to disk, the situation is more complex. If the system allows asynchronous writes, the user process may be allowed to continue once the data has been copied into a kernel buffer. Thus, the only thing that is going to prevent continuation is a shortage of buffers. The actual write to the disk could be delayed for a long time, and there is no way for the user program to determine when it happens. This can cause problems for programs which are concerned with the consistency of the data on disk and in memory. Should a much-delayed write fail, it will be reported back through `stderr`.

It is possible for programs to circumvent some parts of the file system and not use the buffer cache. In some sense, such a program accesses the disk directly with read and write system calls. This is done by opening what is called the *raw* disk device in UNIX. The system calls are identical with the exception of the name used to reference the *disk-as-file* in contrast to a *file on a disk*. The system recognizes this name. Only a process with very special privilege will be allowed to mention this ineffable name, but if you have those rights, you get access to the full disk as is and where is with no restrictions. Raw disk data is transferred directly between the disk and the user's memory buffer, rather than a queue of kernel buffers. In this mode, the *device* is represented simply as a continuous stream of bytes without other structure. You might wonder which process(es) would get the privilege to open a whole disk and why it would want to intrude into a disk without the benefit of the file structure. One obvious application would be to *create* the file structure. Disk drives are usually partitioned into separate logical units, each of which has its own structure. Keys to this structure reside in tables on the boot disk, but much of the data for each partition resides on the disk in the partition itself. It follows that one must have raw access permission to create this partition data. Another very important reason to "go raw" is if the file structure has become damaged. It is often possible to reconstruct all or at least most of the file structure by scanning the raw disk. Another similar reconstruction that is done periodically is defragmentation. Normally, this is done immediately after backup. It is an effort to accomplish two desirable and related objectives:

- to place all of the blocks of each file in contiguous sectors on disk to speed up multi-block transfers
- to place all of the free sectors (in some sense, the *file of free sectors*) in a single contiguous array to allow the allocation of substantial helpings of contiguous sectors for new files and for file extension

After we have gone through a conventional UNIX file system, we will spend a bit of time on an alternative system (for UNIX) which does defragmentation as needed while all of the other processes are happily doing *apparently* conventional I/O.

Both raw and buffered transfers are necessarily asynchronous at system level. In the buffered case, both the driver software and the buffers are part of the ever-present kernel; with *raw* mode, the buffer file is in the user space. Since user processes are blocked during disk transfers and may even be swapped out of memory, if raw transfers are being mixed with normal ones, the kernel has to ensure that the user buffer area stays in memory throughout the disk transfer.

Figure 7.3 provides an overview of the principal layers for disk I/O in a typical small UNIX system. In scanning that figure start by recalling that the two basic calls for any file transfer are `read()` and `write()`, which specify

- a *file descriptor* which specifies the file index and an associated file pointer
- a (user-space) buffer from which to take or in which to put the data
- the number of bytes to transfer

From the program's point of view, the file is a stream of bytes. All of the knowledge of actual disk structure which will be needed to extract that byte stream is handled by the system. That potentially very complex extraction problem is transparent to the user. All requests are for contiguous data, and any such request can be broken down into a series of requests for logically sequential blocks on disk. The logic of their sequentiality is considerably different for raw and buffered I/O because raw I/O treats the disk as a linear array of sectors while the buffered I/O views the disk as an assembly of files indexed by a hierarchical file system (also on disk). Figure 7.3 shows the I/O request going to the left if the raw name was used and to the right if a buffered-file name was used. Consider the right branch. Each individual buffered request will be turned into n requests for blocks, where the blocks will include the bytes requested and usually a bit of overrun on one or both sides. To get the block numbers, the *buffer-cache routines* start with the index. To allow large files with modest directory overhead, the directory system is hierarchical. We will provide details of the UNIX directory system in the next section, but just the fact that UNIX has indexes whose entries point at other sub-indexes says that acquiring one block of data can require the acquisition of

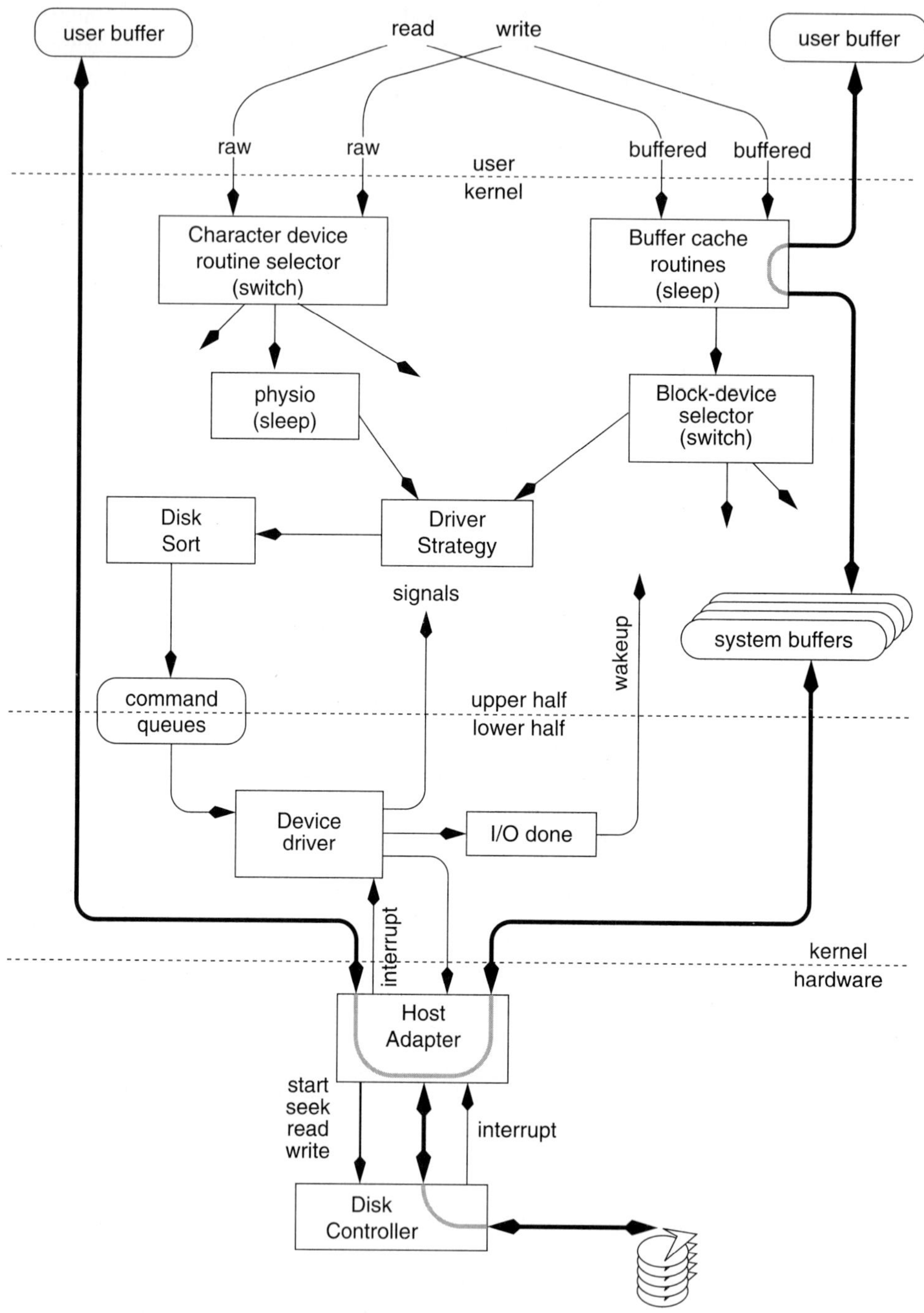

FIGURE 7.3 Command flow and data flow in the UNIX disk I/O routines. The bold lines show the flow of data to and from the disk. Lines of lighter strength show the flow of commands and signals.

several blocks of index. Locality of reference implies that caching indexes can be even more profitable than caching data blocks. The I/O system can now translate the original request into specific disk blocks to be read. Once this translation of bytes requested to blocks to be transferred has been accomplished, the block numbers are passed, one or two at a time, to the disk *strategy* routine. Once those few are passed, *buffer-cache* calls `iowait()` which in turn calls `sleep()`. Accordingly, the UNIX kernel breaks a long request for buffered input into a series of short requests which may well—in fact, most likely will—be interleaved with requests from other processes.

When the *buffer-cache routines* are determining the block numbers on a `read`, they often *look ahead* under the assumption that if you have read from *here* to *there*, you are quite likely to read from *there* to a bit further on. UNIX typically reads one block ahead. That little bit of anticipation can often prevent a considerable delay and several context switches. That cannot be done on writes, quite obviously; it is impossible to anticipate what the data will be. Writes present yet another problem. The partial blocks that are likely at the two ends cannot be handled directly at the disk. On disk, a block is a coherent whole. It includes not only the owner's data but also critically important encoding that becomes an integral part of the block. If there is a partial block to be written at either end, the whole block at that end must first be read, decoded, error-corrected, and written into a system buffer. Then the new data is copied into that same buffer. Finally, the whole block is copied back to disk, being encoded on the way back. Figure III.6 on page 575 shows this transformation. That appendix gives a brief introduction to the physical operation of disk drives.

While what we have just written focused on the *buffer-cache* operation, a similar scheme goes on in the *physio* routine on the left. Everything must still be done in whole blocks, but in the absence of buffers, look-ahead reading is not possible. Two tasks that are unique to the left path are that *physio* must mark the user's buffer as unswappable and it must convert the user's buffer's *virtual address* to *physical addresses* for the *host adapter* to use. It also breaks up long requests to limit the maximum individual transfer, typically to 64 KB.

The *strategy* routine receives single-block requests from the buffered side. *Strategy* too has a translation task. In this case, it must go from logical sector numbers to physical sector numbers. Not only can disks be divided logically into several independent "disks" (called *partitioning*), but even if the disk is a single logical structure, the files are generally not arranged contiguously. Essentially *strategy* must unshuffle the deck. It gets its name because what it is doing is specific to each disk. *Strategy* passes its list of physical sectors to *sort*, which attempts to order the stream of requests in an optimal manner. The reason for the sort is that moving the heads on a disk from track to track takes a long time. If each disk request were serviced in the order received, most I/O time would be spent moving heads back and forth. Instead, *sort* attempts to order them so that the next request to be taken is close to the current position of the heads. Strictly taking the closest one each time is usually not a good algorithm, because it results in the heads staying near the middle of the disks, delaying unfairly requests for tracks near the edge. The algorithm used by the UNIX disk sort routine called *C-scan* is not unlike your TV's sweep. It moves the heads steadily in one direction across the surface of the disks, taking the nearest request in the direction that it is moving. When it reaches the end, it returns immediately to the other edge. Although this *sort* routine is provided in the UNIX kernel, each device driver can use any method it wants to order its requests, and other algorithms are sometimes used. See Chapter 12 in [Deitel, 83] for other disk-scheduling algorithms.

If the device driver (lower half) is idle (empty queue), the strategy routine wakes it up, but all transfers between disk and driver are controlled by the interrupt routines. Usually a transfer consists of two steps: a seek to move the heads to the correct track, and the actual transfer of the data between memory and disk. The average seek takes about 10 ms, but once data starts streaming off a modern hard drive, the data rates can tax even the best integrated circuits. It is usually inefficient to have the central processor handle the individual bytes. Even on very small, single-user microprocessor systems, the transfer of data is usually done by a DMA controller (see Figure 1.1 and Figure 7.3). In its basic configuration, a DMA controller is a rather simple-minded finite-state machine that increments addresses and decrements a transfer count to move a single block of data between disk controller and memory. When the count gets to 0, it issues an interrupt to the host and stops. That interrupt brings up the driver, which checks that the transfer was successful, wakes up the process that requested it, and starts the next transfer on the disk queue.

Notice that the disk routines can be divided into upper and lower halves, just as the terminal routines could, and the two halves operate asynchronously. In most cases, they communicate only through shared data structures, such as the command queue. As in the case of the terminal routines, the lower half of the disk driver could be executed on another processor which shares the memory. Mainframe computers normally do their I/O operations through separate processors, which IBM calls *channels*. They can significantly reduce the number of interrupts to the CPU and allow it to devote more time to user processes. In fact, one can move all of the device-specific functions off the host and onto sophisticated device controllers. In Figure 7.3, that would mean that everything from *Driver Strategy* on down would be part of the device controller. The host routines can then treat files logically or even as simple byte streams. These sophisticated controllers are often as computationally proficient, at least at integer arithmetic, as the hosts they serve. They may be endowed with considerable disk-caching capability and given the task of controlling access, optimizing search sequences, distributing files over an array of disk drives, and even maintaining redundant backups. These topics form a central theme in Chapter 8, which focuses on physical limits to the speed of I/O operations. At this stage, however, we want to complete the system's view of I/O. To that end, let us look at how files are organized on disk. We begin with *directories*.

7.2.3 Directories in UNIX

In the best of worlds, all files would be contiguous. If such a state could be preserved, a file could be specified entirely by its starting point and length. Such a system of perfection can be maintained at considerable cost in flexibility by imposing two rules for writing files:

- Upon opening a file for WRITE, that file preempts the entire length of the longest string of contiguous free blocks on the disk. (Upon closing the file, any remaining blocks are released.) Since this *all-of-the-largest* algorithm is very restrictive if there is only one open area (e.g., an empty disk), an interactive alternative has the application specify the size of the desired file. The system can then select the smallest contiguous region which can accommodate the request.
- If the file being written grows to exceed the blocks it has preempted, the WRITE (and generally the program doing it) must be terminated.

If the system is willing to live with these rules, some important benefits are obtained. These include:

- a very low-cost and simple file directory
- very fast and very predictable data transfer rates
- a higher degree of recoverability if the file directory is destroyed or damaged

Some simple systems have adopted these rules—for example, UCSD's Pascal environment for the Apple II and the PDP-11's RT-11 operating system—and they are sometimes obligatory in real-time operating systems where transfer speed and predictability are so important. In such a system, the user or system manager must *crunch* the disk reasonably frequently to move the scattered groups of free blocks into a single, contiguous unit. Inevitably, doing this requires that the disk unit be taken off line.

Most operating systems do not find the constraints listed above acceptable, even if the benefits are real and desirable. Instead, they use what you would now recognize as a virtual memory system where the application sees a file as a contiguous record of bytes while the I/O system must deal with files comprised of blocks arranged in various degrees of disorder. Address translation is required, and just as with the TLB, caching such translations for frequently referenced blocks can be quite advantageous. However, one critical difference between primary and secondary memory systems persists. Primary memory provides random access; most secondary memory is essentially serial. Accordingly, unlike paged virtual memory, there is considerable benefit to keeping disk files compact and sequential.

Files that are off line can be and often are put in a pristine state, but once the file system is on line and some shuffling of the deck is allowed through writes and rewrites, the law of ever increasing entropy guarantees that a file's blocks will become scattered about the disk, or *fragmented.* Allowing fragmented files requires that the disk directory keep track of where each block of a given file currently resides. Easy rearrangement generally requires a fixed, relatively small block size. Even such inherently continuous media as tape are divided rather arbitrarily into blocks of small size. Since disks are inherently divided into *cylinders* containing some small number of *sectors* of fixed length, one normally chooses a block comprising a small, fixed number of sectors, generally with the small number being commensurate with the number of sectors in a cylinder. Two factors restrict the block size to a small number of sectors:

- Since the number of sectors per cylinder can increase slightly from the inner to the outer cylinders, keeping the number of sectors in a block commensurate with the number of sectors in a cylinder requires the block size to be a very small integer.
- Many files tend to be short, under 1 KB. Accordingly, if the minimum size of a block is much larger than the typical small file, substantial amounts of disk space will be wasted (*internal fragmentation*).

Limiting a block to something between 0.5 and 4 KB means that files of many megabytes now begin to look like a substantial cataloging problem. A 1-MB file of 1-KB blocks will require the cataloging of 1024 block pointers. Once again, to avoid wasting space for cataloging small files, we must have a cataloging system which apportions space for these block indices only as needed. Since files can grow or shrink, the apportionment must be both adaptable and smooth. It should also be efficient. Let us consider how UNIX achieves adaptability, smoothness, and efficiency in its file system.

A file has several attributes, including:

- file type
- date of creation and of last modification
- date of last read
- length of the file in bytes
- ownership
- access privileges
- number of directory entries referencing this file
- index to the blocks

Generally, the *name* is the item that programs use to gain access to the index and the other specific information. A program will issue the `open(char *filename,...)` command to open an extant file. The file may be opened for READ, WRITE, or READ&WRITE. The program can then `lseek()` to any point in the file without worrying about how to get there. This fits UNIX's philosophy that all files are simply streams of bytes.

The name is a directory entry. Along with the name, the file entry includes a file ID which points to the file's attribute table. UNIX allows multiple names in different directories to reference a single file simply by having the same ID. When a user deletes a file, his or her directory entry is deleted and UNIX decrements the count of directory entries referencing the file. When that count gets to 0, the file is actually deleted. A directory is simply a structured file of directory entries. (*Structure* should sound incompatible with the philosophy that all files are simply streams of bytes, but in the same sense, one can describe all literature as ergodic, stochastic streams of characters. The structure to such streams is in the eye of the beholder. In most cases, the brain behind the eye requires remarkably deep context to see the structure. Directories are much simpler.) Directories are seldom so long that how you search them is much of an issue.

Thus, when you issue the `open()`, the file system will search your current directory (or a substituted list of other directories) to see if that name can be found in any of the entries. (`ls` in UNIX or `DIR` in VMS will scan down the same list and deliver all the names to the designated output.) Let us follow down the system's response to the user's request as if the directory files are already in memory, ready for the system to treat as structured data. (Were any missing, the memory manager would recognize that fact and order that the missing directories be brought into memory.) The file manager searches each *filename* element in the list until it gets a match or gets to the end of its search list. Let us presume a hit.

Once a match is found, the system can access the *index table* or *inode*, which will contain the data listed above. Our immediate interests are the last two items in the list: the length and the index. The index is a small structure containing the disk locations of 13 blocks. An entry can also be a *null* location, indicating that there is nothing stored there. (A file's length can include blocks not yet written—a hole in the middle of the file—but the parsimonious file system does not assign disk space to nothing.) The first 10 of the entries in the inode index locate blocks of the file itself. Then next three locate, in order: a block of pointers to blocks of the file itself; a block of pointers to blocks of pointers to blocks of the file itself; a block of pointers to blocks of pointers to blocks of pointers to blocks of the file itself. A picture, obviously in order, is provided in Figure 7.4.

It is important to see how the file system scales to discover what the maximum-size file would be. After all, one of the objectives was to put no practical limit on the maximum file size. As you can see in Figure 7.4, if a block contains B bytes and it takes A bytes to specify a block location, so that a block of pointers can specify I = B/A more blocks, then our inode system can specify a total of

$$T = (10 + I + I^2 + I^3)B \text{ bytes}$$

It is clear that very large files will require larger block sizes, with $T \approx B^4/A^3$ as I gets large. A modest example would be a 300-MB disk with sectors of 512 bytes. Thus, there are 600K sectors requiring an address space of no less than 20 bits. If we used a word (32 bits) as our block address, a block of addresses can reference 128 blocks, giving a maximum file size of 1 GB, well in excess of the whole disk. If we went to four sectors per block, keeping our disk address a word, we get the prodigious maximum file size of 2^{38} or 256 GB. The principal problem with supporting this huge span is that the most common file is much less than one such block. As the blocks get large, the small files waste a lot of space. To the end of allowing the tailoring of the block size to the special needs of different applications, UNIX allows the system manager to set the block size (in units of sectors) for each partition. Note that if you want to include files longer than 4 G sectors, the system must allow file pointers longer than the usual 32 bits.

Note what the burden is to read a random block from the file of Figure 7.4. If the file is short and the inode index already in memory, one block is obtained with a read of one block—100 percent efficiency. If no inodes from the disk are in memory, that one-block read becomes a lot more painful. The steps include:

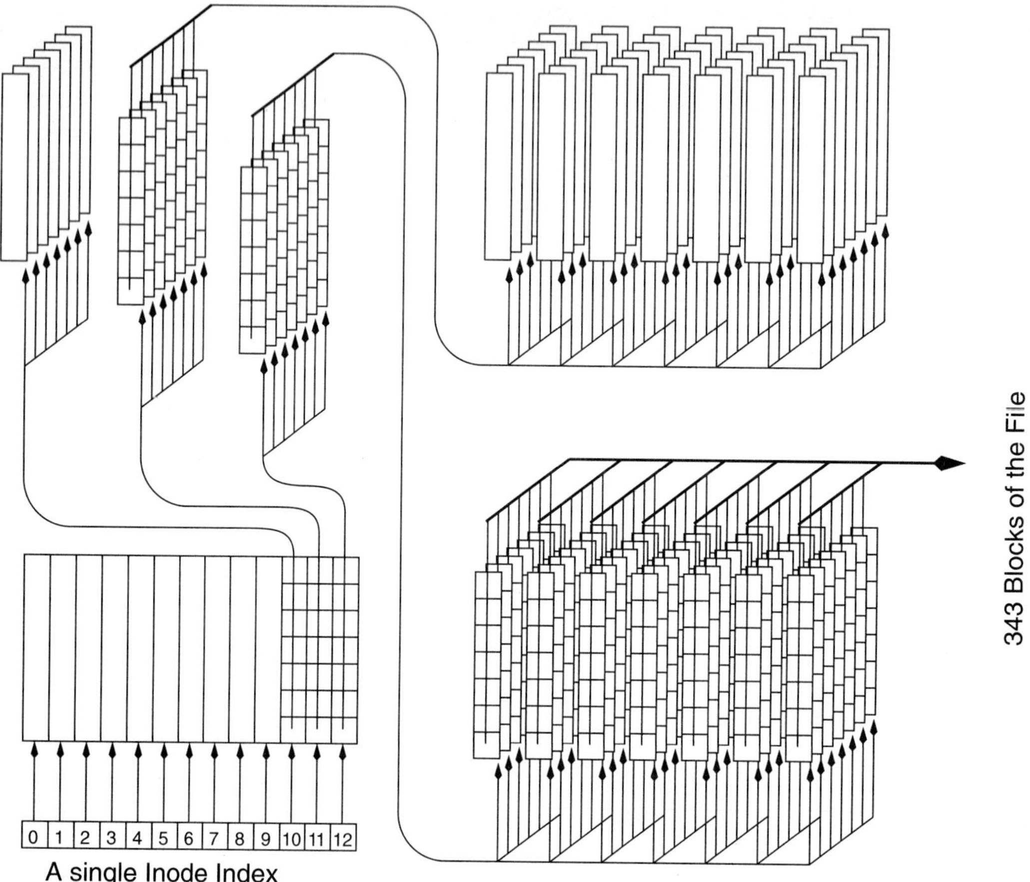

FIGURE 7.4 The expansion of an inode index. A single index, containing 13 block pointers, is the key to any whole file. The first 10 entries in the inode point at blocks of the file. These are shown in the figure as clear rectangles. The last three entries also point to blocks, but these blocks contain only pointers to other blocks. Each block of pointers is shown broken up into seven squares, each containing the location of another block. Thus, pointer10 points at a single block containing pointers to 7 more blocks of the file. At this point, 17 blocks of file have been specified. Pointer 11 points at a block containing pointers to 7 blocks but with each block divided up to contain pointers to 7 more. Thus, 11 provides doubly indirect access to 49 blocks of the object file. Now the total is 66 blocks. Finally, pointer 12 provides access to 343 blocks through triple indirection. The total here would be 409.

- a read of the inode for the directory
- a read of the directory
- a read of the inode for the file
- a read of the file

If all of these are one-block reads, reading the single-block file required four separate reads. Now we are down to 25 percent efficiency. That sounds bad—it is—but it gets worse when you consider that disks are at their very worst when asked to read single blocks.

The problem, which we expand upon in Chapter 8, is that it takes a disk a very long time to get to the start of a block and almost no time to read or write it. Getting to the beginning is called *seeking*. It is limited by how large an acceleration one may apply to the disk head. This is a mechanical constraint on a macroscopic object. For this reason, there has been only modest progress in reducing seek times in the 30+ years since IBM introduced the Mother of All Disk Drives. Today, it takes a typical drive roughly 10 ms to do the average random seek. One should compare that time with current processor speeds of 10 to 100 MIPS. One seek is taking between 100,000 and 1,000,000 instruction times! Once the head reaches the beginning of the block, the data rate can challenge the very best of electronic circuits. The reason for this wide disparity is that bit densities can be improved with techniques of miniaturization similar to those which have proven so remarkably effective in integrated circuits. Disk drives also may be paralleled to even further enhance the data rates. Seeks, however, remain, and while seeking, no matter how fast the potential data rate, nothing is being transferred. Limiting the number of seeks per transaction is of vital importance. As we shall see, it is one of the areas where there is great potential for increasing disk system performance.

Dynamic growth is relatively easy with a file system like this. One of the structures on the disk is the array of free blocks. To keep this potentially immense list compact, Berkeley UNIX stores the map of free blocks as a bit array at a known location on the disk; AT&T UNIX uses a linked list of free blocks. Another system structure is a list of free inodes. UNIX puts inodes at known locations on the disk. The file ID identifies the inode which contains the file description. Files begin by acquiring an inode. Files grow by acquiring blocks from the free file; they shrink (or vanish) by adding their blocks to the free file. As files grow by picking blocks from the free file, they become fragmented. Every so often, a disk should be taken off line and defragmented to speed up file transfers. Often this is done at backup time to assure that data will not be lost in defragmentation. Fragmentation is rather like bald tires: The problem grows slowly to a point where it cannot be ignored.

A much more serious problem with this dynamic disk organization involves the differences between the buffer cache and its image on disk. Much of what is buffered is directory and inode data. Since the inodes are modified (updated) while resident in the computer's memory, it is often the case that the inodes on the disk do not correspond to the file blocks on the disk. Systems do crash. Now you really do have a problem. Some systems provide a special emergency shutdown program built into the kernel, which allows the computer operator to attempt to write out the buffer cache *after a crash.* Since software crashes generally result from fatal inconsistencies in the operating-system data, such a recovery requires that the buffer cache be at a known physical address, that the machine be restartable at a recovery routine that is basically independent of the now wounded operating system, and that the cache be checkable for self-consistency before writing it out to disk. Another approach is to mark file blocks themselves so that an after-the-fact scan and recovery are possible. UNIX provides an elaborate program called *fsck* to check the consistency of the file system and attempt to repair it if possible. To minimize the extent of the potential disaster, UNIX automatically updates (or *synchronizes*) the on-disk inodes and directories every 30 s and allows manual updates on demand. The critical records are stored in three different locations on each file partition to provide redundancy. Synchronization requires the system get itself into a fully self-consistent state in which all the I/O requests have been completed and all the inodes and directories have been updated and written out to disk. To get into such a state, all the processes which generate I/O have to be backed into the wait queues and left there until this consistent state has been achieved. Stopping all activity until the ducks get in line eats lots of CPU cycles. That makes it expensive. It is done for the same reason that insurance is purchased—to prevent excessive loss.

A rebuild after a crash is certainly not a trivial or inexpensive activity. It is not unusual to have *fsck* run for 10 to 15 minutes to complete its task in rebuilding the file system to a self-consistent state. That self-consistent state may *not* correspond to the state that the users thought they had just prior to the crash. In fact, it may end up with dangling files (which end up, quaintly, in *lost +found*) and lost data. At worst, it should be close to correct at the time of the last synchronization.

This is a good introduction, but there is lots more. See [Bach, 86], [Leffler, 89], and [McKusick, 84] for more details on the UNIX file system. Try Problem 7.4 to test your understanding of the inode system. File systems for larger computers typically provide additional functions, particularly in supporting database operations. For a description of the record management system in VMS, see [Kenah, 88].

7.2.4 Alternative Organizations of a File System

While UNIX's approach to file organization is global, hierarchical, and delightfully regular to observe, it is by no means a recognized optimum in file design. Several criticisms may be raised about the system. We would include among these:

- cost of the index for long files
- speed of directory searches
- speed of file transfers
- cost of file recovery after a system crash

The indexing cost has to do with the essentially linear structure of the inode index—every block requires a block pointer. If you use little blocks, long files require many pointers; if you use long blocks, short files and the inevitable mismatch between files of arbitrary length and blocks of fixed size will lead to wasted space within the allocated blocks, *internal fragmentation*. The problem is shown in Figure 7.5. A typical sector on a hard disk stores 512 bytes. You may construct blocks of any integral number of contiguous sectors, but blocks in any disk or disk partition are of a fixed size. If you make blocks of one sector, then you have devoted almost 1 percent of your disk to pointers; on the other hand, if you reduce the overhead by going to multisector blocks, you waste space in files much shorter than these larger blocks. An insidious but often unmentioned corollary to the size of the file description is the problem of holding large parts of the file index in memory. If the file descriptions are vast, you will find that:

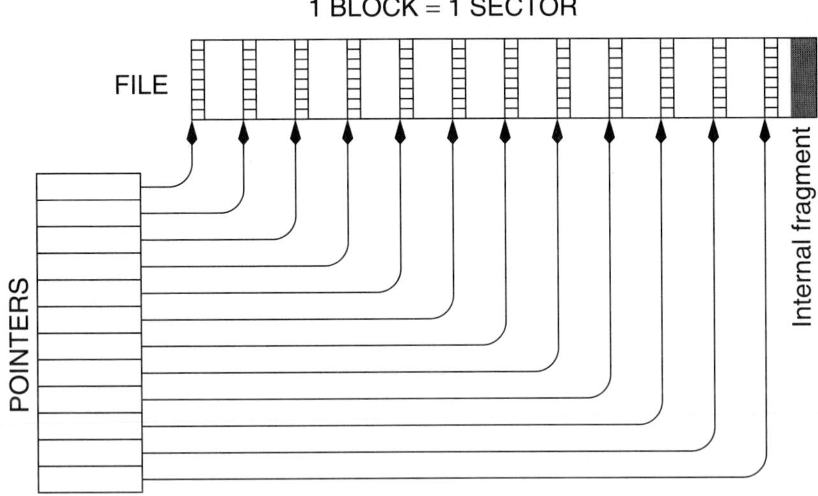

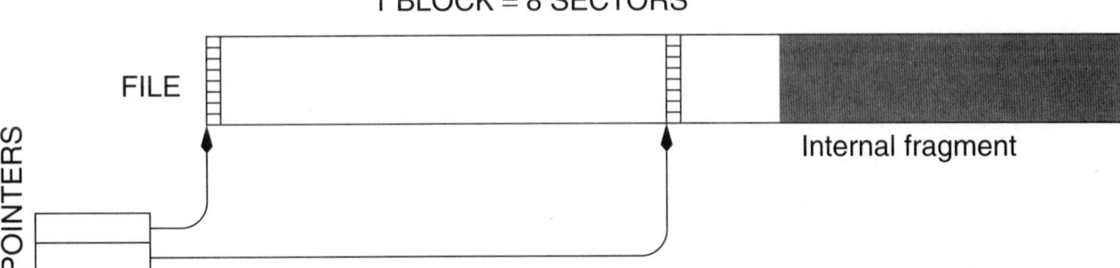

FIGURE 7.5 Consequences of block size on internal fragmentation, number of pointers, and number of headers in a linear growth system such as UNIX. Each block is shown with an identifying header which may be used to reconstruct a damaged file system. The same file is shown distributed over 12 blocks in the upper case and 2 blocks in the lower case.

- If your cache of such descriptors is small, you are spending a large fraction of your I/O effort merely in acquiring and reacquiring the file block directory.
- If your cache of such descriptors is large (to avoid the first problem), then your write-back or synchronization of the cached and disked file directories is too expensive to do often and a lurking disaster if not done often enough.

Finally, there is the issue of recovery. To be sure of getting the whole file system back together when the inevitable system crash fails to return the updated file structure from cache to disk, you would have to store some header information at the beginning of each block. Since this connectivity data would have to sit at the head of every sector but contribute nothing to the data therein (other than some hope for the future), using small block sizes would mean more header. This is shown quite conspicuously in Figure 7.5 Clearly the linear system gets more painful as the file length increases.

In most systems, header data is too expensive. Instead, rather complex reconstruction techniques are employed, and the system lives with the possibility of some loss of the most recent data. What are the alternatives?

The most obvious improvement that can be made is to take advantage of the fact that in any well-run computing system, disks or partitions spend most of their time in a largely defragmented state. (That comment is not true if the disk or partition is almost full and subject to frequent changes. Fragmentation grows rapidly as the almost full disk gets shuffled, a state that is endemic in swap disks and certain other applications.) If you run a fragmentation test on your hard disk, you typically get numbers of 1 percent or less. This means that the longer files are built of a few long strings of contiguous blocks called *extents*. Two major advantages can be obtained from contiguous blocks:

- a drastic reduction in the number of long seeks in reading or writing long files
- a reduction in the number of entries in the inode index

In this section and the next, we take a brief look at two quite different applications of extents in modern file systems and the benefits that obtain from them.

If files can be built of long extents, it is much more economical to store a starting address and a length in sectors than it is to store every sector's address. This type of variable-length block is the standard for the Macintosh hierarchical file system (HFS) [Mac, 86]. In the limit of lengths of 1, it reduces to the inode concept of a linear list of fixed-sized blocks, except that now you need a pair of numbers to describe a block rather than one. In well-defragmented systems, it provides

- faster disk transfers for longer files, both because contiguous files are inherently faster and because the required directory data is more compact
- the ability to use small blocks, with a major benefit in minimizing internal fragmentation, while keeping the size of the directory structure small both in cache and on disk
- reduction in the amount of header information which must be stored to reconstruct a damaged directory

HFS allows a file to be made up of an array of extents, just as UNIX uses an array of block pointers. Thus, a file can be composed of an essentially arbitrary collection of odd-sized extents. There is no practical limit to growth, no external fragmentation, and little internal fragmentation. Any grouping of contiguous sectors from 1 to the maximum length is usable. It is clear at the outset that HFS depends on reasonable disk housekeeping. File fragmentation must be kept low to get much advantage from extents. For badly fragmented files, HFS is no wonder. In an environment where the average extent is but one or two blocks HFS provides only the benefit of the ability to use small blocks to reduce internal fragmentation. But for the usual environment, where disks get defragmented as needed and where disks are kept below 90 percent of capacity, the extent is a better way to describe a file. For a dramatic if somewhat extreme view of the power of the extent at its best, consider the structure of a disk just after formatting. It comprises a root directory, a list of bad sectors, and a list of free sectors. Were we to keep that list in the form of a standard file—neither UNIX nor Macintosh does—we would have a measure of the cost of storing the largest file that the disk drive could hold. If we had a 100-MB disk with a sector of 512 bytes and if there were 0.01 percent bad sectors, then the average free-sector or extent length is 1×10^4 sectors. There would be only 21 extents to describe that list or 42 32-bit words. To describe the same list with an inode structure would require 2×10^5 entries! Not to overstate the case, that huge list of entries is still only 1 percent of the file space. But with applications running tens of megabytes and disk drives commonly holding hundreds or thousands of megabytes, compactness of the file structure is beneficial and speed of file transfer critical to good system performance.

The several developers of UNIX have not been unaware of the original UNIX file system's limitations. In the early '80s at Berkeley, considerable improvements were introduced over the logical but inefficient file system just described. This new system was called the UNIX Fast File System (FFS) [McKusick, 84]. Its principal improvements are:

- Larger blocks are used (typically 8K) with a mechanism to split a block into pieces so that very short files, or the ends of longer ones, can share parts of a block. Without this addition, internal fragmentation with the large block size would waste 46 percent of the disk space in a typical UNIX system; with the use of block fragments, FFS gets back some of the advantages of HFS's efficient use of small blocks while retaining all the advantages of large blocks for long files.
- To reduce seek time, partitions are broken into cylinder groups (see Appendix III), each of which contains some of the inode structures, and the system attempts to allocate the data blocks for a file close to its inode.

Alternatives to FFS are a subject of ongoing research, driven in part by new hardware. As processor speeds soar and memory costs plummet, new paradigms for data storage are becoming essential. Processor speed makes or will soon make the cost of seeks for randomly accessed short files simply unreasonable. Inexpensive memory chips make it possible to devote ever larger chunks of memory to disk caching. Since streaming transfers are fast and getting faster while seeks are slow and staying that way, the way around the seek bottleneck is always to write long files, distributing the cost of seeking the first byte over the transmission of a megabyte or so. But why would one want to read in or write out a megabyte if all the user had asked for was to change one 512-byte sector? The answer is the heart of the innovative Sprite Log-structured File System under development by Rosenblum and Ousterhout [Rosenblum, 91] as an alternative to FFS.

Rosenblum and Ousterhout focus on the cost of writes, assuming that large memories will make reads efficient through caching. To create an efficient *write*, they cache all writes in memory as a *log of writes* until they can assemble this disparate, unrelated collection of blocks and all of the inode and directory information into a single, extent-long list in memory. The extent is transferred to disk as a single entity. There are problems to be solved, to be sure, but the basic idea is that long transfers distribute the seek (actually one long seek and then several very short ones to acquire adjacent cylinders) over so many blocks that the seek cost per block is negligible.

The log gets transferred quite rapidly, but that leaves the question: How do you keep track of the locations of the blocks in the several files to which they belong? The question is resolved in a fashion not very foreign to FFS, but with some noticeable advantages in minimizing the cost of crash recovery.

In order to be able to "get at" the data in a disk when it is *mounted*, the system must have a key or keys in known places on the disk. Keys contain disk identification and organization data as well as directory structure. In FFS, the inodes are located in fixed positions on the disk. In that sense, upon mounting a disk (an interaction between operating system and disk in which the first sector is read in, the disk is identified, and its name inserted into the pathname tree structure), the disk's inodes can be read without further "research." This can be very helpful when trying to recover from a crashed system. When any file is in use, its inode index and some or all of its extensions will be cached in memory. The crash problem arises when the data which had been in memory before the crash is different from the last copy of that inode on disk. The recovery process is an effort to make what is in the inodes coherent with data blocks on disk. What one gets by this process of reconstruction is not necessarily the latest information that was current in cache when the system crashed. For example, if a file had just been deleted, you might well resurrect it in the recovery process. It generally takes some interaction by both the system manager and the file owners before the transient state is fully resolved and even then, what is recovered may not correspond exactly to what was lost in the crash.

Sprite also uses inodes, but they do not reside at known locations. Instead, they become part of the log itself. Finding them is accomplished normally by a table of inode locations—the *inode map*—which is also part of the log. Somewhere, at the root of all this freedom, must be a map, located in a known place, which provides a key to the location of files. In Sprite, this is the *checkpoint region*. It has a map of the inode maps, and in Sprite, it is the root item which resides at a fixed and known place on disk. A figure is obviously called for and provided in Figure 7.6. Keep in mind that both FFS and Sprite will have large fractions of the active indexes cached in memory, so at least some of the location steps illustrated will not normally require a disk access.

As each log is written, it contains all the new data except for the entry point to the inode map. The two new files shown in Figure 7.6 are completely contained within the log, along with their directories and inodes. If there are additions to or deletions from files that are currently resident on disk in one or more other logs, only the additions along with updated inodes and updated directories will be written to the new log. (Deletions are entries in inodes and, for whole files, directories.) Observe how different the distribution of files is in FFS. The whole disk (or partition) is available for block storage. Inodes are at known locations, which means that updates have to go to those locations. While the drawing suggests FFS simply rolls dice and puts the next block where the dice decide (not an entirely incorrect description of the system which FFS replaced), FFS really does attempt to keep long files as contiguous as it can. The problem that FFS encounters is that even with such optimization for long files, it spends something of the order of 90 percent of its available disk bandwidth on the seeks asso-

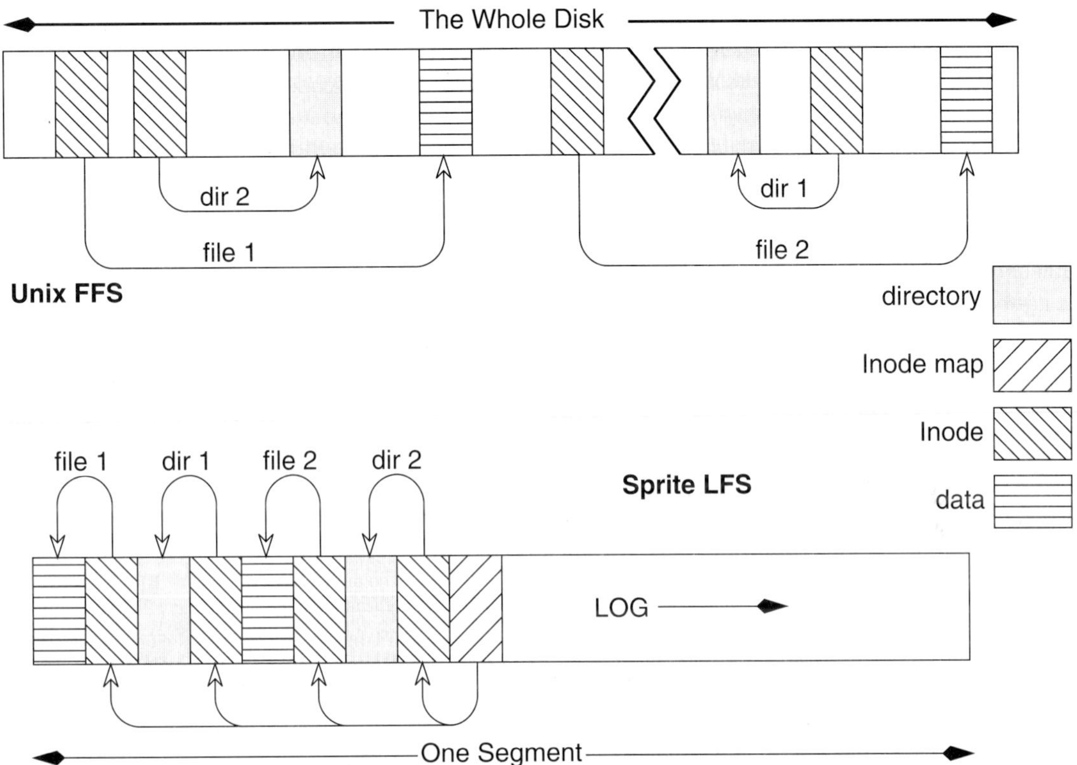

FIGURE 7.6 Comparison of the organization of the modified blocks after the creation of two single-block files, `dir1/file1` and `dir2/file2` in UNIX FFS and SPRITE LFS. In the FFS system, the inodes are at known, fixed locations, while the objects pointed at by the inodes are wherever there is room for them. In the LFS system, the file and its inode and the directory and its inode are written out together, followed shortly thereafter by an inode map which locates all of the current inodes. The extent of the transaction in FFS is 10 short, widely spaced writes; in LFS it is a single, long, contiguous write. Some other structures are written to each log along with what is shown here. In general, the log would not be written out until it was relatively full. After [Rosenblum, 91].

ciated with *short* files. To write out a short file—by far the most common kind—the system must put out a directory and a data block (writes to two separate files) and sooner or later update the inodes involved. That requires writes and possibly reads that are scattered all over the disk. Sprite will have similar seek obligations if it is reading, but on writes, it packs the whole thing together and ships it out in a fast, continuous stream. It is this compaction of many small writes into one long write which gives Sprite its greater efficiency. Shades of Federal Express!

Note that by maintaining the FFS inode concept, Sprite has reading ability equal to FFS. The log itself does not have to be scanned to determine its structure. If a read is required from a file that has not been recently active, both systems must acquire first the directory through one inode and then the data requested through another inode—a minimum of four random, sequential reads. This is a heavy burden on that first acquisition, but after that, the newly activated inodes and the directory are cached. Subsequent reads will go straight to the desired data, with only an occasional dip into indexing to pick up extensions to the data file's inode structure.

Two important issues have not been addressed:

- How is Sprite assured that there will be a big hole to dump each log into?
- If we lose the current checkpoint on a system crash, how would we ever rebuild the system, since old, invalid inodes are now distributed about in the many logs.

Both of these issues focus on *garbage collection*. The first issue is satisfied by continuous, selective compaction by elimination of old versions that were rendered invalid through either deletion or replacement. The second question is answered by having information in each log which makes it possible to identify what is garbage. Getting rid of garbage is a critical and often costly part of any file system. Let us compare the methods in FFS and Sprite.

7.2.5 Midden Building

Students new to computation often take great pains to zero registers and memory before they write some other numbers there. If pressed, they admit (often uncomfortably) to holding onto an analogy with the blackboard. The chalk must be removed (or more likely, uniformly distributed) before new chalk can be applied. Obviously, in computers you just abandon old data. If you later want to reuse the space, you simply write new data therein.[2] This brings up the question of what constitutes *empty* or unused space on a disk. Empty blackboard is distinguishable, but how can you recognize when a block has valid data?

FFS knows its free blocks by the freeblock bitmap. One typical way that blocks get returned to the free pool is by deleting a whole file. In FFS, this will free up not only the file blocks but the file's inode as well. In FFS, there are a fixed number of inodes per disk or partition, so they, just like the blocks, represent a resource that the system must conserve. A free inode goes back on the free-inode list. Other transactions also will affect these structures and their related data blocks. For example, if you add or delete a block in a file, the inode and/or its extensions will be modified. Extension modification will be obtained by writing the new version and moving the pointer from old to new. File blocks and inode extensions are written first and the old ones invalidated later by updating the inodes. Until the inode is updated, the new blocks "do not exist." After the inode in memory has been modified, the old data is essentially invisible. Once the *valid* bit is cleared in the freeblock bitmap, the space may be overwritten. The

---

[2] There is another paradigm—the *demand-zero page*—which applies when passing memory space from one user to another, but there the extra work of erasing the space before delivery is to prevent snooping by the recipient.

problem in a crash is that the more recent updates to the inodes or two freelist structures may not have migrated yet from memory to disk. The system on reboot[3] then finds itself with uncollected garbage—old, invalid blocks and out-of-date inodes. A critical question is: How can a recovery program rebuild a coherent disk from the mix of garbage and goodies that it finds on the disk? In effect, it must sort through the midden of material, identify the latest versions—*the good stuff*—and reconstruct an up-to-date index to it all. It would be nice to have a header on every block with some information which identifies where the file goes and when it got created. Otherwise, how could you know? One byte looks pretty much like another. Let us postpone the description of what must happen while we develop a brief description of the comparable but distinctly different midden structure in Sprite.

In Sprite, the perceived structure of the disk is quite different from FFS. The disk is divided into very long extents. Rosenblum and Ousterhout have been using extents of 0.5 to 1 MB, which they call *segments*. They are of fixed length, comprising 500 to 2000 blocks as contiguously placed as the underlying disk structure permits. The contents and structure are illustrated in Figure 7.6. The critical difference here is that the *relevant* inodes and the new inode map are written out at the same time as the new data. Once again, the rule is that if the full log has not been written out, nothing in the extent has any validity. No broken potsherds in this archaeology. Once a full log has been written, the only missing piece is the *checkpoint region*. This is supposed to point to the latest inode map. If it has not been updated since the last log, the data on disk points to an older map. Once again, unsorting that will require time stamps on the logs. But before getting back to the reconstruction problem, which clearly favors Sprite, let us consider Sprite's biggest problem with its midden.

Sprite requires an orderly midden. To keep writing out these long tales of activity, Sprite must have empty extents. Just as with FFS, new writes in Sprite render old blocks invalid. Every time it writes a new log, it invalidates blocks in other extents—if nothing else, the inode map of any log older than the latest is invalid. In active files, file deletion and modification will leave a scattering of invalid blocks. While Sprite can clean middens and do regular process work at the same time, let us consider the cleaning activity independently. To clean out a segment, Sprite copies out its valid blocks and then lists the segment in its *cleanlist*. The valid blocks from that old segment are now resident in memory. The system must update the inode structures which point to these blocks, and then the blocks and their inodes are added to the current load awaiting a write operation. Several partially valid segments will combine to generate one new, full segment. As soon as a segment's worth is aggregated, it can be shipped out in one of the blazing writes for which Sprite is designed. The extents filled with the most active files rapidly go out of date and not long after creation may contain only 10 per-

---

[3] *Reboot* is an ancient term in computation which derives from the practice, circa 1960, of manually loading a *bootstrap loader* program by keying it in with panel switches. That little program loaded a more powerful loader from card or paper tape which then would load a program to run whatever the machine was to do next. This practice faded with the invention of the ROM but the name has stuck and generally means: "Press the reset button."

cent valid blocks. These can be compressed with great "profit," 10 extents yielding 9 clean ones. Note how small a structure Sprite needs in order to know where to write. Its only list is the list of clean segments—typically a list of fewer than 100 entries. There is no block bitmap nor list of available inodes. In Sprite, inodes are not a limited resource; they are just pieces of a log.

Sprite must have a low-cost way of cleaning segments. It starts with one thing already going for it. A segment is read as efficiently as it is written. The throughput is high because a segment is not a random read; it is a contiguous read. Sprite tries not to get too uptight about cleanliness. The only point in combing the midden is to acquire enough clean segments. Cleaning is a *float-level process*. It starts when the available segment count drops below a certain level and stops when it rises above a certain level. The range is roughly *on at 20* and *off at 60 to 100*.

Once Sprite starts neatening the midden, how does it distinguish the live blocks from the dead ones? Each log includes a segment summary file which provides identification for each block in the log. For data, for example, it provides:

- file number (identifies the file in which this block will be found)
- block number (identifies the position of this block in the file)

The first item can be used to find the inode of this block's file and the second can be used to find the entry in the inode directory which should point at this block. If it does, the block is live; if not, the block is dead. This certainly works, but it is a little slow in coming. Sprite optimizes the search by one more degree. More often than not, blocks become dead when files are deleted or truncated to zero length. Rather than pursue each and every block, Sprite includes a version number with the inode map. Whenever a file is eliminated as a whole, the version number is incremented. The file number that is used is a combination of this version number and the locator in the inode map. The common symptom of block invalidity is a mismatch in the version number. If that shows up, the system need go no further.

The purpose of all of this sorting was to extract the valid blocks of the just read segment, pack the good remnants with those from other segments, and then write a full segment back out to disk. Some substantial optimizations in this process can be obtained. Consider that typically only a fraction of the disk files tend to be active at any one time. Many files may be effectively dormant. It would seem a shame to keep on sorting and filtering unchanging segments. This suggests that the cleaner ought to spend its time where the customers are dumping the garbage. That turns out to be wrong, as was discovered during simulations by Rosenblum and Ousterhout [Rosenblum, 91]. They were startled to find that focusing cleaning on the most active segments reduced the efficiency. They suddenly realized that this was like trying to keep the garbage truck clean while it was in use. Instead, what one wants to do is to squeeze the "bubbles" out of the more inactive segments. The work to get that free space will be much longer lasting than a similar effort on a rapidly changing segment.

To accomplish that objective, Sprite's authors have constructed a benefit/cost expression for cleaning a particular segment and then added one more structure, the *segment usage table*, to enable the system to make wise decisions on which segments to clean. The benefit/cost expression is reasonably direct. The benefit to be obtained is the number of blocks freed times the length of time that the space recovered is likely to stay free. Now just a minute! How do you know how long the space will stay free? You don't, of course. The best you can do is play weatherman and predict that the future weather will be like the past. If the segment has not been updated in a long time, then it is a good guess that it will not be updated in another long time. Think about the large pile of diskettes that you own and the small number of them that work very often. The general truth of the statement is clear, and that is all we need. Accordingly, if we keep track of each segment's last change, the oldest segments will be the most likely to give up their bubbles for the longest time. The cost is even more direct. The cleaning process must read the whole file and write back the useful part of it, *u*. The benefit/cost ratio then becomes

$$\frac{\text{benefit}}{\text{cost}} = \frac{\text{free space recovered} \times \text{segment age}}{\text{read cost} + \text{write cost}} = \frac{\text{age} \times (1-u)}{1+u}$$

By applying this formula, the cleaning process squeezes all the air out of the unused files but cleans the busiest ones only when they approach emptiness.

To work this policy, the system must keep track of both segment age and utilization. Consider segment X. X starts life with $u \approx 1$ (a segment may not be 100 percent full on inception and all segments age by losing utility) and little age, so the benefit of cleaning X when it emerged is ≈ 0. Each time that the system deletes or replaces a block which resides in X—for example, when it updates one of the inodes which was written to X by writing its new version to Z and changing the map to point to Z—the system must delete 1 from the count of useful blocks and reset the clock on that segment. These two numbers—useful blocks and time of the most recent change—reside in the *segment usage table*. This is not an overly large structure. For example, for a 300-MB disk with 0.5-MB segments, we would need only 600 entries of time and block count. That makes the whole structure only a few blocks long. The system is *not* writing this data into the segments that are losing their youth and gaining wrinkles. They sit passively out there on the disk until the cleaner decides to extract the free space. These changes occur only in the segment usage table. All of the transactions and all of the data for the transactions are in memory, where life is conducted at 10 to 100 MIPS. The only times that the system would go out to the segments themselves would be

- to retrieve uncached data
- to clean a whole segment
- to write a whole segment
- to rebuild after a system crash

It is only in the last of these that there is any reason to reference structural data on disk. It is now time to consider that infrequent but onerous task to see why Sprite's disk structure makes it easier to get it together.

7.2.6 After the Crash

When the system comes apart, it loses the structures it was caching in memory. Normally, one must reboot, load the system itself, generate anew the internal system structures, and then prepare to run other processes. Knowing that this reboot did not follow a proper shutdown, the system manager must intrude and run *fsck* or its equivalent to restore the disks to a coherent state. If this were FFS, what would *fsck* have to go on? What constitutes "coherence" in the disk structure?

When you go to disk as a user, you want to `open()` a file and then access it with `read()` or `write()`. To make that work, the system must be able to find the file entry you have specified in the appropriate directory. Prior to any access, the system manager or the boot program must *mount* the volume. Among items that get read on mounting are the partitions, block sizes, and for each "volume," the inode locations and the root directory. From this, *everything else* must be derivable in an orderly, hierarchical fashion. If it is not, the disk is in an incoherent state. Apart from the possibility that the disk was physically damaged and rendered unreadable in whole or part, the usual reason for incoherence is that the data on disk is newer than the inodes or the directories. That would mean that the inodes point to invalid or stale data while nothing points to the new data. Or to show the extent of the confusion that can result, the data written to disk and properly indexed by the inodes lost in the crash may have overwritten a stale directory block and thus wiped out the version of that directory last written out to disk. This means that all subdirectories of that directory and all files listed in that directory have suddenly become orphans even if their data is fully up to date. One objective of *fsck* is to find the orphans and attach them to the file system and to bring up to date all of the active inodes. The orphans will not be attached where they belong; that "where" vanished in the crash. Instead, they will be attached to *lost +found*. There they reside until the system manager finds them a proper home. Such is life for an orphan.

How does *fsck* find orphans? Well, to begin with, FFS is reasonably careful about the order in which things are written to the disk. This helps, but something has to be written first and it can be presumed that something will be amiss with the disks after a crash. Certain things about the disk structure are fixed. Inodes are at known places. Inodes which have not been used will be marked invalid. In other words, there are clues, but reconstructing the whole from its parts is neither entirely deterministic nor rapid. For example, an inode extension may identify its inode but the inode may not point back at the extension. Instead, the inode points at an older or a newer extension. A time stamp may help sort this out, but a look at the absence of inherent structure for the FFS disk in Figure 7.6 should convince you that sorting out all of these inconsistencies is a lengthy task. It is not uncommon for a UNIX system running FFS to require 10 or 15 minutes to reconstruct its disks after a crash. That is 10 or 15 minutes that the machine is down.

The advantage that Sprite has going for it is very basic. Because writes are so cheap and because changed inodes and the inode map are updated on disk on every segment write, there is always much more coherence there to begin with. The root structure—the *checkpoint*—will be out of date and the data still cached awaiting the next segment to be written will have been lost. But the system starts with a much more orderly and regular midden in which to build coherence.

The checkpoint structure is more than the simple pointer to the inode map that it was represented to be above. It contains a complete map of the blocks of the inode map and the segment usage table. It is also time-stamped when its very last block gets written out to disk. There are two checkpoints and they are used alternately. The one to use on recovery is always the one with the latest time stamp. Should a crash occur while transmitting the checkpoint, its time stamp will not get updated. Thus, the latest one is always coherent. The writeout of a new checkpoint is always preceded by a complete synchronization. Getting all the ducks in line requires that the system have all of its cached file structures—inodes, directories, maps, and segment usage tables—in a coherent state and that it then write them all out without any changes allowed until they are transferred. In other words, all I/O activity from normal running must stop. Once a fully coherent and finished copy of the file structures has been written out to disk, a new checkpoint can be written out and the disk is completely up to date. This, of course, is what is done for an orderly shutdown. It is also done periodically during normal running, but it is moderately expensive. The longer the system can wait between checkpoints, the more "useful" work it can get done.

Now let us consider restart after a crash. One could, for example, simply start a disk from its last checkpoint. That checkpoint will point to an inode map that was correct at the time of the last checkpoint transfer. However, data written since the last checkpoint would be lost, and, since checkpoints are written infrequently, the amount of data loss might be unacceptable. We assume that there is no possibility that the segment(s) written at the time of the last checkpoint, which contain a full synchronization of what was in memory with what is on disk, could have been *cleaned* in the interval. That scenario is preventable by, say, introducing the idea that the minimum segment age is "1" and that an age of "0," which renders the profit 0 and thus prevents cleaning, is never advanced. With that assumption, the state represented by the checkpoint is self-consistent.

The checkpoint is certainly the place to begin. The objective is to recover as much of the work that was done in the interval as possible. Sprite's *roll-forward* program scans the summary blocks of all of the segments. If a segment has a more recent time stamp than the checkpoint, its inode or inode map blocks can be used to update the map from the checkpoint. Since several transactions may have affected the same inode, the rule is always *newer replaces older*. The same data can be used to update the segment usage tables. There are not that many segments, so the task of scanning the summary blocks is not immense—tens of seconds versus the tens of minutes for FFS. In particular, the update is very regular and provides monotonic convergence to the latest complete version.

What about orphans and zombies? Zombies? Hang in there a minute. Orphans are the result of breaks in a directory hierarchy. This causes directories and what they point to to become detached, unreachable. Zombies are the data-file equivalent, with an inode becoming detached from the directory structure. Even to excise a zombie, it first must be attached; it must become part of the structure to be deleted. Otherwise it wanders perpetually through the file system, occupying space but unobservable and unkillable. The zombie occurs because multiple directory entries may point to one inode (and thus one file). The inode maintains a link count. The file is deleted only when the link count goes to 0. Crashes can produce *orphans* by losing a directory and *zombies* either by losing a directory without decrementing the link count or by deleting a directory entry but losing the decrement operation (update to the inode). In a sense, the orphan is simply the zombie of directories.

To catch and handle orphans and zombies, Sprite adds yet one more structure to the logs. This is the *directory operation log*. For each change in a directory structure—*create*, *link*, *unlink*, and *rename*—there is a corresponding entry into the log. The write-out of the directory operation log precedes the associated updates to the directories and inodes. If the operation log does not get written, the whole transaction effectively "never took place." No inconsistency can arise from the absence of a transaction. If the log gets written but the crash prevents the updated directories and inodes from being written, the log allows *roll-forward* to recreate the transactions. After reconstruction, a new checkpoint is written.

CHAPTER SUMMARY

This chapter was devoted to determining how the disparate interests of many processes could be satisfied by a single I/O system. Our first focus was terminal services. Both the electrical and logical connections between a terminal and the processes which had been created from that terminal were developed. The terms UART, MODEM, LAT, and TELNET were defined with a simple multiterminal configuration using UARTs and MODEMs shown in Figure 7.1. Questions on input and output were raised and answered. On input:

- You can "type ahead," writing characters that the program is not yet looking for. What happens to characters that are typed ahead?
- How does the operating system know which program should receive the characters that you type?
- When should the characters be echoed?

On output:

- When a program writes characters to `stdout`, how does the operating system decide which terminal to send them to?
- Characters are produced by an application at processor speed—some characters per microsecond. They are delivered to the screen at rates of the order of $^1/_{1000}$ of processor speed and generally at times when the generating process is not the current process. How are the different rates and asynchronism accommodated?

The UNIX programmer's view of files—all files are streams of bytes with any structure or meaning strictly in the eye of the beholder—helped organize the presentation of terminal file handling. Figure 7.2 showed the logical or programmatic layout of the interconnect between terminal and process. On the logical level, the terminal device services were divided into a program-driven upper half and an interrupt-driven lower half communicating through shared data structures. The figure showed how data could travel in either direction and how echoing was accomplished. It did not answer the question of which of the several processes launched from a single terminal would get the input data. As it turns out, there are several possible answers:

- The simplest solution is to let the little kids go first. Most often, processes which create other processes simply suspend themselves until the child process has finished. While sitting in the *wait* queue, they take no input and generate no output.
- The second choice is to redirect the child process to take its input from some other source. Obviously, to do that, suitable file input must exist, so redirection is not always possible.
- A last, considerably more complex, and increasingly popular option is to use some kind of windowing program (e.g., Macintosh or X-windows), which allows the terminal to act like two or more virtual terminals, one of which is connected to each process *which chooses to appear as an independent interactive application*. For programs which so choose, program input and output are directed to the correct window-dependent destination while keyboard input goes to the *current* (user-selected) window, of which at any moment there is only one.

The need to have "smart" responses to the terminal input stream brought up selective echoing. Letting the user program provide the "smarts" introduced the first form of *raw* mode.

From the relatively simple and slow transactions which go on with terminals, we next turned to the considerably more complex and critical subject of disk I/O. While the UNIX programmer's view of files still prevailed, the underlying structure and the need for reliability and high speed transfers in data storage introduced many new needs and solutions. The set of seven simple C file commands were our starting point:

- open — Opens a file for Read, Write, or Read & Write
- creat — "Rewinds" an old file or opens a new one for R, W, or R&W
- close — Disconnects a file from the operating system
- read — Reads N bytes from an open file starting at the current position
- write — Writes N bytes into an open file starting at the current position
- unlink — Removes a file from the current directory (file vanishes)
- lseek — Moves the current position to any valid position within an open file

The logical connections of a UNIX disk file system were shown in Figure 7.3. Once again there was *raw mode* and *buffered mode*. While both were described, the focus was on normal transactions which go on in buffered mode. In UNIX, there are both process and system buffers. The process buffers are what the user sees with his or her `read()` and `write()` commands. The hardware transfers go on between the system buffers and the disk.

The picture of *block-structured devices* fitted well with the buffering concept and made it easy to introduce the idea of caching blocks for both *look-ahead* reading and *delayed* writes. Files were broken up into blocks and stored as blocks on disk or tape. The organization of the blocks on the device did not have to be contiguous with the organization of the blocks in a file. Finding one's way into the block structure brought us to the idea of *directories* (a file of file names with access numbers directing the system to the file descriptors) and *inodes* (the descriptors including the file-ordered index to the file blocks on disk). Figure 7.4 showed the inode and its extensions. The steps to read a single, random block of data from the disk comprise:

- a read of the inode for the directory
- a read of the directory
- a read of the inode for the file
- a read of the file

If it is necessary to follow down extensions to the inode, that random block could take up to three more reads. Additional structures in the UNIX file system included the free-block bitmap or linked list and the free-inode list.

Once we had the basic structure, we could begin to criticize it. Some of the problems included:

- the indexing cost of storing long files
- speed of directory searches
- speed of file transfers
- cost of file recovery after a system crash

Two alternative organizations were considered. Each solved some but not all of the problems just listed. The first considered was the Macintosh HFS. We focused on that system's use of variable-length *extents* to reduce the indexing cost. Next we considered Sprite, a modern alternative UNIX file storage system currently under active development. The Sprite system is designed to take advantage of the extraordinary decline in memory prices and to use memory buffering to cache all of the inevitably short writes in a log of both data and updated inodes. When a sufficient accumulation of writes have been gathered into the log, it is written out to a very long, fixed-length extent. Because the extent is essentially contiguous, the entire write of 0.5 to 1 MB is conducted at full peripheral bus bandwidth. There is but one long seek for the whole write. It is this optimization that is the primary motivation for the Sprite system, but in the construction of the whole system, some substantial improvements were obtained in ease of crash recovery. The operation of the Sprite system required that there be a pool of free extents (or *segments*). This introduced the differences in garbage generation and collection in FFS and Sprite. Some of the structures which Sprite maintains both for cleaning and for crash recovery include the segment summary table, the segment usage table, the inode map, the directory operation log, and the checkpoint.

The process of rebuilding after a crash in FFS and Sprite was compared. FFS had a particularly difficult time not only because of the rather random use of blocks around the disk but also because of the lack of orderly advancement from the last full synchronization. The problem of zombies and orphans was explained. Then we considered the much more orderly *roll-forward* reconstruction possible in Sprite.

PROBLEMS

7.1. Assume that terminal I/O buffers contain 80 bytes of data and forward and backward links. Let there be 60 interactive processes. Half of them are word processing and using spreadsheets. To a first approximation, these use a buffer for every character. The other half are line-oriented applications including shells. The average command is 23 characters long. The average typist is putting characters in at a rate of 1 per second. All input characters are echoed one character to a buffer. On the average, 10 processes send 1 line per second to their terminals as output beyond the echoing. Each of these lines averages 38 characters. All output buffers are queued after 1 second or after a line is entered. The baud rate corresponds to 40 char/s. Each person's input-consuming process runs twice per second and essentially instantly consumes its input.

(a) What is the steady-state number of buffers not on the freelist?

(b) If the system sets aside twice as many buffers as you found in *(a)* to provide a bit of cushioning for surges, how much memory is devoted to terminal I/O?

(c) If handling an interrupt for input or output of a character (which might require acquiring a new buffer or even both dequeuing and enqueuing) averages 3 μs, what fraction of the CPU time is spent on terminal transmission and reception?

7.2. Let us say that we had a maximum UNIX file size of 4 GB. If disk sectors are 1 KB and disk addresses are 4 bytes, what is the smallest block size that we may use? Remember that blocks must be an integral number of sectors and generally some power of 2. Do all of the arithmetic as powers of 2 (e.g., 4 GB is really 2^{32} bytes).

7.3. Contiguous file systems, so simple in concept, quickly become very constricting in real practice. Let us say that such a system has a 100-MB disk. Let us say that the system allows two files to be open for writing at one time. When it opens a file, of course, the system has no idea how large it will be. Accordingly, to have two files open, it allocates half of the largest open space to the first and then the largest remaining window to the second.

(a) With that rule, how many of the following operations can be completed before the first crunch is required? (Assume that the first file is closed before the third is requested in each case.)

(b) How many crunches will it take to complete the list? (Always assume that the first of two finishes writing and closes before a third is opened.)

- create file A and write 2 MB
- create file B and write 11 MB
- create file C and write 3 MB
- create file D and write 27 MB
- delete file C
- create file E and write 13 MB
- delete file A
- create file F and write 1 MB
- create file G and write 33 MB

- delete file D
- create file H and write 7 MB
- create file I and write 9 MB
- delete file F
- create file J and write 12 MB
- delete file H
- create file K and write 13 MB
- delete file G
- create file L and write 3 MB
- create file M and write 1 MB

7.4. A simple UNIX file system has a block size of 512 bytes, and each block number is 32 bits (4 bytes). Suppose that the inode structure for a file contains the following block list (all numbers are decimal):

```
50 51 52 53 77 78 79 80 99 31 32 96 81
```

and the contents of some of these blocks are (as 32-bit integers):

```
block 31: 27 28 29 ...
block 32: 65 97 24 ...
block 80: 44 45 46 ...
block 81: 89 92 91 ...
block 89: 94 95 88 ...
block 90: 41 42 43 ...
block 91: 57 58 59 ...
block 92: 60 61 62 ...
block 93: 67 68 69 ...
block 94: 36 37 39 ...
block 95: 47 48 49 ...
block 96: 93 98 90 ...
block 97: 83 84 85 ...
block 98: 72 73 74 ...
```

Which disk blocks must be read for the following pairs of operations? Answer both in logical blocks and in physical blocks. Any page already read need not be read again.

(a) lseek(file, 2000, 0); read(file, buffer, 1024);
(b) lseek(file, 4650, 0); read(file, buffer, 1024);
(c) lseek(file, 70656, 0); read(file, buffer, 1024);
(d) lseek(file, 136250, 0); read(file, buffer, 1024);
(e) lseek(file, 8524800, 0); read(file, buffer, 1024);

REFERENCES

Operating systems textbooks

[Deitel, 83] Deitel, H.M., *An Introduction to Operating Systems*, Addison-Wesley (1983). Good coverage of asynchronous processes (Chapters 3–6), memory management (Chapters 7–9), disk-scheduling algorithms (Chapter 12), and VM/370 (Chapter 22).

Descriptions of actual operating systems

[Bach, 86] Bach, M.J., *The Design of the UNIX Operating System*, Prentice-Hall (1986). This is the best publicly available description of the algorithms used in the AT&T UNIX kernel, and it is very readable.

[Kenah, 88] Kenah, L.J., R.E. Goldenberg, and S.F. Bate, *VAX/VMS Internals and Data Structures*, Version 4.4, Digital Press (1988). An extremely detailed description of VMS, but not easy to read.

[Leffler, 89] Leffler, S.J, M.K. McKusick, M.J. Karels, and J.S. Quarterman, *The Design and Implementation of the 4.3BSD UNIX Operating System*, Addison-Wesley (1989). A description similar to [Bach, 86] of the Berkeley version of UNIX.

File systems

[McKusick, 84] McKusick, M.K., *A Fast File System for UNIX*, **ACM Transactions on Computer Systems 2**(3), 181–197 (1984).

[Rosenblum, 91] Rosenblum, M. and J.K. Ousterhout, *The Design and Implementation of a Log–Structured File System*, **Operating Systems Review 25**(5), 1–15 (1991).

[Mac, 86] *The File Manager*, **Inside Macintosh IV**, chapter 19, 89–212, Prentice Hall (1986).

General

[Tiberghien, 81] Tiberghien, Jacques, *The Pascal Handbook*, Sybex (1981). An excellent, readable and rather complete exposition instructions of the Pascals current on small machines at the time of publication.

Synchronization

[Snaman, 87] Snaman, Jr.,W.E. and D.W. Thiel, *The VAX/VMS Distributed Lock Manager*, **Digital Technical Journal 5**, 29 (1987). This whole issue was devoted to communication, file management and reliability in VAX clusters.

CHAPTER 8

WHAT LIMITS THE SPEED OF INPUT/OUTPUT?

RUSH HOUR ON THE PIKE

8.1 VITAL SIGNS

Hennessy and Patterson [Hennessy, 89] begin their chapter on I/O with the statement: "Input/output has been the orphan of computer architecture." Not true. Some of the most impressive integer processors, including the "mother of all RISCs," the IBM 801, have been applied in I/O applications. I/O architectures abound and have been the recognized as critical elements in system performance since the earliest days of computation. What is true is that I/O has been the orphan of computer architecture *texts*. The subject is really too big for a chapter. It includes a vast panoply of disparate disciplines ranging from Maxwell's equations to system software, from network modeling to magnetic recording. Those who do make a serious pass at I/O usually pick out some respectable but decidedly limited subset of the overall problem and focus on that. Obviously, we too must concede to reality and pick and choose. We began in Chapter 7 with the interface between the I/O system software and the hardware. In this chapter, we get down into the hardware. The development in this chapter is supported by Appendices II and III and two pieces of software on the text's associated disks. Our specific objective is to answer the question on limitations to speed posed in the chapter title. I/O is a layered system. It follows that there is an answer to the limitations on speed to be found in each layer. We will examine the three main layers:

- data transmission on a bus
- communication protocols and bus overhead
- data protection and the organization of secondary memory

In most cases, the only hands-on experience that an advanced student has had with I/O itself is waiting for it to happen. This contrasts with CPU architecture, where the typical advanced student has been an interested and aware user for several years. The complexity and great importance of busses and peripheral architecture should be brought home by the fact that the two biggest players in computation, DEC and IBM, have put some of their most powerful integer processors out there among the "peripherals" and have been responsible for a continuous proliferation of bus architectures in an endless effort to meet I/O demand at acceptable prices. The I/O system as a whole is both the blood supply and nerve network of the computer. All levels of information transfer—even those on chip—are part of the picture. If any part is a subperformer, the rest of the system will run well below its capabilities. As you know, it takes but one lane under repair to turn a six-lane highway into a long parking lot. The processor of infinite speed can eat instructions only at the rate at which they are delivered; superfast memory can feed the processor only with data that has been delivered from the outside and over a bus that is currently free; and finally, for most users, it is response time, not throughput, which counts for speed. If someone or something is waiting for the answer to an inquiry, you will get no credit for keeping the CPU busy with *other work* while the expectant inquirer twiddles his/her/its thumbs. We have a tight little processor system. Let us connect it to the outside world.

8.2 INITIAL THOUGHTS ON CHOOSING A BUS

The first thing we must do to get some idea of the communications needs of our processor is calculate the data flow rates at the several busses throughout the systems. Note the phrase "several busses." Few modern designs use only a single interconnect. Figure 8.1 shows the components of a two-processor *cluster* in which a pair of processors share several disks. With proper software, the pair could talk directly to each other, each treating its opposite as simply another *peripheral* capable of delivering data and services—a *server*. Shown are three *different* busses with multiple copies of several of them. Each of the busses shown connects a variety of devices. Some of the devices serve as *bus adapters*, permitting data to flow across disparate busses more or less as a thruway interchange permits one to move from a congested city street to a high-speed, multilane highway.

Devices sharing a bus must take turns, with only one user "talking" at a time. The need to share the bus equitably and to ensure that all of the subsystems on the bus can function properly leads to a variety of bus protocols, *rules of the road* for bus usage. These protocols and the physical configuration of each different bus determine the data rates and also whether a bus is robust enough to sustain this rate under demanding circumstances.

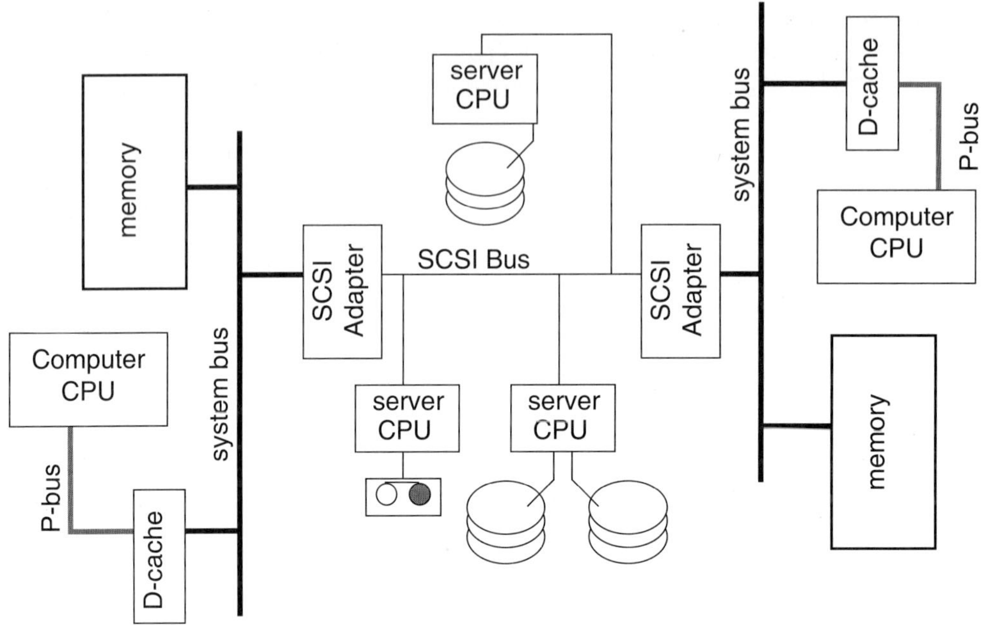

FIGURE 8.1 A pair of (our) processors sharing a common disk file system. The secondary storage peripherals include a double disk drive, a single disk drive, and a cassette tape drive. Note the potential for direct computer-computer communication.

Table 8.1 presents a 1989 view of "well-established" and "emerging" system busses. As this book is completed a few years later, all of the "emerging" busses have moved into active and widespread application and all of the "widely used" list have come up with new versions whose speed has been doubled or quadrupled. Do not take all of the data rates in Table 8.1 at face value. Some are measured (Micro Channel) and others are *best case* or simply hand-waving guesses.

Let us start with a rough estimate of the traffic which the busses of Figure 8.1 would be expected to sustain. Then we would like to start at the bottom and see what James Clerk Maxwell had to say about the speed limit for driving real data around on real busses.

Look at the hierarchy of the busses in Figure 8.1. Data moving among the elements which comprise the CPU environment—CPU chip, D-cache, and coprocessors—travel over the P-bus. This bus is quite local and would undoubtedly be designed to match this particular application. Moving out from the D-cache, which also serves as a bus adapter, we find ourselves at the system bus. If we want to connect standard components to this bus, such as memory boards or SCSI adapters, we will find it much to our advantage to use a standard bus. You can buy ready-made memory boards for most of the busses listed in Table 8.1. Not only is this cheaper in the first place; it generally permits owners to upgrade their machines with minimum pain and cost at some later date. That makes it easy to say "Pick a standard bus," but in picking (or creating) that standard, you are choosing a whole set of conventions and rules with which your machine must live and for which your customers must pay.

TABLE 8.1 Current and emerging system busses as viewed in 1989. The timing column indicates whether the timing protocol is synchronous or asynchronous and whether the address is time-multiplexed with the data. Three semi-open industry standards are included. Two are competing offerings for evolving PC (IBM) and PC-clone (non-IBM) designs and the third a bus architecture by Sun Microsystems. Sometimes these industry architectures are adopted by a committee and become a truly public standard. For example, the VMEbus began at Motorola and the NuBus at Texas Instruments (as a derivative of an MIT design). The S-bus has been adopted by the SPARC standards group, which includes all the companies developing SPARC boards. The Fastbus began as an effort by the high-energy physics community to solve their problems in recording vast amounts of data from diverse instruments. This special need is reflected in its high data rate as well as the fact that its definition includes an auxiliary bus with 195 additional pins. The maximum data rate is an estimate based on a lot of assumptions. Only the MicroChannel number represents an actual measurement. The others would inevitably suffer reductions if rules from real life were applied. Similarly, the pin numbers are often not what they seem. In general there are multiple ground and power pins, so two busses with the same number of pins may have quite different numbers of independent signals. Where different address and data widths are indicated, the same bus conventions and protocols can operate with any of the widths shown. In this way, systems with 8-, 16-, and 32-bit widths can be constructed using the same software and much of the same hardware.†

Bus	IEEE standard	Address width	Data width	Timing	Max data rate, MB/s	Driver technology	Max pins
Well-established 32-bit system busses							
Fastbus	960	32	32	async/m	165	ECL	130
VMEbus	P1014	16, 32	16, 32	async/nm	40	TTL	96/128
NUbus	P1196	32	32	sync/m	37.5	TTL	96
Multibus II	P1296	16, 32	16, 32	sync/m	40	TTL	96
IBM Micro-Channel		16, 24, 32	8, 16, 32	async/nm	17	TTL	198
Extended Industry Standard (EISA)		16, 24	8, 16, 32	sync/nm	33	TTL	198
Newer, emerging 32-bit busses (all in use by 1992)							
Sun S-bus		32	16, 32	sync/nm	57	CMOS	96
Futurebus+	P896.1	32, 64	32, 64, 128, 256	async/m	400 (32-bit) 3200 (256-bit)	BTL	192 (64 bits)
Scalable Coherent Interface (SCI)	P1596	64	64 (logical) 16 (physical)	not yet defined in 1989	1000 per node	ECL	not yet defined in 1989

† Adapted with permission from [Borrill, 89].

How much bus do we need at each point in our system? Some of the numbers are easier to come by than others. The P-bus is the easiest to estimate. Running at full tilt, the P-bus delivers one word per clock. That constitutes a flow of 40 MB/s. Since that flow is quite real, the P-bus must be designed so that it really can sustain that flow. Looking at the more popular *system* busses in Table 8.1, the P-bus data rate may look pretty imposing. However, as you will see, its tiny size, tightly clocked protocol, and limited loading permit faster performance than that easily sustainable on the typical system bus.

The system busses—the next layer down—have data rates which are much harder to pin down. The problem is not inconsistent with the difficulties in estimating traffic flow on a new highway. Your customer, not you, is going to decide who rides on that road or that bus. You can limit the number of ports (interchanges?), but once the basic box is out the door, it is hard to say what is going to transpire upon delivery to the customer. With a little care, we can estimate the load that our processor will put on it. If we have a D-cache large enough to produce a 96 percent hit rate, the memory will be accessed on 4 percent of the P-bus cycles. Each access entails a read of four words and, on the average, a writeback of 1 word. Accordingly, the system bus rate is about 20 percent of the P-bus rate, or 8 MB/s. In contrast to the P-bus, the system bus average rate is comfortably within the performance capability of all of the busses in Table 8.1.

Many caveats are in order here, however. Foremost, our 10 MHz clock rate is lethargic by 1993 standards. With a 40 to 50 MIP machine, the upper half of Table 8.1 shows only Fastbus with adequate bus performance. Average performance is not the only issue. The processor gets particularly hungry when switching contexts or handling infrequent interrupts. As it loads up, not only would it completely consume all available bus cycles, but it would likely find itself spending a lot of time stalling for instructions from memory. Since all the peripherals on the bus are going to need bus cycles as well, it will be not only unfair but probably quite unhealthy to let the D-cache tank up at the expense of everyone else. While rules of the road may help with the issues of fairness, nothing but a high throughput rate will ease the traffic jam at rush hour. Today, a modern system will need a bus with sustainable data rates well in excess of 40 MB/s. Everyday 32-bit-wide, 80-ns DRAM, doubly or quadruply interleaved, can sustain data transfers at several times 40 MB/s.

How about the peripheral bus—SCSI in this example? Here we get culture shock. The required data rate is not determined, at least to the first order, by the CPU/BUS/MEMORY system or even by the application. The principal rate determinant is the peripheral hardware. Peripheral busses are shared in the same sense that the courts at Wimbledon are shared. A full match is played and then the next user gets a turn. While lots of little messages are exchanged between servers and clients, the typical peripheral device handles *blocks* of data. One or more full blocks are transmitted at a time. While the system bus admits transfers of 4 to 128 bytes, the peripheral bus will typically be dealing in unbroken transfers as long as 4K or 8K bytes. In the extreme, consider writing to disk in Sprite's log file system (Section 7.2.4 on page 386). You would be sending a megabyte in which the data is completely sequential on disk. A break in the data flow could mean missing a whole rotation of the disk. The bit rate here is determined by the peripheral device itself. As a disk spins or a tape streams under the read/write head, the bits go out at a rate determined by the recording density and mechanical speed of the device. Appendix III gives a reasonably thorough discussion of the mechanics of reading and writing on hard disks. The raw rate quoted in 1993 for IBM 3.5", 5400 RPM drives is 5 MB/s. The rate at which data is inserted into or extracted from this raw bit stream depends on the recording format. Typical extraction rates range from one-half to two-thirds of a data bit per raw bit, so today's small disk drives can deliver data at rates of about 3.5 MB/s, saturating the nominal 4 MB/s bandwidth of the SCSI bus. To put the picture in perspective, the 1-MB log would require 286 ms to write. Picture a 2-mile-long funeral train passing through an interchange. The rest of the clientele will get antsy. Such megatransfers are normally not allowed. Other devices must be able to get their two cents in as well. Today data is usually buffered at both sides, allowing it to move in brief bursts of modest length, 8 KB or less. To accommodate multiple server–client relationships, the data rate must be well in excess of the streaming rate of any single peripheral device. Is it any wonder then that when hard disk data rates approached SCSI's bandwidth, we were visited with SCSI-II with quadruple the data rate?

As the demand for disk transfer rates goes up, the intelligence needed to order and efficiently manage the data flow to or from the disk is moved away from the CPU and out to the drives themselves. Since a shared peripheral bus is not always quickly available when data passes under the head of a disk drive, one of the things that a server is usually charged with is buffering data to permit substantial asynchronism between bus transmissions and disk reads or writes. In other words, the server will have enough RAM to store one or more full transmissions. When a server gets its turn on the peripheral bus, transmission speed is limited only by the bus itself. In the example shown in Figure 8.1, a total of three disk units and a tape unit could be active simultaneously. If all four units could be expected to operate at average rates of say 700 KB/s, the bus would have to handle 2.8 MB/s. As a general rule, whether it be highways or busses, the *transaction time* for independent, competing transactions begins to fall off as the artery reaches about 50 percent of its nominal capacity. Throughput may continue to rise for a while, but the time from request to delivery will begin to increase. Thus, the little system shown in Figure 8.1 would be close to saturation delivering 2.8 MB/s on a 4-MB/s SCSI bus. Specifying SCSI-II would be far better.

This brings us to a very fundamental question in I/O: Why is SCSI's data rate 4 MB/s? What is the fundamental limitation on data transfer on a given bus? As it turns out, the answer is composed of several interacting facets—electronic, electromagnetic, and rules of the road. We begin with the electromagnetic limits, and these, in turn, will lead us to the others.

8.2.1 The Speed of Light and Other Fables

Almost no one would argue that signals travel along a bus at somewhat less than the speed of light, c. c is a pretty good speed, no doubt, but it has only a limited impact on how fast data can be transferred on most busses. Of all the busses listed in Table 8.1, only SCI can make a claim to transmitting at the speed of light. On all of the other busses, we must consider in some detail what is often called a *loaded line*. The loads are the terminations and connections to the line, which both make it useful and also limit its performance. We begin with the classical analysis of a single length of transmission line and then extend the analysis to strings of such lines joined together at loads. This structure can be well represented on a spreadsheet to provide us with a readily available tool for the analysis of the transient response of rather complex, realistic bus structures.

The classical transmission line can be represented by a differential T network comprising a series impedance and shunt admittance which are analogs of the differential energy stored and lost per unit length along the line. Radiative losses are one particularly important manifestation of the conductance. We can construct a model of a line as shown in the network of Figure 8.2.

Kirchhoff's laws lead immediately to a pair of differential equations:

$$\frac{dv}{dx} = -ri - li_t \qquad \frac{di}{dx} = -gv - cv_t \tag{8.1}$$

The circuit parameters are in units such as ohms/meter (Ω/m) or farads/meter (F/m).

While we can certainly solve this pair of coupled equations using classical separation of variables, the easiest way to deal with this equation pair is to note that all waveforms can be represented by a sum or integral of sinusoidal functions. Using the classical Heavyside formulation,[1] the two equations quickly become

$$\frac{dv}{dx} = -ri - j\omega li = -zi \qquad \frac{di}{dx} = -gv - j\omega cv = -yv \tag{8.2}$$

The time dependence is still there in the form of a term $e^{j\omega t}$, which is included in both v and i. With this form, we can easily combine the two equations to obtain a single second-order equation in v or i:

$$\frac{d^2v}{dx^2} = zyv \tag{8.3}$$

Note that

$$zy = -\omega^2 lc + rg + j\omega(rc + gl) \tag{8.4}$$

with the units of 1/m^2. Let's define $k^2 = -zy$. With that substitution, we obtain the classical wave solution for v of

$$v = v_a e^{j(\omega t - kx)} + v_b e^{j(\omega t + kx)} \tag{8.5}$$

where we have reinserted the time dependence. If we observe the position of constant exponent as time increases, x increases for the term on the left and x decreases for the term on the right. In other words, as time increases, the wave represented by the term

[1] For those of non-EE persuasion, in Oliver Heavyside's method, instead of driving with sin(ωt) or cos(ωt), one uses $e^{\pm j\omega t}$. Simply algebraically convenient here, it becomes exceptionally useful in other applications. Complex coefficients carry both a magnitude and a phase angle. If trigonometric notation is used, these must be included explicitly.

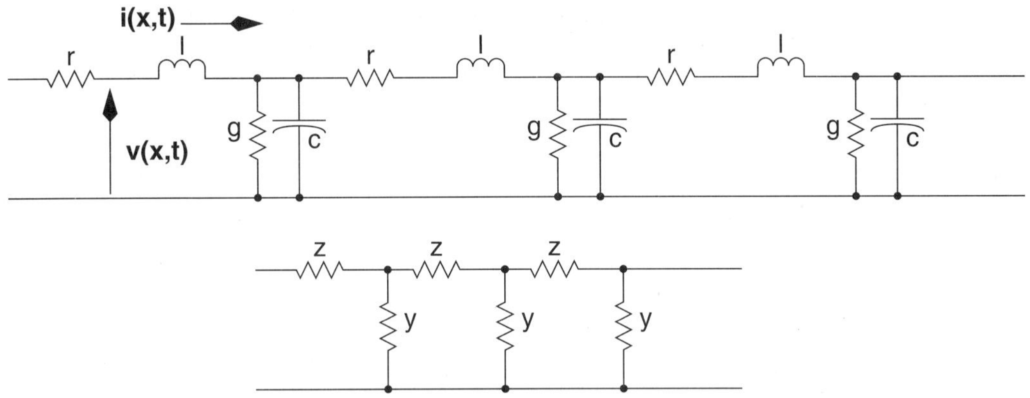

FIGURE 8.2 Two representations of the same set of differential circuit parameters for a general two-conductor transmission line. r and g model energy losses per unit length; l and c represent energy stored in the magnetic and electric fields per unit length. At a given angular frequency, ω, $z = r + j\omega l$ and $y = g + j\omega c$.

on the left is *moving to the right*, and the term on the right represents a wave *moving to the left*. While not exactly a surprise, we have arrived at this very fundamental result quite simply. What we have derived is the fact that waves travel on the line. If the *propagation constant* k is essentially real, then we have also found that in each wave, a particular phase angle moves along the line with a velocity $v_p = \omega/k$.

Now using equation (8.5) and the first equation in equation (8.2) we obtain i:

$$i = \left(\frac{jk}{z}\right)[v_a e^{j(\omega t - kx)} - v_b e^{j(\omega t + kx)}] \tag{8.6}$$

Many find this result astonishing: The current is related to the voltage by a term (k/z) which contains in it *nothing but the parameters of the line*. In other words, for any wave traveling up or down the line, the ratio of the voltage to the current is simply z/k, or, using the previous definition of k, we obtain for each of the two waves in equation (8.6) the important result

$$\frac{v}{i} = \pm\sqrt{\frac{z}{y}} = \pm\sqrt{\frac{r + j\omega l}{g + j\omega c}} \equiv \pm Z_0 \tag{8.7}$$

The quantity Z_0, which is a function only of the line parameters, is called *the characteristic impedance of the line*. In the especially interesting case where the line losses are negligible over the length of the line ($r = g = 0$), $Z_0 = \sqrt{l/c}$ and $k = \sqrt{\omega^2 lc}$.

Since the two parameters Z_0 and k are functions only of the line parameters (and frequency for k), it should be possible to make some nearly universal statements about these two parameters covering most of the structures which we call transmission lines. As a starting point, we should observe that Maxwell's equations, from which Kirchhoff's equations derive in the limit of objects small compared to the wavelength, can be solved for $\boldsymbol{E}$ and $\boldsymbol{H}$ in essentially the same fashion as we have just done. The result is that in free space, electromagnetic waves propagate with ***E*** and ***H*** perpendicular to each other and to the direction of propagation. (TEM waves, just as in a transmission line!) Furthermore, the ratio of $|\boldsymbol{E}|$ to $|\boldsymbol{H}|$ is a function only of the medium and is given as

$$\frac{|\boldsymbol{E}|}{|\boldsymbol{H}|} = Z_0 = \pm\sqrt{\frac{\mu_0}{\varepsilon_0}} \tag{8.8}$$

In free space, this ratio turns out to be 377 Ω, from which one derives the comment: "The characteristic impedance of free space is 377 Ω." When one puts a couple of metal wires in the configuration, the impedance will change. The amount of the change depends on how much the wires dominate in determining the field pattern. In typical open-wire structures such as power lines or TV *twin lead*, Z_0 is roughly 300 Ω. In coaxial lines, where the field is much more constrained and where ***E*** is frequently reduced by the presence of a dielectric (i.e., Z_0 is reduced), the characteristic impedance is typically between 50 and 75 Ω.

8.2.2 Transmission, Reflection, Traveling, and Standing Waves

Waves traveling down (or up) a line are intellectually interesting, perhaps, but unless you interrupt the wave in one way or another, you will never know it is there. What we want to look at is what happens when a traveling wave hits a discontinuity. If the world is *linear, time-invariant* (LTI), we can use superposition at any point of the incident and reflected waves to satisfy the boundary conditions. It should be noted immediately that if the boundary or load impedance at any point is Z_0, then any and all waves traveling by satisfy the boundary condition at that point and no reflection occurs. For any load impedance other than Z_0, the sum of the incident and reflected voltage and current waves at any discontinuity must add up to the values correct for that discontinuity.

Consider Figure 8.3, with an impedance, Z_L in the middle of a transmission line of characteristic impedance Z_0. The two Z_0 loads are in there to make our problem simple, as you shall soon see. Consider the incident wave with parameters v_i and i_i. This wave travels out from the voltage source, and, as with all traveling waves on the line, we have

$$\frac{v_i}{i_i} = Z_0 \tag{8.9}$$

Let us say that we start tracking the signal at $x = 0$ and $t = 0$. Let the phase at that point be 0. That phase will move out with phase velocity $v_p = 1/\sqrt{\mu\varepsilon} \cong c$, the speed of light. Thus, at a time $t_1 = p/v_p$, the phase on that traveling wave at p is 0. If the wave that we are considering is $V_0 e^{j(\omega t - kx)}$, then it is associated with a current $I_0 = (V_0/Z_0)e^{j(\omega t - kx)}$. That is all very good while we are out on the line, but when we get to p, the ratio of total voltage to current must be the effective impedance at that point. Looking at Figure 8.3, you can see that the effective impedance must be $Z_0 \parallel Z_L$. The Z_L term is conspicuous in the figure; the Z_0 term less so. However, if you note that any voltage which appears across Z_L must of necessity also be across the transmission

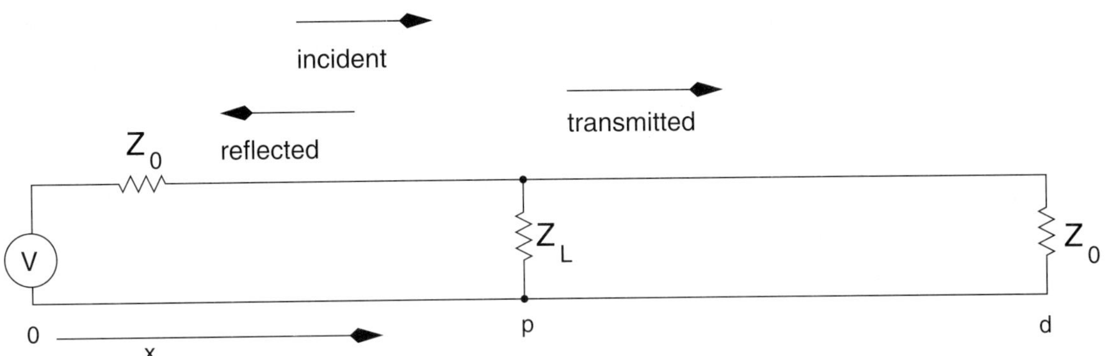

FIGURE 8.3 The setup for determining the relationship between the three waves at a single discontinuity in a line.

line to the right, then there must be a wave traveling out from p toward d with the voltage across Z_L as V_2 and the current of $I_2 = V_2/Z_0$. That puts a Z_0 in parallel with Z_L. The problem is that we do not yet know what the reflected wave will be. Kirchhoff will not let that situation long endure.

At the point p as at any point, the currents into the node must sum to 0 and the sum of the incident and reflected waves' voltages must add to the voltage across Z_L. With the added fact that for each and every wave on the transmission line have $V/I = \pm Z_0$, we are home free. We may write immediately

$$I_0 + I_1 - I_2 - I_L = \frac{V_0 - V_1 - V_2}{Z_0} - \frac{V_2}{Z_L} = 0 \qquad (8.10)$$

$$V_0 + V_1 = V_2$$

If we let $Z_T = Z_0 \parallel Z_L$, then we may solve equation (8.10) for the result

$$\frac{V_1}{V_0} = \frac{Z_T - Z_0}{Z_T + Z_0} = \mathcal{R} \qquad \frac{V_2}{V_0} = \frac{2Z_T}{Z_T + Z_0} = \mathcal{T} \qquad (8.11)$$

The term $\mathcal{R}$ is called the *voltage reflection coefficient*, or more often simply *the reflection coefficient,* and $\mathcal{T}$ the *transmission coefficient*. Note that there are three important cases of particularly simple form:

for $Z_T = Z_0$,

$\mathcal{R} = 0$ $\quad \mathcal{T} = 1$ *matched case*

for $Z_T = 0$,

$\mathcal{R} = -1$ $\quad \mathcal{T} = 0$ *short circuit*

for $Z_T = \infty$,

$\mathcal{R} = 1$ $\quad \mathcal{T} = 2$ *open circuit*

The open-circuit $\mathcal{T}$ is formally correct, but it really indicates only the magnitude of the voltage at the open termination. Nothing is transmitted. It you computed the *power transmission coefficient*, it would be quite satisfactorily 0.

Go back now and look at the line that was set up in Figure 8.3. Notice that it is terminated at *both ends* in its characteristic impedance. That means that none of the waves which reach the ends get reflected again. Their energy is absorbed by the resistors at the ends. Why do we care?

Well, consider a transient wave. Something like a step function. If the line is *nondispersive*—that is, if the phase velocity is independent of frequency—that step will move coherently as a wave down the line. It will come to the load in the middle, where it will reflect and transmit in appropriate proportions. When these reflected or transmitted components get to the terminations of Figure 8.3, they are totally absorbed. What simplifies our analysis is that we do not have to keep on adding reflections of reflections to our waves. As the number of mismatches grows, the formalism remains the same but the problem of visualization quickly becomes overwhelming. It is similar to throwing stones in a clear pond. The first one produces a beautiful circular pattern; the second generates some nice interference patterns; the third simply makes the water rough. What we want to do is develop a method which applies well to our designated problem: a line short enough that it has little damping or dispersion but one that has multiple mismatches distributed in some not necessarily uniform pattern. This we now proceed to consider.

8.2.3 The Short Bus as a Transmission Line

Physically, a typical backplane bus comprises a very large number of wires arranged in a flat array on a printed circuit board. Usually the back side of the PC board is also used to get enough wires. To a first approximation, the lines on the back can be considered to be a ground plane. The reason for the huge number of wires is not simply superwide data or addresses but the necessity for shielding one line from another as the frequency increases. Quite often, each active line has a ground line on either side. (The ground lines are not "wasted." To begin with, many ground lines are needed. Second, the boards receive power from the backplane, and these DC lines are equally good "AC grounds.") The configuration comes out to be something like the arrangement shown in Figure 8.4. That figure shows the equipotential lines surrounding a pair of active lines with one of them driven to +5 V and the other at 0 V. It is clear that a large fraction of the field lines that begin on the 5-V line will terminate on the ground plane and the two ground lines rather than on the adjacent active line. The diagram is quite accurate, having been calculated by finite-element techniques. That method also provides for capacitance calculations. These data are presented in Table 8.2.

The capacitance from the 5-V line to ground is 96 pF/m; the capacitance from that same line to the next active line is 1 pF/m, not very different from the capacitance to the rest of the universe (the 0.4 pF unaccounted for in the sum of cross terms compared to the self or diagonal term). This indicates that the PC-board layout with adjacent active lines separated by ground lines provides very good line isolation indeed. One of the consequences of the tight shielding is a lower Z_0. For the somewhat

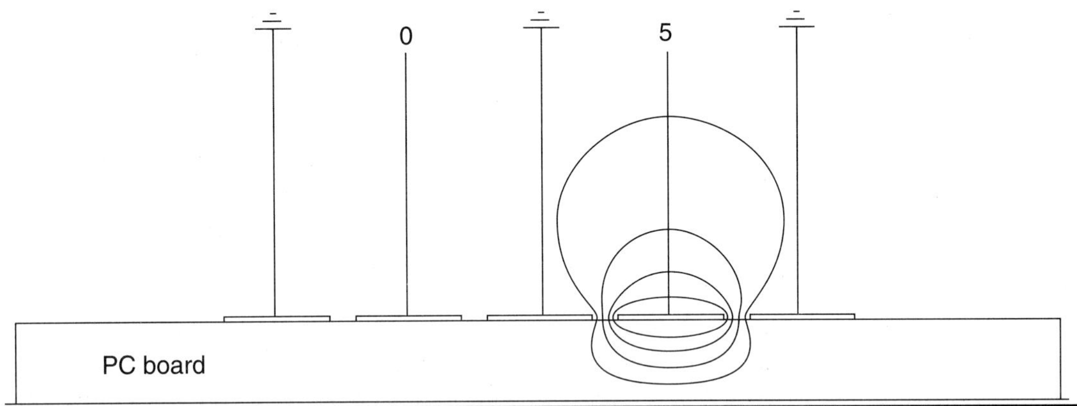

FIGURE 8.4 The 1- to 4-V equipotential lines around a PC-board bus with two active lines, one driven to 5 V and the other held at 0. There is a ground plane at the bottom of the board. The relative dielectric constant of the board was taken as 3.5. One can see, by mentally constructing curvilinear squares to the equipotentials, that most of the field lines would terminate on the grounded surfaces. The lines are 2×0.1 mm on 2.5 mm centers and the board is 1.6 mm thick.

arbitrary dimensions in Figure 8.4, a value of roughly 65 Ω is obtained. For the calculations developed below, we have used 100 Ω for this "unloaded" Z_0. This is closer to the dimensions and board materials currently employed.

Circuit-board connections are made to the backplane structure illustrated in Figure 8.4 by using a female connector on the backplane and then using either the edge of the board as the male (typical of devices designed to minimize cost) or by having high-precision connectors on both the backplane and the circuit board. When the boards must be multilayered to accommodate the wire density, attaching the connectors to all of the layers becomes both complex and expensive. A fairly complete description of today's bus structures and interconnects can be found in [Di Giacomo, 90]. Figure 8.5 illustrates a typical two-layer backplane. What we wish to do at this point is take advantage of the isolation and shortness of the lines in the typical backplane bus to simplify the calculation of the transient response to a bus driver pulling down or releasing a bus.

TABLE 8.2 **Capacitance matrix (in pF/m).** The capacitance matrix relates the voltage between two elements to the charge found on those elements. The self term is the charge on that element if 1 V were put on that element and all other elements were at 0 including the proverbial point at infinity.

	Active A	Ground	Active B
Active A	97.5	-96.1	-1.0
Ground	-96.1	236.4	-96.1
Active B	-1.0	-96.1	97.5

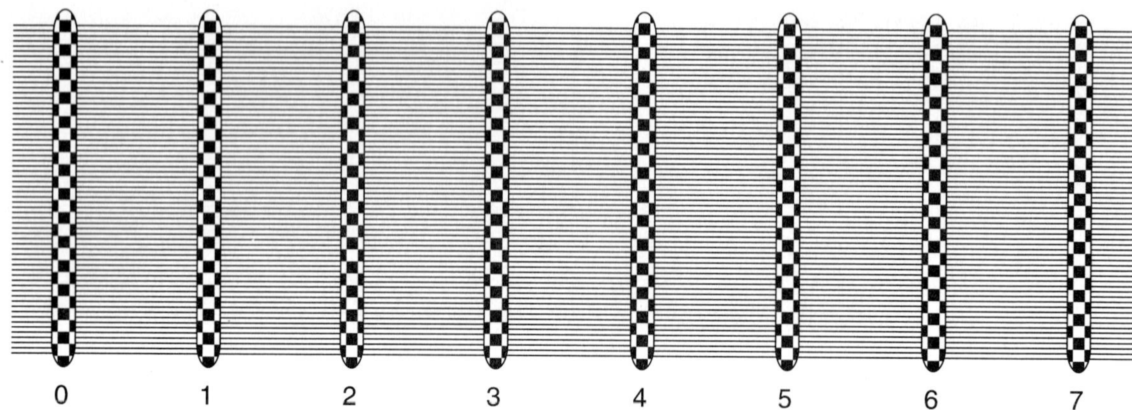

FIGURE 8.5 A 64-line bus laid out on a two-sided backplane board with eight slots for circuit boards. Connections to the back side must be made through holes (called *vias*) drilled through the board. All in all, it is an expensive technology. Proper terminations on the bus require resistors at both ends of all active lines.

Consider some simple approximations to a typical bus setup shown in Figure 8.6 with only a single transceiver indicated. The line's structure will give us a $Z_0 \approx 100\ \Omega$ to start with. As you start adding the capacitance of the feedthroughs on the board and the connectors themselves, this comes down to something closer to 60 Ω. This is called the *loaded* Z_0. Most bus specifications define upper and/or lower bounds on all of the parameters shown as well as limiting the number of slots and being quite specific on the mechanical configuration(s). We are going to illustrate the signals on two busses, VMEbus [VME, 87] and Futurebus [Futurebus, 90]. Some typical values for the components of Figure 8.6 are given for VMEbus in Table 8.3 and for Futurebus in Table 8.4.

FIGURE 8.6 The loaded VMEbus with four slots occupied. Each slot has a transceiver with a capacity of 20 pF. The board in slot 4 is shown with a pulldown transistor whose characteristics are shown in Figure 8.7.

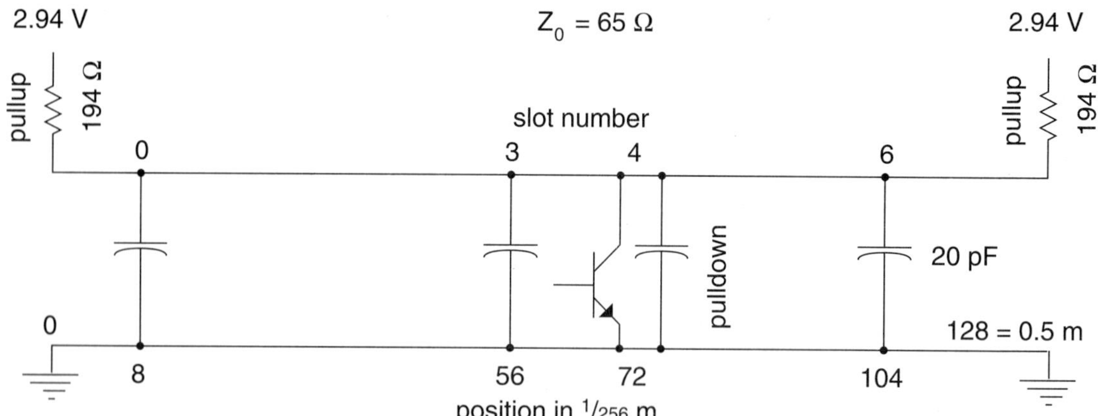

TABLE 8.3 Specifications used for the VMEbus simulation

Z_0	65 Ω	V_{CC}	2.94 V
I_d	65 mA	C	20 pF
x	0.5 m	Z_L	194 Ω

What we have done in our simulations is to put loads in four of the slots in Figure 8.5. This is shown in Figure 8.6. The objective is to see how the different bus specifications are met and how those specifications determine the maximum transfer rate on the bus. As far as the electromagnetic limitations to bus performance are concerned, the tale can be told by looking at a pulldown and a pullup transient. That is, we will let the bus stabilize with the switch open or the switch shut. Then, at $t = 0$, we will flip the switch and watch the voltage at each of the stations. Each will see a decidedly different pattern, showing the delays for signals to propagate not only through the short sections of line but also to get past the capacitors.

An analogy of the circuit of Figure 8.6 is a line of deep, narrow ponds interconnected by pipes. If we let this arrangement of ponds come to equilibrium, the surface of all the ponds will be at the same height. At $t = 0$, we will pull the large plug at the bottom of pond 4. As the level falls rapidly in pond 4, a negative pressure wave travels out to ponds 3 and 6. It gets to 3. The pressure at the bottom of 3 cannot change instantaneously. It is determined by the height of water in the pond. Accordingly, the negative pressure wave is *reflected* as a positive pressure wave back down the pipe to pond 4. Note that the positive pressure wave will push water from 3 to 4 just as the negative wave sucked water from 3. This causes the level to drop in pond 3, which will be seen in later waves. Just a bit later, the wave toward 6 gets there and reflects. Pretty soon, that reflected wave gets to pond 4. After a while, waves from 3 get to 0 and from 6 get to the termination (in the analogy, an infinite reservoir with a smaller pipe than the pulldown). As all of these time-dependent waves start overlapping and bouncing back and forth, we quickly run out of patience and pencil lead. It is at this point that we call in the spreadsheet. Details of the method are presented in Appendix II. Here we will present only the solutions and conclusions therefrom. However, the method is relatively easy. The problem set encourages doing some examples and the spreadsheets, which are part of the software associated with the book, provide the wherewithal to solve the example in Figure 8.6.

Just before the transistor is driven on, the system would be uniformly at 2.94 V. While the transistor is in the off state, there is essentially no current flowing in it. With the transistor on and line voltages above about 0.7 V, the transistor will act as a constant

TABLE 8.4 Specifications used for the Futurebus simulation

Z_0	60 Ω	V_{CC}	2.1 V
I_d	65 mA	C	10 pF
x	0.5 m	Z_L	39 Ω

current drain of about 65 mA. When the voltage gets below 0.7 V, the transistor *saturates* and as the voltage continues to fall, the transistor conducts less and less, essentially shutting off at 0.2 V. A reasonably effective transistor terminal model employing three straight lines is given in Figure 8.7. As the transistor is driven on, the capacitance at slot 4 starts to discharge rapidly. This is shown by the curve marked *drive* in Figure 8.8. Note that the time scale on that figure is in nanoseconds. You can see the delays before the first inklings of the coming change arrive at each of the receivers. The first receiver to find out that things are changing is the closest, 3. Not long afterward, 6 finds waves on its doorstep. Finally, about 1.8 ns after the initiating event, the message gets to *last to know,* slot 0. Notice how the signals get dragged up and down by the waves bouncing back and forth. One of signals—the drive—even goes negative and that in spite of the transistor turning off completely because of saturation.

The VME spec requires *low* at a threshold of 0.8 V and *high* at 2, as shown in Figure 8.8. Things keep rattling around for another 10 ns or so. "Eyeballing" Figure 8.8 suggests 6 ns to the *low* state. In general, the receivers employ some hysteresis so that once a line has gone to the *asserted state* (low), it must climb a considerable distance before it is regarded as *deasserted.* The 2/0.8 specification is the "guaranteed" transition level, but the space in between is no-man's land.

Now consider the pullup. With 130 pF to be charged through 97 Ω (the two ends in parallel), the RC time constant is 12.6 ns. That is a lot more than our pulldown figure of 6 ns. To run this case, you start the line in the steady-state pulldown condition. From

FIGURE 8.7 The model of the pulldown transistor that was used in simulating the line behavior. This is a reasonably good model for typical low-power Schottky bus drivers.

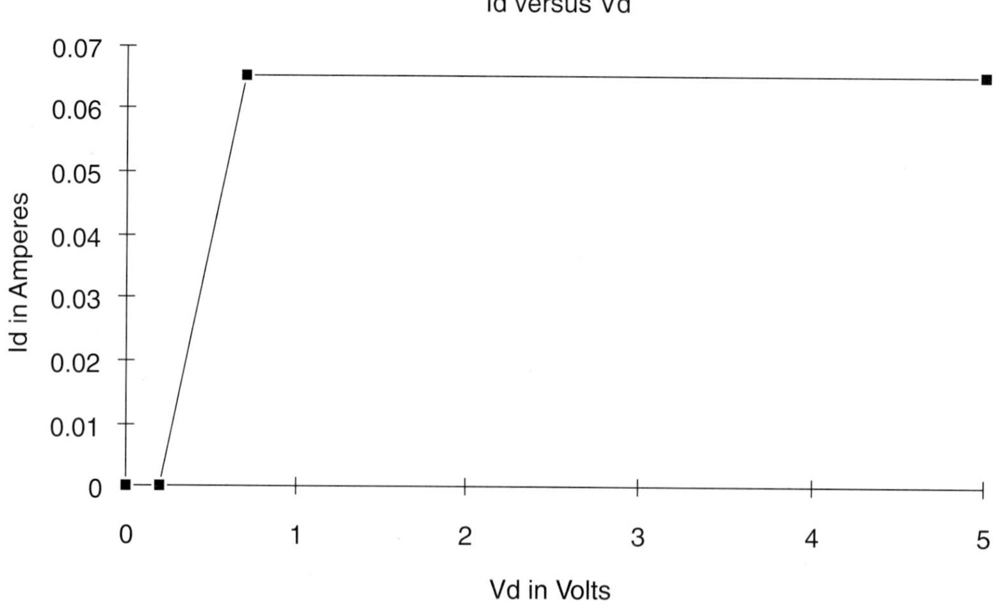

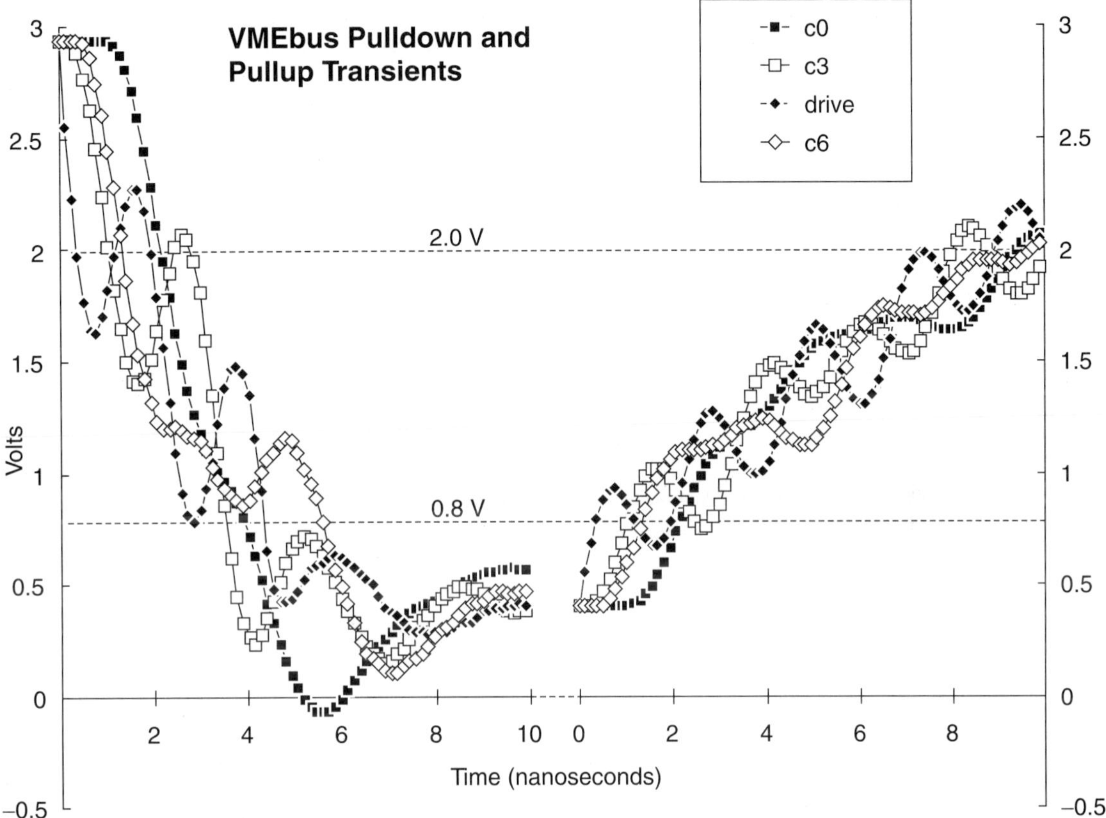

FIGURE 8.8 The circuit of Figure 8.6, with the open-collector transceiver initially driven on at $t = 0$ and then, after stabilizing at 0.4 V, opening at $t = 0$.

Figure 8.7 and the pullup resistors, we obtain the value of 0.4 V for the steady-state pulldown voltage. The pullup waveforms are shown in Figure 8.8. Once again, we see oscillations which have their origins in the waves echoing back and forth in the "hollow" spaces of our line. While the waveforms are interestingly different at the four slots, they are much less wild. It is clear that all the signals reach the high, unasserted state after 10 ns. That the pullup takes longer than the pulldown is a consequence of the choice of pullup resistor. It would be easy to say, "Make it smaller and go faster," but the choice of termination resistor determines, at least in part, the amount of current that the pulldowns must sink. Since each of the drivers and receivers leak a bit, the pulldown can be pushed beyond its limits if the pullup resistances are to low. To do better, one must change either the technology of driving the bus or the methodology of signaling on the bus. Futurebus attempts to improve things by making both kinds of changes. We will look at Futurebus in a moment, but first let us collect our thoughts on what we have achieved.

The conclusion from this simulation is that on these loaded lines, there will be ringing which can significantly extend the time between the assertion or deassertion of a signal and its reception at another load. The length of the line enters into the damping rate for these oscillations. Accordingly, to be able to guarantee a delay, a bus design generally has to specify

- a maximum length of a line and also the maximum number of loads
- the maximum size of a load (generally assumed to be capacitive)
- the sinking capability of the drivers and the minimum pullup resistor value

If one is obliged to communicate at maximum speed over long lines, then matched-line, point-to-point communication is the way to go. This is the design choice of the superfast SCI bus mentioned in Table 8.1. If such point-to-point communication is the choice, to make all the delays the same, all the lines must be of the same length. In Cray machines, where a nanosecond is a serious piece of change, such sets of matched lines are much used.

The total drive current for a backplane bus driver is a very serious problem. Since the typical system bus has 100 to 200 signal lines, the driver chips must be able to sink *amperes* of drive current to be able to pull down all of the signal lines at once. Delivering amperes over the ground lines while holding the ground voltage very close to 0 requires lots of ground lines. This is why they are so plentiful in the ground plane. It is also the reason why it is critical that the power and ground lines be "decoupled" by having buffering capacitors at every daughter board and every chip.

The previous paragraph may suggest that the way to go is to use optical communication. After all, light travels at the speed of light, doesn't it? Well, not always, and there is nothing un-lightlike about the electromagnetic waves traveling on the busses we have considered. The reasons for the almost universal swing to fiber-optic communications has almost nothing to do with the speed of visible and infrared light. For long lines, the point-to-point fiber-optic system provides three outstanding benefits over an equivalent matched copper twisted pair or even coaxial line. These are:

- an extraordinarily low rate of attenuation, permitting much longer distances between repeater stations or lower drive power for single segments
- much higher bandwidth per line, at the moment limited only by the bandwidth of the electronics associated with modulation and detection
- high packing density and inexpensive installation compared to coaxial lines, twisted pair, or stripline

As you can see, it is economic considerations, not propagation speeds, which are driving the conversion. For the short distances of interchip communications, optical links are under very active development. Here again it is economic considerations which are the motivation. Printed circuit board costs become very high when large numbers of wires must cross over or get around each other. With the high pin counts of modern chips, multiple-layer crossovers become inevitable. Furthermore, with all those lines to drive, the chip must devote much area and a huge fraction of its power budget just to driving bus lines. If chips could be well aligned, then one could use the air above the chip for chip–chip communications [Dickinson, 89]. The concept uses a common off-chip optical power source and integrated modulators on chip. Since it takes far less power to modulate the optical beam than it does to drive an electrical bus and since the technique would increase the interconnectivity, it could have much promise.

Returning to more common shared-conductor busses, we next take a very brief look at the issue of how one might improve upon the VMEbus while still retaining the same basic technology.

8.2.4 Pushing (and Pulling) the Bus

We have stated that the transmission line specification for VMEbus is a well-balanced, locally optimal design. To do much better, different technology must be invoked. As you will note in what follows, it isn't really all that different—just clever.

Low-impedance drivers are essential to fast bus performance. In general, that means *go bipolar*, but the traditional bipolar technology—TTL—takes away on one hand what it gives with the other. The problem with TTL is that it comes with lots of collector capacity. All of the open switches are big buckets which have to be drained by the active driver or filled by the pullups. The VMEbus standard gives an expected budget for a daughter-board transceiver:

typical capacitance of a receiver	3–5 pF
typical capacitance of a driver	10–12 pF
typical capacitance of a transceiver	15–18 pF
typical capacitance of a 5-cm PC trace	2–3 pF

You can certainly see where the 20 pF/slot spec came from. If we apply the Tchebyschev rule of thumb, then our first effort to speed things up is to drop the transceiver capacitance to 3–5 pF. "Ha!" you say, "and just what do we propose for a high-conductance, low-capacitance driver?" Fortunately, textbook jockeys generally do not have to be too original. Others have done the thinking for them. That better driver has arrived and is much in demand. Let us see how the reasoning goes.

A bipolar junction transistor (BJT) is at its capacitive worst as the voltage across the transistor falls toward and below 0.6 V, just the conditions which obtain as the driver lets go to start the pullup. The collector junction becomes forward-biased and lots of charge moves into its base and collector regions. To pull all of those open collectors down, the active pulldown is obliged to push all of that charge into the junctions. Then, to pull the voltage up, all that charge must be sucked out again. To meet this problem, most of the newer busses have resorted to a better method, called *backplane transceiver logic* (BTL). That could just as well be for *bipolar transistor logic*, which is still at the heart of its high current-sinking capability. What BTL accomplishes is to maintain the excellent pulldown capability of TTL while drastically reducing the capacitive load presented by the undriven pulldowns.

The newer method begins by taking advantage of the fact that a forward-biased Schottky barrier has a relatively small voltage drop (typically 0.25 V) and that, being a majority device, its capacitance in either bias is quite small. By putting the Schottky in series with the BJT, one isolates the big capacitance from the line. In fact, you need not pull down the open BJT collectors at all, saving both the pulldown and pullup from that load. Figure 8.9 shows the circuit. For simulation, we use Figure 8.7 simply shifted right by the Schottky-diode's drop of 0.25 V.

The other side of the BTL circuit is equally important. It is pretty obvious in Figure 8.8 that a large portion of the delay derives from the time it takes the bus to traverse the full length of the deadband in the middle. While many students think that that deadband is defined by the required noise immunity, it is really defined, at least in how small you *can* make it, by the swing necessary to convince all receivers that you meant *high* or that you meant *low*. A digital circuit's noise immunity is defined properly as the differences between its steady-state signals and the edges of the dead band. How big the differences must be to make a circuit work reliably depends on noise on the sensing technology. The biggest source of noise on the bus is nicely illustrated in Figure 8.8. It is the bouncing of the signal on the bus. Unless you are running your bus in a noisy environment (which is quite possible), the other principal source of noise is coupling between adjacent lines in the bus. Good design—running ground lines between signal lines, decoupling all of the power supply and ground lines, and placing the lines themselves close to a ground plane—can reduce coupling noise to quite modest proportions of the bus swing itself. Since all of these noise sources are directly proportional to the bus swing, all of this invites us to reduce the bus swing and the associated noise-immunity band. Let us say that we used a 1-V swing. This will limit the deadband to a few tenths of a volt. That, in turn, will call for a much more precise detection of the voltage than the usual receiver will deliver. Accordingly, a "precision comparator" is employed.

What is earned by this circuit is a loading typically of 7 to 10 pF, the powerful pulldown of a BJT, high speed, and very reasonable power demands. Furthermore, in the most modern circuits, bipolar and CMOS are realized on the same chip in BICMOS

FIGURE 8.9 The backplane-transceiver logic system. The transmitter or pulldown is a BJT isolated from the bus by a Schottky diode. The receiver is a comparator which compares the line voltage against an internal reference and registers a hard 1 or 0 on either side of a narrow band.

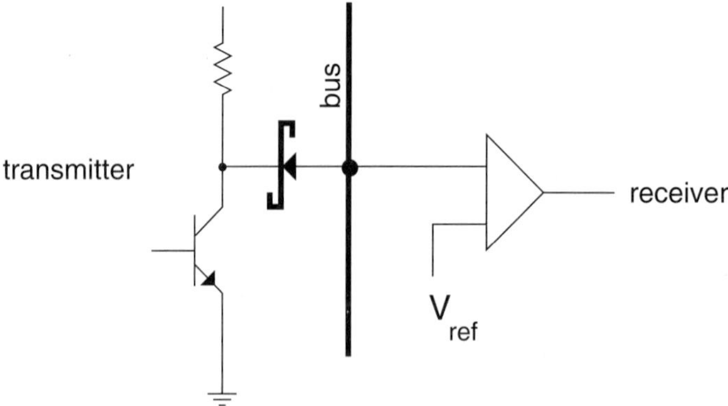

technology. Accordingly, these drivers are quite suitable for on-chip drivers. Not having to go from chip to chip to get onto the bus saves anywhere from 5 to 15 ns. Combining this circuit with the Futurebus definition leads to the characteristics shown in Table 8.4. Compare this table to Table 8.3. The most significant differences are the halving of the capacitance and the substantial reduction in the termination resistance. The latter is not a result of a more potent pulldown transistor. Quite the contrary. I_d is identical in Futurebus. What has changed is the required voltage swing. This, in turn, is a direct consequence of having a precise transition voltage rather than a deadband of more than 1 V. Since we will not have to traverse the deadband to achieve a transition, we need not swing so far. It is the distance from the transition voltage to the high and low DC values which determines the noise margin. Futurebus, with its BTL transceivers, provides 0.6 V of noise margin and yet requires a swing of only 1.2 V.

Simulation of the Futurebus transitions using the methods of Appendices II leads to the results shown in Figure 8.10. Once again, the complexity of the BTL is replaced with Figure 8.7 shifted right. We see a nicely balanced pair of transitions with at least some argument that would say that the delay is about twice the fundamental one of the

FIGURE 8.10 Pulldown and pullup on a Futurebus. The specifications for the bus are given in Figure 8.4. The dashed line is at the nominal transition threshold of the precision comparator.

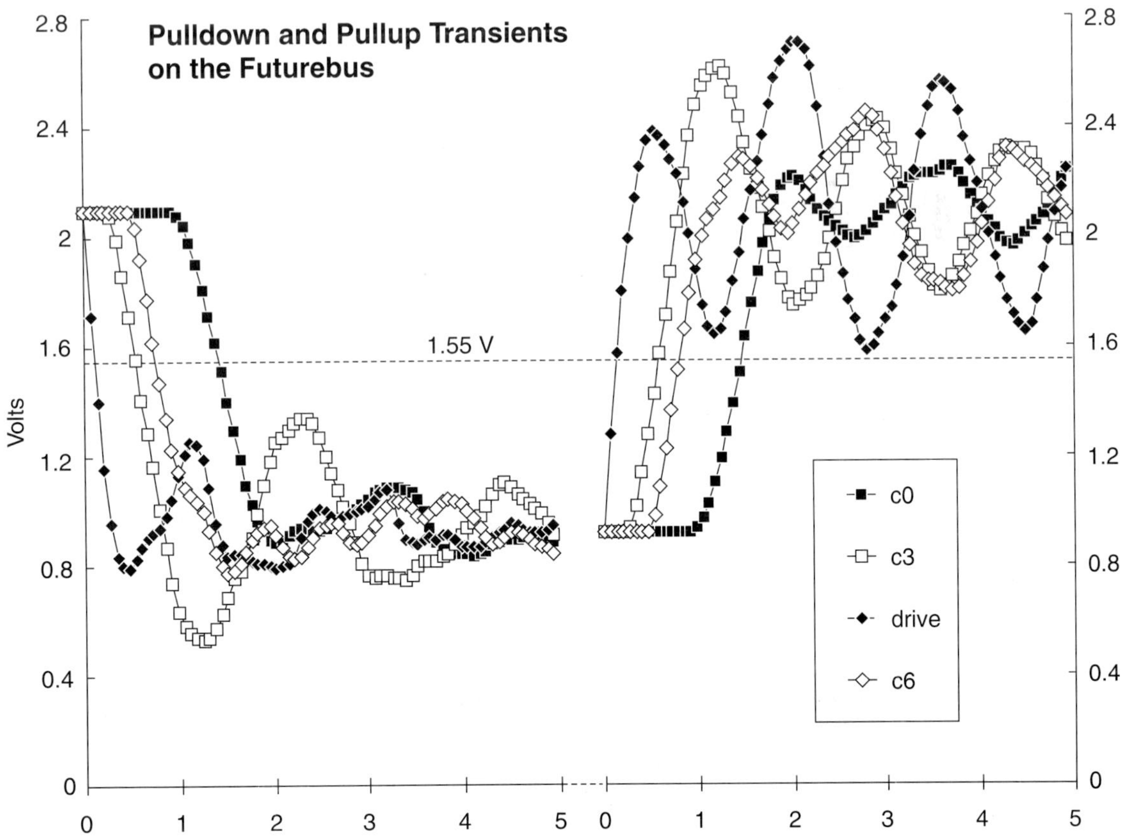

speed of light. You can see that the transition in each direction is "threatened" by oscillations. To deal with these potential *wired-OR glitches*, the Futurebus specification requires that the receivers have a low-pass filter whose response time is no less than a round trip on the bus. Such a filter would conceal the oscillations in Figure 8.10 and make the transitions look smooth and uncomplicated. If speed-of-light considerations are all that limit transactions, then the bus with these drivers on a 0.5-m line could approach 150-MHz clock rates. However, the bus specification has two rather interesting features which would limit this optimistic assessment to values closer to 80 MHz.

The first feature is the specification [Futurebus, 90] which states that "to minimize noise problems on the boards, bus drivers may be used that have controlled output transition times of not less than 3 ns." There is also the lower limit that "the rise or fall times for all signals shall be no greater than 10 ns under all permitted loading conditions." There is no doubt that a controlled rise or fall in Figure 8.10 would get rid of the threatening oscillations. Under those circumstances, the transitions will be clean, and the specification makes very good use of this fact. This introduces the interesting topic of how the receiver knows when the signal represents a correct value.

8.3 BUS CYCLES

8.3.1 Synchronous and Asynchronous Busses

Active busses have some form of signal on them all the time; the signals change rapidly with time and have no inherent characteristic to identify when the signal is valid—that is, when the values at the receivers correspond to the transmitted values. To avoid the essential noncausality of having someone read a message before it is written, some method for synchronizing the writes and the reads must be employed. Busses are normally characterized as "synchronous" or "asynchronous" according to how this synchronization is achieved. This somewhat misleading nomenclature really describes whether the bus timing line or some other signal lines, driven by either the current bus master or one of the bus slaves, signals when to write and when to read.[2] The synchronous system is timed with a universal clock; the asynchronous system uses a direct *handshake* between sender and receiver to do all the timing. The interaction brings to mind the justly famous, oft repeated, Danny Kaye routine from *The Court Jester*: "Get it?" "Got it." "Good."

The advantage of asynchronous operation is that it allows a slower device to control its environment without necessarily limiting the faster devices in their interactions. If all devices use the clock, then all of them must be in lockstep. If the designer wishes

---

[2] Still other even more misleading usage is made of these words. On a SCSI peripheral bus, *asynchronous* is used to mean that every byte transmitted is accompanied by an immediate handshake while *synchronous* means that the handshakes can get somewhat out of synchronism—that is, you can get several bytes and then get several handshakes. There are good reasons for having the two conventions on that bus, but the English language is hardly so short of good words as to have required that abominable construct.

to raise the clock frequency on a synchronous bus, any component which cannot keep up must be replaced. On an asynchronous bus, life just slows down when the deficient performer is on line.

The previous paragraph would suggest that everything favors the asynchronous bus. That is far from the case. A synchronous bus requires fewer lines and leads to simpler circuits. Those are decided advantages. Conforming to the VME and Futurebus standards is more expensive than the NUbus or S-bus. Looking at Figure 8.1, you can see that the latter two are synchronous; the former two are asynchronous. Apple and Sun chose the synchronous route. Apple rejected using the VMEbus for Macintoshes even though that bus was specifically designed for MC68000-family compatibility. Cost is generally not an irrelevant factor for those who have chosen to stay in business.

Neither are performance and adaptability irrelevant. The ability to conform to the needs of many boards often makes it worthwhile to accept the cost of the asynchronous busses. For example, Digital Equipment recently adopted Futurebus as a DEC standard. The effort is to let DEC's computer systems talk directly and simply to a wide variety of high-speed peripherals that are being developed for this bus standard. To get the broadest range of adaptability, the choice is an asynchronous bus.

Without going into all of the details, we want to take a look at the different sets of interactions that VME and Futurebus use to transmit a single block of data. You will see how the very long and arduous task of defining and implementing the Futurebus has led to a data-transfer protocol which is as responsible for its high performance as is its superior drivers.

8.3.2 Bus Arbitration

Since a single bus can have only one transmitter active at any moment, any bus with more than one potential master must have some way to "arbitrate" between the competing demands of its users. The sequence of states which is traversed to transfer some data comprises:

1. check for bus free
2. contention among the potential users for bus access
3. selection of a single master (arbitration)
4. address, data direction, and data size driven onto the bus, usually by master
5. data driven onto the bus (this step may be repeated) by master or slave as appropriate
6. bus released

Each of these states must be unambiguously defined in duration and format. The definitions must allow time enough for signal propagation and stabilization, so they are not independent of the technology employed. Within those hardware constraints, there is still much room for different definitions. Timing for each step in the series above can be determined by a master clock, by specific delays with respect to an event such as the release of the bus (this is essentially timing by local clock), or by specific handshaking—the get-it–got-it–good routine. Many bus definitions mix these methods.

As you can see from the list, there is some overhead—an unavoidable delay—in getting to the meat of the operation, which is certainly steps 4 and 5. To reduce percentage of time devoted to that overhead, two steps can be taken:

- First, whenever practical, it is good to transfer as much useful data as possible for each acquisition of the bus. What militates against transferring too large a block is that a subsystem such as the CPU may grind to a halt waiting for a turn on the bus. With backplane busses, maximum block sizes are typically four to eight transfers. On a 32-bit bus, that means 16 to 32 bytes, with block transfer cycles of less than a microsecond. With a peripheral bus such as SCSI or DSSI, where some degree of buffering on both sides is presumed so there are no critical immediate demands, block sizes are much larger—typically 1 to 16 pages, with block-transfer cycles of 1 to 2 ms.
- Second, recognizing that some users, such as the CPU, will make much more use of the bus than other masters, some bus definitions include the concept of *parking*. That is, the last user does not release the bus even if it is idle unless told to do so by some other user. There is only a small penalty—the time to release the bus—and the potential savings from eliminating steps 1 . . . 3 and 6 for most transfers can be quite large indeed.

Once contention begins, how does the *arbitration* proceed? VME and Futurebus are quite different in their mechanics but similar in objectives. To begin with, each defines two different ways of ordering the requests: *priority* and *fairness*. In priority, the order is prescribed; in fairness, the initial order is generally prescribed, but after the first turn, each served user must wait until there are no other contending users until it can contend again. The need for both modes arises because some users cannot wait very long—obtaining the bus is part of their *critical path*—thus obligating short queues for some users; on the other hand, a greedy user may starve other users and finally bring the system essentially to a halt.

Quite independent of how one selects the next user, there are two physical ways of determining the queue order. These are by *daisy chaining* and by *assigned number*, equivalent respectively to standing in line and to taking a number at the bakery. Daisy chaining is arranged, as shown in Figure 8.11, by having each chained group connected in parallel to the **bus request** line but in series to the **bus grant** line. The grant to user N must pass through users N-1, . . . , 1. Each one in the chain can prevent grants to higher numbers from passing through, so only if all users $< N$ are satisfied will N see that it has been granted the bus. If the wire making the connection between n's **out** and $(n + 1)$'s **in** is part of the bus, then the order of selection is determined by the distance of the card from the arbiter. In other words, slot position is queue position. Alternatively, if the wiring is independent of the bus, as it would be if several potential masters shared a single card/slot, then geographical and numerical order need not be identical.

To make a daisy chain behave under priority rules, each master opens its switch whenever it needs the bus. Since that means that lower priority positions can never be served while a higher priority master wants the bus, you definitely have a priority system and not a fairness system. To get the daisy chain to act in fair fashion, the rule is that once you have had a turn, you may not pull down on the request line until no other

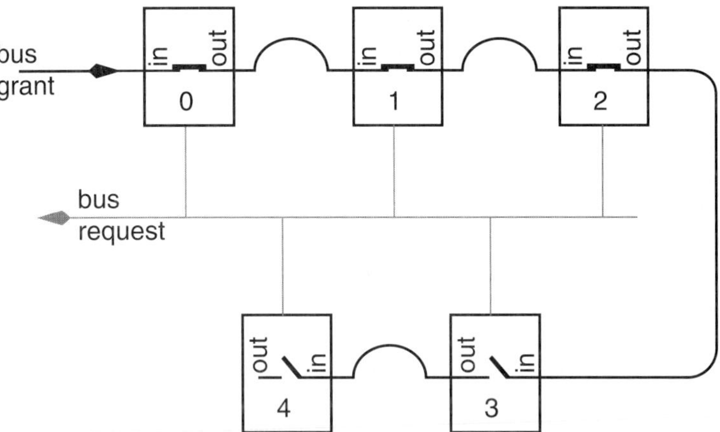

FIGURE 8.11 Five users daisy-chained together. Any and all can pull down on the bus-request line. Users 3 and 4 wish to use the bus so their series switches are open. User 3 can see the bus grant line but until 3 closes its switch, 4 cannot.

user is pulling down on it and while you are waiting, you must keep your **bus grant** series switch closed. Thus, in Figure 8.11, if user 3 got a turn, it must allow 4 to see the **bus grant** line. Only when the **bus request** line is free (unasserted or high) for some prescribed interval can 3 regard itself as *in line* again. The cost in bus lines for the daisy-chain system is three. These comprise **bus request**, **bus grant**, and **busy**, the last being the line that the assigned master pulls down to indicate that it is using the bus. (The state *bus free* is essentially having **busy** in the unasserted state, though most busses require several other conditions to be met as well.) A rather obvious potential problem for daisy chaining is the delay time for having the **grant** signal propagate through all of the series switches. That delay will extend the time devoted to stages 1 . . . 3, stages in which no "useful" bus activity is possible (although see the later discussion of overlapping the arbitration stage with the previous data stage).

The *assigned number* scheme for sorting out the order of requests is either *high is first* or *low is first*. In general, some scheme is adopted which allows all users to assert their numbers during the *contention* phase. Then, either a specified arbiter or the users themselves recognize the current top dog and all others back off. The winner asserts **busy** and gets on with its business. Having everyone asserting a number simultaneously requires enough bus lines to accommodate that action. For the SCSI peripheral bus, the eight data lines are used with each of the modules assigned one line. Obviously, the SCSI bus is limited to eight users, but arbitration is certainly simple. The high wire gets the bus.

VMEbus uses four **bus request** lines BR3. . .BR0 and four **bus grant** lines BG3 . . . BG0. In the VME scheme of things, these lines should be thought of as *class-priority* arbitration lines. Then, within a class, if further subdivision is required, a daisy-chain scheme is employed. Thus, the arbiter enables a single class and then the daisy chain determines which member of the class is selected. When *fairness* is desired, some scheme of switching fairly among the classes as well as among the daisy-chained users must be considered. Since the VME system uses a single arbiter, located perforce on card 1 (counting from 1), the arbiter can enforce class fairness by cycling through the classes like a sweep-second hand marches through the seconds. Such a fairness algorithm is called *round robin.* Within a class, however, fairness (or unfairness) among the daisy-chained is distributed among the several users on a chain. There is a considerable liability with the centralized arbiter scheme and that is that the whole system fails if the arbiter board fails or vanishes. The daisy chain is similarly subject to losing users if a board fails or is removed. In systems which must support genteel degradation upon component failure (*fault-tolerant systems*) or which would benefit by permitting live (system electrically active) board replacement, contention and selection must be available to all users all of the time. The VMEbus does not meet this requirement. Few busses do.

The Futurebus specifically makes fault tolerance an objective. Accordingly, it strives to eliminate any "single-point" failure modes where a single component brings the whole system down on its knees. *Assigned number* is the queuing convention and each user does its own determination of the correct outcome of contention. In other words, arbitration is *distributed* among all of the modules and is not dependent upon the presence of any card. The contention number has seven digits **ab6 . . . ab0**, five of which are really identification (**ab5 . . . ab1**). **ab0** is used to assure that all asserted numbers have odd parity and **ab6** separates priority IDs from fairness IDs. The Futurebus provides each slot with a *hardwired*, geographically determined identification number, GA4 . . . GA0, but the slots are permitted to use other numbers (and even change number) as long as they meet the requirement that no two slots have the same number. Along with the seven-digit ID, each Futurebus board uses four lines to handshake the six steps involved in a bus-ownership transfer. This handshake is quite unlike the *get-it–got-it–good* convention. Instead, using pairs of pulldown lines, one to mark the old state and one to mark the new, all users connected to the bus—even those not currently involved in any transaction—walk through the steps in virtual unison. A transition is started when the first to make it pulls down on line B and is complete only when *everyone* has released line A (which should follow pulling down on B), which marks the previous state. Instead of *get-it–got-it–good*, we have "All together now, one, two, two, two . . . two." Since it is the absence of anyone holding down line B which signals the new state, the removal of a board does not interrupt the transitions for any other board. Do not be too quickly swayed by this argument. The Futurebus does allow live insertion and removal of boards, but this does not make it completely fault-tolerant. Obviously a "stuck closed" switch can bring the system to a halt and certain combinations of open switches could be mighty confusing. The only way to deal with a "bolted fault" in the control lines or certain multiple failures is to provide some redundancy which permits error correction. For a high level of fault tolerance, redundant I/O structures must be used.

In terms of arbitration costs, a full VME-spec bus uses 12 lines and requires each board to have four transceiver gates for passing daisy-chained **grant** signals. It also requires a single bus arbiter to select the next user. Its logic, even for the round-robin scheme, is quite simple. A portion of the arbitration logic for *fairness* systems must reside on each daisy-chained user.

For the Futurebus, the costs include 11 lines on the bus and possibly complex logic on each board. The complexity can be avoided, but if such concepts as changing

IDs and moving back and forth between fairness and priority are incorporated, the arbitration system costs can become important.

8.3.3 Bus Parking and Overlapped Arbitration and Data Cycles

Some masters of the I/O system work actively most of the time; others will be sporadically active. It seems foolish not to let the I/O system adapt a bit to accommodate activity shifts. One simple method for doing this is *parking*. With this scheme, which is available for both the VME and Futurebus, the current user does not automatically relinquish control of the bus when it finishes its current transfer. Instead, it *parks* on the bus, giving up control only when another user requests bus mastery. If the CPU is opening up a new routine, for example, it will be packing many new words into the cache. Why go through bus release and arbitration for each transfer? If the backplane bus can be devoted to feeding the cache for a while, the CPU will be able to run at something close to full throttle. This was the state that we assumed in developing the state machine of Figure 5.20. Parking is the normal mode for Futurebus and an optional mode for VME. When parking is the operating mode, an arbitration cycle begins with a request for the current owner to relinquish the bus. The response to the request depends on whether the request is to be looked at as an order to yield or simply as a *no parking* sign. Both busses make provisions for immediate, unconditional release of the bus for such impending disasters as a power failure, but in the absence of a genuine emergency, both busses permit the current user to continue until a convenient time for a break occurs. The definition of what constitutes a reasonable delay is so dependent on local circumstances that it would be improper to make it part of the bus definition. Local bus designers must ask themselves whether anybody on the bus will starve to death if they cannot get on the bus in say 10 μs. If the answer is yes, then a maximum delay of 5 μs or less may be called for. Since the size of transfers is usually not adaptable, what this does is to constrain block transfers such as those needed to pack full lines in the cache. If memory is designed to function efficiently with block transfers, then it may be possible to transfer all of the data with a single address transmission. Transfer rates can easily spurt up a factor of 10 in a block-transfer mode. On the other hand, if some device that you really want cannot wait, then you must give it the access it needs.

Once the bus is released, a new owner can assert control. If arbitration is held up until release, there will be a nonproductive hiatus between release and reassertion of control. For a peripheral bus such as SCSI, where the data lines themselves are used for arbitration, you have no other choice; you have to let go of the bus before arbitration. This is not a bad choice for SCSI because its transfer blocks—typically one to eight pages—are so long compared to the time for arbitration. The ratio is typically 500 or 1000 to 1. Backplane busses, on the other hand, will have frequent master changes and transfers of typically no more than four to eight words. Separating these short bursts with the punctuation of contention and arbitration would detract from bus performance. Instead, both busses carry on their arbitration over lines which are devoted to that cause. This allows arbitration before the bus is free so that the new master knows it has won and can assert control as soon as the bus itself is free. Many VMEbus implementations do not use these features of parking and overlapped arbitration and data cycles, but for maximum performance, they are necessary. Let us see what delays are entailed in getting from user A to user B.

For Futurebus, the operation requires 11 lines (AP, AQ, AR, AC, and AB6 . . . 0) and three or six steps, depending on whether *fairness* is inhibiting all interested masters. Figure 8.12 illustrates the state transitions, showing the three handshake lines, AP, AQ, AR. State 1 is the state where the master-elect becomes master and sets off to use the bus. In this state, everyone—every possible master—is pulling down on (asserting) AR. When any user—even one inhibited by fairness—needs the bus, it asserts AP. Upon observing the transition in AP, each module asserts AP, releases AR and starts progressing through the bus handover. However, nobody gets to state 2 until everyone releases AR. In this way, the slowest or the last to hear of the change determines the speed to arbitration. During this first transition, any module that is not inhibited by

FIGURE 8.12 State transition diagram for the Futurebus. All potential masters step through the sequence shown regardless of state or desire. Line AC determines if a six- or three-transition sequence is followed.

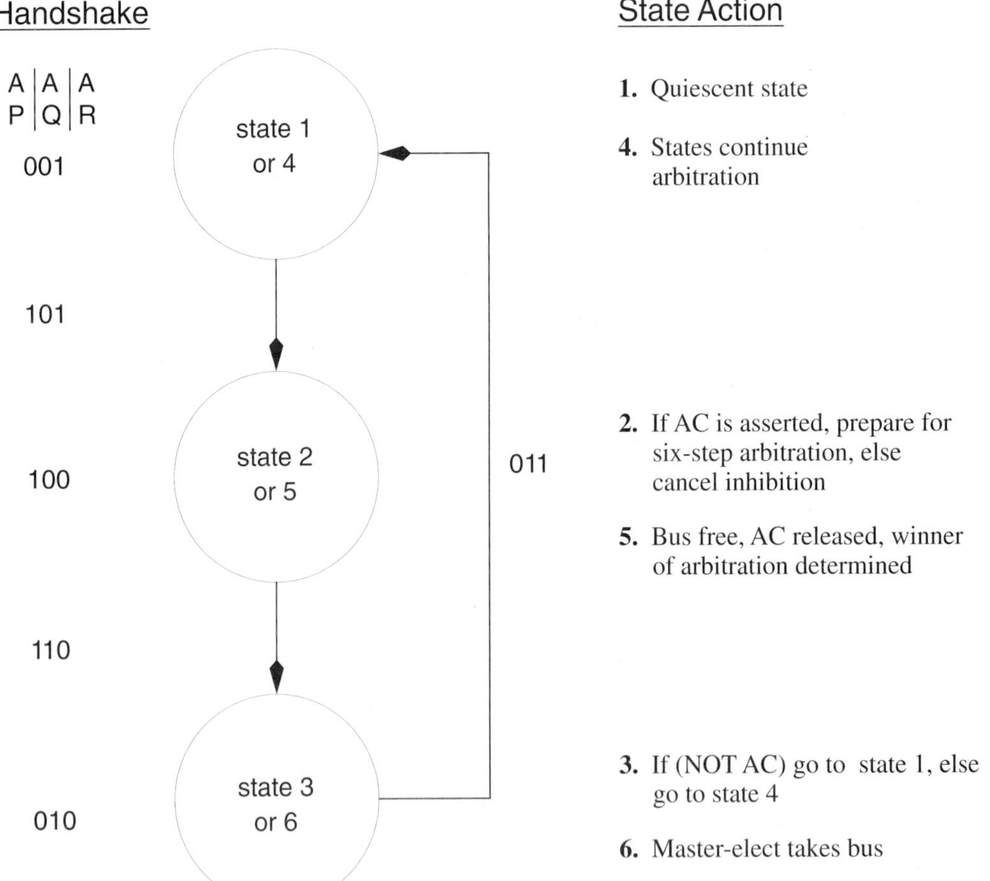
Handshake
State Action
A A A
P Q R
001
101
100
110
010
011
state 1 or 4
state 2 or 5
state 3 or 6
1. Quiescent state
4. States continue arbitration
2. If AC is asserted, prepare for six-step arbitration, else cancel inhibition
5. Bus free, AC released, winner of arbitration determined
3. If (NOT AC) go to state 1, else go to state 4
6. Master-elect takes bus

fairness and wants the bus asserts line AC to indicate that it is contending. If AC is asserted, that indicates to all devices that this will be a six-step sequence. Upon reaching state 2, if AC is asserted, all contenders assert their arbitration code on lines AB6 . . . 0. If AC is not asserted, all of the fairness-inhibited devices cancel their inhibitions and become either free bystanders or competitors. They can then arrive at 1 ready to contend for the bus on the basis of their pecking order.

The act of arbitration in the six-step version proceeds as follows: Each competitor, asserting its number, does a high-to-low comparison of its arbitration number with the bits asserted on AB6 . . . 0. At the first bus "1" that is not matched in its own number, it is obliged to release all bits of lower value. For example, if A is asserting the 1's in 0110111 and B is asserting 0111011, A would be obliged to switch to 0110000, in effect leaving on the line B's whole number. In this way, only the biggest number is left on the AB lines. If your number is left, you have won. The six transitions may be thought of as:

$1 \Rightarrow 2$ Modules note the current bus master (if necessary) and if they want the bus and are not inhibited, assert AC. (For each module, timing of the arbitration interval begins when AC is detected. Note that each module does its own timing.)

$2 \Rightarrow 3$ Based on whether AC is asserted, all modules decide whether a three- or six-step cycle is under way. If AC is not asserted, the inhibited modules cancel inhibition and become either contenders or free bystanders; if AC is asserted, all contenders assert their arbitration number and the master, if not competing, removes its number.

$3 \Rightarrow 1$ No action. Bus still belongs to original master, but a six-step sequence for transfer can now begin. This is how an inhibited module can force transitions until it gets a chance to get back into the queue.

$3 \Rightarrow 4$ This serves as setup time so that each module is prepared to stop or go on depending on the number of cycles to step through. Timing of the arbitration interval continues if this is a six-step sequence.

$4 \Rightarrow 5$ All competing modules must complete their arbitration interval before moving to state 5.

$5 \Rightarrow 6$ Master initiates this transition to indicate that the bus is now free. Each module checks to see if it has won. AC is released. (At this point, all modules do a validity check of the arbitration result. If a parity error or selection error occurs, AC is asserted to force a retry of the whole sequence.)

$6 \Rightarrow 1$ Master-elect assumes mastership; all others cease asserting their arbitration numbers.

Note that fairness does not preclude a module from insisting that others get on with their business and let those inhibited get back in line. Furthermore, the overlap is as complete as possible. As soon as the bus master releases the bus in the $5 \Rightarrow 6$ transition, the bus may be acquired by the master-elect.

How long does all of this take? The duration does not detract from maximum bus performance under contention, since it is overlapped, but from a parked state, the length of the arbitration effort determines how rapidly another user can get on the bus. The Futurebus does all of its transactions by observing transitions, not values. As you can see by Figure 8.12, a transition is started by one module pulling down on AP, AQ, or AR and is completed by all modules releasing another of those three. Each of those transitions is then limited by the round-trip delay time (crudely 3 ns) and the delay through the integrators and on-board logic at the modules. If we assume that these add another 5 ns or so, the minimum time for a step is then 8 ns. Since such things as parity errors are checked, it behooves the careful bus committee to allow enough time for all the bits to get there and get settled. To this end, the Futurebus committee established a minimum arbitration time—the time which must elapse between transition $1 \Rightarrow 2$ with AC asserted to the completion of transition $5 \Rightarrow 6$—as eight times the longest of those bit settling times plus four round trips on the bus. With the crude wave-of-the-hand numbers above, we have this minimum time as $4 \times 3 + 8 \times 5 = 52$ ns. This is roughly how long it takes to transfer bus ownership with a quiescent bus. Another way to look at this same number is to say that there is no point in giving any user less than about 0.1 μs on the bus since a new user won't be in place before then. While that is currently the cycle time for "ordinary" memory chips, considerably faster ones are available. Accordingly, if we do some memory interleaving, it does not look as if we would find any reason to inhibit the transmission of full cache lines on a Futurebus version of our computer.

Now let us consider VMEbus. Recall that arbitration is conducted by a single arbiter on module 1 on four prioritized request lines and that the four bus-grant lines are daisy-chained. Bus release is independent of arbitration, being recognized by the release of both BUS-BUSY (BBSY) and ADDRESS-STROBE (AS) on the data-transfer bus. The only time constraint specified on arbitration is that upon receiving the grant, a module must hold the bus (assert BBSY) for at least 90 ns and that that same module must release its bus-request line at least 30 ns before it releases the BBSY line. This constraint is to assure that the arbiter can separate outstanding requests from the one currently being served. The dearth of constraints derives from having all of the action at one place—the arbiter. Along with deciding who gets the bus, it also decides when. Consistent with the objective of overlapping data transfers with arbitration, the arbiter watches the BBSY line. It releases the bus grant line when BBSY goes low and asserts a grant line only when BBSY is high. To accomplish the overlap, the spec *recommends* that the current bus master release BBSY after starting its last data transfer. During that period, it will be asserting AS. As soon as that last transfer is accomplished, AS will be released and the new master can take over.

The *parking* mode on VME is accomplished by use of the BUS-CLEAR (BCLR) line. That line, driven by the arbiter, simply informs the current master that a higher order request is pending. (Note that there is no provision specified for having round-robin arbitration use BCLR, but it is not forbidden. Accordingly, one could design an arbiter which pushed the current user along whenever there was a request pending.) Let us assume the same conditions that we did for the Futurebus—user parked on bus but no bus activity. Time to obtain the bus would comprise the following parts: asserting request (half a round trip on loaded bus plus one receiver time), 15 ns; asserting BCLR (setup, half a round trip on loaded bus plus one receiver time), 30 ns; release of BBSY (setup, half a round trip on loaded bus plus one receiver time), 30 ns; assertion of bus-grant line and transmission through three stages of daisy chain (setup, half a round trip on loaded bus plus one receiver time, plus three daisy-chain transmission gates), 45 ns. The total is 120 ns, more than twice what Futurebus requires. Note that this doubling of time is partly the slower round-trip time for the TTL-loaded bus and partly the bus conventions.

8.3.4 Data Cycles

Getting to be bus master is like getting a dial tone on a party line. It just empowers the user but it establishes neither a connection nor a data-transfer convention. Bus designers try to avoid putting the module designers into straitjackets while still meeting the standards of robust, error-free data transfers. The variety of possible transfer modes which our example busses support is really quite marvelous. Each bus must provide not only the lines for data and address and for handshaking (or clocking) the transfer but also the ability to control the format and conventions of the transfer. Consider, for example, that in snooping, snarfing, and intercession (Section 5.6.3 on page 265), a single address may reference multiple modules. Futurebus explicitly allows for *intervention*. A CPU asks for *datum_A*, fully expecting an answer from memory; the data arrives right on schedule, but not from memory. There had to be some way for the cache holding the latest version of *datum_A* to tell memory to hold its peace. (Neither snooping nor snarfing requires a bus convention.) Another substantial efficiency is to have data blocks transferred with only the first address. While that puts the burden of incrementing addresses on each and every module, it can almost double the data transfer rate. It is a useful idea, but consider the analog of the page fault: What happens when the master sends or asks for data that exceeds the slave's immediate capacity? Obviously, the slave must be able to communicate its saturation to the master.

What emerges from these two examples is the need for a reasonable number of control and control-data lines and for a complex set of conventions in their use which permit the master and slaves to define precisely what is going on. Both of our example busses do this.

Table 8.5 shows the set of 55 lines which Futurebus uses for data transfers. Two of them are for a "future spec"; 53 are currently employed. Two approaches are rather novel in this bus definition: the *edge definition* of transactions and the concept of all the modules participating at some level in all transactions. The edge definition is similar to the edge-triggered flipflop. An event has "happened" when the correct edge arrives. For example, for each slave (selected or not), the address transmission is over when the AS is asserted. Similarly, for the master, the address phase is over when, depending on function, AK is asserted or AI is released. Since it is critical to causality that the data be there simultaneously with the edge-defining strobe, the definition defines a critical line or lines for each transaction and specifies the *skew* or delay between this line and all other lines as being positive at all points on the line. Previous bus definitions all involved *setup* and *hold* times to allow for a particular technology's need. Once so defined, the bus is bound by that definition even if improved technologies like BTL would permit much faster operation. With edge definitions, the recipient can react as rapidly as its current technology permits. Another interesting outcome of this definition

TABLE 8.5 The 55 lines comprising the data section on the Futurebus

	Asserted by	Use
CM<5 . . . 0> **CP**	Master	**Command.** Used in both address and data transfer cycles. Establishes the transfer mode during address transfer. During a data transfer, establishes data direction, which bytes (of 4) are invalid, and whether a third party is involved in an otherwise two-party transfer. CP is the command parity bit (odd).
AD<31 . . . 0> **BP<W . . . Z>** **TG,TP**	All	**Address/Data.** Addresses always go from the master but data may go in either direction. AD31 is most significant. BP provides the byte parity (odd) for each of the 4 AD bytes. TG (tag) and its odd parity bit (TP) are for future use.
AS	Master	**Address Sync.** Asserted as soon as valid command and address information is on AD and held throughout the data transfer interval.
ST<3 . . . 0>	Slave	**Status.** Used in both address and data transfer cycles. Indicates when an address is recognized or when an error condition obtains. Also can indicate that the module addressed is busy, out of room, or locked.
AK	Slave	**Address Acknowledge.** The acknowledge handshake to AS. Remains asserted throughout data transfer phase.
AI	Slave	**AK Inverse.** A supplementary handshake to AS. Being the *inverse* of AK, it permits the master to observe when *all* slaves have acknowledged AS by releasing the AI line.
DS	Master	**Data Sync.** Toggled each time valid data is on (master) or to be put on (slave) the AD lines.
DK	Slave	**Data Acknowledge.** The acknowledge handshake to DS.
DI	Slave	**DK Inverse.** When used as the inverse of DK, it permits the master to observe when *all* slaves have acknowledged DS by releasing the DI line. When used independently, it allows intervention by an unselected slave.

is the use of both edges on the data strobes. In other words, you don't have to recock to fire. You transfer data on the assertion edge and on the release edge. This has to save 5 to 10 ns on every datum in a multiple transfer. Obviously, it leads to greater complexity in the bus interfaces—for example, you have to do something different to conclude an odd number of transfers than with an even number—but with modern integrated circuits, the added burden is small and the potential benefit large.

The idea of shared responsibility for monitoring the bus, while not entirely unique, is carried to unusual limits in the Futurebus definition. Not only can any module intrude if a bus error is detected but a much more positive sort of interaction is envisaged: the ability of an unselected slave to intervene and respond when that is called for by the state of the system. The use of inverted pairs of strobes is a natural consequence of thinking of every module as sharing in bus control. By pairing the strobes, the master can watch both for the first to pull down and also the last to let go. This leads to excellent possibilities for *broadcast* (write) and *broadcall* (essentially, *snarfing*) to multiple modules. For example, in a system of many processors where the same data may reside *at the same address* in multiple local memories, a single address can arouse all of the devices holding that address to read the data following. In the broadcast protocol (signaled by asserting CM1 during the address phase), the DK/DI line pair is used to log each datum in, with the line which happens to be asserted *prior to the start of each datum transfer* being watched to see when it is released. At that point, the last receiver has obtained its data.

Consider a block transfer of three words to a group of slaves. An odd block transfer is about the most complex regular transaction. Figure 8.13 provides a timing diagram to illustrate the handshaking and will allow us to estimate time for a block transfer. The transaction begins with the master driving onto the bus the address appropriate to all of the slaves to be selected and the command in which INTENT TO MODIFY (CM4), BLOCK TRANSFER (CM2), and BROADCAST (CM1) are asserted. With appropriate care to avoid negative skew, the master then asserts AS. As soon as *each* module sees AS asserted, it compares the address to its range. If it has been selected, it asserts AK, drives the appropriate status lines [SELECTED (ST2) is all that is expected but BUSY (ST0) and ERROR (ST1) are also possible], and releases AI. When AI goes high, the master reads the status lines. Assuming that no slave indicated an error or busy, the master starts driving the data onto the line. Each datum is followed as quickly as skew permits with a switch of DS. Each slave responds as soon as it can with ST and then a switch in DK and DI. The master has finished the transmission and may read ST when the low line of that pair goes high. At the conclusion of the last data transfer, the master releases AS, which tells the slaves that the transmission is complete. The slaves respond by releasing DK and asserting DI. The transaction, however, is not

FIGURE 8.13 Odd data count, block broadcast transaction on the Futurebus. All lines are *wired-OR* and are asserted by being driven low. The equal spacing of the master and slave intervals is an artifact of the drawing. In Futurebus transactions, the recipient of a signal may act as soon as the appropriate strobe is observed to change.

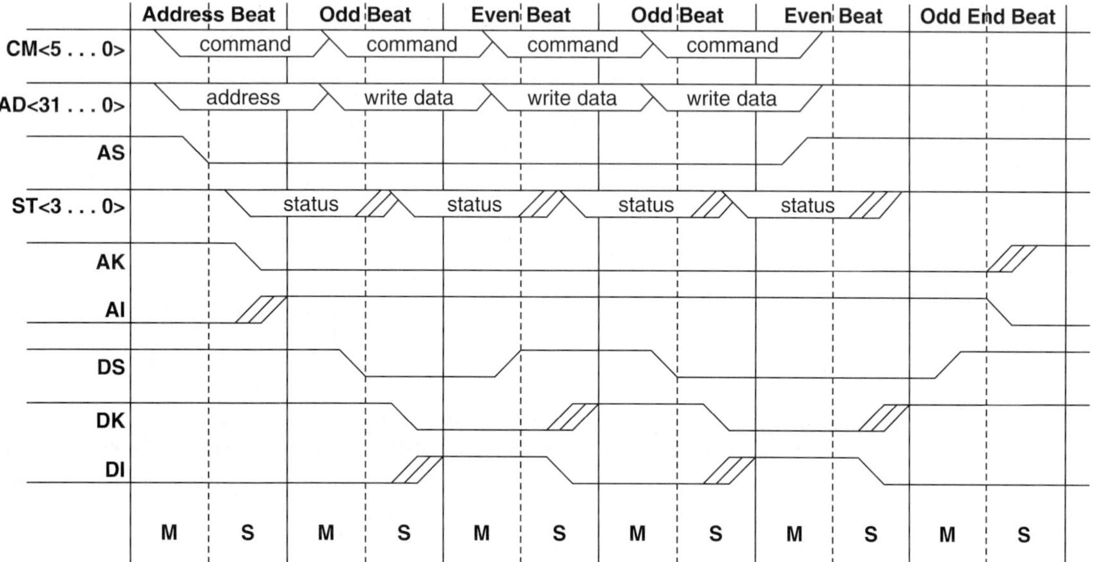

complete; DS is still being asserted. To get back to "GO," the master releases DS and the slaves respond by releasing AK and asserting AI.

To estimate the total time for a transmission of a block of N words, we can make the not-unreasonable assumption that the time for each half-step (M or S) in Figure 8.13 is a transit of the loaded bus plus four gate transitions. Both numbers are quite independent of the bus definition—a central objective in Futurebus. Using 3 ns for the loaded bus and 1 ns for each gate layer, one obtains 9 ns for a half cycle in Figure 8.13. For N words in a block, the total time is $T = (N+2)\times 18$ (N odd) and $(N+1)\times 18$ (N even). Were we advertising the bus using a philosophy of "Tell 'em the best; ignore the rest," we would state the data capacity of this bus as the limit of the block transfer or 4 bytes in 18 ns or 222 MB/s. In Table 8.1, the claim was made that Futurebus had a 400 MB/s capability. That is only 5 ns per half-cycle, which seems pretty optimistic. If we were to assume that our D-cache was parked on the bus and always read four words, the sustained rate using our numbers would be 178 MB/s. Futurebus can achieve that rate.

When we look at the data cycles on the VMEbus, we can see the reasons why the Futurebus attempted to get a technology-independent definition. Even though VMEbus is asynchronous, it requires TTL-derived hold times. All VME-compatible modules must hold for those times no matter how fast their technologies. However, before being too critical of the design, it should be stated that when this bus was developed, it was designed for the MC68000 and the family of microprocessors which could reasonably be expected to grow out of that chip. It has served well and nobly in that roll and only recently has begun to show some signs of age as applications with multiple MC68030 or MC68040 processors have come into use. (A new, 64-bit wide version of VME attempts to meet the competition while retaining the ability to use all of the VME-compatible devices already on the market.)

Table 8.6 presents the data section of VMEbus. It is noticeably wider than Futurebus even though it has no parity bits and no inverse strobes. Its extra width is devoted entirely to separate data and address sections. Given that busses as old as Digital's SBI (the VAX backplane in the model 780) were multiplexing address and data onto the same lines when VME was being designed, one might well ask what the designers had in mind when they devoted this rather expensive resource to parallel transmission of data and address. According to Shlomo Pri-Tal, the decision was based on the observation that vast majority of bus operations were the processor reading instructions. Pri-Tal states: "It does this by executing single-transfer read cycles." By having separate address and data structures, the single-datum transfers could be handled more rapidly. Obviously, this focus on the single-datum transfer, quite valid in its time, did not foresee line-reading caches on systems run by microprocessors. That day has already arrived.

To give VME its due, its separate bussing does permit the overlap of *last* data and *next* address in what the spec calls "address pipelining." If you were operating as expected without doing block transfers, this overlapping would definitely wring a bit of speed out of the bus. With writes, the case for separate address lines is more obvious. Address and data can be sent together rather than sequentially.

The VMEbus does admit multiple data transfers. In fact, it specifically permits the transfers to walk off one module and onto another, something absolutely forbidden

TABLE 8.6 The 77 lines comprising the data section of VMEbus

	Asserted by	Use
A<0 . . . 31>	Master	**Address.** These lines hold the address throughout the transaction. A0, A1, DS0, DS1, and LWORD work to define both the number of valid bytes in the 4 and alignment of those bytes in the 32-bit word transmitted.
AM<0 . . . 5>	Master	**Address Modifier.** Used to specify privilege, whether program or data reference, whether this will be a block transfer, and whether the address uses 16, 24, or 32 bits. Among the 64 possible codes, several are left for user definition.
D<0 . . . 31>	All	**Data.** The specification allows the bus to be configured with either 32 or 16 lines.
DS<0 . . . 1>	Master	**Data Strobes.** On write cycles, the first data strobe indicates that valid data is on bus. On read cycles, the release of the first data strobe acknowledges receipt of the data. See A<0 . . . 31> as well.
LWORD	Master	**Longword.** Simply a modifier to specify which bytes are valid. It really signifies a byte selection which is not available from a 16-bit memory such as an odd-address pair, 3 bytes or 4 bytes.
AS	Master	**Address Strobe.** Indicates that a valid address is on A<0 . . . 31>.
BERR	All	**Bus Error.** Indicates an illegal code or operation or a timeout. There is no bus parity check so BERR does not indicate a literal bus error.
DTACK	Slave	**Data Acknowledge.** On WRITE operation, it acknowledges receipt of data; on a READ operation, it indicates that valid data is on the data lines.
WRITE	Master	**Write/Read.** Asserted by the master to indicate that the data is going from master to slave.

on Futurebus. VME limits this strange permission by adding the rule that no block transfer may cross a 256-byte address boundary. This rule appears more onerous than the permission could ever be beneficial. You would have to put hardware on all block-transfer masters which would deal with this artificial line of demarcation. Furthermore, if there can be a change in the slave designated based on the slave's perception of the current address, then all potential slaves must track any block transfer. It is small wonder that few VME busses use block transfers. Apart from that strange permission and its even stranger constraint, VME's block transfer bears many likenesses to Futurebus. Since we have analyzed the timing for a Futurebus block transfer and since block transfers will certainly be important for cache filling and cache writeback, let us do the same analysis for the VMEbus even though we might not want to use it in this mode.

On both busses, the block transfer is declared on the first address. After that, the slave is responsible for (and must be able to do) address incrementing. Each transfer is clocked through with a "get-it–got-it" handshake, or, in the case of VME, "get-it–got-it–good." That extra strophe is the reset required by relying only on the assertion edge for the transfer handshake. The principal differences between VME and Futurebus are these:

- VME's use of a single strobe from the slave implies that there can be only one slave at a time (no broadcast or broadcall modes in clocked data transactions).

- The VME bus uses only assertion edges for data strobes. Accordingly, both strobes must be reset before the next datum can be sent.
- VME specifies hold times and minimum delays on certain portions of the signals.

Laying out the principal parts of the full transaction for a 16-byte block transfer with the required and expected delays leads to Figure 8.14. The timing between the slave's response (DTACK) and the data is a bit strange. On a read (slave's data ⇒ master), DTACK really means "that's my address" and can precede the data by up to 25 ns; on a write (master's data ⇒ slave), DTACK is both acknowledgement of the address and a signal to the master that the data has been read and may be removed; the data must be valid 30 ns prior to DTACK [VME, 87]. The expected delays were obtained by assuming 5 ns to pull down, 5 ns propagation time, and 10 ns from the arrival of DS to the assertion of the data. This might seem a little pessimistic, but if you use those numbers with the requisite delays of 30 ns between data assertion and DTACK assertion and the 40 ns between DS release and DS assertion, you get 110 ns per data cycle. In the limit of long block transfers, that gives you 36 MB/s—essentially what is claimed in Table 8.1. Adding on the required delay between address assertion and AS assertion slows the average data rate to 34 MB/s on block transfers of four 32-bit words. That should be compared to the178 MB/s performance we obtained for the Futurebus.

8.4 I/O STRATEGY AND I/O INTELLIGENCE

To this point in the chapter, we have been building the bottom layer—the physical interconnect and the limits imposed by Maxwell's equations and by the protocols and

FIGURE 8.14 Timing diagram for a block read of four 4-byte words on the VMEbus. The WRITE and LWORD lines have been left out to simplify the diagram. They would pull down for the duration. The lines that are driven up as well as down are shown as spreading. The address strobe is released after the last transaction. The BBSY line (not shown) could be released during the last data transfer to allow arbitration to begin. The bus is not released until AS and DTACK are released.

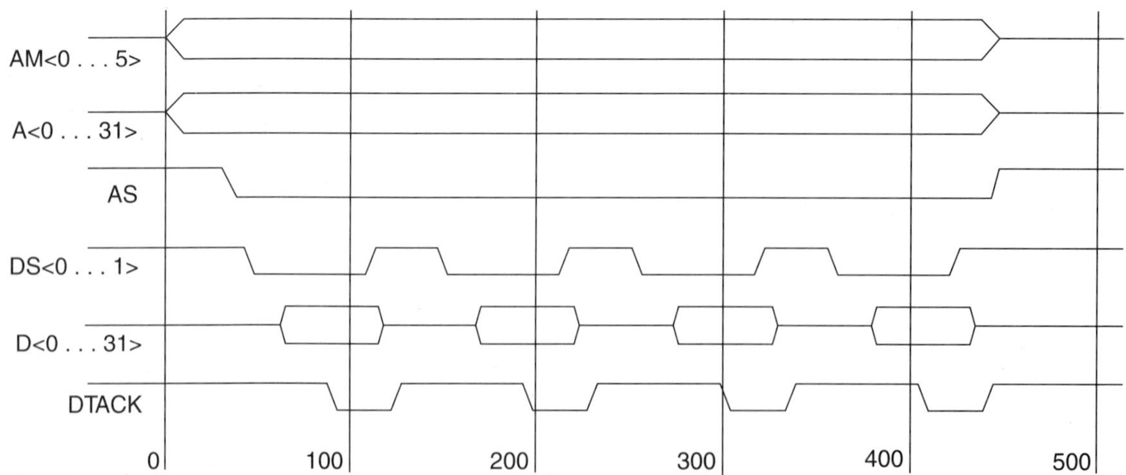

formalisms of the bus definition. Once the interconnect has been selected, making efficient use of its bandwidth demands the design and tuning of an effective I/O system. There are many strategic decisions to be made. The bus-speed examples we developed are devoted entirely to the cache-memory interaction, particularly the operation of loading the cache. While this is critical to the performance of the CPU—how can you do one instruction per clock if you don't have one instruction per clock to do?—the cache-loading issue assumes that your data and program are in memory. To be there, they had to get there. You can hardly make progress on programs or data while they reside way out there on a disk file. The operation of bringing something into memory can be quite complex. It can involve making room in memory by swapping something out; it can require the fetching of pages of hierarchical index and protection data; reliability considerations may require that any file must be recoverable in spite of the failure of any disk at any time; and in large systems, any given I/O operation is apt to be inextricably interconnected to operations going on another machine in the same *cluster.*

The strategy for controlling all of this coming and going in some coherent and efficient fashion will entail choices in both software and hardware. Take a look at Figure 8.1 again. That diagram shows two of our host processors sharing a common disk and tape system and interconnected to each other through a SCSI bus. This layout is derived from configurations which can be used in interconnecting small- to medium-sized VAXs into clusters over the Digital DSSI bus. In that form, the separate systems would probably also have their own "personal" disks, connected either through other DSSIs or other peripheral busses. These personal disks can also be available to other hosts with the local host acting as *server.* That is, the remote host sees the local host as an intelligent disk controller, no different from any other disk controller on the DSSI bus. Let us follow the course of a request from a host to disk server on such a bus.

The description of the transaction we are about to give is frequently dissected into a stack of horizontal transactions which are reminiscent of a telephone call. The analogy is a good one in the sense that:

• callers talk to callers	logical layer
• analog phones communicate to analog phones	transport layer
• interchanges exchange digital packets	network layer
• packets are encoded and decoded	data link layer
• transmitters talk to receivers	physical layer

Each of these layers interacts only with the layers immediately adjacent; each layer can be considered independent except for the interface. By having well-defined interfaces, totally independent designers and manufacturers can develop products which can be stacked up and work well as an integrated system. There is such appeal to this organization and such demand for open (i.e., *public*) system definitions with competition among independent firms to supply equipment and software for one or more layers that many firms, the IEEE, ANSI, and the International Standards Organization (ISO) have developed public or semipublic open standards for information interchange. Such standards are found in all sorts of communication networks, from international phone networks down to single computer hosts talking with their own disk controllers. For DEC, the semipublic standard is called the Mass Storage Control Protocol (MSCP). We will walk a read request down through the layers to see both what must be done and why it takes so long.

8.4.1 Delays, Delays, and More Delays

As you have undoubtedly noticed, the time for getting from here to there is seldom limited by such elemental considerations as the adhesion of your tires to the road. Similarly, the speed of light is seldom the ruling limit in I/O operations. The typical I/O request in a VAX/VMS system is for four pages. There are lots of one-page requests and relatively few very large transfers, most of which result from swapping out programs which are waiting (most often for I/O) to make more room for programs which are running. Normally, there are numerous requests pending at any moment. Two rates of data transfer must be considered. These comprise the *data rate*, the average flow of data measured say in megabytes per second, and the *response time* measured in seconds (or, more often, fractions thereof) of delay between the request and the availability of the data. While a high data transfer rate may assist in shortening the response time, one frequently finds that optimizing data transfer rates is done at the cost of longer response times. Why should this be so? Consider a highway example.

If you want to get from point A to point B on the Massachusetts Turnpike, you do best at 3 a.m. with the road empty and the police asleep. On the other hand, the Turnpike Commission is happiest between 7 and 9 a.m. when the maximum flow through the turnstiles occurs. Your personal arrival will be delayed by sharing the "bus" as well as delays in entry and exit, so your response time and frustration will be higher. Interestingly enough, 4:30–6 p.m. is bad for everyone, because the road jams and the booths jam and both total flow and personal speed decline. Drivers take other routes. Very similar behavior can be seen on I/O systems. The cures to the bottlenecks are very similar as well: more lanes, more booths, more efficient booth strategies, better on and off geometries, and finally, and only sometimes, higher speed limits. Let us look at the individual operations for the disk-read transfer of a four-page block contiguous in virtual memory in a VAX operating under VMS. Our objective is to look at the delays and the data rates.

A four-page request frequently begins with a page fault. This need for more program or data is conveyed to the operating system. This is the top of the *logical level*. An operating system function sets aside a four-page buffer in the operating system's data space. If the data direction were outbound, the data would be copied from the user's space to the buffer. The operating-system driver then posts a request, or in DECspeak, it "queues an IO request," or QIO. This is the bottom of the *logical* level. The transaction will get back to this level when the lower levels finish their tasks and word of success or failure percolates up through the *transport layer*.

The queuing operation is quite reminiscent of the queues discussed in Chapter 3, with all of the requirements for locks and semaphores to keep the queues coherent. In VMS there are four *command* queues for each I/O adapter. (Look at Figure 8.1. It shows a single SCSI adapter for each system. A system may have up to four SCSI adapters and other types of host-bus adapters to serve other I/O bus configurations.) The four queues provide a way to prioritize requests. The adapter will empty the top one (3) before starting on the next and will stop taking new requests from 0 if a previously empty higher queue gets a request.

Each request is stored in an *envelope*, a block of host memory big enough to hold any of the messages defined for the particular I/O system. The message itself contains a header—essentially an address block—which contains (among other things):

- message length in bytes
- message type (e.g., request, response)
- destination
- a unique ID number
- an error code byte (used in acknowledge messages)
- some control bits (e.g., saying if the adapter should separately acknowledge message transfer completion as well as data transfer completion)

This header tells the adapter everything it needs to know to handle delivery of this piece of mail. The rest of the message is, like a letter, intended for and meaningful only to the recipient.

At startup the adapter's registers have been loaded with the addresses of the queue headers. Furthermore, if the operating system puts an envelope on a queue that was previously empty, it sends an interrupt to the adapter to let it know that there is new mail on that queue. Accordingly, the adapter is always aware if there is mail in a particular queue, and it has the wherewithal to go get it. This means that the adapter is an independent customer on the host bus, seeking bus mastership whenever there are messages to transmit or when, as a slave to a peripheral on the peripheral bus, it is told to transfer data in either direction.

The step down into the *transport layer* is taken by the adapter when it accesses a QIO. It does this by snipping the envelope off the head of the *command queue*. *Snipping* is the correct term, as you shall shortly see, because after that transaction, the piece of memory constituting the envelope has quite vanished from the VAX's ken. Only the adapter knows where it is—that is, it "has a pointer to it." Following the Figure 8.1 configuration, where the adapter is a SCSI or DSSI adapter, the adapter will then contend for the SCSI bus, and upon becoming master, it will acquire as its slave the destination specified in the message header. The adapter obviously has to behave on one side as a VAX backplane bus device and on the other side as a DSSI or SCSI device. These operations comprise the *data link* and *physical layers*. Generally, the primitive functions on both sides are handled by small state machines with all supervisory or intelligent functions carried on by an internal adapter CPU or state machine. The lowest smart level is the *network layer* which keeps track of the success of transactions in the state machines. In this sense, the transport layer, recognizing that it has a message for customer 5, tells its network layer to start its little state machine on the SCSI side to "connect me to 5." The state machine handles the primitive operations of waiting for the bus to become free, contending repetitively until it wins mastery, and then signaling that 5 should be slave. When 5 responds, the supervisor tells the state machine to signal "write" (i.e., receive), and then starts by sending its own SCSI or DSSI header, containing data similar to the VAX QIO header but meeting the SCSI or DSSI standard. It follows this header with the message that was under the header in the VAX QIO.

The transfer is completed with both vertical and horizontal parity checks. The network layer can try several times if there are transmission errors. If the QIO header specified an acknowledgment or if the transfer was unsuccessful even after several tries, the adapter turns back to the VAX, takes (*snips*) an envelope from the *free queue* (or uses one of those it has been caching for just this purpose), copies back the header and message it just transmitted, changing only the message type and result bytes, and queuing it on the *response queue*. If the transfer was successful and no acknowledgment is required, the adapter can return the envelope to the host's free queue or hold it (really the pointer to it) in a strictly limited cache. (Since the memory representing the envelope vanishes from the VAX's view while the adapter is holding it, it would never do to have the adapters stuff large globs of host memory away in their little gunny sacks. On the other hand, getting or returning an envelope costs host bus time and adapter processing time, so letting the adapters hold a few envelopes can speed things up.)

The ball is now in the server's court. The server's logical level must interpret the message. In our case, the host sent it a message to transfer four pages from disk to memory. The message contains the address of the first page in host memory and the positions of all four pages on disk, the offset into that first page, and the number of bytes to transfer. If there is some disk fragmentation resulting from the repeated writing and deletion of data on the disk, the situation might be like that shown in Figure 8.15. (If you are not familiar with the structure and operation of disk drives, read Appendix III.) The head happens to lie on a cylinder containing none of the sectors addressed. Accordingly, the controller must first get the head on cylinder 1 or 3, settle, and identify the sector under the head. Once the rotational position is known, it is only a matter of waiting for the sector to pass under the head.

Notice that the data is not contiguous. Where fragmentation is present, a single transfer can require two or more seeks (getting the head over the proper cylinder) and then waiting a rotational latency for the data to come under the read head.

When the data comes under the head, the controller must be ready; otherwise, it would have to wait for a full rotation (twice the average rotation latency) before it can read or write again. It is definitely a *use it or lose it* situation. Many modern disk controllers use local memory buffering to decouple the arrival of the data under the head from the exigencies of having an active bus connection to use for data transmission. An alternative, used by telephone long line systems and by IBM in mainframe systems, is to have enough busses serving each peripheral so that there is seldom any difficulty in getting a transmission link. For the DSSI system, buffering in the disk controller is always used, but some inexpensive SCSI systems simply assume that the bus will be available when needed, and on those occasions when it is not, the system just swallows another full rotational delay. This assumption of bus availability is well founded, because on inexpensive SCSI systems, there is no assumption of intelligence at the storage device. In general, at this most primitive form of SCSI, the commands may be

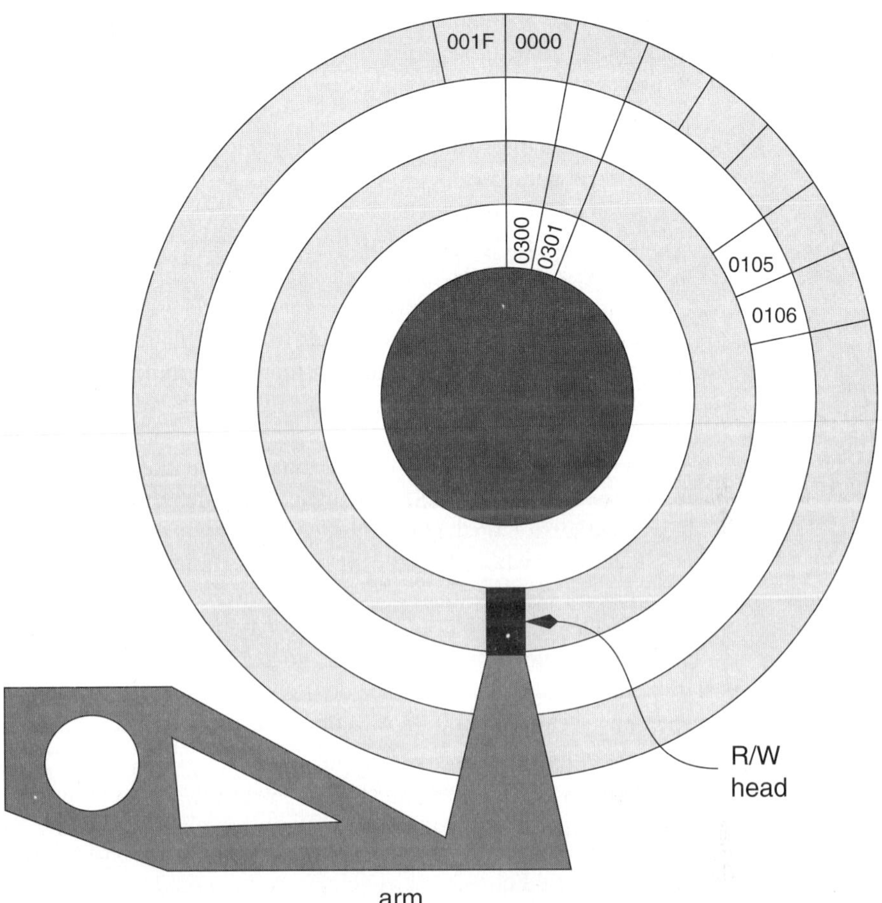

FIGURE 8.15 The position of the nominally contiguous four pages on a disk in which fragmentation is present. The disk is shown to have four cylinders and 32 sectors per cylinder. Sectors 0105, 0106, 0300, and 0301 contain the information being sought.

limited to simply reading or writing specific sectors. All indexing functions and all file organization issues are handled by the host. DSSI and VMS assume more intelligence on the part of the storage device.

Once the data is ready for transmission, the adapter has the task of moving it. This effort down at the data link and physical layers involves addresses and packing bytes into longwords on the VAX side and handshaking, byte counting and parity checking on the DSSI/SCSI side. The DSSI adapter does not know what is coming (it doesn't read the mail it delivers), so the DSSI storage device must preface its data transmission with a header which gives the length of the transmission and an appropriate starting address. The DSSI adapter is slave at this point. All of the data to do the job was contained in the command message, so the storage device is just parroting back to the DSSI adapter whatever data came with the command. For the most sophisticated DSSI single-host adapter chip (SHAC), that address is a *virtual* page address with pointers to the beginning of the process's pagetables. With a virtual starting address and the pointers to the process pagetables, the physical addresses of a transfer contiguous in virtual space are determined. The burden of doing the virtual-to-physical address translation is left up to the SHAC. For most other VAX adapters, the operating system feeds the adapter a table, usually to memory-mapped storage in the adapter itself, containing the physical addresses in the order needed. With that approach, all that must be passed is a pointer to the first page's PA[3] in the adapter's memory and the offset in that page. As each page boundary is crossed, the new page PA is used for generating the address of the bytes being stored. For typically more primitive SCSI systems, transfers are done by a simple DMA (direct memory access) device which, at best, can store the current page address plus the next one. It then becomes the master's task to update that waiting address to keep the data flowing. For the most primitive systems, only transfers contiguous in memory can be handled by a single setup of the DMA device. For a paged virtual memory system, that limits the continuous transfers to a single page.

On the VAX, which is our current example, the transfer is not limited by addressing issues, though the DSSI timeout spec requires transfers to be limited to eight pages in a single session on the DSSI bus. (After that, the bus must be released and contention will determine who gets the next turn.) Assuming that address generation is done in parallel with the data transfer—almost always a good assumption—and further assuming that the system bus is available for transfers whenever the DSSI adapter needs them, this portion of the transfer can go at the full DSSI bus speed, 4 MB/s.

Getting the data into place does not finish the transaction. The logical level in the operating system doesn't know a thing about it yet. The data-storage device must generate a report on the transaction. It does this by taking the very command message that asked for the transfer and modifying it to indicate that the transaction was (or was not) successful. It sends this back to the DSSI adapter, labeled as a *message*. The DSSI adapter recognizes this as a *response* and puts it back into an envelope with a standard VAX header and queues the envelope on the *response queue*. If that queue were previously empty, the adapter may have been instructed to interrupt the VAX to inform it that it has mail.

Posting the transaction response on the response queue effectively finishes the peripheral activity, but the reader may still remember that this data has been written in a buffer. It is not yet available to the process which required it. To achieve that end, the data is then copied to pages assigned to the process. This transfer of data rather than just assigning the pages to the process may seem like unnecessary busywork, but at least two benefits result. The first is that the buffer pages, which are an operating-system resource, are managed quite independently of the assignment and deassignment of process pages. For many VAX adapters, PAs rather than VAs are used for the buffer pages. If the PAs were constantly being given away to processes, the drivers would be constantly asking for buffer pages and having to update pagetables which reside in the adapters themselves. If the adapter was using that table for other transfers, then the

[3] Since VAX pages are 512 bytes long, all page addresses end in 9 zeroes.

operating system would have to be aware of what portion of the table was active and what could be changed. By this double buffering, the system can greatly simplify its task of keeping track of the buffers.

The other big issue is the problem of data consistency. If the data is to be written out of an active process, there is no reason why the process cannot continue to run *as long as the data to be written out remains unchanged during the transfer.* One could do this by suspending the process and putting it in the *waiting for I/O queue* until the transfer is complete. Alternatively, the data can be quickly moved to the buffer—thus recording it at the moment of the request—and then the process can continue, free to change its own copy of the data. The latter is consistent with VMS's use of asynchronous I/O.

The transfer complete, it behooves us to consider the delays which may occur at each stage to see what limits the real performance of the peripheral system to something considerably less than the DSSI bus rate of almost 8,000 pages per second.

8.4.2 Throughput and Response

An example DEC system from 1990 might comprise a five-platter, 5-inch, 3600 rpm disk drive, a DSSI bus, a SHAC adapter, and a 10-MIPS VAX (the 4000-300, for example). (Two properties of the disk drive would be different today. The same data would be contained on fewer, smaller platters and the rotation speed would be 5400 rpm. Appendix III discusses such a drive.) Let us begin with a single isolated request for one page. By isolated, we mean that there is by assumption no other disk activity on that bus at that time. In this way, we can look at the steps involved in fetching the data without considering how the different requests normally competing for the bus and disk will interact and interfere, nor will we consider any possibilities for pipelining or other optimizations which can be brought to bear on a stream of requests. What we wish to look at throughout this section is:

- What is the delay from request to data availability (the *response time*)?
- What is the average data rate for the whole transaction (the *throughput*)?

As you will see, the delay will increase slowly with load but the data rate will improve dramatically as the load increases.

If you break down the disk transaction into its component parts, it is possible not only to analyze what is "taking all that time" but also to consider some alternative strategies for increasing the throughput. Figure 8.16 shows the steps in relative proportion. What jumps out in startling detail in that graph is the enormous fraction of the time that is devoted to getting the read/write head over the data and the tiny amount of time that is spent on the heart of the matter—transferring data. This presentation is both correct and badly misleading. What is misleading is that it represents a worst possible case for the mechanical issues and a best possible case for the electronic and bus issues. The assumptions were that the read was an isolated event and that it transferred but a single page. In a multiprocess, virtual memory environment there is so much disk traffic that an isolated search for a particular sector is a rare event indeed. Furthermore, the aver-

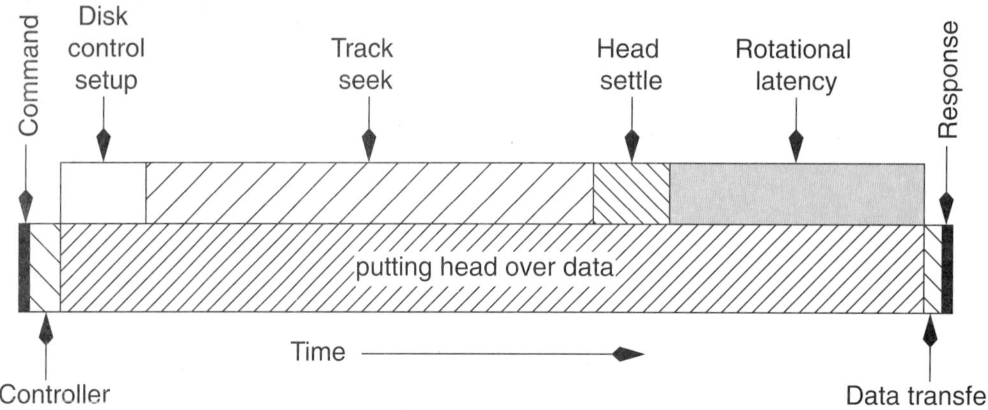

FIGURE 8.16 The delays in processing a single, isolated request for a single page of data on a 10-MIPS VAX using the SHAC/DSSI system and a Seagate Wren Runner-2 disk. The total delay from initiating the request to having the data available to the process is about 20 ms.

age VMS request is roughly four pages, not one. In light of the tiny amount of time given to the actual data transfer, it is clear that far better performance will be obtained by acquiring more pages at once. Let us look at the times which make up this extreme example and then consider how an optimizing controller and the nature of the request stream tend to increase the throughput without badly impacting the response time. The data are presented in Table 8.7. Some of these data come from articles by Kenneth Bates [Bates, 89] [Bates, 90], others from Seagate literature, and those on the SHAC and DSSI from personal experience with the chip. It should be noted that the Seagate disk drive would require adaptation to make it compatible with MSCP. It was chosen for the disk data because its size and speed are good measures of the then-current state-of-the-art products.

The elements shown in Table 8.7 represent a sequence of events which, for any single transaction, cannot be overlapped. In that sense, they spell the average time that an *isolated* random read of one page would take. The data rate is then 512 bytes/20 ms or a measly 25.6 KB/s. However, since the data transmission time was so small a portion of this operation, we could jump to 125 KB/s just by asking for five pages which happen to be contiguous on a single cylinder.

While the data rate is abysmal, the response rate is not bad. A user tends to regard anything that happens in less than one second as *instantaneous*, and even at the machine level, the 20 ms is only a couple of process time slots. As long as the machine has something else useful to do, this response rate will not slow things up materially.

8.4.3 Improving the Data Rate by Software

A number of things can be done to improve the performance of the disk system without attacking the fundamental slowness of mechanical access in the disk drives themselves. Some of these are almost at the level of housekeeping. The first thing to do is to look at disk requests and see what typical read and write patterns look like. If the typical read

TABLE 8.7 Delay times for each of the steps in transferring a single page in an isolated transaction from disk to memory over the DSSI bus and SHAC adapter

Transaction	Time, ms	
Command out		
Posting command	0.13	VMS responds to request by putting command on command queue.
Transmit command	0.03	SHAC responds to entry in command queue by transmitting it to controller.
Controller	1.00	Controller interprets command and sets up buffer and disk command.
Data in		
Drive setup	2.50	The controller tells the disk drive which cylinder and sector and which buffer.
Seek	8.3	The disk drive moves the arm from where it is to the desired track.
Settle	2.00	Time allotted for homing on track after slewing motion of arm and head.
Rotate	5.6	Sectors identified until desired sector appears under head.
Data to buffer	0.15	Data is read from disk and copied to controller buffer.
Data to memory	0.13	Data is transferred from buffer to host memory through DSSI and SHAC to the buffer specified in the command.
Response in		
Response	0.03	The command is modified to become a response and sent through the DSSI and SHAC to the host's response queue.
Processing response	0.13	The host reads the response, processes it, and moves the data to the user's memory space.
Total	**20.00 ms**	

request is a page fault, then most requests will ask for a single page. However, just as in memory accesses, where a request for word n is most often followed by a request for word $n+1$, a request for disk block m is very often followed by a subsequent request for block $m+1$. How long this typical chain extends will depend on the applications running on that host and certainly on block size, but a not untypical result of analysis of the request string on the VAX (with its 0.5-KB page) is to show that *look-ahead* reading of the next three blocks substantially improves the throughput. This optimization sets off the efficiency of fewer seek and settling times against the waste of reading some unnecessary pages. Also, be assured that no *look-ahead* page is ever delivered to a process until it is requested and its request is checked for proper authorization. These *lookaheads* are simply being cached in system memory on the presumption that many of them will be accessed in the near future. If they are not accessed by the time that the buffer is needed for another transfer, the data in them is trashed. In this way, unwanted pages evaporate from main memory.

If the average read has now been extended to something in excess of four pages by these *lookaheads*, then we would be well advised to take care to see that the disks are not badly fragmented. The situation indicated in Figure 8.15 shows a 33 percent fragmentation with one break among four pages. It will require two seeks and settles to read these four pages, greatly reducing the throughput that the look-ahead read was intended to achieve. How much would it reduce it? This turns out to be a much more complicated issue than the simple analysis that we applied above.

Let us begin by specifying a few parameters for the disk structure itself. The numbers are circa 1991. Both the rotational rate and the data density are higher than those that give the Bates data. Newer drives have substantially higher data densities. Let the disk be a 300-MB affair with five platters plus a servo platter. In other words, we will have 10 platter sides to write data on. That puts 30 MB on a side. Using data from Table 8.8, we can estimate that each track could contain about 20 KB of user data. That will require 1500 tracks per platter surface and it will occupy the outer 1.5 cm of disk surface. Since the heads are all connected to the same drive shaft, all tracks on a given cylinder are aligned. At any moment, any 1 of 10 tracks is accessible. This puts 200 KB—400 VAX pages—in easy reach without another seek (but with a rotational latency). That is a lot of turf. The clever controller will assign logically adjacent blocks to the closest possible free sectors. It is cheaper to go up or down than sideways. Even if an entire cylinder is filled—quite possible if the disk is reasonably full—with steps of 400 pages per cylinder, if there is much fragmentation, there are bound to be some open pages within a distance of a few tracks. This immediately suggests that basing the calculation on having a second seek of one-third of the way across the disk is much too

TABLE 8.8 Parameters for new medium-sized hard drives circa 1991

Capacity	300 MB
Platters	5
Tracks/side	1500
512-byte sectors per track†	40
Rotation speed	5400 rpm
Rotation period	11.1 ms
Lateral acceleration	1.73×10^{7} tracks/s^2
Data rate†	1.8 MB/s

†Would normally be a function of the radius in stepwise fashion.

pessimistic. More than just the likelihood of reasonable adjacency is the fact that a sophisticated search algorithm will be used in any high-throughput I/O system. The idea is that if you have multiple requests, you can vastly improve throughput (though not the response rate) just by ordering the requests (and page-sized fractions of a request) to match an optimized search algorithm. In the old days, the management of this search strategy was a task for the host; today, many systems move it out to the disk server. On Digital's disk controllers, the optimizer snaps into action as soon as more than eight QIOs have been queued up for action. This has the curious effect of making the ninth request appear to speed up the previous eight. The improvement possible by reordering is important, but not quite as large as Table 8.7 might suggest. In slewing the head from one track to another, the actuator normally applies full acceleration for half the distance (22 g) and then full deceleration for the remaining half. This leads to a triangular velocity pattern and a seek time $\tau_s = 2\sqrt{n/a}$, where n is the number of tracks and a is the head acceleration (22 g = 1.73×10^7 tracks/s^2). This number shows that a seek of 5 tracks will require only 1.1 ms, or only 10 percent of the "average" seek of 500 tracks. That is not the end of the benefit. The settle time is proportional to the error in slewing. This goes up roughly as the square root of the peak velocity, or essentially proportional to $\sqrt{\tau_s}$. Thus, to go the 5 tracks will require a settle time of 36 percent of 2 ms or 0.72 ms. Now our seek and settle is only 2 ms, a considerable improvement over the 10 ms we were looking at in Table 8.7.

Rotation is also amenable to reordering. This is important since we see that real seek and settle times may be under 1 ms. Once the heads have settled, they will shortly report that they are at sector j. If the first sector desired is in $j-1$ and the next at $j+50$, wouldn't it be a shame to read them in that order. The difference is 5.6 ms less latency, certainly significant in a 20-ms per random-page system and overwhelming in the much more rapid sequence of reads possible with well-ordered seeks. The calculation of the average rotational latency is obtained by assuming a random position for the first sector identified and then assuming that the reads will be in whatever order the sectors first appear under the head. With multiple surfaces, calculating the exact average rotational latency becomes an interesting problem in combinatorics. Consider transferring multiple sectors in a single cylinder, remembering that a cylinder comprises one or more rings of sectors. With more than one platter surface, there is a significant possibility that two or more of the sectors to be transferred have the same angular location. They are one above the other. Were three of them vertically aligned, it would take two full revolutions plus one sector's rotation to get them all. Figure 8.17 shows how the rotational latency increases with the number of sectors transferred. These data suggest that a multiple-block read will require 0.8 to 0.9 revolutions. For $n = 80$ and a read of 5, perfect reordering could reduce the average latency to 0.57. The saving at 3600 rpm is 5 ms; at 5400 rpm it is 3 ms. Both are significant improvements. The program which generated the data of Figure 8.17 and a companion program which does the case where adjacent sectors cannot be read are found on the program disk associated with the text.

The ultimate internal reordering is defragmentation. This exercise in battling entropy must be applied at frequent intervals to have much impact, but it is an exercise difficult to pull off while the system is active. Consider what must be done to

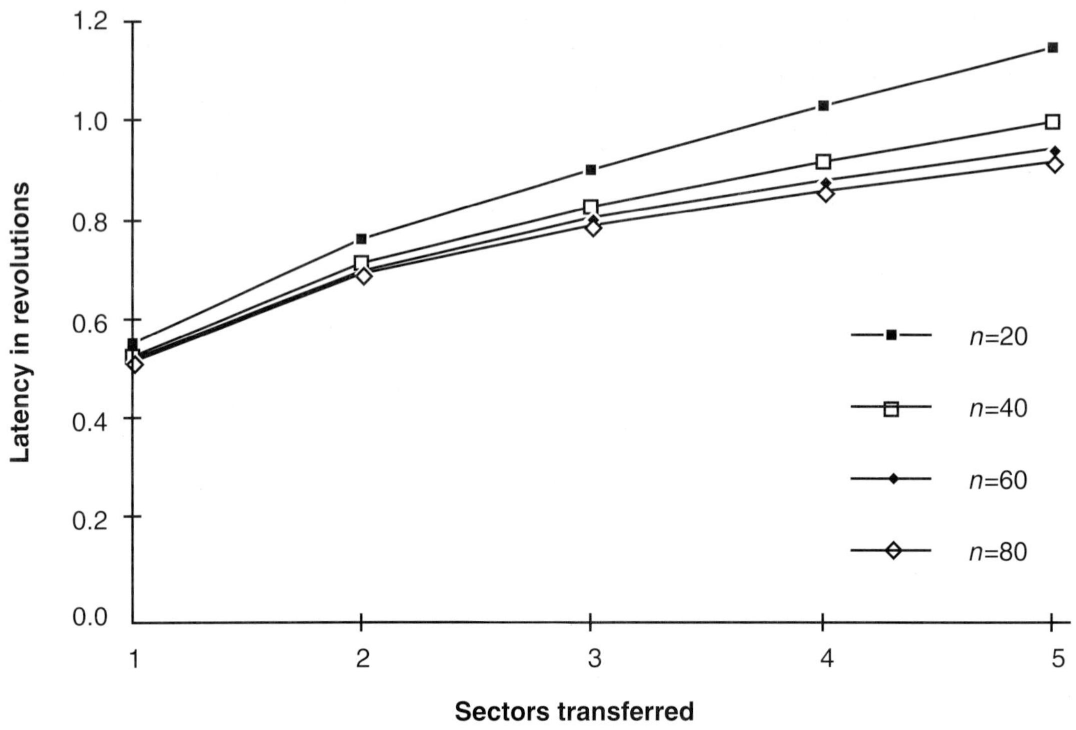

FIGURE 8.17 Rotational latency as a function of the number of sectors being transferred in a given cylinder. Calculations were done assuming that adjacent sectors could be read in a single pass and that there were five or more platter surfaces. n is the number of sectors per track.

defragment a disk that is almost full. To eliminate a break in the first file that is broken, enough space must be opened at the first break to accommodate all of the remaining parts of the file. The file's girth could exceed available memory, so brute force copying to memory is not possible. Instead, the unraveling is done by lots of smaller exchanges through memory. Keeping track of this gross reshuffling of memory is hard enough with a static file system. Allowing some other witless process to access the mess is clearly an invitation to file failure at an early age. In fact, the whole operation is tenuous enough that a defragmentation is normally not attempted until a full backup of the file. Full backup and then defragmentation is a lengthy process that must be done off-line. It is frequently relegated to 2 o'clock on a Sunday morning. To keep the system up and running most of the time, one lives with a certain measure of fragmentation. Disk accesses may be better on Monday morning than Friday afternoon, but you did have access late Tuesday night when you needed the machine. Since we must live with moderate amounts of file fragmentation, there is considerable effort expended at reducing the cost of fragmented files. The earliest efforts at latency reduction were directed at software which reordered the search pattern to minimize the impact of mechanical delays.

What gets worse in all of this reordering is response time. It is the old problem faced by public transportation. If you use one vehicle to cater to the individual needs of many riders, you will spend a great deal of time loading and unloading and much less time traveling. For the individual user, this equates to a longer ride. The alternative is, of course, to take a cab—higher cost but much more rapid response. The cab is a form of partial parallelism—many individually directed carriers sharing a common road. The same approach is used in machines from workstations to mainframes. In fact, it was one of the principal motivations in DEC's decision to develop the DSSI system. Recall that DSSI (and SCSI) provides eight slots. This allows up to seven peripherals feeding one host. All share the same bus and adapter, so the throughput benefit in having multiple disks on this one peripheral bus has got to be the possibility of overlapping disk operations—setups, seeks, and rotational latencies. The problem with this approach is that it requires that the system manager tune the storage allocation algorithm so that with each particular system's typical load, the set of requests is well distributed over the set of disk controllers. Resisting this optimization by demand pattern is the normal human need to regularize storage. We all sort the laundry. That is no different from putting all the students on those disk drives and all the faculty on this one, with the system disk over there and the active images on the one in the middle. Doing that kind of organization certainly makes flushing of all student accounts at the end of the year a lot easier. It also means that the system will have some hot disks and some quiet ones. With all that we have said so far, it should be clear that unequal loading will lead to suboptimal performance. Values of only 50 percent of potential throughput are not unusual. While jawboning system managers to do a better job of file assignment may improve the performance, it is clear that people will have been considering hardware solutions which will get close to optimal performance while allowing the manager to organize logical disks as he or she would have them. Let us consider several of these.

8.4.4 Improving the Data Rate by Hardware—Shadowing, Striping, and RAIDs

Just as having multiple platters and heads makes many tracks simultaneously accessible, one might think of combining several physical disks into one logical disk. This leads to three rather different concepts, each of which attacks one or more of the problems with disk storage. The first is called *shadowing*. It combines two disks, each an image of the other one. Whenever you write a page to this structure, it is put on both disks. However, the disks need not be in synchronism. Software on the server or in the host arranges for the two writes. If the data is buffered in the server, then less bus traffic is required (at the cost of a larger buffer requirement). There is clearly no speed benefit in a write; in fact, there may be a small speed penalty. On a read, however, the host is served by the first available disk. While reads dominate at the application-operating-system interface, with ever larger and less expensive memories, buffering can reverse the dominance of reads at the disk itself [Rosenblum, 91]. Still, with two disks operating asynchronously, and with a large number of requests pending, shadowing can provide a very measurable performance improvement. Curiously enough, that is the secondary reason for adopting shadowing. Its primary objective is reliability. What you have with shadowing is an instantaneous backup against the possibility of disk failure. Backup serves two functions: archival ("Sir, I erased my paper but my Professor wants another copy.") and failure recovery ("We're dead! The disk with our accounts receivable just crashed!"). Disk shadowing serves only the latter. If disks A and B both have the accounts receivable, the death of A is not the death of the firm—although its continued survival requires an immediate archival backup and then the replacement of A with an available spare.

The principal advantage of shadowing is that the recovery from failure is taken essentially from the state just before failure. Any formal backup procedure will have the potential for losing data between the time of backup and the time of failure. The cost is a doubling of disk storage costs. You will be buying two disks where one would have done, and you will also have to buy a system or software which does the shadowing. For this you will get your immediate backup and some noticeable speedup of read accesses.

The improvement in read access that one obtains from having two choices in where to make the access suggests that even more improvement could be obtained both by regularizing and further spreading the search pattern. This train of thought has produced the concept of *disk striping* [Salem, 86]. In this approach, one takes a number of disk drives—say, four—and distributes all records across all disks. The first question that occurs here is the same question that arises in any effort at improving throughput by parallelizing an inherently serial operation: What is the grain size? Do we put adjacent bytes on adjacent disks? Adjacent bits? Or adjacent pages?

There are some enormous differences between the possible organizations. A page-oriented distribution system adapts naturally to any number of disks n just by adopting a disk-addressing scheme which uses *page address* mod n as the disk pointer. In other words, it is a *round-robin* distribution scheme. If you own three drives with such a system and buy a fourth, all you would have to do to upgrade would be to copy the files from the three to tape, add the fourth (changing some hardware and, if it is not self-organizing, the server software so that it knows about the change), and then copying the data back onto disk.

Bit or byte organization would have to be done at the hardware level. It would require some complex buffering to accommodate the inherently asynchronous response from the disks. Furthermore, such hardware would expect to see n disks where n is the right number. Upgrades could not be incremental. However, this fine granularity has some surprising advantages. It is exactly what is done in a RAID, which we discuss below. In striping, however, the basic scheme is page-oriented.

Consider a four-page striping scheme with the typical read being four pages. By the addressing scheme we described above, any record of four pages or more will be distributed across all the disks. This ensures that, regardless of the particular workload, all four disks will participate with an essentially equal workload. While there are some hardware possibilities for having all four transferring data at once, this would make incremental upgrades more complex, and in any case, a higher peak data rate is not the source of the principal speedup. As you can see from Figure 8.16, the data transfer delay for a one-page access is almost trivial. No, the saving is in having overlaps between seek and rotational latencies. Over a period of time, the fragmentation of the disks will have the disks operating asynchronously. This means that while one is doing a long seek, another is transferring data. Note that there is no asymmetry between reading and writing in a striping system as there is with shadowing. One of the big advantages of the striping approach is that four disks give you four disks' worth of storage. However, one of the obvious hazards here is that the whole record structure now depends on the health of all four disks. Since the disk directories reside on disk, losing any of the disks effectively wipes out a lot or all access. Disk reliability is not all that good anyway. Reducing it by a factor of 4 does not make it better. Let us consider this issue with some care, because it promises to become dominant as storage systems grow.

No manufacturer publishes real failure rates for disk drives, but a good philosophy of data storage is to say: "It is not *if* the drive will fail but *when*." If you depend on the data, you have to back it up. The more you depend on it, the more carefully you attend to the issue of how a single incident—a lightning strike or earthquake or fire—can destroy both the original and the backup. As you get closer to the host system, the problem switches from preserving a recent copy with a probability of 1 to preserving the last version with high reliability and a minimum loss of time and performance. It is to this issue that RAIDs are directed. Upon observing that the best buys in disk drives were in the highly competitive PC marketplace, Patterson's group at the University of California–Berkeley proposed that large storage systems employ great farms of these inexpensive units in place of the very much more expensive massive disk drives of the mainframe market [Patterson, 89]. Right from the start, they recognized that they had to "get around" disk frangibility. Gibson and coauthors write, ". . . even with disks 10 times as reliable as the best on the market today, the first unrecoverable failure in a nonredundant array of a thousand disks can be expected in less than two weeks" [Gibson, 89] also [Gibson, 92]. By the way, lest that number of 1000 disks sound a little grandiose, at 300 MB/drive, that would amount to something on the order of 0.3 TB. There are at this writing several tens of systems which are handling more than 1 TB of active storage.

The disk failures which are a problem here are those not addressed by the loss of small parts of particular records. These are handled by rereading the data and by reconstruction through Reed-Solomon codes [Rao, 89]. What we are concerned with here are total losses such as those which result from a head crash or a failure of the mechanical drive or the electronics. These failures announce themselves in clear and conspicuous fashion. Detecting them is no problem. Once they have been observed, there are two problems: recovering from the loss and minimizing the chance that a second failure will prevent recovery. The idea is to design a system which meets a given *mean time to data loss* (MTDL) with a large array of disks whose individual elements may have *mean times to failure* (MTTF) either below or above the object MTDL.

The basic concept is to distribute data uniformly across an array of N disks. The distribution could be bitwise, round-robin bytewise, or round-robin blockwise, but the essential feature is that you could consider the data as having been written on N parallel stripes. Figure 8.18 shows the scheme applied to four data disks and one parity disk. Regardless of whether the system perceives this data as representing blocks or bytes vertically or nibbles horizontally, a parity bit is written to a fifth disk representing the odd parity of each horizontal stripe across the four disks. To write a new block on a single disk, the driver must read the old data and old parity bit, deliver the new data bits, and update the parity bit depending on the change that is made; to read, you need only

0	1	2	3	P
1	1	0	0	1
1	0	0	1	1
0	0	0	0	1
1	1	1	0	0
0	0	1	0	0
1	1	1	1	1
1	0	1	1	0
0	1	1	1	0

FIGURE 8.18 Data distributed on four disks with an odd parity bit on a fifth disk.

read the data bits. This puts a considerable penalty on a write, but writes are relatively infrequent. Alternatively, if the data is written bitwise or round-robin bytewise across the whole array, no read is necessary since the parity bit is determined by data held by disk controller. This operation removes entirely the penalty on a write, restoring the essential symmetry between reads and writes.

On first consideration of reading and writing across the set of five disks, you might wonder how it would be possible to hold them in proper synchronization. While it could be done with elaborate feedback and just a little local buffering [Kim, 86], it is much easier and more logical to do the necessary data shuffle in memory. For example, on a round-robin bytewise organization, the memory on the server handling the set of five would be four-way interleaved and double-ported so that each disk drive would each have its own piece of memory. Figure 8.19 shows a reasonably regular organization of memory. Each 32-bit word written on the left generates one byte of parity bits on the right. The DMA chips would provide memory address sequencing for transfers to and from the disk drives. It may be necessary for the server to know when the last of the disks has finished its transfer. This is done by ANDing the five DMA interrupt lines to produce an interrupt only when the last one completes. Any structure as regular as this is a natural target for integration. However, while it is tempting to put all your eggs in that one neat little basket, we must worry about any common failure mode which could render the data inaccessible.

One interesting question is: In either bytewise or blockwise organizations, is there a hot disk? For the bytewise organization, the answer is: "None is hotter than any other." All disks will operate on any operation. This may sound as if we are overworking the drives, but in fact, the data is more compactly stored so the disks will be progressing in gentle fashion and loose synchronization across their surfaces. Instead of having five platters operating on one shaft, we would now have five (or 20) operating on five shafts. For the blockwise operation, the situation is a mix. Disk P is read first and then written to every time that a write occurs, but it is never accessed on a read. A

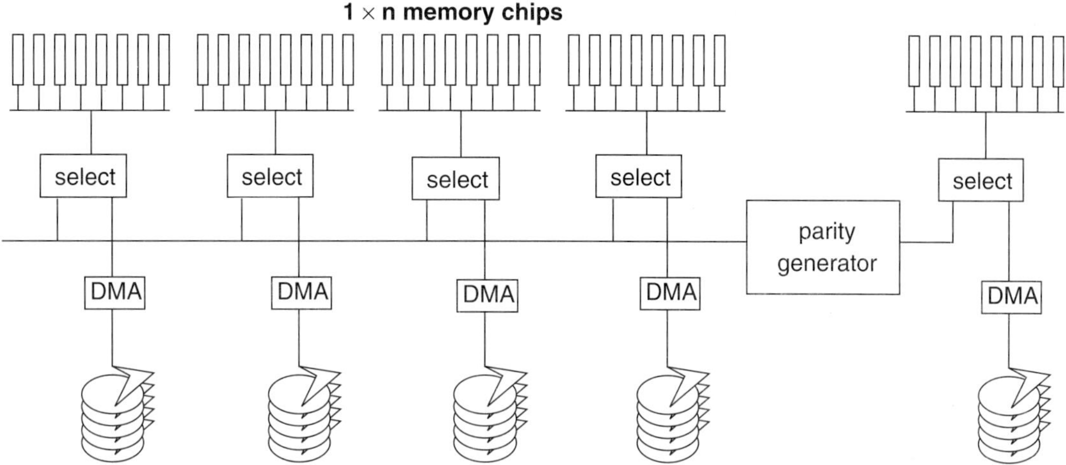

FIGURE 8.19 An organization of server memory which would enable five conventional disks to work independently of each other while handling data that is distributed round-robin by byte over the first four disks. The bytes written to the fifth disk are parity bits for the other four, as in Figure 8.18. The horizontal bus goes to the server processor. On reconstruction, the parity generator can be programmed to replace any one of the five bytes.

first guess is that P's average workload is not a problem. On the other hand, if a fragmented file is distributed over several disks, the data disks will have a chance for parallel operation, while poor old P will be jumping back and forth in a dance that will be slow, full of hard accelerations, and difficult to improve even with clever coordination. One can improve the load on P by going to a better correction code. Several such codes are presented and discussed in [Gibson, 89]. Another technique is to distribute the parity just as you have distributed the data. Such an arrangement is shown in Figure 8.20.

Now consider what happens if any one of the five disks fails. To reconstruct the data one need only read the other four disks and replace the missing bit on the basis that

FIGURE 8.20 Figure 8.18 rearranged to distribute the parity bits uniformly across the five disks.

0	1	2	3	4
P	1	1	0	0
1	P	0	0	1
0	0	P	0	0
1	1	1	P	0
0	0	1	0	P
P	1	1	1	1
1	P	0	1	1
0	1	P	1	1

the parity must be odd. This is not the end of the issue, however. There is always a finite possibility in any finite interval that a second disk of the set of five could fail. If that were to happen, you have lost it all. To escape from that dire fate, you may take one of two paths. The first is to make the interval very short. If you can replace the failed disk and reconstruct the missing data within a time that is short enough compared to the MTTF of any individual disk, then the probability of loss of data will not decrease the MTDL below what is acceptable. This requires that you have a unit ready to plug in and that the time to reconstruct the data on the replacement disk is short enough. If disk drives were "plug-in" units and the system had 24-hour attendance, this method might well suffice. On the other hand, if the system ran unattended over the weekend or overnight, precious data might be more at risk than was acceptable.

Note that there is a simple relationship between the number of disks protected by one parity bit and the length of time which can be allowed between failure and repair. If we were protecting 8 bits instead of four, we would have to act to recover in half the time. However, the cost of having the redundancy would be halved. One can extend the acceptable time frame to any degree desired by adding more redundancy. To keep the cost modest, it is desirable to be clever in distributing the parity bits so that the fewest number of extra drives are required. Gibson et al. cover this subject to a fare-thee-well.

Note that the reconstruction can take place while the system continues to operate, but until the new disk is rebuilt, all disk operations must include reconstruction.

One final caveat is in order. RAID treats only the independent disk failure mode. Common-mode failures—fire, electrical transients, earthquakes—require careful remote siting, uniteruptable power supplies, and often redundant computer facilities.

8.4.5 Some Simulation of a Disk Drive

All that remains is a look at the speed which we could expect from this group of five loosely coordinated disks. Let us consider two cases: round-robin bytewise and round-robin blockwise organizations. We will assume that the parity bits for the blockwise organization are distributed as shown in Figure 8.20. Isolated reads or writes are both artificial and not particularly important. Let us consider a rather large number of reads and writes, make some reasonable assumptions about the locations and fragmentation, and then do an analysis of how fast the data transfer will take. A set of "reasonable assumptions" is provided in Table 8.9. A total of 100 reads and writes are distributed into records varying from 1 to 16 pages. These two columns give you the weighting values for lengths of records for both reads and writes. The assumption made in generating this table is that all reads of fewer than 4 pages are extended to 4 pages as a look-ahead strategy. For writes, on the other hand, the most common form of a write will occur when a process buffer (one page) is filled. As soon as that happens, the data is written out and the buffer is reset to empty. Accordingly, the most common write is one page. One other fairly common page number is 16 pages, corresponding to a partial swap-out of a process waiting for something like input. Note that the weighted average read is 5.77 pages and the weighted average write is only 2.25 pages. Clearly, a log-file system such as Sprite would give vastly different statistics.

The right two columns of Table 8.9 are used with a random-number generator for selecting the track for the next page. The random-number generator generates a flat distribution of 16-bit integers. The random number modulo 20 becomes the index for the track step. The number to the right of that index is then the step to the next track. Since the number of tracks is 1500, the track step is modulo 1500.

TABLE 8.9 **A table of "reasonable assumptions" for the analysis of data transfer between a disk array and a host.** The number of reads and writes for each size are for a total of 100 reads or writes respectively. The sector step table is to be used with a random-number generator to obtain the distance to the next block. Note that almost half of the sector steps are 0.

Size	Reads	Writes	Track step	
1	0	68	0	0
2	0	13	1	0
3	0	8	2	0
4	55	4	3	0
5	15	1	4	0
6	8	1	5	0
7	5	0	6	0
8	3	0	7	0
9	3	0	8	0
10	3	0	9	1
11	1	0	10	2
12	2	0	11	4
13	1	0	12	7
14	2	0	13	14
15	1	0	14	27
16	1	5	15	53
Weighted average	5.72	2.25	16	102
			17	200
			18	387
			19	750

What remains is to create a program which generates a table of, say, 20 reads and five writes distributed according to these tables. Having created the table, the program must then do the task of the server, sorting the data transfers to optimize the search into a sawtooth pattern. That is, we will employ a batch mode, starting each batch from track 0 and then slewing back to 0 to start the next batch. Then, using values for each of the latencies, it is possible to keep track of time as the data is transferred. From these, one can extract numbers for both throughput and response. By repeating the program a reasonable number of times good statistics can be extracted.

Once the program is written, it is not hard to show where the bottleneck is in each case. Then, by devoting more resources to that bottleneck (that is, widen the neck by pushing money through it), one can advance slowly to a system which gives the best performance possible with the basic underlying technology. As a start in this process (which is continued in the problem set), we have provided a program which generates a task set and then orders it and does the seek, rotate, and read routine to obtain the values for throughput and response. The program is included in the software on the disk that is an accessory to the text. The weightings of Figure 8.15 are employed and the statistics derive from 10 sweeps of 25 QIOs each on the IBM model 0662 drive from Appendix III—about 9 seconds of disk operation and 1258 pages transferred. These data are presented in Table 8.10. Several QIOs from the last batch are presented in Table 8.11. Some conclusions can be drawn.

The most important conclusion is that random reads on a single high-performance disk drive can barely scratch the performance capability of a SCSI or DSSI bus. Note that the data transfer rate averaged over 10 batches is 206 pages/s or 106 KB/s. The bus is comfortable with 4 MB/s. While there will be some traffic associated with the command and response messages, a very large fraction of the bus's availability will be idled away. This conclusion is in full consonance with the bus designers' intentions. The central reason behind the design of the SCSI system and for its adoption by so many system designers is that it can handle a substantial number of peripherals without becoming a bottleneck. However, remember that this conclusion is based on random reads. A very different conclusion will be drawn for long, coherent writes as in Sprite or reads and writes on some powerful single-user workstations. In a coherent write operation, that one IBM model 0662 drive would overwhelm SCSI. To increase the data bandwidth, SCSI-II was developed. It comes in three flavors: *fast*, *wide* and *fast and wide*. In synchronous mode, *fast* has a 10 MB/s bandwidth over an 8-bit bus; *wide* has the same clock rate as SCSI-I but a 16-bit bus to give it 8 MB/s; the combination of *fast and wide* gives 20 MB/s. The IBM drive comes with either *fast* or *fast and wide*. This text is being written on a Macintosh FX with a very fast 500 MB disk drive, but the two are joined by a slower than usual SCSI-I drive. The SCSI drive is a bottleneck that you become very conscious of every time that a chapter backup is done or a new chapter read in, a reasonably coherent transaction of about 400 KB.

The average response time is interesting and potentially a little misleading. If you look at the sample QIOs in Table 8.11, you can see that the track values, distributed according to Table 8.9, are rather badly fragmented. The first thought might be that this value could be much improved simply by doing a routine defragmentation. In our model, this would be a revision of Table 8.9 to have fewer long steps. That, however,

TABLE 8.10 Statistics for the operation of a single high-performance disk drive. Statistics from 10 runs of 25 QIOs each.

Average rate	205.95 pages/s, with $\sigma = 7.88$
Average response	349.81 ms, with $\sigma = 180.46$
Average block size of a QIO	5.03
Maximum rate	225.10 pages/s
Maximum response	672.52 ms

will not cure the problem here. The issue is really the fullness of the disk, not its fragmentation. In a triangular scan pattern, a moderately full disk implies that a collection of limited-sized QIOs from completely independent applications will distribute themselves pretty much over the whole disk. To finish the whole batch, the head will have to seek from one side to the other, stopping frequently in between.

Since the response latency must spread rather uniformly from files near the beginning to files near the end, the average will be a file in the middle and the worst case will be a file at the end. This is exactly what you see in Table 8.10. The average response is 0.35 s, the worst is 0.67 s, and the standard deviation is about half the mean. Looking at the finish times in Table 8.11 gives similar results. Jobs 1 and 4 deliver the same number of pages and neither is badly spread out, yet the response time for job 1 is

TABLE 8.11 Five QIOs from the last batch in a run of 10 batches

Job 1	READ of 4 blocks.					
TRACKS:	2944	3331	3331	3331		
		Start time: 0.00 Finish time: 449.78 Increment: 449.78 ms.				
Job 4	READ of 4 blocks.					
TRACKS:	886	886	887	887		
		Start time: 0.00 Finish time: 103.88 Increment:103.88 ms.				
Job 9	READ of 10 blocks.					
TRACKS:	2966	2993	2994	3008	3008	3022
	3022	3022	3029	3029		
		Start time: 0.00 Finish time: 402.05 Increment: 402.05 ms.				
Job 21	WRITE of 1 block.					
TRACKS:	1754					
		Start time: 0.00 Finish time: 251.27 Increment: 251.27 ms.				
Job 22	WRITE of 4 blocks.					
TRACKS:	1021	1021	1021	1021		
		Start time: 0.00 Finish time: 148.89 Increment: 148.89 ms.				

four times that of job 4. The reason is simple. Job 1 did not start until well after job 4 finished. It was further along the disk. Since moderately high utilization of storage capacity lowers the cost per unit of storage, the delays inherent in multiple, independent QIOs on a single disk are inevitable. A more dynamic search strategy, which would not use the triangular sweep and batch processing, might decrease the response time a little, but the real solution must be multiple independent disk drives. This, of course, is what we were considering above in the discussion of RAIDs, but we had not yet made much of a distinction between organizing a RAID group as a set of essentially parallel units representing a single storage entity or as a group of essentially independent disks sharing parity. With this little bit of simulation in hand, it is not hard to see which system would provide the best performance.

As discussed earlier, if one treats the disks as independent devices sharing parity, then the execution of a write requires that the RAID system read both the data to be overwritten and the current parity block prior to writing. Then, the new parity block becomes the bitwise XOR of the two old files and the new data file. Thus, a write becomes a read and a write on each of two disks. This might seem only to require two rotations for every write, but it is more complicated than that. Much speedup can be obtained by operating the disks in some loose synchronization and using lots of buffering to hold data in a random-access medium until the controller has sorted out all of the parity changes which have to be made. Further, by spreading parity sectors across all of the disks, different pairs could be working in different places. Working out this scheduling on the fly calls for a great deal of computing power in the RAID controller. It also means that there can be some substantial lags in having the parity data written out from the buffer.

Having a bit of lag (order of 1 s) in the parity block's currency means that when a disk fails—and it will fail—some of the data necessary for rebuilding may be in RAM, not on disk. Now what happens if the lights go out? Even without the disk failure, a power failure presents a RAID or any buffering disk system with a critical problem. The write to disk must never get further behind than the panic-mode time upon discovery of an impending power failure. Since that time depends completely on the availability of standby power—where UPS stands for *uninterruptable power supply* and not the ubiquitous package delivery service—it may not be a problem or it might be an overwhelming one. Let us leave that particular issue with the observation that one should not install a RAID without at least a few minutes of backup energy supply. Many of the modern units have keep-alive batteries to make RAM essentially permanent.

With that caveat, we can consider the impact on performance of having the extra rotation for each write. The latency for an isolated write would then include one full rotation—an extra 11 ms according to the data in Table 8.7. Of course, if you happen to have two or more writes on that same track—not all that unlikely—then you can distribute that delay over the N writes and the burden looks proportionately less. Estimating that the ratio of QIO reads to QIO writes is 4/1 (including the read-before-writes) and that the average task will include 25 QIOs (the case considered in the simulation), we can use the value we derived of average rotational latency of 0.85 and come up with an estimate of the average extra rotational latency of 1.85 rotations or 20.4 ms. Since we have allotted 5 out of 25 QIOs to writes, the burden of the extra reads will add

102 ms to the average response latency. That is certainly not insignificant. In fact, it is an 18 percent degradation. The flow of data, however, will have increased by the number of data drives. The parallel disk operation is even better. It avoids the added response latency and the gives the same improvement in data rate. In fact, apart from dramatic differences in reliability, one could look at the parallel operation as being little different from having all the platters on a single shaft with groups of read/write heads operated in parallel.

In a RAID, synchronization delays might be obligatory while one or more disks wait for other disks to catch up with a read and then write. One simple synchronization method would be to take advantage of the back sweep for doing the writing. In this scheme, the disks proceed in the forward direction at their own pace, accumulating read-before-writes in the buffer and delivering all normal reads to memory. All pause at the inside cylinder until the last drive reaches the inside. Then all proceed at their own pace back toward cylinder 0 performing all of the writes. If a disk fails during the read portion of the cycle, the write is not performed and the disk array is in perfect order for reconstruction; if a disk fails during the write portion, the other disks are updated and in perfect order for reconstruction. Assuming that the disk loading is reasonably uniform, the synchronizing delay at the end should not be overly burdensome.

What do you get for this complexity? Well, whether you run your disks in parallel or as independent devices with common parity, you get protection and recovery capability. How good is it? At the '93 PC Expo in New York, Legacy Storage demonstrated an 8-drive RAID. When asked if they could pull a disk drive right out of the working stack, the salesperson looked quite appalled and said that she would ask the Vice President. He grinned and invited the inquiring customer to pull the drive of his choice. The RAID proceeded to rebuild itself while continuing to serve its normal traffic. The Vice President then reinserted the drive into the operating stack. Again the stack was rebuilt without down-time observable to the user. Nothing was turned off or on in the whole procedure. Impressive.

There is more than security to be obtained. What you get from the parallel connections is great potential for faster throughput. And we should not leave out the ID in RAID. These devices provide vast storage at much lower cost than their large predecessors.

CHAPTER SUMMARY

I/O is a vast topic, worthy of a text in itself. We have bitten off two principal parts of I/O technology in this chapter and presented them in modest detail. The first part was a look at busses, the backbone of data transfer between primary and secondary memories and between memory and the processor. The second half of the chapter focused on the connection to and operation of the disk drives. In both cases, our principal objective was insight into the mechanisms, fundamental or otherwise, which limited the speed of our computer.

The nominal objective in the chapter was selecting the system and peripheral busses. To this end, we began with Figure 8.1 and a table of bus specifications. While it would seem that all busses were much the same—parallel wires—the table revealed that different busses had very different levels of performance. In an effort to understand why similar arrangements of wires gave different results, we took a close look at the physics of busses, at bus configurations, at bus transceivers, and finally at the handshakes and conventions of bus transactions.

Our major comparison was between the VMEbus and the Futurebus, one a well-established, widely used, and versatile bus that became popular in the '80s and the other a newly emerging bus of similar size but much higher performance. Part of this performance was extracted from the design of the transceivers, substituting *backplane transceiver logic* for the more traditional TTL drivers; the remainder of the added speed was obtained from improvements in the bus protocols. The two busses shared certain conventions which tend to improve performance. In particular, both admit to *parking*, which allows the busier users to get more data transferred between delays for bus contention and arbitration, and both have methods for transferring multiple data with a single address. What differentiates the two busses is that the designers of Futurebus—with the advantage of most of a decade of hindsight—made their bus less sensitive to single-point failures, used timing conventions which allow speed to improve with technology, made the multiple data transfer much more readily accessible, and made it much easier to sink data in multiple receivers (*broadcast mode*). One of the observations which one should extract from this analysis is that the oft-quoted maximum data rate is achieved only under circumstances where data can be transferred without intervening addresses. This puts a premium on designing memory chips and peripherals to move data in bursts of several words.

A spreadsheet methodology was developed in Appendix II and used in this chapter for simulating bus transactions. While simple representations of the active drivers were employed, the spreadsheet simulation produced reasonably accurate pictures of the bus transitions as a function of position and time. The effects of loading, drive, line length, and termination impedance were all clear. Transient diagrams for both pulldown and pullup transitions were extracted for both VME and Futurebus (Figures 8.8 and 8.10).

With the basic interconnect well described, we turned to the sequence of transactions which are traversed in the course of transferring a block of data between memory and disk. Our model was the VAX using a DSSI/SCSI peripheral bus with a SHAC bus adapter joining the DSSI to the system bus. We began by watching a read request created in the host and delivered through all of the layers of the protocol to the server; the server responded by delivering the data back to the host through those same layers; finally, the server delivers a response to the host, who finally completes the transaction by moving the data into the user's domain. The principal delays in all of this were the mechanical ones of positioning the read/write head over the correct data tracks. For a single page transfer, the data rate was startlingly low—only 25.6 KB/s. That focused our attention on getting more performance, but with the caveat that the two measures of performance, *throughput* and *response time*, are in inherent conflict—optimize one and "pessimize" the other.

A simple modeling tool was constructed which developed statistics for data throughput and response times for the random requests from independent processes. The model used a triangular sweep with 25 tasks of weighted random length and distribution. The data rate increased by 4.5 times while the response rate declined by an order of magnitude. The simple search algorithm can be improved to decrease the response rate, but the data rate is reasonably close to maximum for this size batch (25 jobs of average length 5 blocks). Since the data rate observed (106 KB/s) is well below the bus capacity (4 MB/s), an obvious conclusion was that the route to improved I/O was multiple, relatively independent disk drives with the load distributed rather evenly over the whole set. A rather different set of results and conclusions would be obtained in any I/O environment where long coherent transfers are made.

Uniform distribution of the load is difficult to achieve and to maintain in any file distribution organized on a logical basis. To get the load distributed across several disks rather automatically, the concept of *disk striping* was introduced. In this system, adjacent blocks are stored on adjacent disks. With data buffering and the random overlapping of seeks and transfers on the several disks, much higher data rates can be sustained.

Unfortunately, distributing your data eggs among many baskets increases the probability of losing one of those baskets between backups. This loss can completely destroy the data on all of the group of disks since the files are rather uniformly distributed across the full set. The need for higher reliability in data storage leads in the short term to *shadowing* and in the long term to RAIDs. The basic concept in a RAID is that the data is distributed across a set of $n + 1$ disk drives with n bits of data and one parity bit. The concept was that data lost from the failure of a single disk could be reconstructed from the data on other disks. The "hit" was just a slowing down while the data was reconstructed. The amount of redundancy required depends on the probability of a second disk failure before regeneration of the lost data. We looked at several ways of organizing raids, one in which the group of disks was operated essentially in parallel and another in which the disks operate essentially independently and where records can be written in any way across the disks with the parity updated as new data is written. The independent mode suffers on a write because data must be read and then written in order to update the parity bits. On the other hand, by making the disks independent, one obtains a great deal of overlap in seeks and transfers, thus obtaining a higher data rate. The parallel mode really gangs the disks together, allowing $n + 1$ heads to read or write simultaneously but doing nothing for reducing the effective mechanical delays. Since the raw data rate from the disk was never the limiting factor, we concluded that in general, the independent mode was likely to give better performance.

PROBLEMS

8.1. Since it is common experience that if you shut the switch "here," the voltage appears "there," you should spend a moment first to disabuse yourself of that concept and then to reestablish the truth of the observation as the end state of a transient response. Consider the line shown below. Let the line be 1 m in length and the point at which the voltage is measured in the middle. Note that the driver is terminated in Z_0. The problem deals with several different types of Z_L. (Parts ***(b)*** and ***(c)*** have generated more different wrong answers than any other problems in this text. Try to work out what should happen, particularly the initial and final values before creating the sketches.)

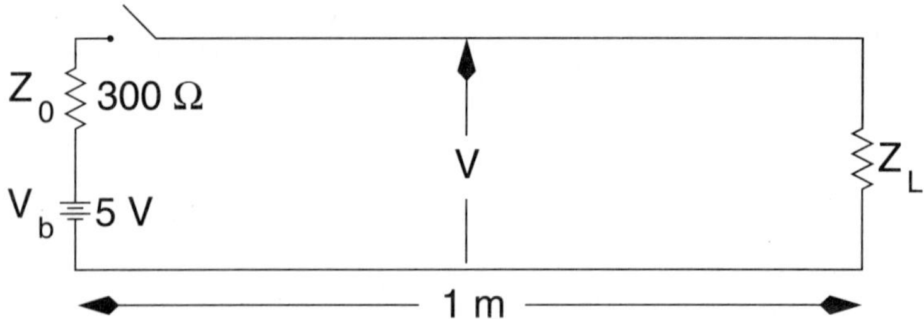

(*a*) Sketch the value of $V(t)$ for the first 6 ns after closing the switch with $Z_L = 150\ \Omega$.

(*b*) Replace the load with a capacitor of 10 pF and sketch the value of $V(t)$ for the first 6 ns after closing the switch.

(*c*) Replace the load with an inductor of 1 μH and sketch the value of $V(t)$ for the first 6 ns after closing the switch.

8.2. Consider Sun's S-bus, a board-level bus with up to six slots. This is a synchronous bus with no termination resistors. Instead, the drivers are used not only to drive and damp the line but also to "reset" the line to whatever its unasserted state might be. The line is designed for CMOS drivers, though today that is hardly the wimpish drive of early CMOS. A drive of 24 mA is available in *either* direction. Let the upper drive voltage be 2.8 V. Let us model each driver as tapering down to 0 starting as the voltage gets within 0.8 V and getting to 0 at 0 V. Let Z_0 be 60 Ω, let the line be 50 cm long, and let there be four transceivers. Each transceiver will represent a capacitive load of 20 pF. Rules of the road are that there can *never* be more than one driver, and that driver must assert the line unambiguously in less than 20 ns and, upon completion of the cycle, drive it back to its unasserted state in less than 20 ns. Let a 0 be anything less than 0.8 V and a 1 anything higher than 2.0 V. Let the driver be in slot 0 and capacitive loads in 1, 3, and 6. Note that a driver is shunted by 20 pF whether it is on or off. Determine the minimum time to assure a switch from 0 to 1 and 1 to 0 with four slots occupied.

8.3. Extend the calculations for pulldown shown in Figure 8.8 to having all eight slots filled. Keep the active driver in slot 4. How much longer is it until the receiver in slot 0 can be sure of receiving a proper 0? Is slot 0 the slot with the longest potential delay?

8.4. To represent the terminations more accurately, one is required to model the stub which connects the transceiver to the backplane. Let the stubs have a Z_0 of 100 Ω and a length of half a slot separation. (This is the same length as the end terminations.) To compare the impact of this change, repeat the problem represented in Figure 8.6 using only two transceivers, but put each transceiver at the end of a stub.

8.5. Most programs contain many small loops, so even as the code is being added to the cache, the cache hit rate is reasonably high. How high must it be if the sustainable transfer rates of the Futurebus and VMEbus are to be able to keep the CPU running at 10 MIPS? How high would it have to be to operate at 40 MIPS? Consider only instruction fetches.

8.6. Compare a disk read of four contiguous pages with four pages requiring one extra seek/settle time. Do the problem assuming that each seek is a 30 percent traverse of the disk and that each rotation delay is half a rotation. Obtain your data from Table 8.7.

8.7. Suppose that a disk has five data surfaces and that each cylinder has 50 sectors per surface per cylinder. If we are looking for five sectors within the current cylinder and if only one head can be reading at any instant, what is the probability that we will be able to read all five sectors in a single rotation? You may assume that the heads are just reaching the start of a sector and that the disk can read that sector if necessary. So the only thing preventing it from reading all 5 sectors in a single rotation would be the possibility that more than one of the desired sectors could be in the same angular position.

8.8. Test the results of the disk latency simulation program by changing the number of runs to see how many runs must be taken before the statistics settle to a steady-state value. Is 10 too few, adequate, or excessive?

8.9. Extend the latency program to handle the RAID write-after-read issue to determine if our back-of-the-envelope calculation was a reasonable estimate of the degradation in response. Distribute the load across five surfaces (total) and use a master clock and four local clocks to see which disk does its next read or write. Distribute the parity and the data across all the disks in regular order. Note that parity bits cannot be written until both old data and old parity have been read.

8.10. As the number of QIOs per second increases, the data rate gets ever better but the response rate ever worse. While increasing the number of disk drives is the real solution to this problem, consider a scheme for limiting response delays while not reducing throughput. In the scheme simulated in the program provided, all sweeps were started from track 0. Instead, divide the load per sweep in half and do alternate sweeps from track 0 and track 1500 respectively. This removes the wasted backsweep, cutting by half the stops from each. In analyzing the delays and rates, you can assume that the computational delays would be halved per sweep so that if half as many stops turn out to require half as much time, then the assumption that the disk delays mask the computational delays will still be valid.

8.11. The batch processing model used in the simulator is not only a bit artificial but also somewhat misleading in terms of what it says about optimization strategy. A better model would be to add new QIOs at periodic intervals and to consider various schemes for ordering the activities. One of the obligations of any strategy is to ensure that no QIO gets set aside in the name of optimizing either data rate or response. A technique which accomplishes this end is to do a back-and-forth sweep across the tracks, adding tracks to the list as the QIOs come in, but continuing in the same direction until the last block waiting in that direction has been reached. To study this scheme will demand a rather major revision of the simulator but one that will give both interesting and different results from what we have above. Using this new approach, determine how the data rate and response time depend on the rate at which QIOs are added.

REFERENCES

[Bates, 89] Bates, Kenneth H., *Performance Aspects of the HSC Controller*, **Digital Technical Journal 8**, 25–37 (1989).

[Bates, 90] Bates, Kenneth H., *I/O Performance, Part 4*, **DEC Professional**, 38–48 (March 1990).

[Borrill, 89] Borrill, Paul L., *High–speed 32–bit buses for forward–looking computers*, **IEEE Spectrum 26**(7), 34–37 (July 1989)

[Dickinson, 89] Dickinson, Alex and Michael E. Prise, *An Integrated Free Space Optical Bus*, **Proceedings of the 1989 IEEE Conference on Computer Design**, (Cambridge, MA), 62–65 (Oct. 1989).

[Di Giacomo, 90] Di Giacomo, Joseph, editor, *Digital Bus Handbook*, McGraw Hill (1990).

[Futurebus, 90] *IEEE Standard Backplane Bus Specification for Multiprocessor Architectures: Futurebus*, **ANSI/IEEE Std 896.2–1990**

[Gibson, 89] Gibson, G. A., L. Hellerstein, R. M. Karp, R. H. Katz, and D. Patterson, *Failure Correction Techniques for Large Disk Arrays*, **Proceedings of the Third International Conference on Architectural Support for Programming Languages and Operating Systems (ASPLOS)** (Boston), 123–132 (1989).

[Gibson, 92] Gibson, Garth A., *Redundant Disk Arrays: Reliable, Parallel Secondary Storage*, MIT Press (1992).

[Hayes, 88] Hayes, John P., *Computer Architecture and Organization*, second edition, McGraw–Hill (1988).

[Hennessy, 89] Hennessy, John and David Paterson, *Computer Architecture, A Quantitative Approach*, Morgan Kaufman (1989).

[Kim, 86] Kim, M.Y., *Synchronized Disk Interleaving*, **IEEE Transactions on Computers C–35**, 978–988 (1986).

[Patterson, 89] Patterson, D. A., G.A. Gibson, and R.H. Katz, *A Case for Redundant Arrays of Inexpensive Disks (RAID)*, **Proceedings of 1988 ACM SIGMOD Conference**, 109–116 (1988).

[Rao, 89] Rao, T. R. N. and E. Fujiwara, *Error Control Coding for Computer Systems*, Prentice-Hall (1989).

[Rosenblum, 91] Rosenblum, M. and J.K. Ousterhout, *The Design and Implementation of a Log-Structured File System*, **Operating Systems Review 25**(5), 1-15 (1991).

[Salem, 86] Salem, Kenneth and Hector Garcia–Molina, *Disk striping*, **IEEE 1986 Conference on Data Engineering**, 336–342 (1986).

[Stallings, 90] Stallings, William, *Computer Organization and Architecture*, second ed., Macmillan (1990).

[Stone, 88] Stone, Harold S., *High Performance Computer Architecture*, second ed., Addison–Wesley (1990).

[VME, 87] *IEEE Standard for a Versatile Backplane Bus: VMEbus*, **ANSI/IEEE Std 1014–1987**

CHAPTER 9

A MICROPROGRAMMED FLOATING-POINT COPROCESSOR

WHEN COUNTING BY 1'S WON'T DO

9.1 COMPLEX INSTRUCTION SETS AND MICROPROGRAMMING

This last chapter in the text presents a design of a floating-point coprocessor that realizes the operations specified in the IEEE floating-point standard [IEEE, 85]. It is certainly proper that we come full circle and consider once again how we will organize this processor. Two things are distinctly different here, two things which will lead us to a rather different design format. These are:

- The basic operations which this chip must deliver, by hardware or through software, are specified in detail by the IEEE floating-point standard [IEEE, 85]. Furthermore, we have loaded a collection of functions onto the instructions for this coprocessor (see Table 2.7). This means that the instruction set is preordained.
- We have not yet discussed the other principal paradigm of computing machine design—microprogramming.

Microprogramming is a logical and rather ancient extension of the concept of a stored-program computer. At its lowest level, the difference between microprogramming and hardwiring is whether the logic is stored in a ROM or a PLA. In that sense, no big deal. You can still retain any of the RISC concepts such as a load-store architecture and one instruction completed on every clock. Some of the early RISCs were microprogrammed. Since both ROMs and PLAs and even gate arrays are programmable, at this lowest level the choice is really between two almost equivalent ways of making the same incoming bits generate the same outgoing bits.

At a higher level, however, the two diverge. Microcoding implies that there is a programmable processor controlling the CPU; hardwiring implies that the instruction itself controls the hardware. That dichotomy is less clear than you might suppose. Both forms of machine go through a sequence of operations to accomplish a single instruction. The sequence can be of fixed length, as our CPU is, or of variable length. Whatever divergence there is is a matter of degree. Some CISC proponents considered the RISC option as "turning microcode into machine language"; some RISC proponents saw the same half-full glass as an opportunity to let high-performance compilers optimize the code that the actual machine ran. Six of one; half a dozen of the other.

In this chapter, we:

- support the majority of the mathematical operations that one rather successful, IEEE-standard-compliant coprocessor supports (the MC68881)
- continue to use the LOAD/STORE model that is appropriate to our RISC architecture
- design a computing structure to provide all of the primitive operations which are needed and which employs parallel operations wherever it is beneficial
- control the computing structure with microcode

Microprogramming came on as the new wave in the mid-1970s, driven by availability of inexpensive ROMs. Yet in truth it was a method of such antiquity that its roots date back to day 1. Microprogramming was invented formally by Maurice Wilkes in 1951 [Wilkes, 51]. Reminiscing two decades later, Wilkes pointed out that in the previous century Charles Babbage had proposed a mechanical equivalent for his Analytical Engine (see pages 198-199 in [Wilkes, 85]). We can view a microprogrammed machine as a processing system run by a microengine which behaves a lot like our RISC processor of Chapter 6. A principal difference is that the instruction that the CPU fetched was the control word for the CPU, whereas the macroinstruction or *command* delivered by the CPU to the coprocessor is essentially a datum for the microengine. The datum contains an address for selecting a routine from the microcode as well as control bits which enable the microcode routine to select the correct data for processing.

Before we start to develop our microcoded coprocessor, reread Section 2.6 to refamiliarize yourself with our basic objectives and the interface between coprocessor and CPU. With that in hand, we may consider the following snippet of pseudo C code as a description of what our coprocessor will do:

```
while (1) {
    command = P_bus;
    if (control_code == coprocessor && command<1:0> == 2) {
        switch (command<27:23>) {
            case 0:{…}  /* here we execute the command FPADD whose opcode is 0 */
            case 1:{…}  /* here we execute the command FPSUB whose opcode is 1 */
            …
```

```
            ...
            case 31:{…} /* here we execute the command FPSTORES whose opcode is 31 */
        }
    }
}
```

This loop runs forever, looking for a command, executing it, and then returning to look for the next. If we expect a steady and rapid stream of floating-point instructions, we might well want to permit a second instruction to begin before a first one had finished, but that does not change the general concept. Nothing in this piece of code suggests that we must execute it in software. Nor, should we opt for microcode, does this software description imply that what we are doing is not simply executing the sequence of hardware steps which gets our job done. All that it does is suggest that we could sequence our steps by doing what one does in code: either take the next instruction in sequence or branch. It is this software perspective that sets microcoding apart from hardwiring.

Look at Figure 6.11 on page 340, which shows a hardwired sequencer of a tight and simple sort. The instruction enters through decode logic—a PLA. The decoded bits, latched into the I register, control the ALU and the output of the register file on the next clock. The contents of the I register are further decoded (more PLA) and passed to the LAST_I register. Here the doubly decoded bits are used to control reads to or writes from the P-bus and the movement of data from the C register or P-bus to the register file. *Sequencing*, such as it is in our processor, is simply the orderly progress of instructions through the decoding logic and I registers. The pump is the clock and the sequence is stepped along by the entry of new data into a register on the chosen clock edge.

What will be the difference for our microcoded sequencer? The PLA has the flavor of a logic-state manipulator: input logic state ⇒ output logic state. The ROM has the flavor of a memory reference: input number ⇒ output bit array. If the *output bit array* happens to be more or less equal to the *output logic state*, you can say that they are the same or you can say that they taste different. Let us see what makes up the flavor.

Figure 9.1 shows one form of microinstruction. It is particularly wide, having as part of the instruction itself the address of its logical successor as well as the address to jump to if some particular condition obtains. As a result, branches—even conditional branches—are folded into the previous microinstruction. In fact, entire loops can often be folded into a single microinstruction. This parallelism can permit an n-step loop to complete in n microinstructions. Lots of other formats are found. One common mechanism is to use an incrementer to generate the successor address. Then only the branch address need be carried.

FIGURE 9.1 A typical microinstruction. Here the sequencing is determined explicitly by the instruction. The control bits serve the same function as the control bits in the I registers of Figure 6.11. They control the hardware of the chip. The other fields determine the next instruction to be read from the microinstruction store.

control bits	branch bits	next address	branch address

It is not uncommon to set up the control bits so that each bit field controls some particular function. Such a fully decoded format is called *horizontal microcode* because of the great width of the resulting instruction. The alternative, encoding functions into a relatively narrow format, then becomes *vertical microcode*. A combination of the two is to have narrow microinstructions interpreted or otherwise translated into wide *nanoinstructions*. This approach originated with the Nanodata QM-1 [Nanodata, 79] around 1970. A simpler version is found in modern vertical microcoded machines, such as Motorola's MC68020 and MC68881.

Many features of current RISC processors were originally developed for microengines. The execution of exactly one microinstruction per clock cycle makes pipelining extremely simple, just as it does with RISC processors. Delayed branches are used by some microengines, just as they are used by some RISC processors. In a CISC machine, it tends to be relatively easy to implement pipelining at the microinstruction layer, but very difficult to pipeline the basic CISC instructions. For this reason, high-performance CISCs sometimes have one machine fetching a sequence of CISC instructions and converting them into a sequence of microinstructions, which is fed into a pipelined microengine. This type of operation may be thought of as a compiler, rather than an interpreter. See [Mishra, 87], [Ditzel, 87a], and [Ditzel, 87b] for examples of this kind of operation. CRISP is a particularly interesting implementation, since it stores the "compiled" microinstructions in a second I-cache, so loops may not need to fetch the original instructions again.

In thinking about Figure 9.1 and the hardware it may imply, consider that other data is available to determine certain operations. In particular, the data to be used and the destination can be specified by the command, the branch can be predicated on bits set by or in the hardware, and so forth. We will soon enough block out a real engine. First, though, we must establish what the coprocessor must do. This brings us face to face with the IEEE floating-point standard. There is much more to it than having a convenient way to write Avogadro's number or the charge on the electron. The standard is the distillation of years of struggling with very difficult problems in numerical calculation. The complexities which result are sufficiently intimidating that the standard specifically permits meeting any (or all) of its requirements in software. Many IEEE-compliant floating-point systems take advantage of this escape clause to handle rare events. Many other floating-point systems are compliant only with a subset of standard.

9.2 IEEE FLOATING-POINT STANDARD

Floating-point arithmetic is very useful in many applications. We hope that that point needs no proof, even though some distinguished people have questioned the proposition (page A-63 in [Goldberg, 89]). But numbers are numbers. Why do we need a *standard*? A standard is desirable from the programmer's point of view because:

- It allows a program run on various computers to get the same answers on all of them. Prior to the development of the IEEE standard, a floating-point program could be expected to give slightly different results on each machine, and if roundoff errors were significant, the results might be completely different. In fact, the program might converge to a correct answer on one and oscillate forever or blow up on another.

- It allows or at least facilitates data exchange between computers of different design.
- It defines the set of special cases—underflow, overflow, inexact, undefined—in a uniform way, as well as the set of tests and comparisons. For example, if you ask if $(-1) + (1) < 0$, should the answer be yes or no? In integer arithmetic, "< 0" is true if the result's sign is negative. Since floating point supports both +0 and -0, the answer is neither obvious nor uniform among nonstandard floating-point systems.

The IEEE standard [IEEE, 85], which evolved primarily from the work of Kahan, has become so pervasively accepted that the only deviants from its rules are found either in architectures which were extant prior to its adoption or in systems which, for reasons of price or considerations of speed, choose to fulfill some subset of the standard. The IEEE standard is good, widely available, and dominant in new designs. Let us see what the standard says.

9.3 REPRESENTATION OF FLOATING-POINT NUMBERS

Consider Avogadro's number, 6.0221×10^{23}. The number itself is not exactly Avogadro's number; it is the best approximation to Avogadro's number that will fit in five decimal digits. The issue of what fits will become important shortly, so we emphasize it right at the beginning. Now name the parts of number itself. Everyone gets "23 is the *exponent*," some will get "10 is the *base*," and barely anyone seems to know that "6.0221 is the *significand*." If you said: "6.0221 is the mantissa," you join an unexclusive club noted only for its ignorance. It would be easy to include in our list of references an appallingly long list of otherwise worthy texts which call the *significand* a *mantissa*, but do not be party to the mob which does not know the difference between a number and its logarithm. Lest you be accused of being of the generation that understands that "logarithms are what you get when you press the log button on your calculator," we present here the correct names for both the floating-point representation and a logarithm:

$$+6.0221 \times 10^{23} = \text{sign} \times \text{significand} \times \text{base}^{\text{exponent}}$$

$$\log_{10}(6.0221 \times 10^{23}) = 23.77975 = \text{characteristic.mantissa}$$

This makes it look as if we could say that $mantissa = \log_{\text{base}}(significand)$ and that $characteristic = exponent$, but a little caution is in order. To begin with, both significand and exponent have signs associated with them. To keep things real, we must restrict the argument of a logarithm to positive real numbers. Accordingly, the *significand* is always a positive real number with a separate sign which is not included in the logarithm. Furthermore, if the significand is represented in *normalized* form, so that $1 \le significand < \text{base}$, then the mantissa will always be a positive fraction. To form the log, we must now add the integer and fractional components of the logarithm. Thus,

$$\log_{10}(0.03) = \log_{10}(3 \times 10^{-2}) = +0.47712 - 2 = -1.52288$$

Just to drive home the point, the fractional part of the logarithm above looks like -.52288, but it is not. The mantissa must be positive and comes from the previous expression; it is +0.47712. As one last tidbit in names, let it be said that the generic name for the period separating the integer part from the fractional part is the *radix point*. For any given base or *radix*, the name can be made specific to that radix by using *binary point*, *octal point*, *decimal point*, and so on.

In designing a format for floating-point numbers in the computer, the obvious choices would pack the sign, significand, and exponent into one or more words, using all of the precision available. The base would be compatible with a binary system—2, 4, 8, or 16. Beyond these choices, the selections become considerably less obvious. The items left to choose comprise:

- division of the bits among sign, significand, and exponent
- which base to use
- signing convention for both the number and the exponent
- ordering the bit fields

We telegraphed the bit-division problem when we stated that "6.0221×10^{23} is not exactly Avogadro's number." Precision is one important parameter; range is the other. Let us consider the problem in the framework of the shortest string of bits widely used for a floating-point number—32 bits, or one word. First let us consider the *range*-versus-*precision* issue.

If we devote 7 bits to the exponent and use a base of 2, the exponent will represent a range of 2^{-64} to 2^{63}. However, if we devote the same 7 bits to the exponent and use a base of 16, the exponent will represent a range of $16^{-64} = 2^{-256}$ to $16^{63} = 2^{252}$. The first is a dynamic range of 10^{37}; the second is a whopping 10^{153}. You may conclude quite correctly that, for a given number of bits of exponent, larger bases increase the range represented. However, larger bases tend to waste some bits in the significand. As usual, there is no free lunch. The price that you pay for a large radix is a loss of significance. This is a little subtle. If we use a base of 16, for example, the bits to the left of the radix point must accommodate numbers in the range $1 \le n < 16$. That calls for 4 bits, leaving only 20 for the fraction. This makes the last bit of our normalized significand of size $2^{-20} \approx 10^{-6} = 1$ part in a million. With radix 2, we need only 1 bit to the left of the binary point, leaving 23 on the right. That makes the finesse a factor of 8 smaller (better) at 1 part in 10 million. Is range important? Clearly. Is precision important? No question. What makes for a good balance? That depends on the application.

Analyzing relative error as a function of the base, exponent, and significand sizes is fairly complex (see [Brent, 73], and Sections 9.2 and 10.5 in [Hwang, 79]). Brent concluded that a base of 4 produces the best RMS values of relative error, other things being equal. However, an additional advantage is possible using a base of 2. If all non-zero numbers are required to be normalized and the base is 2, then the most significant bit of every significand must be 1. In that case, there is no need to store that bit as part of the number; it carries no information. Removing this redundant bit from the storage format gains an extra bit of precision in the significand. With this change, base 2 becomes the best choice in terms of RMS relative error. But note:

- The bit removed—the *hidden bit*—must be restored to its normal place when the packed storage format is unpacked for doing any arithmetic operation. It is hidden but not absent.
- There must be a way to distinguish between 0 and 1.0×2^n. See Section 9.3.2.

The use of base 2 with a hidden bit is older than electronic computers. It first appeared in Konrad Zuse's relay computers beginning in 1936 [Zuse, 36]. The IEEE standard uses base 2 with a hidden bit. The size of the bit fields for one- and two-word representations (*single* and *double* precision) are given in Table 9.1. The dynamic range does not include the *soft zero*, which is part of the IEEE specification. We will add that to our discussion below.

Now we turn to the last two items in our short list above: signing convention for both the number and the exponent and order of the bit fields. When we made the choice of 2's *complement* for the integer format, our objective was the best possible format for our most common arithmetic operations: addition and subtraction. In floating point, the choice is based on the operation *compare*. This may seem a strange focus but consider our objective and then our defense. First our objective:

> If we choose a format which makes large floating-point numbers look like large integers, and small floating-point numbers look like small integers, then we can compare floating-point numbers using integer comparisons.

To begin our defense, let us start with where the comparison issue arises: addition and subtraction. Consider the task of computing $3.5732 \times 10^{-12} - 3.5665 \times 10^{-12}$. The very first thing you must do is determine which of these numbers has the *larger magnitude*. You then will subtract the smaller from the larger, taking the sign of the larger for your result. Determining the *larger magnitude* is the comparison task that concerns us. You did it when you looked at these two numbers, *A* and *B*, by:

TABLE 9.1 **IEEE standard storage formats for IEEE floating-point numbers**

	Single	Double
sign	1 bit	1 bit
exponent	8 bits	11 bits
bias	127	1023
significand	23 bits	52 bits
dynamic range	$\sim 10^{74}$	$\sim 10^{614}$
precision	1 part in 10^7	1 part in 10^{16}

```
if (expA > expB) then choose A
else if (expB > expA) then chose B
else if (signifA > signifB) then choose A
else choose B;
```

Exponents first, then, if necessary, significands. That suggests putting the exponent field to the left of the significand field, since a number with a larger exponent will be larger, regardless of the significands. Furthermore, we must make the exponents *monotonic* so that a larger exponent, represented as an integer, is always bigger than a smaller exponent. Neither a complement nor a sign-magnitude representation has this monotonicity. To achieve that end, we must put our smallest exponent at 0 and count up to our highest exponent. Such a system will put *exponent* = 0 somewhere in the middle, just as you might put your 0 in the middle of the *x*-axis. Since you can think of this as simply adding a *bias* to the real exponent, this format is referred to as a *biased number system*. Alternatively, if you view the operation as removing the bias to get the true value, you might apply the other name *excess "bias value" notation*. For example, the IEEE single-precision format will use *excess 127 notation*, indicating that by subtracting 127 from the exponent you get the true exponent. With this notation and with the order of the bit fields being *sign-exponent-significand* and with the hidden bit concealed from view, we get the two storage formats from Table 9.1 as shown in Figure 9.2.

Choosing the bias involves a tradeoff between the largest representable magnitude and the smallest representable magnitude. The IEEE standard uses this to balance the range of representable numbers, so that almost every representable number has a representable reciprocal.

We have described all of the basic issues but one: What do you do when a result lies outside the range of the number format you are using? While it is but one question, it brings up hints of a host of answers. The IEEE has set aside the largest and smallest exponents for special purposes. For example, in single precision, biased exponents 0 and 255 do not mean biased exponent 0 or biased exponent 255. You can think of them as flags saying: "Read this as something else." *Something else* can include numbers

FIGURE 9.2 Formats of the two most common IEEE floating-point representations.

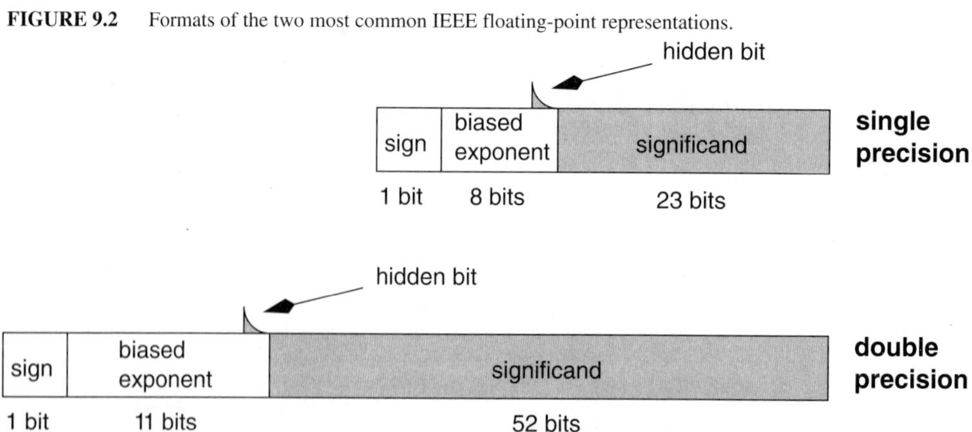

either too big or too small, indeterminate results, inexact results, or even results that are not numbers. Let us consider first the subject of numbers that are too big for format.

9.3.1 Overflow

When a result is too large for the format, we say that the result has *overflowed*. The two customary ways of indicating overflow are to set an overflow flag or to trap. The IEEE standard includes both. The user program should be able to control whether overflow causes a trap or not, and it should be able to test an overflow bit to determine whether overflow occurred even if the trap is disabled.

The question of which value an operation should return when overflow occurs is more complicated. We could simply regard the result as meaningless when overflow occurs. IBM did that in its earliest 360 models [Gifford, 87] but later was forced to modify all of the machines it had sold. The problem is that many programmers want to find the correct answer after an overflow. There are two reasonable ways to return useful results after an overflow. The first, which was used on Zuse's relay computers in the 1930s [Knuth, 81] and on the CDC 6600, is to assign certain patterns to represent "infinity." *Infinity* here means *too big*, not necessarily mathematically infinite. In many cases, very large numbers can be considered to be infinite, and, if the program can accept *too big* as a result, it can continue to perform computations. The assigned patterns for $\pm\infty$ in the IEEE single-precision format are shown in Table 9.2. The only difference between the two is the sign bit. Note that the structure for infinity comprises the largest possible exponent and a zero significand field. That same formula works for the double-precision format but with longer fields.

Of course, once you allow infinities among your programming toys, some otherwise ordinary operations can produce indeterminate results. $\infty - \infty$, $0 \times \infty$, and ∞/∞ are some conspicuous examples. What in the world can a coprocessor do with *indeterminate*? "Too big" is specific; "I really don't know" is difficult to write as a number. While the IEEE committee could have introduced a set of responses specific to particular outcomes, just as it did with infinities, the committee chose instead to be nonspecific in a conspicuously specific way. The IEEE spec is complete in all respects but one: reasons for what the committee did. So what did it do in its specifically unspecific fashion?

First, it introduced what is called a *NaN*, not a number:

> A *NaN* is any floating-point number with a maximum exponent, as in Table 9.2, but whose significand is *not 0*.

TABLE 9.2 IEEE single-precision infinities

	In hex	In binary showing the three fields
+infinity	7F800000	0 11111111 00000000000000000000000
-infinity	FF800000	1 11111111 00000000000000000000000

The standard discusses using different NaN patterns for a variety of things, such as uninitialized variables and complex-affine infinities, but specific patterns and uses are not defined. The standard does specify two types of NaNs which must be provided: *quiet NaNs* and *signaling NaNs*. Signaling NaNs can cause traps if you try to operate on them; quiet NaNs simply cause the result to be another quiet NaN. While it is left up to the designer to implement in whatever fashion he or she chooses, here the intention of the IEEE spec is specific:

> Two different kinds of NaN, signaling and quiet, shall be supported in all operations. Signaling NaNs afford values for uninitialized variables and arithmetic-like enhancements (such as complex-affine infinities or extremely wide range) that are not the subject of the standard. Quiet NaNs should, by means left to the implementor's discretion, afford retrospective diagnostic information inherited from invalid or unavailable data and results. Propagation of the diagnostic information requires that information contained in the NaNs be preserved through arithmetic operations and floating-point format conversions.

Retrospective diagnostic information? Doesn't that sound fascinating! Let us consider that with the infinities.

One possible choice when overflow occurs is to provide more detailed information about the result of the operation that overflowed. In fact, the hardware often knows what the correct result is, but cannot return it because it will not fit into the rigid format. Some programs could proceed to compute correctly if they could get the information which is available inside the floating-point hardware. A simple way to allow this is to return the correct significand and an exponent which is simply the least significant part of the true exponent. At the same time, we must indicate that overflow has occurred, so the program can account for the missing high-order bit of the exponent. Notice that this is sufficient for simple arithmetic operations like addition, subtraction, multiplication, and division (not including either hard or soft 0), since they never change the exponent by more than a factor of 2. More complex operations, such as exponentiation, can require more than one extra bit.

Kahan, who was responsible for many of the features of the IEEE standard, implemented a more elaborate mechanism on the 7094 [Kahan, 66]. It allowed a program to select what was called *counting mode*, in which case a special location was incremented whenever overflow happened and decremented whenever underflow happened. This automatically kept track of the upper part of the exponent through an entire sequence of multiplications and divisions. For example, the binomial coefficient

$$\binom{100}{50} = \frac{51 \times 52 \times 53 \times \cdots \times 100}{1 \times 2 \times 3 \times \cdots \times 50} = 100891344545564193334812497256$$

$$\approx 1.0089 \times 10^{29}$$

has a value which can be represented, at least approximately, in IEEE single-precision format. Computed by alternating multiplications and divisions, it reaches the final value without overflow. But what happens if we compute the numerator first, then compute the denominator, and divide to get the final result? The numerator would be approximately 3.068519×10^{93} and the denominator would be approximately

3.041409×10^{64}. Both of these are too large to represent using IEEE single precision, which is limited to numbers smaller than 3.4×10^{38}. By using counting mode, computations like this can be performed in any convenient order.

The IEEE standard does not include counting mode, but it does provide a mechanism to determine the correct result if traps are enabled on overflow. In that case, the standard requires the correct significand to be returned, with an exponent that is 192 less than the correct exponent in the single-precision case, or 1536 less than the correct exponent in the double-precision case. These bias values were chosen so that the returned exponent will tend to be near the middle of the range, to reduce the chance of another overflow if the computation is continued. Using this mechanism, it is fairly easy for a software trap handler to implement counting mode or some similar mechanism to deal with very large numbers.

Before we go much further, two items deserve a moment's note. To begin with, what does this "if traps are enabled" comment mean? There are several ways that a computation in floating point can blow out a gasket. The IEEE spec often provides two responses:

- Take an exception and handle the problem directly.
- Return the best value that you can and continue.

Returning $\pm\infty$ is an example of the latter, while the "subtract 192 ..." is an example of the former for the case of an overflow. In general, the way that particular traps are turned on or off is to have a status register for the coprocessor with a set of bits set aside for enabling specific traps. Other bits indicate whether a particular trap has occurred. The program can write to the coprocessor status register to set trap-enables as desired. Upon context switch the coprocessor status must be part of the context.

The second point is whether we *need* microcode to handle all these special cases. Certainly a programmer's prejudice is to write program to handle the many choices, but think of the state machines in Chapter 5. They certainly handled special cases. Software is certainly easy to upgrade and install, but similar tools now exist for PLA and gate array designers. We will do it with microcode, but we do not have to.

9.3.2 Underflow and Soft Zero

Underflow is similar in many respects to overflow, but the mechanisms used to deal with it are somewhat different because the problems underflow entails are different. The most common approach has been simply to ignore it. That is, if the result of an operation is too small to be represented in the format being used, a zero is returned. This solution is called *flush to zero*. It is simple to implement, but it causes some strange results.

First a direct example. Suppose we want to multiply three numbers, 2^{-60}, 2^{-70}, and 2^{+80}, using a single-precision format which cannot represent numbers smaller than 2^{-128}. If we begin by multiplying the first two numbers, the product will be flushed to zero, so our final answer will be zero. But if we begin by multiplying the last two numbers, our final answer will be the correct value 2^{-50}. This example invokes a curious philosophical question: How close is 2^{-50} to 0? If powers of 2 are not your forte, try 8.88×10^{-16}. A number, by itself, has no size. Throw units at it to get some sense of importance. You could consider this number as "fewer dollars than you would ever worry about" or "a charge of 5500 electrons, which is a pretty big signal in a CCD video detector." In one case, truncating to 0 concurs with your sense of proportion; in the other, you have indeed disposed of baby and bathwater. If you want more absolute comparisons, consider that the appropriate scale is logarithmic. On that basis, the step from 2^{-50} to 0 is infinite. Now that is a step! It leads us to ask what impact such a step might have on numerical solutions.

A subtle but insidious problem arises with the introduction of a step of noise into any iterative calculation that can be thought of as solving a differential equation. Such calculations cover a huge amount of computer activity. Truncation to zero introduces a step function of noise into the system that is being solved. Step functions generally result in some ringing behavior in the solution which may or may not be well damped. The result can be oscillatory behavior or even nonconvergence in the iterative procedure. Worse yet, such behavior may depend critically on the starting values, making it rare and very hard to debug.

The IEEE standard takes its usual two ways to deal with the underflow problem: trapped detection or, if traps are disabled, simply a better, more controlled response than a raw flush to zero. The value returned depends on whether a trap is enabled. If a trap is taken, the correct significand is returned with an exponent that is rebiased by adding 192 (single precision) or 1536 (double precision). This allows the trap routine to implement counting mode or some similar mechanism. If no trap is taken, the underflow flag is set, and tiny numbers move toward zero in a progressive manner called *soft zero*. The idea here, also due to Kahan, is to trade precision for range. In the IEEE standard, the exponents 0 and max_EXP are reserved. Max_EXP signaled infinities and NaNs. 0 will signal *soft zero* (denormalized number). To see what that implies, begin with what all other exponents imply:

> All other exponents imply a normalized number with a *hidden bit*. The (implied) radix point is right behind this hidden bit.

To see this idea clearly, first consider the numbers 1, 2, 3, and 4 as shown in Table 9.3. These are certainly most ordinary numbers but they are also easy to comprehend and useful for illustration. Since $1 = 2^0$, the EXP (exponent) field is simply the bias (7F in hex). The visible part of the significand—the fraction—is 0, so the number becomes $1.00 \times 2^{(127-127)}$. Thinking of 2 as 1 + 1, we have $(1.00 \times 2^0) + (1.00 \times 2^0) = 2.00 \times 2^0 = 1.00 \times 2^1$. Again, no surprises, but look at the rather unfamiliar form that you see in Table 9.3. 3 becomes 1.5×2^1, and 4 is simply 1.00×2^2. In each case, one normalizes the number to be of the form 1.xxx, puts the .xxx part into the significand field, and remembers the hidden bit. A zero significand field means 1.000.

Next, let us consider how one stores the tiny numbers 1.5×2^{-126}, 1.5×2^{-127}, 1.5×2^{-128}, and 1.5×2^{-149}. These numbers are shown in Table 9.4. Consider the first entry. Note that the biased exponent is 1. That signals a normalized significand with a hidden bit in front of the implicit binary point.

TABLE 9.3 Some examples of small integers represented as IEEE single-precision floating-point numbers

	In hex	In binary showing the three fields
1	3F800000	0 01111111 00000000000000000000000
2	40000000	0 10000000 00000000000000000000000
3	40400000	0 10000000 10000000000000000000000
4	40800000	0 10000001 00000000000000000000000

If we employ the symbol *B* to mean "2 to the power of" just as we often use *E* to mean "10 to a power of," and using decimal-based true exponents and binary significands, the four numbers are shown in Table 9.5. With the first number, you can see the ".10" of 1.10, but the 1 is hidden. All of the rest of the numbers shown in Table 9.4 present a biased exponent of 0—the same exponent even though they range over 2^{22}. In fact, 0 is not the exponent; 1 is! All of the numbers in Table 9.4 have biased exponent 1. What the exponent 0 indicates is that the significand is denormalized. That is, no hidden bit or "What you see is what you've got." Accordingly, you accommodate the changing exponent by shifting the significand right, *trading range for precision*. Notice that you can see the "11" in the second and third cases, but in the fourth, something very strange seems to have happened. The lower order 1 has been traded for a 0. Why?

The answer is not so strange. The IEEE standard specifies rounding. 1[1000000], where the number in the bracket contains the bits to the right of the window, fits a rather special case, which we will discuss in a moment, but for now, it looks just like your usual rounding rule: If it is 0.5 or greater, round up. Had you really been counting right shifts (Binary notation is awful for human computers!), you would have seen that 1.5 had been replaced by 2 when the .5 part went off the right end.

Rounding brings up another careful prescription in the standard: *inexact*. How would we get to this value of 1.10B – 149 which we have been forced to represent as

TABLE 9.4 Some example tiny IEEE single-precision floating-point numbers

	In hex	In binary showing the three fields
1.5×2^{-126}	00C00000	0 00000001 10000000000000000000000
1.5×2^{-127}	00600000	0 00000000 11000000000000000000000
1.5×2^{-128}	00300000	0 00000000 01100000000000000000000
1.5×2^{-149}	00000001	0 00000000 00000000000000000000010

TABLE 9.5 Numbers from Table 9.3 in mixed binary-decimal format

	(binary) B (decimal)
1.5×2^{-126}	1.10B – 126
1.5×2^{-127}	1.10B – 127
1.5×2^{-128}	1.10B – 128
1.5×2^{-149}	1.10B – 149

1.0B – 148? By an arithmetic operation such as division or by conversion from other representation. Whatever the route, you have to admit that $2 \neq 1.5$. To let the perspicacious programmer into the secret that the result is *inexact*, the standard requires that even if you are using soft zero rather than trapping on underflow, the coprocessor must signal an inexact result by setting an *inexact* bit in a status register which the program may test. If it is running with soft zeroes enabled (underflow traps disabled), it will set the *underflow* if the result is both *denormalized* and *inexact*.

Do note that underflow is defined differently by the IEEE standard depending on whether the underflow trap is enabled or not. If it is enabled, then any nonzero result which is too small to represent as a normalized number will cause an underflow trap, and the correct significand will be delivered to the trap handler with an exponent biased by 192 or 1536. The coprocessor always keeps 24 or 53 significant bits in the significand. If the underflow trap is disabled (the standard default), the underflow flag will be set only if a nonzero result is too small to represent as a normalized number *and the result is inexact*. If the result contains all the bits which can be obtained from the calculation, it is not inexact, so neither the underflow flag nor the inexact flag will be set. This means that addition and subtraction cannot underflow with traps disabled, although they can produce either denormalized or inexact results. To see that reasonably subtle point, note that one shifts the subtrahend right until the minuend and subtrahend exponents are equal. To have a bit "hanging over the end" to cause an inexact result, you must shift the subtrahend. That means that the minuend's exponent must be greater than the minimum exponent of -126. Accordingly, if there is to be a remnant hanging over the end, the result must be at least as big as 1.0B – 126. Thus, only three outcomes are possible:

- an inexact but normalized result
- an exact and normalized result
- an exact but denormalized result (which includes true 0)

While the true 0 is the limiting case of a soft zero, it is specifically exempted from underflows. Note that none of these will set the underflow bit. The first will set the inexact bit.

9.3.3 Rounding

You will be surprised by how much the IEEE standard can say about rounding. Rounding seems like a simple concept:

> Get one-half of a place more precision in the last place by *rounding up* if the residue of bits hanging off the end equals or exceeds a half in that last place.

It is a pretty small correction in any case. Some machines, such as Crays, simply throw away any extra bits. This *truncation* is very easy for the hardware to do, so it allows the processor to run fast. But if truncation is not good for your calculation, correcting for it in software will be expensive compared to hardware rounding [Kahan, 66].

Truncation is not *not rounding*. It is one form of *directed rounding* called *round toward 0*.[1] The IEEE standard attempts to enable the programmer to select any reasonable form of handling the residues. There are several reasons for allowing this diversity:

- It is often highly desirable to have two disparate machines running the same HLL program get identical results for identical input data. To assure that result, the two machines must be able to round in the same way. Accordingly, a processor that is compliant with the IEEE standard should be able to adopt the rounding mode of a machine that is not fully compliant.
- A different rounding mode may be appropriate in different circumstances. The IEEE standard makes every effort not to burden the programmer with inappropriate methods that require software workarounds.

The standard provides four precisely defined rounding modes. The definitions are all based on a signed-magnitude significand:

- *Round to 0*. This is truncation.
- *Round to* $+\infty$. If the magnitude of the residue is greater than 0, the number returned is the smallest representable number that is algebraically greater than the exact result. This rule results in truncation of the residues of negative numbers and adding 1 to the least significant bit (LSB) of the significand of positive numbers with nonzero residues.
- *Round to* $-\infty$. If the magnitude of the residue is greater than 0, the number returned is the largest number that is algebraically less than the exact result. This rule results in truncation of positive numbers and adding 1 to the LSB of the significand of negative numbers with nonzero residues.
- *Round to nearest*. This comes the closest to your conventional rule for rounding. The standard says that the "representable value closest to the infinitely precise result shall

[1] Being yet more precise, truncation on signed-magnitude significands is *round to 0*; on twos-complement significands (not IEEE) it is *round to* $-\infty$.

be delivered." In other words, if the magnitude of the precise result is greater than $^1/_2$ in the LSB, you add 1 to the LSB of the magnitude; if it is less than $^1/_2$, you truncate. Now what if the coin you have flipped lands on its edge? In a digital computer, it certainly can come out precisely $^1/_2$ in the LSB. What you do then strikes most students as so bizarre that we provide an explanation before the result. The problem is to avoid biasing the result unwittingly. (Directed rounding is "biasing it wittingly.") In repetitive calculations where the precise value of $^1/_2$ in the LSB occurs with some frequency, you would find the answer slowly but steadily drifting off base if you always rounded $^1/_2$ in the same direction. Consider adding and then subtracting the number 1.0B – 24 to and from 1. If we always round up on $^1/_2$ in the LSB, the result drifts off to 2. To avoid such unreasonable behavior, the IEEE standard attempts to distribute the *residuals* as evenly as possible. While a truly random distribution would accomplish that end, were it really random, then repetitions of the same problem could give nonidentical results. The method had to be deterministic but effectively random. What the standard requires is that if the residue is precisely $^1/_2$ in the LSB, then the rounding is accomplished by adding the LSB to itself—that is, your result is always that the LSB becomes 0. (This is often called *round to even*, but since the significand is a number between 1 and 2, you well might question that name.) The reason for choosing to make the least significant bit even, rather than odd, is that we tend to get results like 1.00000000 rather than 1.00000001 or 0.11111111. Although it makes no difference in terms of accuracy, the results look better to humans when they come out with more trailing zeroes.

We have motivated *round to 0* and *round to nearest*, but why would one want the directed rounds to $\pm\infty$? Consider trying to get some bounds on the rounding error in a complicated calculation. Many problems are solved by repetitive calculations with many millions of floating-point operations. With all of those rounds, what do you know about your result? By performing each operation twice, using two different rounding modes, the programmer can obtain one result which is less than or equal to the exact answer and another result which is greater than or equal to the exact answer. By combining in appropriate fashion the ranges for each calculation in the whole sequence of calculations, one can obtain bounds on the errors. This approach is called *interval arithmetic* because instead of doing arithmetic with individual values, it is done with intervals or ranges of values. Interval arithmetic has many subtleties. See [Ulrich, 90] or Section 7.4 in [Sterbenz, 74] for more details.

The IEEE standard discusses rounding by talking about the difference between the *representable value* and the *infinitely precise value*. Do they really expect floating-point processors to retain infinite accuracy? Hardly. The infinite precision applies only to whether the residue is

- zero
- greater than $^1/_2$ in the LSB
- equal to $^1/_2$ in the LSB
- less than $^1/_2$ in the LSB

What is required in the hardware to answer this question to infinite precision? Let's consider a simple addition example. Initially, we ignore the possibility of NaNs and infinities as inputs or results. The steps in doing a floating-point addition starting with the storage format and carrying through to returning a number are:

1. Choose the larger of the two magnitudes for the augend
2. For each of the operands, do

```
if (biased_exponent > 0)
    significand = significand+hidden;
    else biased_exponent = 1;
```

3. For the addend (the smaller number), align the radix points by doing

```
while ((exp_addend< exp_augend) && (signif_addend > 0)) {
    ++exp_addend;
    addend = addend >> 1; /* right shift of 1 place */
}
```

4. Form the sum by doing

```
if (sign_augend == sign_addend)
    significand = significand_augend + significand_addend;
else significand = significand_augend - significand_addend;
```

5. Renormalize by doing

```
if (significand >= two) {
    significand = significand >> 1; /* right shift of 1 place */
    ++exp;
}
else while (significand < one && exp > 1) {
    significand = significand << 1; /* left shift of 1 place */
    --exp;
}
```

6. Round (discussed below)
7. Renormalize by doing

```
if (significand >= two) {
    significand = significand >> 1; /* right shift of 1 place */
    ++exp;
}
```

8. Reassemble and return (essentially reverse 2, use sign of augend)

While this is pretty much the whole routine, the rounding issue for addition is our central focus. Let us consider several specific single-precision examples which will drive home the method and bring up the issues which arise in rounding and keeping track of that *infinitely precise result*. The first case is to sum

```
3D7FFFFF + 3FFFFFFF
```

A quick eyeballing of these two numbers shows that both are positive and that the second is the larger of the two and should be the augend. That covers the first step; we show the other seven in Figure 9.3. First the augend and then the addend are expanded from the storage formats. Then the binary points are aligned (exponents made equal). In the process, 5 bits in the addend are shifted into the *extension*. The extension of the augend is simply 0. Addition is performed. At that point, the extension is greater than ½ in the LSB of the significand. It would look as if a round up should be done, but no—first normalization, then rounding. After the first normalization, you can see that no round is in order. Here we displayed 8 bits of extension. The question that we wish to raise is: How many extension bits are necessary to be able to handle all possible rounding situations to *infinite precision*?

Before we work our way through the answer, make sure that you understand both the steps and the representation of the steps in the figure. As a warm up, you might try

FIGURE 9.3 First example of floating-point addition in the IEEE single-precision format.

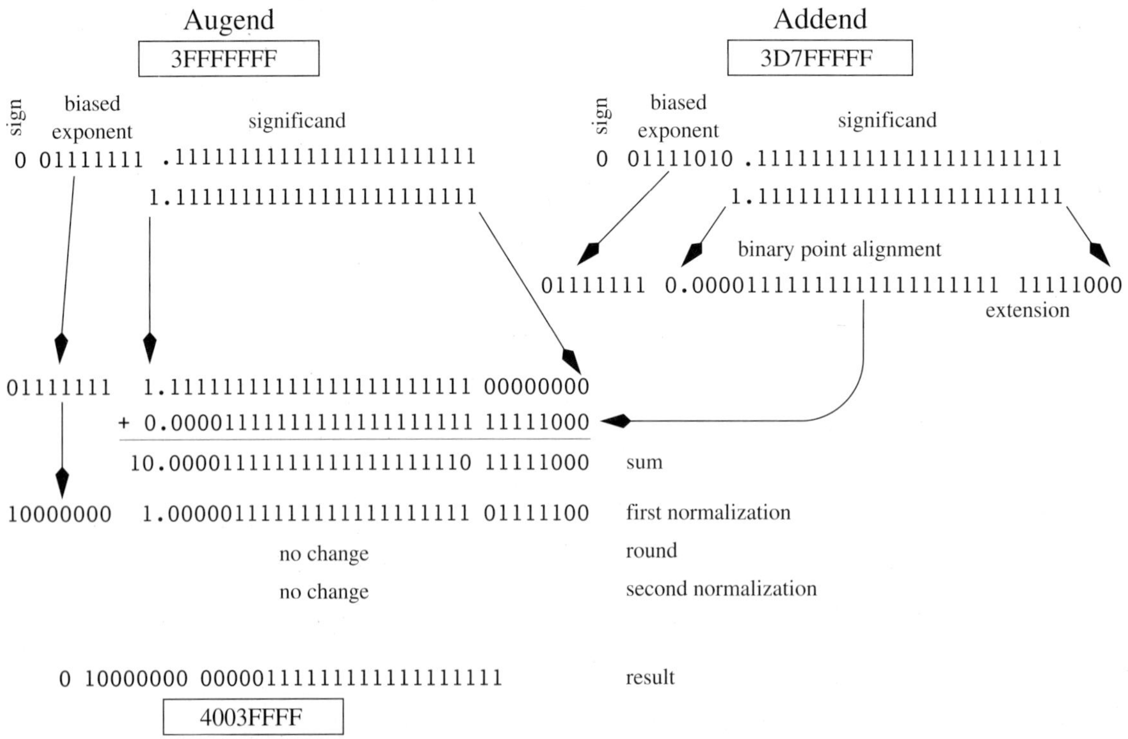

```
Augend                                    Addend
[3FFFFFFF]                                [3D7FFFFF]

sign  biased      significand             sign  biased      significand
      exponent                                  exponent
0 01111111 .11111111111111111111111       0 01111010 .11111111111111111111111
           1.11111111111111111111111                 1.11111111111111111111111
                                                 binary point alignment
                                          01111111 0.00001111111111111111111 11111000
                                                                             extension

01111111   1.11111111111111111111111 00000000
         + 0.00001111111111111111111 11111000
          10.00001111111111111111110 11111000   sum
10000000   1.00000111111111111111111 01111100   first normalization
                  no change                     round
                  no change                     second normalization

0 10000000 00000111111111111111111               result
[4003FFFF]
```

adding by hand 1.0 (3F800000) to 8.5 (41080000) to get 9.5 (41180000). The principal difference between what you would be doing there and in Figure 9.3 is the *extension bits*. These are simply the bits that get shifted out upon alignment. With the 1.0 + 8.5 = 9.5 problem, all the bits shifted out are 0's so nothing seems to happen out there.

Now take a look at the problem in Figure 9.3. After the add, the extension is well above $^1/_2$ in the LSB, but the significand at that moment has 25 bits. Accordingly, the rightmost one really belongs in the extension and ends up there after normalization. Note also that normalization preserves value by incrementing the exponent when it shifts the significand right. At this point, you can see that the extension is less than $^1/_2$ in the LSB. Accordingly, the default form of rounding (round to nearest) changes nothing.

Now we want to look at just which bits we *really* had to retain. There are only three things that can be required in the first normalization after doing an addition. (We include subtraction here since we do not constrain the sign of the operands.)

- The sum is $\geq$ 2.0 so the normalization which is needed shifts a bit right into the extension.
- 2.0 > sum $\geq$ 1.0 so no normalization is needed.
- 1.0 > sum so a normalization which shifts bits left is required.

Remember that for the rounding step, we must be able to discriminate three states:

1. less than $^1/_2$ in the LSB
2. greater than $^1/_2$ in the LSB
3. equal to $^1/_2$ in the LSB

The first state is true only if the most significant bit (MSB) of the extension is 0. That is clearly a pivotal bit, so let us name it the *round bit*. To discriminate between the last two states, we must know if *any* of the bits to the right of the round bit are 1. Since all of these bits got there by being shifted right through the round bit, what we want is a single bit that is 1 if any bit that passed through was a 1. Because the passage of a 1 forever sets the bit, it is said to be a *sticky bit*. Thus, if the round bit and the sticky bit are set, round up (state 2), whereas if only the round bit is set, you have the *round to even* case. It should be clear that this works for addition of numbers of the same sign. It is less clear when the numbers are of opposite sign. In that case, if the two numbers are almost equal, you can end up normalizing by shifting many places left. How can 2 bits retain enough information for that?

The issue is easily resolved if you but consider that *many shifts to the left* occurs only if the two numbers are almost equal—for example, 2.0 and 1.9999999. An *almost equal* example is presented in Figure 9.4.

This particular example is good because it shows a shift for alignment of binary points even though the numbers differ by the smallest difference possible in this format. An alignment shift of at most one place will occur if the numbers are almost equal, and only if they are almost equal will the difference be less than half of the augend. In other words, there are only two cases:

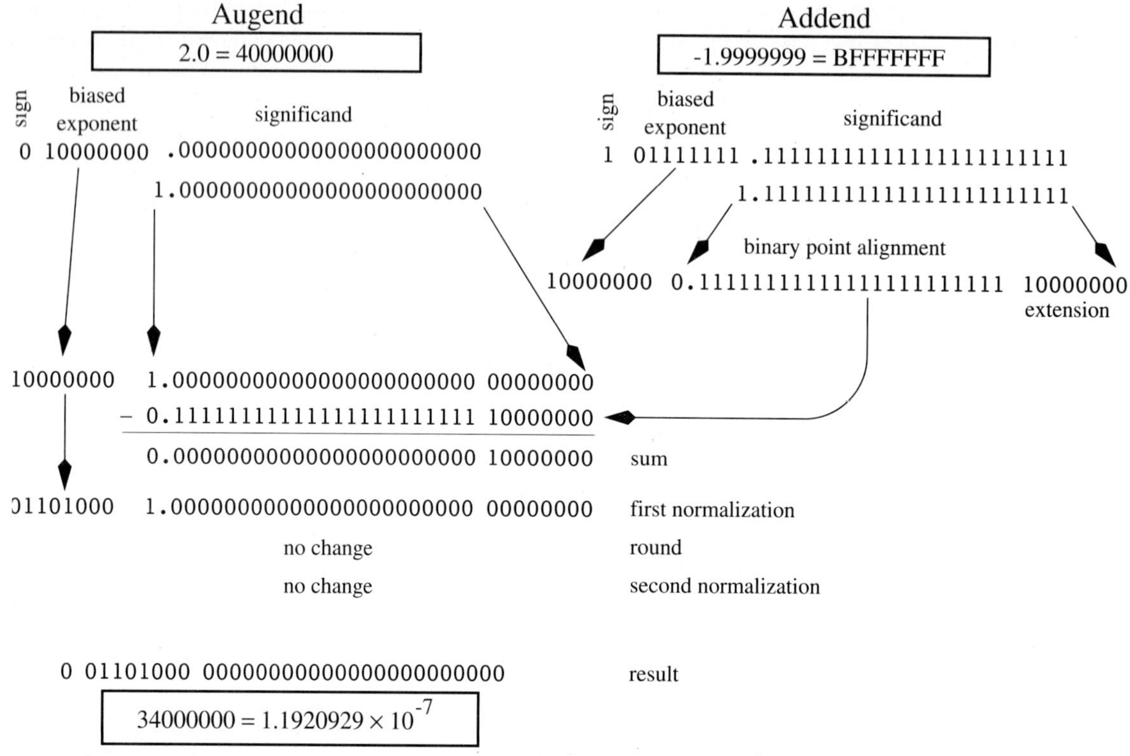

FIGURE 9.4 An example of subtraction of almost equal numbers in IEEE single-precision format. The problem is stated in decimal so the binary result has been converted back to decimal. The error from conversion inexactitude is 19 percent. While that may look bad in the extreme, we have obtained the difference between two numbers equal to within 1 part in 10 million in a system whose least significant bit is 1 part in 16 million. The accuracy obtained was what can and should be expected.

- *Augend and addend almost equal.* The maximum alignment shift is 1 place but the difference can be as little as 2^{-24} of the augend and require a shift of 24 places to normalize. (True zero can also occur, of course, but there is no alignment or normalization issue there.)
- *Augend and addend differ by more than a factor of* 2. Any alignment shift is possible, but renormalization will never require more than a left shift of one place.

Once again we ask: How many trailing bits do we need? Now we can answer. In the first case, we have the possibility of only one right shift and many left shifts. Since there is at most one right shift, the round bit stores the correct value to shift in and the sticky bit tells us that all the rest of the bits are 0. Thus, for the first case, 2 bits do the job to *infinite precision.*

The second case has any number of right shifts followed by at most one left shift for renormalization. Here 2 bits are insufficient. After the shift to the left, we would be left with only the sticky bit to decide between the three rounding scenarios. But 1 bit cannot define three scenarios. We need 2 bits hanging off the right end in order to discriminate between exactly $^1/_2$ in the LSB and more than $^1/_2$ in the LSB. This extra bit is called the *guard bit*. The order of the bits is *round*, *guard*, and then *sticky*.

We should look at how these bits are treated in additions and subtractions. The left two are just extensions on the LSB of the addend/subtrahend. They are treated like any other bits. The sticky bit, if 1, implies at least one 1 there or to the right. If the sticky bit is 1, adding it or subtracting it still leaves 1 in that place. Since the rightmost 1 on addition or subtraction will always leave a 1 (because the extension of the augend/minuend is always 0), and all that we want from the sticky bit is knowledge on whether there is a 1 somewhere out there, the sticky bit may be treated like any other bit in forming the sum/difference.

One final example presented in Figure 9.5 should illustrate the use of these bits. Initially, all three are 0. Upon alignment, the four rightmost bits, 0001, are shifted through the round, guard, and sticky bits. While the 1 passes right through, the sticky

FIGURE 9.5 An IEEE floating-point example showing the development and use of the round, guard, and sticky bits. Note that in normalization, 3 bits are retained to keep the round algorithm the same.

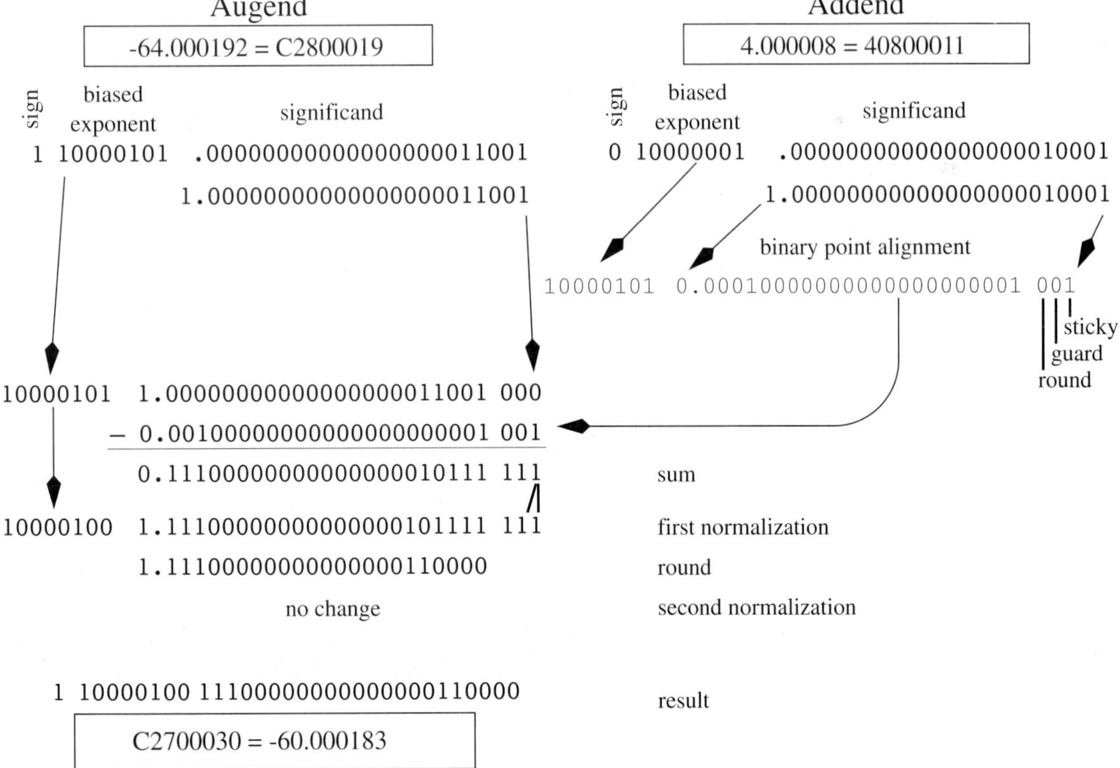

bit retains the fact that a 1 had been there. Then the extended significand is subtracted from the extended significand of the augend. Since the result is less than 1.0, renormalization requires a left shift of 1. The left shift does not affect the sticky bit, so the rounding algorithm is the same, although the case 101 will never occur.

One final comment about inexactitude. The decimal answer that is given in Figure 9.5 would seem to be off by 1 in the LSB. That last digit, however, is out at the end of the resolution limit for single-precision numbers. Any number between -60.000182 and -60.000185 will translate quite properly to C2700030. The resolution is 1 part in 16 million. That is all you get.

9.3.4 Operations Which Yield Infinity and NaNs

While it may seem obvious which operations result in $\pm\infty$, the directed rounding modes may generate some surprises:

- *Round toward 0.* The magnitude of the result of any operation which overflows is *defined to be* the largest finite number which can be represented, not $\pm\infty$.
- *Round toward* $-\infty$. If the operation overflows in the positive direction, the result is set to the largest finite number, rather than $+\infty$.
- *Round toward* $+\infty$. If the operation overflows in the negative direction, the result is set to the most negative finite number, rather than $-\infty$.

Having operations which "ought to" yield infinity but do not is certainly counter-intuitive. The arithmetic operations which produce NaNs are more reasonable if you look at returning a NaN as saying: "I have no numeric representation for this result." The operations which generate NaNs comprise:

- Any operation on a quiet NaN, which produces a result, produces a quiet NaN.
- Addition or subtraction such as $(-\infty) + (+\infty)$ produces a quiet NaN.
- Multiplication of $0 \times \infty$ produces a quiet NaN.
- Division of 0/0 or ∞/∞ produces a quiet NaN.
- X REM 0 or ∞ REM X produces a quiet NaN for any X.
- Square root of a negative number produces a quiet NaN.

Operations on signaling NaNs cause traps if enabled. Otherwise, they result in quiet NaNs.

Since the functions that we have defined in the floating-point instruction set (Table 2.7) can be calculated using series expansions, they are covered by the rules above. How these functions deal with $\pm\infty$ for an input, however, varies from function to function. For example FPSIN(∞) would yield a quiet NaN, as would FPASIN(3). However, FPATAN(∞) should yield $\pi/2$.

TABLE 9.6 Required operations for an IEEE standard floating-point processor

Addition	Remainder
Subtraction	Square root
Multiplication	Comparison
Division	Round to integer
Conversion between integer and floating point	
Conversion between different floating-point formats	
Conversion between decimal strings and floating point	

9.4 ALGORITHMS FOR FLOATING-POINT ARITHMETIC

The IEEE standard requires the operations listed in Table 9.6 to be implemented. In this section we will cover the algorithms that might be used to implement these operations, and the problems that we can expect. This will be helpful when we design the hardware in the final section.

9.4.1 Floating-Point Addition and Subtraction

Figures 9.3 to 9.5 provide good numerical examples of floating-point addition. To complete that picture, we present below a C subroutine which performs all of the steps necessary to accomplish a floating-point add with the default rounding mode (*round to nearest*). While reading someone else's code is only slightly better than reading a newspaper in a language you have not mastered yet, we commend this program to you because it handles each of the issues in the standard in a competent and *executable* fashion.

Note the definitions of hexadecimal constants at the top of the program. Some are used as masks; others are values to return (e.g., *infinity* and *indef*). A little routine at the top handles the three extension bits. You should look at how these are handled in the subtraction operation as well.

Each operation is set off with a comment. Where necessary, comments also illuminate obscure operations on a line.

```
#define SIGN     0x80000000
#define EXPO     0x7F800000
#define HIDDEN   0x00800000
#define ONE      HIDDEN
#define EXPO_1   HIDDEN              /* one in the exponent field */
#define FRAC     0x007FFFFF
#define UNSIGN   0x7FFFFFFF
#define INFINITY EXPO
```

```
#define TWO       0x01000000
#define NAN_IN    0x7F800001            /* not part of IEEE std */
#define INDEF     0x7F800002            /* not part of IEEE std */

unsigned long bitshift(unsigned long x, unsigned long rounds)
/* shifts the LSB of x into round, and correctly updates guard and sticky bits */
    {
        rounds = (rounds >> 1) | (rounds & 1); /* preserve sticky bit */
        rounds = rounds | ((x & 1) << 2);
        return(rounds);
        }

unsigned long FPADD(unsigned long a, unsigned long b)
           /* does IEEE single-precision add with round to nearest */
    {   unsigned long as, ax, bs, bx, rgs;
        int n, m;
                      /* remove signs to separate registers */
        as = SIGN & a; a = a & UNSIGN;
        bs = SIGN & b; b = b & UNSIGN;
                      /* largest magnitude into a */
        if (b > a) {
            rgs = b;  b = a;   a = b;
            rgs = bs; bs = as; as = bs;
            }
                      /* NaN in check */
        if (a > INFINITY || b > INFINITY) return(NAN_IN);
                      /* infinity in check */
        if (a == INFINITY || b == INFINITY) {
            if (a == INFINITY) {
                if (b != INFINITY) return(a + as);    /* infinity + x */
                else if (as == bs) return(a + as);    /* infinity + infinity */
                else return(INDEF);                   /* infinity - infinity */
                }
            else return(b + bs);
            }
                      /* decompose */
        ax = a & EXPO; a = a & FRAC;
        bx = b & EXPO; b = b & FRAC;
                      /* hidden bit or exp restored */
        if (ax != 0) a = a + HIDDEN;
            else ax = ONE;
        if (bx != 0) b = b + HIDDEN;
            else bx = ONE;
                      /* align radix points */
        rgs = 0;
```

```
while (bx < ax && (b > 0 || rgs > 3)) {
    rgs = bitshift(b, rgs);
    b = b >> 1;
    bx = bx + EXPO_1;
    }
          /* add or subtract significands including residue bits */
if (as == bs) a = a + b;
else {
    if (rgs == 0) a = a - b;
    else {
        rgs = 8 - rgs;
        a = a - b - 1;
        }
    }
          /* first renormalization */
while (a < ONE && ax > EXPO_1) {                /* properly handles soft zeroes */
    a = (a << 1);
    if (rgs > 3)      a = a + 1;
    rgs = ((rgs & 3) << 1) | (rgs & 1);         /* preserve sticky bit */
    ax = ax - EXPO_1;
}
if (a >= TWO) {
    rgs = bitshift(a, rgs);
    a = a >> 1;
    ax = ax + EXPO_1;
    }
if (ax == EXPO) return(EXPO + as);              /* return signed infinity */
          /* round */
if (rgs > 4) a = a + 1;
else if (rgs == 4) a = a + (a & 1);             /* round to even */
          /* second renormalization */
if (a >= TWO) {
    a = a >> 1;
    ax = ax + EXPO_1;
    }
if (ax == EXPO) return(EXPO + as);              /* return signed infinity */
          /* reassemble and return */
if (ax > EXPO_1 || a >= ONE) return(as+ax+(a & FRAC));    /* remove hidden bit */
else return(as + a);          /* return soft zero */
}
```

A caveat is in order. This program has been thoroughly tested but it has not been subjected to an official verification test for compliance. It clearly handles only the default case for rounding. With those limits and warnings clearly stated, we believe it is robust. In Problem 9.5, you are asked to demonstrate this routine's competence.

9.4.2 Floating-Point Multiplication

Multiplication of floating-point numbers is rather what you would expect with a few complications that you might not expect. Apart from those complications, the task requires:

1. separating the fields and restoring the hidden bit in multiplier and multiplicand
2. adding the exponents in the following form to end up with a properly biased exponent:

   expa = expa + (expb − bias)

3. multiplying the significands
4. renormalizing (includes getting the exponent in range if possible)
5. rounding
6. renormalizing
7. returning the reassembled number

Multiplying the significands has some very interesting possibilities. In single precision, we would be multiplying two 24-bit significands to arrive at a 48-bit product. Since the range of input values is $1 \le x < 2$, the product of two such numbers is $1 \le x \times y < 4$. That suggests that we will have at most one right shift after multiplication. However, before deciding on that happy result, let us look a bit more carefully at the product itself. The significands are really being treated as integers. That binary point that we see so clearly in Figure 9.5 is really only in our mind's eye. Staying aware of the fact that we are multiplying integers, we can still think of 1.0×1.0 as

```
  1.00000000000000000000000|
 ×1.00000000000000000000000|
 -----------------------------------------------------
 01.00000000000000000000000|00|000000000000000000000
```

Nobody will argue much with the result, but it is important to think of what the alignment means. As with MUL in Chapter 2, the product is formed by adding/subtracting and shifting right. Only the bits in the partial sum that are to the left of the tall line participate in the next sum. The 2 bits set off by the two lines will be used as a *round bit* and *sticky bit*; the remaining bits are unnecessary. As we show in a moment, all shifts are right shifts so 2 bits suffice for rounding "to infinite precision."

The algorithm for this integer multiplication is entirely up to us. We could use a 2-bit (radix-4) Booth recoding as we did for MUL. Since the numbers are both positive, we could use a purely additive scheme. We could throw money at it and use an array multiplier. This last technique will require some fancy footwork to get the round and sticky bits right, but it can be done [Santoro, 89]. A very thorough review of the possibilities is found in [Goldberg, 89].

How will we deal with denormalized numbers (soft zeroes)? They complicate multiplication. Since denormalized numbers are relatively rare, high-performance implementations sometimes trap when they encounter them to let system software accommodate them. However, "rare" means rare in general. Some programs generate lots of very little numbers. Those programs slow down considerably if denormalized numbers are relegated to software solutions. Dealing with denormalized numbers is not a basic problem; it is just an extra burden on the system. A simple and quite appealing method for handling soft zeroes is to normalize them by shifting left and counting the shifts. If that count is *shifts*, then the expression for *expa* in 2 above becomes

expa = expa + (expb – bias) – shifts

Everything else is the same. Problems 9.6 and 9.7 ask you to develop the descriptions for the multiplier section of the coprocessor. The main action is pretty much what you would expect, but special cases must be considered.

Having decided to normalize all numbers, we may say that in all cases but multiplication by 0, the significand product is between 4 and 1. At most, a single right shift will generate a normalized significand. This says nothing, of course, about where the exponent now lies. In single precision, the biased exponent might have overflowed to as much as $2 \times 128 + 1 + bias = 384$ or descended to the depths of $2 \times -149 + bias = -171$. Note that both of these numbers can be represented if traps have been enabled. For overflow you would subtract 192; for the underflow you would add 192. What about the case where traps are not enabled? For the big ones, we must return a result according to the rounding instructions as specified in Section 9.3.4 and signal overflow. The tiny numbers are somewhat more complicated because we can denormalize (but only if *round to nearest* is selected and underflow traps are disabled). The significand must be shifted right (denormalized) with the exponent increased by 1 on each shift. One of two things happens. The significand gets too small even for a soft zero or the exponent reaches 1:

```
while (expa < EXPO_1) {
    exp += EXPO_1;
    a = a >> 1;                              /* assumed to include the rounding bits */
    if (a == 0 && !round_bit) return(as);    /* signed hard zero */
    }
round();                                     /* flags set as appropriate */
if (expa > EXPO_1 || a >= ONE)
    return(as+expa+(a & FRAC));              /* remove hidden bit */
else return(as + a);                         /* return soft zero */
```

We must not round before getting the significand in the correct position. If the round bit or the sticky bit is set, the result will be inexact. The inexact condition bit must be set. If the result is denormalized, the round or sticky bit should be set, and if traps are disabled, the underflow flag should be set.

9.4.3 Floating-Point Division

Division just tends to be slower. There are numerous algorithms, none fast enough to be really satisfying. We cannot comfort ourselves with the truism of integer arithmetic which asserts that division is so rare that you do not care how slow it is. Floating-point division is really part of the working set of instructions. You can certainly sell chips and whole machines which do not do integer division in hardware. Do not try to sell a coprocessor that does not do floating-point divide in hardware. (Well, Cray almost does that. The Cray provides reciprocal. If you want *a*/*b*, calculate 1/*b* and then multiply 1/*b* by *a*.)

Just as FPMUL could be thought of as adding exponents and multiplying significands, so FPDIV can be described as subtracting exponents and dividing the significands. The normalization and rounding steps are essentially the same. Only the integer division operation stands between us and a speedy response. Just how fast would it have to be to make us happy?

The rule of thumb is "one-third the speed of multiplication" [Goldberg, 89]. While this does not define speed in absolute terms, it gives us some measure to go by. In our integer unit, the nonrestoring DIV instruction runs at half the speed (half as many bits per cycle) as the MUL instruction. That certainly meets the 1/3 ratio. But let us say that we were willing to put lots of dollars into faster multipliers, but not willing to put that much muscle behind the divide operation. This decision tends to represent real chips. For example, the Weitek 3364 chip in double precision does an FPMUL in the same time that it does an FPADD! That is a screaming multiplier, no doubt about that. On the other hand, it takes more than eight times an FPADD's time to do FPDIV. The question that we wish to raise and answer in the affirmative is: Is there a way to take advantage of the very fast multiplier to do division? While we will answer: "Yes," it is really "Yes, but. . . ." The technique that we will demonstrate is trusty old Newton's method.[2] Watch with enthusiasm as we "solve" the division problem, but remember that there are *buts* coming.

The object of the exercise is, given x, to find a sequence of y_i such that $y_i \Rightarrow {}^1\!/x$ very quickly with increasing i. In Newton's method, we create an error function, $E(y) = \frac{1}{y} - x$. The root of this equation is the y that we seek. If we take a good guess, y_0, then we may estimate the root of the equation by extrapolating the derivative $\frac{d}{dy}E\big|_{y_0}$ to the intersection with the x-axis. Figure 9.6 illustrates the method.

By Newton's method, we obtain the sequence of y_i which converge very rapidly on the reciprocal that we seek:

[2] Newton published a method for solving cubic equations in 1669. In 1690, Joseph Raphson used it to find the roots of polynomials. Raphson's method has been generally adopted and often called *Newton-Raphson.*

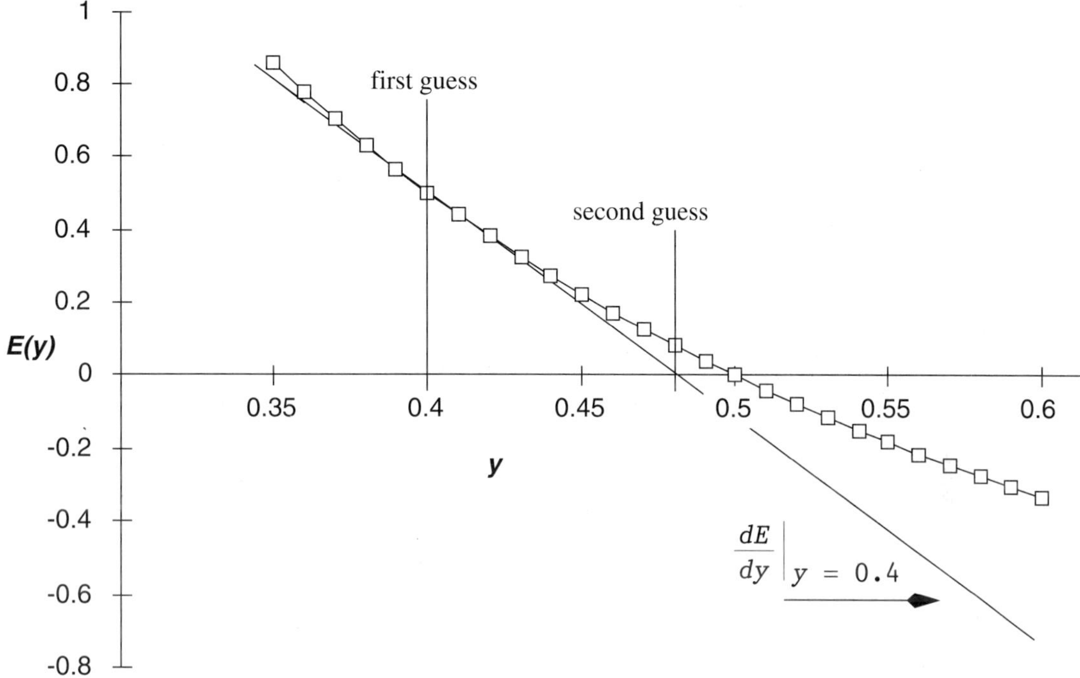

FIGURE 9.6 The function $E(y) = {}^1\!/_y - x$ and the slope at the first guess ($y = 0.4$) used to obtain the second guess ($y = 0.48$) by extrapolating to the value $E = 0$. The figure illustrates one step in Newton's method.

$$y_{i+1} = y_i - \frac{E(y_i)}{\left.\frac{dE}{dy}\right|_{y_i}} = y_i - \frac{\frac{1}{y_i} - x}{-\frac{1}{y_i^2}} = y_i(2 - xy_i)$$

With a nice smooth function like $1/x$ on numbers between 1 … 2, this process converges with a mighty hand. Consider a silly guess for the inverse of 2. If we take 0.4 as the first guess, the sequence of y_i in Table 9.7 results. These are done at approximately double precision. The number of accurate digits essentially doubles on each iteration. Impressive. With a better guess, we could cut out one or even two iterations. The first question is: How do you make a clever guess of the reciprocal of 1.34567?

Let us consider the problem in binary. If we start with guesses that are accurate to 8 bits, two turns of Newton's crank will earn us answers good to 32 bits. One more will deliver 64 bits. Every guess will involve two integer multiplications. Thus, the total effort to find the inverse will be five multiplications. Alternatively, a guess good to 16 bits requires only one turn to reach 32 and two to make 64. Actually, we are doing a little better than this, because the first bit of the reciprocal, y, is as well known as the first bit of x. Thus, we are really going $9 \Rightarrow 18 \Rightarrow 36 \Rightarrow 72$ or $17 \Rightarrow 34 \Rightarrow 68$. The guesses will be stored in a ROM, so what we are considering is the size of a ROM versus the

TABLE 9.7 Newton's method applied to finding the reciprocal of 2

x	y_i
2.0	0.400000000000
	0.480000000000
	0.499200000000
	0.499998720000
	0.499999999997
	0.500000000000

speed of the calculation. To generate the ROM data for a 256-guess table, we run the following few lines of code:

```
#define ONE ((double) 0x40000000)                    /* 2 to 30th */

unsigned long guess[256];

unsigned long round(double x)                        /* rounds to integer */
    {   long n;

        n = x + 0.5;
        return(n);
        }

void tablegen()
    {   double a_256th = 1.0/256;
        double a_512th = 1.0/512;
        unsigned long a, b;
        double x, y;
        int n;

        x = ONE;
        y = 1.0;
        for (n=0; n<256; n++) {
            guess[n] = round(x/(y+a_512th));
            y = y+a_256th;
            }
        }
```

The 256-element table is represented by two lines in Table 9.8. The first entry in the table will represent the inverse of $1+2^{-9}$ or halfway between the two points (in binary) 1.00000000 and 1.00000001. To see why 3FE00FF8 should represent $1/1.00195 = 0.99805$, observe in the program that *ONE* is defined as 2^{30} (0x40000000).

Think of that as 1.0000 ... and you will see that 3FE00FF8 is indeed just on the other side of the radix point or 0.111111.... Now how would we use this table?

Say that we wanted the inverse of 1.5×2^6 or 42C00000 in IEEE single-precision format. The high-order eight bits of the significand fraction (0x80 or 128) will form the index into the table of guesses. The value 2A9C7683 is returned. Think of this as a *fixed-point* rather than as an *integer* operation. We drag the significand left to provide the same resolution as the reciprocal within the 32-bit word. (We will consider precision and rounding in a moment.) This is shown in the upper part of Figure 9.7.

Newton's crank is turned twice. This is shown in *hex* in the box. Each new y is obtained by applying the formula $y_{i+1} = y_i(2 - xy_i)$. You can see the precision increase as the A's propagate to the right. The final result is then shifted right to occupy the proper bits of the significand and then rounded. The proper *biased* exponent is found from

$$\text{inverse exponent} = \text{bias} - (\text{exponent} - \text{bias}) = 2 \times \text{bias} - \text{exponent}$$

If we make a special case of the inverse of significands = 1.0, all other inverses are between 0.5 and 1.0 and the renormalization is always a shift to the left of one place. Accordingly, we must subtract 1 from the exponent. While shown as two steps in Figure 9.7, this would be one step in a real process. All that remains is reassembly, using the sign of the original number.

To the method shown in Figure 9.7 must be added the special cases of infinities, large numbers which invert to soft zeroes, NaNs, and numbers too small to have a representable inverse. Problem 9.8 has some fun with the exceptions.

In doing examples, you can work single-precision problems on most calculators simply by reducing the values of x and y to their appropriate ranges $2 > x \geq 1$ and $1 \geq y > 0.5$. Do the Newton's method steps to completion. Any of the values that you want to look at in the *fixed-point* hexadecimal version above can be multiplied by 2^{30} and then converted to *hex*. Some calculators (e.g., HP 32s) provide this conversion service. To get the numbers positioned properly for the significand, you would multiply by 2^{23}.

O.K. We have this dandy way to find a reciprocal. Does it do the job? Unfortunately, it does not comply with the IEEE standard, because even a properly rounded reciprocal is not sufficient to guarantee that we will get a properly rounded quotient after we multiply the reciprocal by the dividend. For example, if you take the reciprocal of 3 to three digits, you have 0.333. Now if what you wanted was $^2/_3$, multiplying by 2 gives 0.666, not 0.667. The *infinite-precision* requirement is much harder to meet using a reciprocal. The problem is that *enough precision* requires that you have precision to correctly round after a product. This may require a full extension of the reciprocal to twice the length of the significand plus 2 bits so that at the end of the product with the numerator, you know exactly how to round. The reciprocal method is too appealing not

TABLE 9.8 Two lines of four elements from guess []

0...4:	3FE00FF8	3FA08F29	3F618C22	3F23056D
128...131:	2A9C7683	2A802A80	2A6403F9	2A4802A5

to have been struggled with. For example, see [Fowler, 89] for another attempt to comply with the IEEE standard using reciprocal. But getting the right quotient is not the end of our problems. The standard also wants *remainder.* This value is a natural and exact result of normal integer division, but it is nowhere to be found in the reciprocal method.

All of those places can be had at modest increase in the steps in the algorithm, but think now about the width of the multiplier (and adder) to do this job. As you undoubtedly noticed somewhere in the fourth grade, the time for a multiply gets longer with the width of numbers being multiplied. We can use that to advantage to speed up the algorithm. The width of useful digits doubles on each cycle of Newton's method. Starting with 8, you obtain 16. If there are only 8 bits with meaning in the 31 that we started with in Figure 9.7, then why bother multiplying with the *meaningless* digits? Set the noise digits to 0 and, knowing that you have done so, process only the uppermost bits. This will save considerable time in the multiplier without compromising accuracy.

We are still left with a choice. Many methods have been used in the past to get faster division. They range over different algorithms and faster hardware. See [Hwang, 79] and [Goldberg, 89] for some good discussions. But in all cases, if we do not do real division, we will find the IEEE standard a hard taskmaster. Let us look at the issue of *remainder.*

FIGURE 9.7 Finding the inverse of 96 (1.5×2^6) using Newton's method.

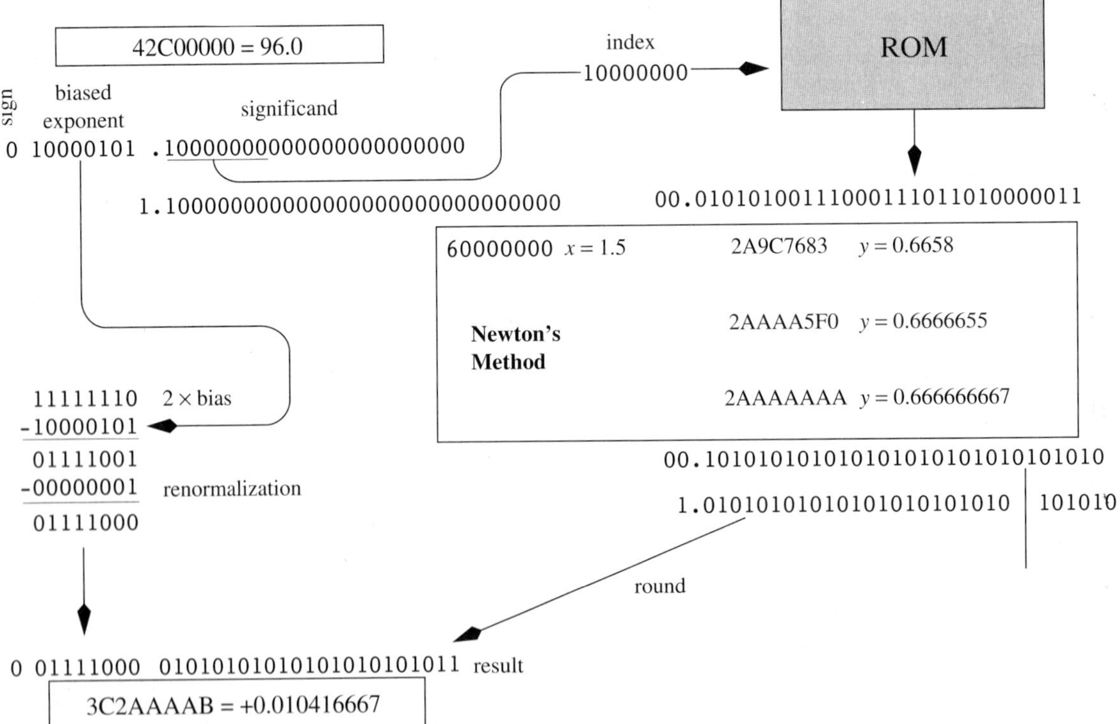

9.4.4 Floating-Point Remainder

The IEEE standard requires the implementation of a floating-point remainder operation, called REM. It is similar to the MOD function of integer division. MOD delivers the integer remainder of an integer division. For example, 17 MOD 5 = 2. The bounds on the MOD function[3] are given by

$$k = j \bmod m \Rightarrow |m| > k \geq 0$$

REM is not quite MOD. x REM y returns the difference between x and $y \times n$, where n is the integer *nearest* to the ratio x/y. Thus, REM returns a number containing both an integer and fractional part and of either sign, regardless of the signs of the operands.

Why do this with floating-point numbers? The most common application is in computing trigonometric functions. Functions such as sine, cosine, and tangent are periodic with a period of 2π radians. The normal algorithms employed for calculating these functions converge only within a limited domain such as $-\pi/2 \leq x \leq \pi/2$. If we want to compute the tangent of a large number of radians, we begin by reducing the number modulo π. That is, we remove some integral multiple of $\pi/2$ from the argument until we get a fractional remainder, such as 0.413π, within the domain of our tangent-function algorithm. Having a remainder function allows us to do this more accurately than we would be able to accomplish by using individual divide, round to integer, multiply, and subtract instructions.

The IEEE standard on REM is a little weird in the same fashion that its rounding is a little weird. It defines the remainder so that its result is as close to 0 as possible with a coin-flip to choose the sign of the one ambivalent case. The definition says:

> x REM $y = x - y \times n$, where n is the integer nearest to the exact value x/y, and if $|n - x/y| = {}^1/_2$, then n is chosen to be even. If y is 0 or infinite, the result is undefined; REM should return a NaN or trap. If the remainder is 0, its sign is defined to be the same as the sign of x.

A strange property of REM is that even though the division x/y might overflow, the remainder can still be computed exactly and must be representable. The definition says that $|x \text{ REM } y| \leq |{}^y/_2|$. If we can represent y, we can represent $y/2$ (which could be represented by 0 even though y may not). While this guarantee of existence may sound comforting, bring a pillow and a good book to read. Getting REM can take a very long while. Let us see why. In doing so, the definition of REM should become a little clearer.

First, let us do a few fairly obvious examples. First consider 5.0 REM 3.0. The integer nearest to ${}^5/_3$ is not 1 but 2. Accordingly, $5.0 \text{ REM } 3.0 = 5.0 - 2 \times 3.0 = -1.0$. Our next example is 5.0 REM 2.0. This puts us at the critical dividing line: ${}^5/_2$ is equally close to 3 and 2. The standard requires that we pick the even n so we take 2 and get $5.0 \text{ REM } 2.0 = 5.0 - 2 \times 2.0 = +1.0$.

---

[3] The definition of MOD is the mathematical one. What gets returned when you ask for $k = j \% m$ in C often has k of the same sign as j and is allowed by the C definition to be machine dependent.

Consider $1+2^{-20}$ REM 1.5×2^{-20} or approximately 1.000000954 REM 1.43051147×10^{-6}. This may not sound like much of a problem. The numbers are exactly representable in single-precision IEEE format. Let's get at it and divide! But wait a minute. What we must do is carry this out until the remainder is $\le 1.5\times2^{-20}/2$ and represented to the full width of the precision. That is a lot of places. The problem looks like this in binary:

```
                         01zzzzzzzzzzzzzzzzzzzz.| rrrrrrrrrrrr
1.10000000000000000000000/100000000000000000001.000000000000
```

What we have done is to multiply the dividend's significand as *a fixed-point number* by 2^{20}. In effect, we have made the two exponents equal by going to the exponent of the smaller number. This appears to add a lot of zeroes to the right, but we do not have to hold the big number in a register. Every one of those zeroes is added, one at a time, in another division step. They come in naturally from the right as the partial remainder shifts left. All those division steps are what is going to take time. Curiously, we really do not care about the value of all of those `z`'s. What we are after in REM is to get that last `z` and do the last subtraction. The number which remains as the last subtraction is done would be your classical fourth- or fifth-grade remainder. It will, in general, have both an integer and fractional part, and some normalization will be required. We are not quite home free yet. If that remainder, `rrrrrrrrrr` > $y/2$, we must subtract it from y. We are still not done. If the result is precisely $y/2$, we must look at that very last digit, `z`. If `z` is odd, we must flip the sign of the remainder. The lurking delay in this operation is that we could have an enormous difference in the exponents. In single precision, the effective exponent range is +127 to -149. That could require 276 divide operations to get to the remainder! While the division operation itself would overflow, note that we have here an algorithm which gives an exact remainder.

A fundamental problem in utility remains. If the principal use of REM is the reduction of arguments of periodic functions to the first period or subperiod, and if the major periodic functions are the standard trigonometry functions, then we will be dividing by π. π is a problem divisor. No matter where you have truncated this transcendental number, you have done some damage to it. Think of a case where you had an exponent difference of 75. This need not be a measured angle. Tan(x) or sin(x) may occur for computed variables. An excellent scientific calculator, the HP 32S, states that sin (2^{75}) = 0.865224291. It gives the same answer for sin $(2^{75}+1000)$, so the answer returned, however boldly stated, means nothing at all. If you really knew that 2^{75} to all 75 places, even though stored as a single-precision number, you would want 2^{75} REM 2π carried out to the usual 24 bits of precision. In the division example above, you would be inserting another 55 zeroes in front of the radix point. There will be 75 divide operations. If we want a correct 24 bit significand remaining, we must have another 24 zeroes to the right of the radix point. To properly deal with all of those bits, the divisor should be correct to $75+24 = 99$ bits. That calls for 2π accurate to 10^{29}. That is a lot of places of 2π; that is an enormously wide subtraction register. If you do not accommodate such wide strings of bits, the error in your representation of 2π for REM on very large arguments eventually will exceed one full cycle. In other words, the remainder that you get, all beautifully expressed and exactly represented, will be pure noise. It will have nothing whatever to do with the angle of rotation.

This is a pretty fundamental problem in the principal use of REM. Two partial solutions are employed:

- The value of 2π is stored to an exceptional number of digits and provision is made to do multiprecision integer subtraction. Obviously, the processor must know that you mean π, so this solution is limited to internal function generators or functions in software which create their own REMs.
- The processor traps if the exponent difference between the two parameters is too large.

Both are used, sometimes together.

Is it a big surprise to find out that many floating-point coprocessors do *not* implement REM? It can be done, however. The Motorola MC68881/MC68882 is an example of a FPCP which does provide this operation. The IEEE standard does not require REM (or any other operation) to run in hardware to be compliant—only that it run. The IEEE standard has nothing to say about the problem with truncation of π. Apparently, that was left to the perspicacious student.

9.4.5 Floating-Point Square Root

Square root is included in the IEEE standard. As usual, no reason is given for singling out this particular function. It is just part of the standard. The only unusual aspect of its definition is that $\sqrt{-0} = -0$. The square root of other negative numbers is undefined and should produce a quiet NaN or trap.

Simple modifications of bit-by-bit division algorithms can be used for square root. They provided nifty ways of taking square roots on the old mechanical calculators. One appends 2 bits of the "dividend" to the partial remainder at each step, rather than 1 bit, and uses the partial value of the "quotient" in place of the divisor. Both restoring and nonrestoring algorithms are possible, as in division. See Section 11.2 in [Hwang, 79] for the details of the nonrestoring algorithm and a cellular array implementation of it.

Square root can also be implemented by converging algorithms similar to those used for division. For example, a direct application of Newton's method would have us define a function $E(y) = y^2 - x$ and from that derive the successive approximation formula of

$$y_{i+1} = \frac{1}{2}\left(y_i + \frac{x}{y_i}\right)$$

As in the case of division, we can find a starting approximation from a small table, and the algorithm converges quadratically, so only a few iterations are required. This method is somewhat unattractive in that it involves repetitive division. A simple variation which avoids division entirely is given in Problem 9.12.

Another rather neat and rapidly convergent method for finding $1/\sqrt{x}$ is found in [Wallace, 64]. For $0.5 \le x < 2$, we set $D_0 = x/2$, $N_0 = 1$ and iterate:

$$N_{i+1} = N_i\left(\frac{3}{2} - D_i\right)$$

$$D_{i+1} = D_i\left(\frac{3}{2} - D_i\right)^2$$

The value of D rapidly approaches $^1/_2$ while the value of N approaches $1/\sqrt{x}$. Note the constraint on x. Problem 9.13 asks you to compare these two rapidly convergent algorithms. It is not obvious from the outside that it will be easy to meet the *infinite-precision* rounding rule with either of these converging algorithms, but to be fully compliant one must.

Another important set of function generators is called the CORDIC algorithms (from COordinate Rotation DIgital Computer). These were developed by Volder in 1959 and can be used to do multiplication, division, square root, logarithms, and exponential and trigonometric functions [Walther, 71]. See Chapter 11 of [Hwang, 79] for discussions of these and other approximation algorithms.

9.4.6 Combinations of Arithmetic Operations

The combination of multiplication and addition is very common in scientific applications and in many graphics and signal processing-operations:

- In matrix multiplication, each element in the resulting matrix is formed by a vector dot product, $\sum_i A_i B_i$.
- In fast Fourier transforms, the basic operation is $A_i + \omega^j B_k$, where, to add a bit of spice, the values are complex.
- Polynomial approximations are widely used for function generation. These are done by Horner's rule: $\{[(a_n x + a_{n-1})x + a_{n-2}]x + a_{n-3}\} + \cdots + a_0$, which is just made for multiplication followed by addition.

High-performance floating-point processors usually include separate multiplier and adder units. Because of the importance of combined operations, these machines normally provide ways to connect multiplication and addition in a single operation. This combined *add-and-multiply* has always been important on grand number-crunching machines like Cray supercomputers and vector processors, and recently it appeared on workstation processors.

The IBM RS/6000 floating-point chip [Olsson, 90] includes four multiply-add and multiply-subtract instructions. Several advantages derive from having these combined instructions in the architecture:

- It allows a single instruction to start both operations, which makes it easier to keep both the multiplier and adder busy, working in parallel all of the time.

- The combination allows the hardware to avoid doing normalization and rounding of the product before starting the addition. In effect, the addition can be started before an ordinary multiplication would have finished.
- All 106 bits of the (double-precision) product are used in the addition, which reduces the roundoff errors that would occur with separate multiplication and addition instructions with intermediate rounding. If the addition involves subtracting similar values, using separate instructions might result in all of the significant bits canceling. Keeping the full precision of the intermediate product, and rounding after the addition, tends to reduce that problem. A small caveat is in order: The extra precision is not compliant with the IEEE standard, so programs which take advantage of this combined operation on the RS/6000 may give different answers on other machines. The RS/6000 takes advantage of both the precision and speed of the combined multiply-add to do division (using Newton-Raphson reciprocal approximation) and transcendental functions (using polynomial approximations). Clearly, the problem that $(1/x) \times y \neq y/x$, which was mentioned in Section 9.4.3, is greatly ameliorated by this extra precision. One particularly interesting acceleration which derives directly from this added precision is the speed of convergence in successive-approximation algorithms. Often, the extra precision leads to convergence one or more cycles prior to a processor which rounds between operations.
- With the primitives being $A \times B \pm C$, one gets $A \times B$ by doing $A \times B + 0$ and $A + B$ by doing $1 \times A + B$.

Intel's i860 [Margulis, 90] provides combined multiplication and addition instructions. These instructions contain a 5-bit field which specifies 1 of 31 different arrangements of the data paths involving the multiplier and adder. The output of either unit can be fed to the input of the other, and there are also two constant registers and a temporary register which can be used as inputs, plus the normal floating-point registers specified in the instruction. Like the RS/6000, this allows a single instruction to control the operation of both execution units, which makes it easier to keep both of them running at full speed. Unlike the RS/6000, however, the i860 does not keep the full precision of intermediate results, so this mechanism cannot be used to increase the accuracy of computations.

9.4.7 Comparison

As we saw in Chapter 1, comparison is central to programming. It is the heart of the whole variety of branch statements. In floating-point–rich programs, many of those comparisons will be between floating-point numbers. As usual, the IEEE standard attempts to provide unequivocal and useful definitions of the operations without constraining the technique employed to achieve the result. There are some problems at the fringes which the standard had to resolve. Let us work our way from the middle to the edges. In floating point, the edges are never very far away.

The standard defines *four* mutually exclusive relationships:

- <
- =
- >
- unordered (symbolized by "?")

The first three may seem rather obvious (apart from the possibly unexpected standard that $+0 = -0$), but consider each with $\pm\infty$. The infinities are said to be *affine* in the sense that $-\infty <$ any finite number $< +\infty$. Consider the compare operation as asking which of the four is true as determined by a subtraction of the second operand from the first. That is,

$$\text{compare}(A, B) = [(A - B) \Rightarrow \text{one of } (<, =, >, \text{unordered})]$$

While not so stated in the standard, there is another outcome: *invalid operation*. For example, you cannot do $\infty - \infty$ but you can do $\infty - (-\infty)$. For the former, the response must be *invalid*; for the latter, *greater than* is the correct reply. Well, if $\infty - \infty$ is *invalid*, what then is *unordered*?

If either of the numbers being compared is a NaN, the result is considered to be unordered. The name may not be felicitous, but if either A or B is a NaN, *unordered* is TRUE.

At this point, the standard expands the designer's choices by providing two quite distinct routes to execute a comparison. In one, there is but one instruction—*compare*—and it either sets one of four states or flags to indicate the result or it signals the *invalid* exception. This fits exactly with what we have been describing as our interface to the coprocessor chip(s). See Table 2.1, on page 69.

The second route is to define a series of queries with TRUE/FALSE responses. Each query will have a unique instruction, such as: "Is $A \geq B$?" A single query can test from one to three of the states listed above so there are $4 + 6 + 4 = 14$ possible combinations, each with the possibility of negation (e.g., = and ≠). The negatives are, as you might expect from *de Morgan's theorem*, represented among the 14. For example, ≠ is identical to ?<>, that is, *unordered* or *less than* or *greater than*. However, even though de Morgan's theorem applies, that lurking *invalid* renders 12 of the negated versions different from the equivalent positive statement. If you consider the negation as occurring after the comparison, you will see why the two statements can be different. The specific rule is that if the comparison includes either > or < but not ?, then if one or both of the operands is a NaN, *invalid* must be signaled. For example,

NOT(>) will signal *invalid* on a NaN

while its logical equivalent

?<= will not signal *invalid* on a NaN

Do note that = does not have a problem with NaN inputs. If you ask: "Is this NaN equal to that NaN?" the correct response is: "No." If either operand is NaN, the result of the comparison is unordered, regardless of what your eyes tell you about the equivalence of two NaNs.

9.4.8 Conversions and Precisions

The IEEE standard defines four formats for floating-point numbers but requires only single precision. The four comprise:

- single precision (Figure 9.2)
- double precision (Figure 9.2)
- single, extended precision:
  significand $\geq$ 32 bits
  exponent $\geq$ 11 bits
- double, extended precision:
  significand $\geq$ 64 bits
  exponent $\geq$ 15

The fuzzy definition on *extended precision* allows the designer to meet any precision requirement and still stay within the standard. One could provide only single precision and still be fully compliant. (In saying "only single precision" we mean as a floating-point storage format. The standard requires conversion between floating-point storage formats and both integer and decimal-string formats.)

The market has made choices and if you want to sell in that market, you either meet the market's expectation or (good luck!) drag the market with you. The market choice is for double precision. To be compliant, you still have to provide single, but many processors provide only single and double. The IBM RS/6000 is an example. Internally, the 6000 converts all inputs to *double* and then, as we described in previous sections, carries substantially greater precision through the combined *multiply-and-add* operation. Notice that what we have in the RS/6000 are three different classes of precision in one machine:

- storage formats (single, double, integer, and decimal strings)
- internal register formats (double)
- internal working format (significands can grow to a maximum of 106 bits)

Only the storage formats are required to meet the IEEE standard.

Why should we select one format over another? Formats were not created at the big bang. Each evolved in the presence of other constraints. Typical of evolution, some got eaten; others got to be dominant. In the beginning, there was indeed chaos and confusion and darkness did cover the face of the earth. Storage and working formats were whatever the designer both fancied and could afford. As computers moved out of code-breaking and trajectory estimation into the public domain, slowly but surely the importance of character manipulation made the byte the "atom" of all other formats. 4 bytes was barely big enough for a floating point, so that defined the minimum—single precision. Single precision is too coarse (imprecise) and has too limited a range for many ordinary problems (e.g., a business spreadsheet). Double precision was big enough. Double precision became dominant.

Going along with these two choices are instruction sizes and integer sizes. Success in the marketplace required making particularly good use of the current capability of integrated circuits. First, there were 8-bit processors with 8-bit data paths. As soon as they could, designers moved to 16-bit machines with 16-bit busses. It was there that the first single-chip coprocessor appeared, the Intel 8087. Created during the committee wars on the IEEE standard, the 8087 attempted to meet what was then thought to be the emerging standard. Pushing VLSI technology to its limits, the chip stretched to include an 80-bit extended double-precision wordlength. 80 bits is 10 bytes.[4] No problem if you are shipping data 2 bytes at a time, but not so compatible with 4-byte transfers and absurd with 8-byte transfers.

VLSI soon provided 32-bit machines. Their swiftness and modest cost guaranteed success. Soon they were totally dominant. Single and double precision are still good, but 80 bits? Nonsense. A number of manufacturers just dropped *extended* formats. The current most popular design is to do internal storage only in double precision. Big busses support that choice. In fact, the rapid development of 16-byte-wide busses and 64-bit processors has started some movement toward defining a quadruple-precision floating point. IBM, Sun and HP have all adopted (different) 128-bit formats that are IEEE-like. The VAX has had a 128-bit format since inception, but it was not widely used and was not carried forward to Alpha.

The IEEE standard requires an implementation to provide conversions between its various precisions, and between integer and floating point, and between decimal strings and floating point. Decimal strings envisage conversion between numbers in the form "7.6359E-27" and its counterpart in any of the IEEE formats. The standard requires that there be at least one decimal-string format, but it allows more. Most computers support at least three:

- integer
- fixed point
- exponential (or "scientific")

The standard is reasonable in its specification. It requires the string to remain within rational constraints. After all, how long is a string? To avoid having to deal with absurdities, the standard limits the string range for a number in the form $\pm S \times 10^{\pm N}$. Two limits are stated which differ only in the upper bound on N. These comprise the set shown in Table 9.9. Several issues are covered under these specifications. One central one is that conversions in either direction cannot always be exact. For example,

```
0.6 ⇒ 0.100100100100...
```

[4] Goldberg reports [Goldberg, 91] that Kahan said that the 64-bit extended double-precision significand was the largest that could be used in the Intel 8087 without having the carry propagation lengthen the cycle time.

TABLE 9.9 Decimal conversion range bounds

	Decimal to binary			Binary to decimal		
	Max S	Absolute max N	Correctly rounded max N	Max S	Absolute max N	Correctly rounded max N
single	$10^9 - 1$	99	13	$10^9 - 1$	53	13
double	$10^{17} - 1$	999	27	$10^{17} - 1$	340	27

The values in Table 9.9 are concerned not only with reasonable ranges for conversion but also with the effort to make it as likely as possible that if you type in 0.6 and later print it back out, you will get 0.6 on your screen.

Consider single precision. The format supports roughly 7 decimal digits of significand and exponents +38 to -45. You are entitled to enter a string with up to 9 unique digits. If you choose to enter an exponent, its value can be well beyond the representable numbers but no greater than the maximum number of decimal digits (2) that can be represented. This means that the conversion routine need only deal with 2-digit exponents. On conversion, S allows for 9 digits. As it turns out, $999999999 \times 10^{-53} \cong 2^{-146}$, which is the smallest value representable in single precision. Why is the upper bound 13 to be correctly rounded? Well, this unobvious issue derives from the fact that 2 to a power does not convert evenly to 10 to a power. For example, 10 itself is 1.01B+03 in our funny mixed-mode notation. As it turns out, the largest power of 10 which can be exactly represented with a 32-bit significand is 13. Those with the stomach to explore this further, see [Goldberg, 91].

What if you type in a fixed-point number of 24 digits? The user is probably entitled to do it. Lots of places of π or what have you. The processor is equally entitled by the specification to treat those extra digits as zeroes.

It is important to remember that it is permitted to realize any and all of the IEEE standard in software. A compliant system need not have a single hardware floating-point operation. Would it be worth it to include conversions to decimal strings in the coprocessor itself? The Motorola MC68881/2 includes *decimal string* as a storage type. Since the standard provides no definition of the string, Motorola defines a 24-byte structure suitable for storing converted double-precision numbers (page 3-12 in [MC68881, 87]). Neither IBM in the RS/6000 nor DEC in the Alpha nor the SPARC consortium includes such a conversion within the floating-point instruction set. Yet all must accommodate decimal input. Clearly, they do conversions in software. Why the different choices?

The difference is partly the result of when they were created. The MC68000 family's coprocessors were created while the standard was being or just had been accepted. Coprocessor designers at that time tried to make their chips comply in every way so that they could say that their coprocessors were IEEE-754 compliant. With a microcoded CISC, putting the conversions in *firmware* was relatively painless. Intel's Pentium continues this tradition while still delivering single-cycle FADD and FMUL. It is likely that the designers of the RS/6000 and SPARC had another perspective. While they determined to make their *system* compliant to the standard, the FPU was just part of the hardware supporting the whole system. What was not done in hardware would be done in software. Any conversion used frequently would end up in cache and run efficiently. They undoubtedly decided that the conversion operation was not frequent enough to put it in hardware.

In truth, decimal-string conversion is more integer than floating point, though floating-point operations may be useful in the conversion. Not only are such conversions generally infrequent events, but also, formats for I/O are usually quite variable, meaning that a conversion to a standard format would be only a precursor to a conversion to a variable format. It seems much more reasonable to relegate to software conversions to and from strings, and that is now the clear trend. A look at our instruction set shows that we can load and store integers and single-precision variables along with the native double-precision numbers.

The rounding specification for the string conversions is really weird, so much so that the IEEE authors felt obliged to break their oath of silence and confess where it came from [Coonan, 84] by putting a reference right in the specification. Enough is enough. We will not discuss this subject further here. See Chapter 8 in [Sterbenz, 74] for a rather theoretical discussion of conversion algorithms. For an operational and carefully considered conversion function in C, we recommend _Stod from the <stdlib.h> in Chapter 13 of [Plauger, 92].

9.4.9 Exceptions, Traps, and Interrupts

The IEEE standard specifies five exceptions:

- invalid operations (such as 0/0, $0 \times \infty$, and $\sqrt{-1}$)
- division by 0
- overflow
- underflow
- inexact result

The standard is concerned that programmers have the option to recover from exceptions in an informed manner and that there be *default* mode where the processor handles the exception in a known way, leaving a record that the exception occurred. An example of the default response is returning a signed infinity on division by 0. Should you use the default? It is an interesting question. You might have a well-tested piece of software which deals with tiny numbers. In that case, division by 0 might be a natural event, and a signed infinity is the correct result of that natural event. In most circumstances, division by 0 is natural only in the sense that it is natural for programmers to make errors. It most often arises from uninitialized variables. The trap will come up saying "Attempt to divide by 0 on line . . .," precisely what the programmer needs. A more general approach to uninitialized variables is to default automatically on initiation to a signaling NAN. Then, if that variable is used before it is replaced, it is trapped.

A mechanism to enable or disable traps on each type of exception must be provided. If a particular type of trap is disabled when an exception occurs, that exception should set the appropriate status bit. The status bits are *sticky*; they remain set until reset by the program.

In our machine, trap flags are tested with the instruction FPFLAGS followed by the appropriate JUMP instruction. See Table 2.1, on page 69, for the 10 flags and their relation to the CPU flags. To store or load a whole status word in our instruction set, we have FPSTORES and FPLOADS. The latter can be used to set the status register to any desired state, as is necessary on a context switch. As we described in Section 2.6, load/store operations to the coprocessor are served addresses by following LOAD/STORE instructions from the CPU. Also from that section, we showed that you could move data between a coprocessor and the CPU with these same instructions.

Some instructions should give different results if traps are enabled than if traps are disabled. The reasoning for doing it this way is that programs which disable traps are either willing to live with the default response or expected to continue a sequence of calculations and check at the end to see if some error has occurred. Programs which select traps are either looking for programming errors (e.g., divide by 0) or have approaches other than the default response for things like underflow or overflow. To that end, the standard specifies the information which must be made available to the trap handler when a trap occurs. The handler should be able to determine which type of exception occurred, which operation caused it, the operand value(s), the destination format, and the correctly rounded result (if it would not fit in the destination format). Note that in our machine, the destination format is either the internal format (double precision) or one of four storage formats (single, double, integer, or decimal string). (*Decimal string* is a storage format only for software routines but traps must still be provided.)

Traps and interrupts pose certain problems for high-performance coprocessors. A more-or-less unexpected jump out of the normal stream of control occurs. In a processor which does no pipelining or other concurrent operations, this is not much of a problem. If the processor is also restricted to relatively simple instructions, it may be possible either to complete the next instruction (in the case of an interrupt) or to move the PC back so that the current instruction will be executed on return from the trap. Complex instructions present another problem. If the current instruction will take a long time to complete, it may increase the interrupt latency enough to be a problem in some applications. This may be a problem in a microprogrammed implementation of transcendental functions, for example, particularly if the hardware does not include a fast multiplier. Some machines, such as the Motorola MC68882, solve this problem by allowing traps and interrupts to occur *within* an instruction. Unfortunately, this requires some mechanism for saving and restoring the internal state of the processor. With the MC68882, this state takes 216 bytes, so it requires a long time to save and restore it. In the case of an interrupt, this may not be necessary. Provided that the interrupt handler does not do any floating-point instructions, the coprocessor can either stop what it is doing, or continue working on its current instruction, until the interrupt handler returns.

In the case of processors which do pipelined operations, there are additional problems. One problem is simply keeping track of which instructions are in progress. This can be a problem with the coprocessors on our RISC machine, because only the CPU chip knows the PC of the instruction. Another problem is that if we try overlapping instructions in a pipelined machine, we may start a second instruction before discovering that the first one got some kind of error. We intend to allow our RISC CPU to continue executing integer instructions after it starts a floating-point add in the coprocessor. Normally this should work correctly, since the result of the floating-point add will go into a register in the coprocessor, and the integer operations in the CPU are completely independent of the floating-point registers. But suppose the floating-point add overflows and causes a trap. The IEEE standard requires that enough information be available to be able to reconstruct what happened in the FPU, but it says nothing about knowing where you were in your program when the bad news came through. Recovery from the floating-point error may be possible, but since you may not be able to simply stuff the corrected value back in the correct FPU register—it might not fit—it is not necessarily true that you can just pick up from where you got interrupted. We will discuss this problem further in the following section.

To meet the IEEE specification on identifying the operands and operation which caused the error, we have chosen to include a latch (or two latches if overlapped instructions are allowed in a particular FPU) to hold the current instruction. This is a 1-word register. The operand registers are accessible as well. All are memory-mapped, just like the internal registers of the CPU. They can be accessed directly by any system routine, one word at a time, as integer data.

In addition to traps caused by exceptions, a particular system may use traps to handle features of the architecture which are not included in a particular implementation. The advantage of this mechanism is that it allows binary compatibility among a wide range of processors. The highest performance processors may implement all instructions in hardware. The lowest performance processors may simply provide trap handlers which do all floating-point instructions in software. Intermediate processors may do some instructions in microcode, and others in software. Or the most common cases of important instructions may be done in hardware, while unusual conditions cause traps and get handled by software. The important point to remember is that these options are invisible to the user program. The trap handlers may have to be added or modified for a particular processor, but user programs do not require changes.

As an example, consider the four *reserved* FP instructions in Table 2.7, on page 105. They are intended for growth to a new *quad-precision* standard. Were that added to old machines which did not support quads in hardware, the older FPU would trap on the illegal instruction. This is an unmaskable trap so the interrupt will occur. There is no question that we can do quad precision in software, but not in an FPU designed to regard *double* as the upper bound. What must be done is to switch to software emulation. This is done by copying all FPU registers from the FPU to memory, converting them to quad precision, and then setting the *off* bit in the FPU. When this bit is set, all instructions trap as illegal instructions and the entire array of floating-point operations switches to software. Slow as glue? Indeed! But it runs. If you did it very often, you would buy a new quad-ready FPU, but if it is once in a blue moon, the new software will run on the old machine. That will satisfy at least the blue mooner.

9.5 DESIGN OF A FLOATING-POINT COPROCESSOR

Let us lay out a microprogrammed floating-point coprocessor. Its speed will depend almost entirely on the speed of the supporting hardware. That hardware can be simple, inexpensive, and relatively slow, or it can be elaborate, fast, and relatively expensive. We begin with some general mechanisms used in microprogrammed processors.

9.5.1 Design of a Microsequencer

Machine code and microcode are different computer languages. Human beings seldom write either. Microinstructions have certain similarities to RISC instructions. Perhaps the most important of these is that each clock cycle sees the completion of one microinstruction. While some of the detractors of RISC were wont to say that RISC just brought the microcode out in the open to the general discomfiture of the programmer, this is not the case. For the two languages to be accomplishing the same task at the same rate, they must bear some close resemblance, yet to say that they are equal is to say that Chinese is the same as English because you can get someone to pass you the soy sauce in either one. Two things are controlled by both computer languages:

- what the processor hardware does
- which instruction gets executed next

With our hardwired RISC instruction, the decoding hardware develops a complete set of control signals for each controllable function in the processor. With respect to controlling the processor, the microinstruction is essentially the decoded version of the RISC instruction. Sequencing of the microinstructions can be done in traditional machine-code fashion (i.e., in the absence of an explicit branch, the *next* instruction is executed) but it is more often accomplished with a built-in branch not unlike the CRISP described in Section 6.3.4. Basically, what microcoding will do for us is to provide on-board programming for the coprocessor, permitting extended operations such as FPEXP or FPSIN to be accomplished while the CPU does something else. Accordingly, what we are really doing is running the FPU on decoded instructions that are stored on board in what is called the *control memory.* The particular sequence that is run is determined by a single CP command from the CPU. That command could result in 1 microinstruction or 100.

Figure 9.8 shows the elements which go into deciding what happens next within the FPU. Except for the fact that the control store has replaced the I-cache, this is not greatly different from the CPU design in Figure 6.11. It should not be that different. RISC instructions directly control the machine; so do microinstructions. We are not starting *de novo.* What we did in Chapter 6 applies here. A few of the terms and control systems will be different. Let us begin with the *microsequencer* (μSEQ).

By *microsequencer* we mean the mechanism to determine which microinstruction should be fetched next from the control memory. This may be a moderately complex integrated circuit on its own chip, or, in our case and many similar machines, it is

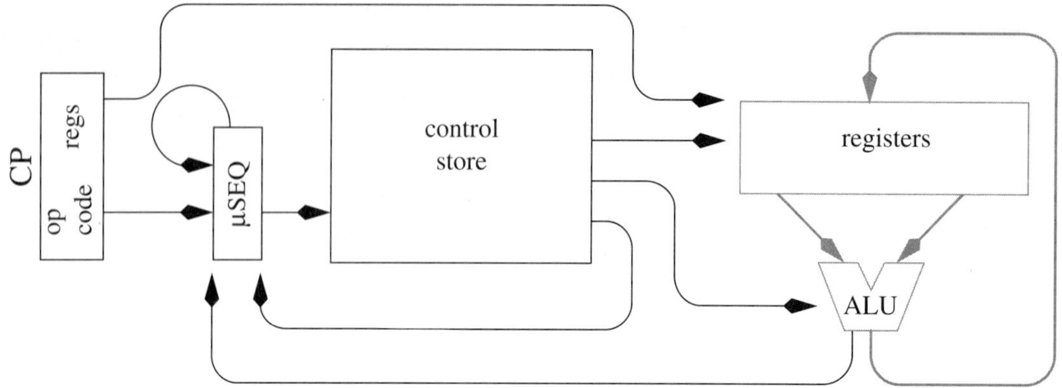

FIGURE 9.8 Data and control flow within the FPU. The CP instruction came from the CPU, carrying information on which microinstruction routine to run and which registers to use. The opcode determines the first microinstruction, but from that point on, the sequence of microinstructions is determined by the current microinstruction and the ALU results. The control of registers is determined in part by the CP and in part by the microinstruction while the ALU operation is determined at each step solely by the current microinstruction.

apt to be simply a MUX with inputs from several corners of the chip. The programming choices for selecting the next instruction comprise:

- *logical next*, which is typified by instruction $n+1$ following instruction n
- *mapping*, which converts the opcode field in CP to an address to start a sequence
- *branch*, which determines whether to pick an alternative to *logical next* based on a test
- *call*, which allows a *branch* while saving *logical next* for a return address
- *return*, which causes a branch to the address saved in *call*

The only one that is new is *mapping*, which covers any of several ways to turn our 5-bit opcode into the address to start a routine. *Logical next* need not generate sequential numbers. An equally good mechanism is to have each instruction carry the address of its successor. In that case, *logical next* means to go to that successor and anything else means not to go to that successor. This covers the programming choices. Now let us consider some hardware issues.

We do not wish to go back to square one. In Chapter 6, we argued forcefully for pipelining. The objective was to divide transactions into a sequence of short, sharp, ordered steps which could each be completed in a very brief clock interval. The pipeline was arranged so that subsequent instructions could be stepping through the pipeline simultaneously, each just one step behind its predecessor. In spite of the fact that any single instruction took several clocks to complete, one instruction per clock emerged from the pipeline. Up to a point, we will want our microengine to work in the same fashion. However, there are two very significant differences between an instruction pipeline and a microinstruction pipeline:

- The microinstruction stream comprises a relatively short burst of instructions. For our FPU, the microengine will frequently be in a holding mode, waiting for the next command. That command may elicit only two or three microinstructions. Accordingly, a long pipeline will give little benefit.
- Each burst of microinstructions is uninterruptable. You have branches on conditions but not unpredictable interruptions.

The first says have a short pipeline. The second allows you to have some more complexity than you would admit into a structure that could be interrupted at arbitrary moments. How short can the pipeline be? Could we do it in a single stage? We could do it, but. . . .

Essentially, a single-stage pipeline or unpipelined system just connects the lines in Figure 9.8 to what they point to. It resembles Figure 6.1. Unfortunately, such a simple approach is replete with slowness. Both the control store and the propagation rate through some of the things that it controls are fairly slow. Since the system clock cycle must be long enough for signals to propagate from the μSEQ, through the control store and ALU, and into the registers before the next clock, a nonpipelined sequencer requires a very long clock cycle. A less obvious problem is that the signals coming from the control store will not be stable during the first part of the cycle, so they can't be used to control anything which is edge-sensitive.

Both of these problems are solved by having at least a two-stage pipeline. The first stage is *get it* and the second is *do it.* An instruction would be in each stage at any one time. In stage 1, the output of the control store is clocked into a microinstruction register; in stage 2, it is the output of that register which controls everything else. Since we can begin fetching the next microinstruction as soon as the first is in the register, the fetch and execute operations are now overlapped. Note the plural of *operations*. We can be doing things to different data groups at the same moment, just as we did in Figure 6.10. If the control store and ALU have similar propagation delays, the pipelined version will be almost twice as fast as the nonpipelined version. We also regain the ability to have the individual outputs of the microinstruction register control edge–sensitive functions.

Figure 6.11 assumes that each instruction steps through the pipeline, controlling at each stage the functions appropriate to that stage. The same sort of scheme works in microengines. It is particularly appealing if the control store is significantly slower than the ALU or other execution units in the processor. Because the microinstruction persists through several clocks, such a system is called a *polyphase* microsequencer [Dasgupta, 79] [Dasgupta, 89]. On the other hand, if the control store is significantly faster than the ALU or other execution units, the microinstruction may be fetched in several pieces, with their execution being overlapped [Retter, 82].

Just as in Chapter 6, we need some way of branching. Should we used delayed branching? Delayed branches were used in microsequencers long before RISCs were developed. If we adopt a delayed branch, our microengine will look like Figure 9.9. Note how many balls a single microinstruction can keep in the air at one time. With the mechanisms shown, a single microinstruction can perform ALU operations, decrement or load a counter, test the results, and branch to a new microaddress if the test is satis-

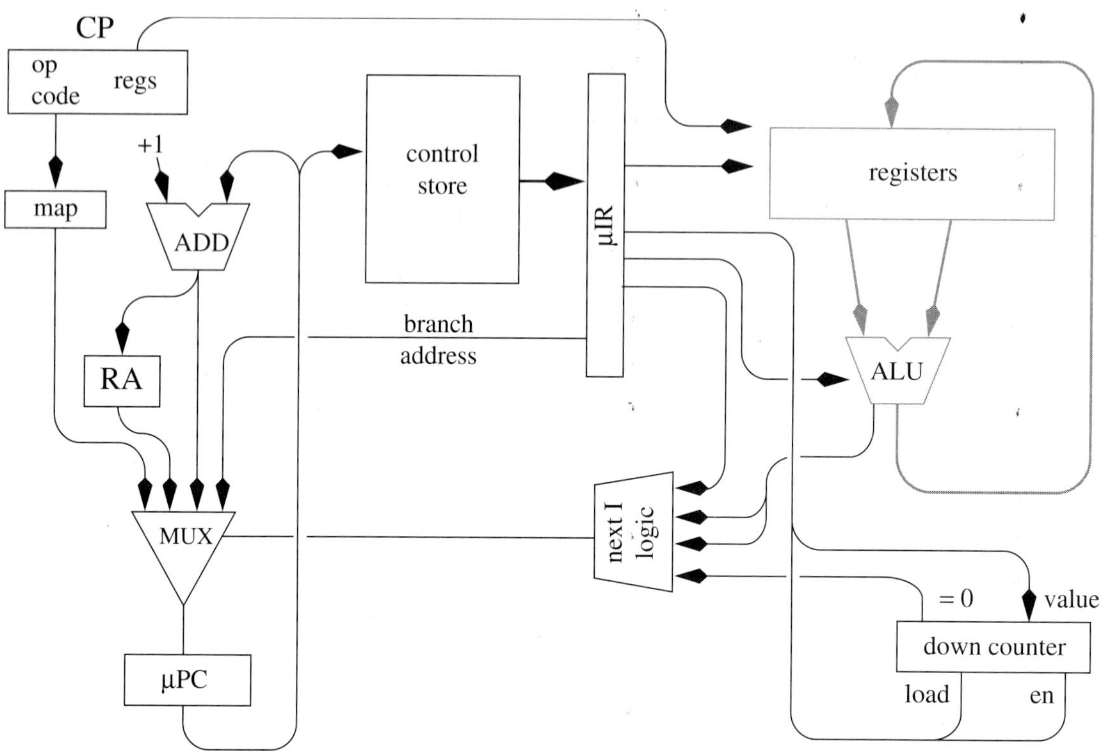

FIGURE 9.9 The microsequencing portion of the microengine with delayed branching. The microinstruction register (μIR) is simply a latch for the current microinstruction. The register/ALU section is deliberately left incomplete to show that we have not yet considered it either for the pipeline or even in functionality.

fied. All four of the branch modes that we identified above are present. Just as with delayed branching in the CPU, the branch would not take effect until after the next instruction is executed. Since the sequence of microinstructions tends to be quite short—the very situation which obtained in the CRISP, where the designers rejected delayed branching—not only would a useful bubble-filler be hard to find, but a NOP would represent a very painful compromise.

Can we build a microsequencer without branch delays? And if so, why could we not do it for the CPU in Chapter 6? The answer is we can for the microsequencer but cannot for the CPU. The reason is found quite directly in our discussion of the CRISP branch-folding scheme of Section 6.3.4. If you recall, in CRISP, branch folding worked only when you could prefigure the address. The bubble of one clock arises in our machine as the time to compute the new address. In that time, you fetch one instruction, so that instruction gets done whether the branch is executed or not. The lesson is: If you know all possibilities for the next address, you do not have to wait. You just pick the right one and head on your way. However, to do this on a result of an ALU operation or countdown to 0, the result must be stable in time to make the address selection. In other words, the result must be there from the last operation. This, of course, was true for the CPU as well.

What do we do to avoid the delay? Simple. All we do is select the address and send it directly to the address pins of the control store. We still need the μSEQ to provide *next* but there is absolutely no reason to delay the address chosen by making it pass through the μSEQ. The concept of *branch folding* is carried one step further in some microengines. There they have two address fields within each microinstruction: *next* and *alternate*. In these structures, every instruction is a branch; the question to be answered is: Which branch is taken? In these machines, there is no μSEQ and no address incrementer, but every microinstruction is wider by the relatively small number of bits in a microprogram address. On chip, wide ROMs are cheap; so is a modest-width fast incrementer.

Look at Figure 9.9. You should be able to see that all four forms of address can be available at the beginning of the cycle. The only one that is new is *map*. Two things are needed to see how this mapping function works and when you do it. Some commands will yield routines that are quite short, some of moderate length, and some rather long (Sin or Exp). But at the end of any sequence, the program returns to the beginning and awaits a new command. The overall program looks like:

```
do {
  if (busy){                          /* CPU executing CP sets busy */
     switch (opcode) {                /* Here is the MAP statement */
         case 0: {execute ADD}        /* Each case executes one FP instruction */
         case 1: {execute SUB}
     ...
         case 31: {execute STORE STATUS}
         }
     busy = 0;                        /* next CP instruction may now be transferred */
     }
  } while (1);                        /* outer loop runs forever*/
```

The Boolean *busy* is set by the FPU when it detects that the CPU is sending it a new FP instruction, and reset upon completion of the instruction. The opcode that is loaded determines the which sequence of microinstructions are started. *Map* is just the equivalent of a *switch* statement in C. In the HLL, such constructs are often referred to by their ancient Fortran name: a *computed-go-to* statement. In other words, at the top, a calculation is performed which carries you directly to the right address for the particular case selected. Since we have a built-in branching method, we could simply make the first instruction of each routine lie in the address corresponding to its opcode. FPADD is in 0, FPSUB is in 1, and so on. We would have a *branch-always* in that first instruction to take us to the second instruction. That works just fine if the first instruction does not have to do a CALL or conditional branch. For the conditional branch, we would need two addresses. If we want to jump to a subroutine in the first instruction, then the two-address format for our microinstruction is the source of the correct *return address*. If our control store uses 14-bit addresses, then the simple mapping function that we just described is the one shown on the left in Figure 9.10. Alternatively, if we wanted to allow starting sequences of four instructions, then we would want to map our opcodes

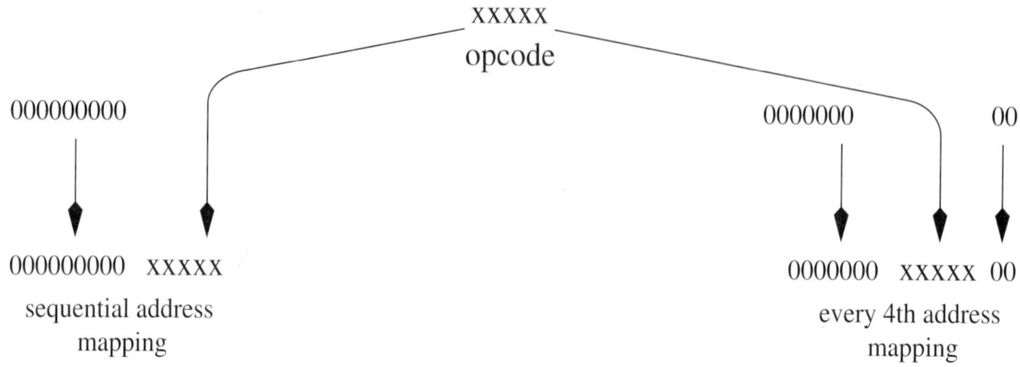

FIGURE 9.10 A mapping of a 5-bit opcode into addresses 0 . . . 31 and another into 0, 4, 8 . . . 128.

into every fourth address. That is shown as the mapping on the right in the figure. As you can see, such mappings border on the trivial even if the concept that an opcode becomes an address is less so.

With the change to *direct* addressing we get the circuit of Figure 9.11, which shows the addresses coming from their original sources directly to the control store. The circuit is capable in any instruction of executing either *next* or *branch*, but if the choice is based on a condition test, the flag signaling that test must have been latched in a previous instruction. This means that if we want to do an operation and then branch on the basis of that operation, it will take at least two instructions. However, because the microinstruction can control many independent actions, even a one-instruction loop may be able to be run as long as it always runs at least twice. Consider that we frequently will want to repeat certain operations until the counter gets to 0. For example, if we use Booth's algorithm for multiplication, it will take a single instruction to perform the add/sub and shifts as well as decrementing the counter. Every time that we go through this essentially one-line loop, we will test the loop end. In the CPU, we would unroll the loop and put 16 MUL instructions in a row. In microcode, we need only observe that we are testing the previous count, not the current result. Accordingly, if the count is set to 15 rather than 16, the loop would execute 16 times. (In the FPU, we will be multiplying 53-bit numbers.) A question that we should ask here is: Is there a way to test an operation which completes not long before the clock edge? Would we be asking if there wasn't? But there is no free lunch. Optimizing the normal route will pessimize the alternative.

Once again harking back to CRISP, we can employ *branch prediction* as well as *branch folding*. The example of multiplication is excellent. We have two 53-bit significands to multiply. If we use a 3-bit Booth's algorithm (base-8), it will require 18 cycles per multiply. Rather than do 18 multiply steps and 18 tests per cycle, it should certainly be better to do 18 multiply steps with the expectation of an immediate repeat and then take a hit of a cycle or two on the miss. In programming in general and particularly in microprogramming, branch prediction is normally very effective. There is a big difference between normal programming and microprogramming:

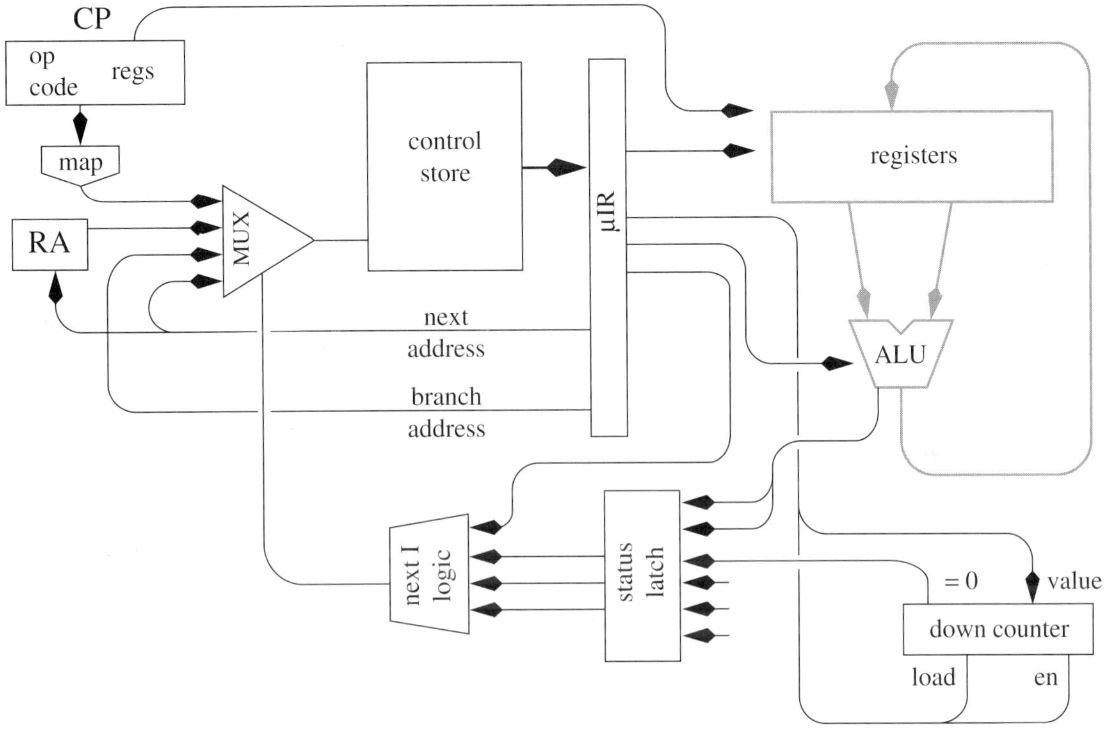

FIGURE 9.11 The microsequencer portion of the FPU arranged for direct addressing. Both *next* and *branch* addresses are contained in the instruction. All condition flags are latched in the status latch in a cycle preceding the test. Accordingly, a branch based on an ALU operation must reference an instruction prior to the current one.

- Typically, normal programming is done in a HLL whose compiled output will run equally well on a whole family of machines sharing a common architecture. All the optimization is done by the compiler and must work on all realizations of the architecture. The issue of *scalability*, or the ease by which the user architecture can be adapted to different pipelines and parallel instruction issuance, is very important in the original specification of an architecture. Branch prediction scales better than delayed branching, a driving consideration in Alpha's choice of prediction over delay.
- The microprogram is unique to a particular implementation of a given architecture, it is extremely small, and normally it is subject to minute hand optimization. There is no issue of scaling. Each implementation gets its own microcode.

While branch prediction is a good choice for either model of programming, it looks almost compulsory in microprogramming.

How would we handle a miss in a circuit equivalent to Figure 9.11? The logic of address selection is either

```
take next unless condition Z occurs in which case take (branch, RA, map)
```

or

```
take branch unless condition Z occurs in which case take (next, RA, map)
```

The problem is that the test condition will not be determined until too late in the cycle to switch between addresses and still get the correct instruction out of the control store. In many ways, our problem here is equivalent to the problem that we had in the CPU when we needed both an instruction and a datum from the D-cache. When that occurred in the CPU, we suspended the CPU clock to provide the one-cycle delay that was needed to move the instruction and then picked up where we left off, but with the instruction on board. We can do the same thing here. Look at Figure 9.11 and ponder for a moment where the clock we are referring to is applied. It is applied to registers. That would include latches on the ALU, the μIR, RA, and the register block. It would not include the status latch because that element will be eliminated from the microsequencer, and it will not include the CP register since that is clocked from the outside. The rest of the items shown are all combinational circuits. In particular, the control store ROM is not clocked. The direct-addressing-with-branch-prediction sequencer is shown in Figure 9.12. This is the structure that we will employ. Problem 9.14 asks you to design the clock circuit.

Let us conclude this section with a look forward to the structure of a microinstruction. Unlike a CPU instruction, a microinstruction tends to be very wide and replete with all sorts of details. To avoid getting too wide, fields may be assigned multiple uses. For example, since very few microinstructions will load the loop counter, it is unreasonable to reserve a field in the microinstruction solely for that count. We have chosen to load it from the next-address field. Naturally, that means the counter must be loaded by a microinstruction which does not branch to a specified microaddress (unless we force the destination address to be equal to the count). A single-bit field in the microinstruction is devoted to *load down counter.* If that bit is asserted, the down counter loads the value in the branch address. For every possible branch parameter, we provide a matching bit in the microinstruction. In the spirit of our branch prediction paradigm, we predict *next* and may choose *RA*, *map*, or *branch* as the alternative if a branch condition is met. The one exception to this rule is a CALL bit which effectively predicts *branch* and saves *next* in RA. For a condition to be met, all of the condition bits asserted in the microinstruction must be asserted in the condition code. Whether the positive or negative sense of condition is tested is controlled by a single bit in the microinstruction.

While we have specified a reasonably effective microsequencer, far more elaborate affairs are available on the market. More complex microsequencers allow nested loops, either by including more counters (as in TI's 74AS8835), or by allowing the counter to be pushed onto the microstack (as in AMD's 29331). Other features which are included on more complex microsequencers include relative branches, microinterrupts, microtraps, and microbreakpoints. However, we are not in competition for a complexity award. We have what we need to proceed. Let us next consider the right half of Figure 9.12, which is the unit that will make our FPU do floating-point arithmetic.

9.5.2 A Simple Microprogrammed Floating-Point Coprocessor

Our next (and final) objective is to apply microprogramming to our particular problem, a floating-point coprocessor. The design of a microprogrammed processor involves several distinct pieces:

- the microprogram
- the instruction format
- program control
- data paths, register sets, and execution units

Each of these pieces interacts with the others; they should be designed together. Clearly, we have already begun on all of these.

- *The microprogram.* We proposed a full algorithm for FPADD (Section 9.4.1) and made a problem out of FPMUL (Problem 9.7). We have discussed all of the basic operations such as FPDIV, FPREM, FPSQRT, and FPCMPR. In our instruction set,

FIGURE 9.12 The microsequencer portion of the FPU employing direct addressing and branch prediction. The figure shows the generation of the internal clock (clk) and the principal items to which it is applied.

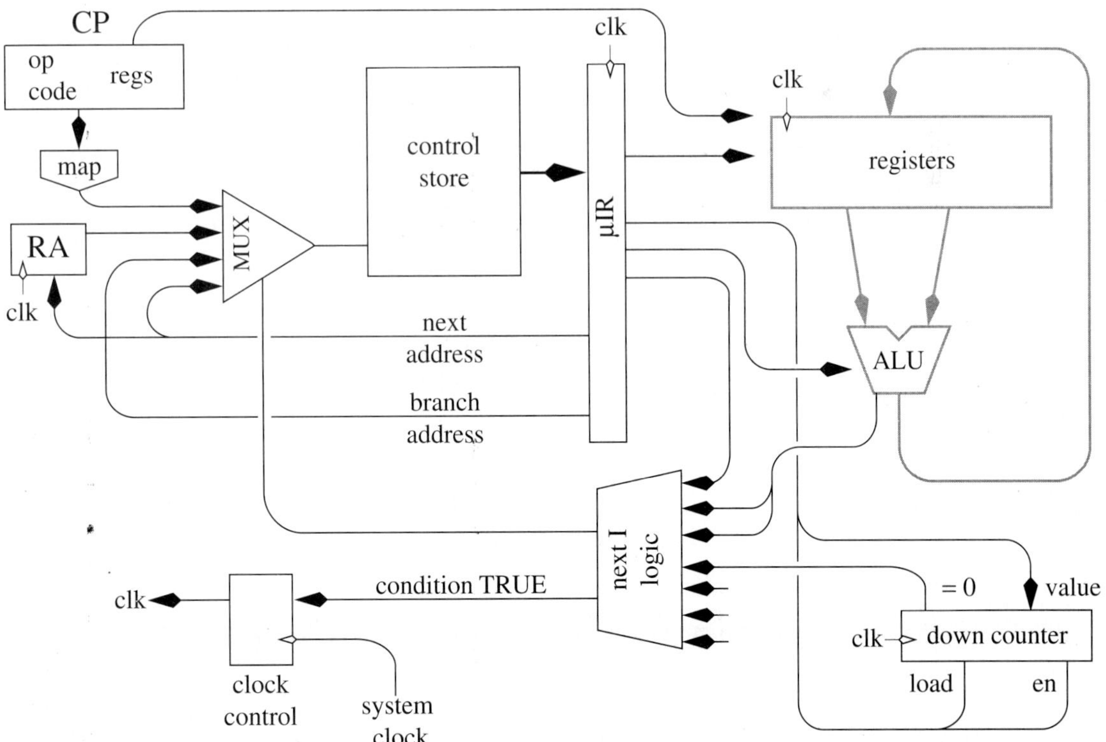

we have a pretty full set of floating-point conversions and load and store routines. What we have not explored thus far are the trigonometric and exponential functions (except see Problem 1.2).

- *The instruction format.* We have many of the fields well defined and others suggested. The order of the bits is at our pleasure. We still need a complete specification of control bits for data paths, register set, and execution units.
- *Program control.* Almost in place in Figure 9.12. What is missing here is the array of conditions that we wish to be able to test for program control.
- *Data paths, register set, and execution units.* This is the least well defined, but even here we have some definitions. We will have 8 double-precision storage registers but have programming space for 32. Each register is 65 bits wide to accommodate the hidden bit. We need a status register for external consumption. We will need a collection of constants for the functions.

Our intention is to work FPADD through completely, lay out the hardware for FPMUL, do one trig function, and worry some about conversions and I/O. Let us start with the effort which lays out a typical addition problem—Figure 9.3 or 9.4. What is obvious in those figures is that the signs, exponents, and significands are treated rather differently. A good layout will have the three parts of each number in different register files. In the process of unpacking the numbers, the hidden bit or the correct exponent (for soft zero) can be restored. We could also include bits to indicate 0, ∞, and NaN, which could be set on storing the number in a register. Let us assume that we have these and walk through the program in Section 9.4.1.

The steps comprise:

1. placing the larger of the two numbers in working register A, the other in B
2. testing A for max exponent (special ending if max exponent)
3. aligning the radix point (skip to step 6 if smaller is effectively 0)
4. adding or subtracting based on signs and operation, result in A
5. first renormalization (special ending if max exponent or underflow and traps)
6. rounding (*inexact* bit set if rounding actually occurs, special ending if trapped)
7. second renormalization and storing (special ending if max exponent)

The basic operations that we require for addition/subtraction are shown in Figure 9.13. As we walk through an addition with the aid of Figure 9.13, you will get a good idea of what will be required from the microcode. You will also see how much of the task is borne by this special-purpose hardware. If the hardware does not carry a good portion of the burden, we might as well do the whole operation in the integer CPU.

The operation indicated that we should do $C \Leftarrow A + B$. There are no restrictions on sources or destination. They could all be the same; they could all be different. We presume that, when the numbers were loaded, they were properly expanded to double-precision floating-point numbers with hidden bit restored. The steps we must follow in

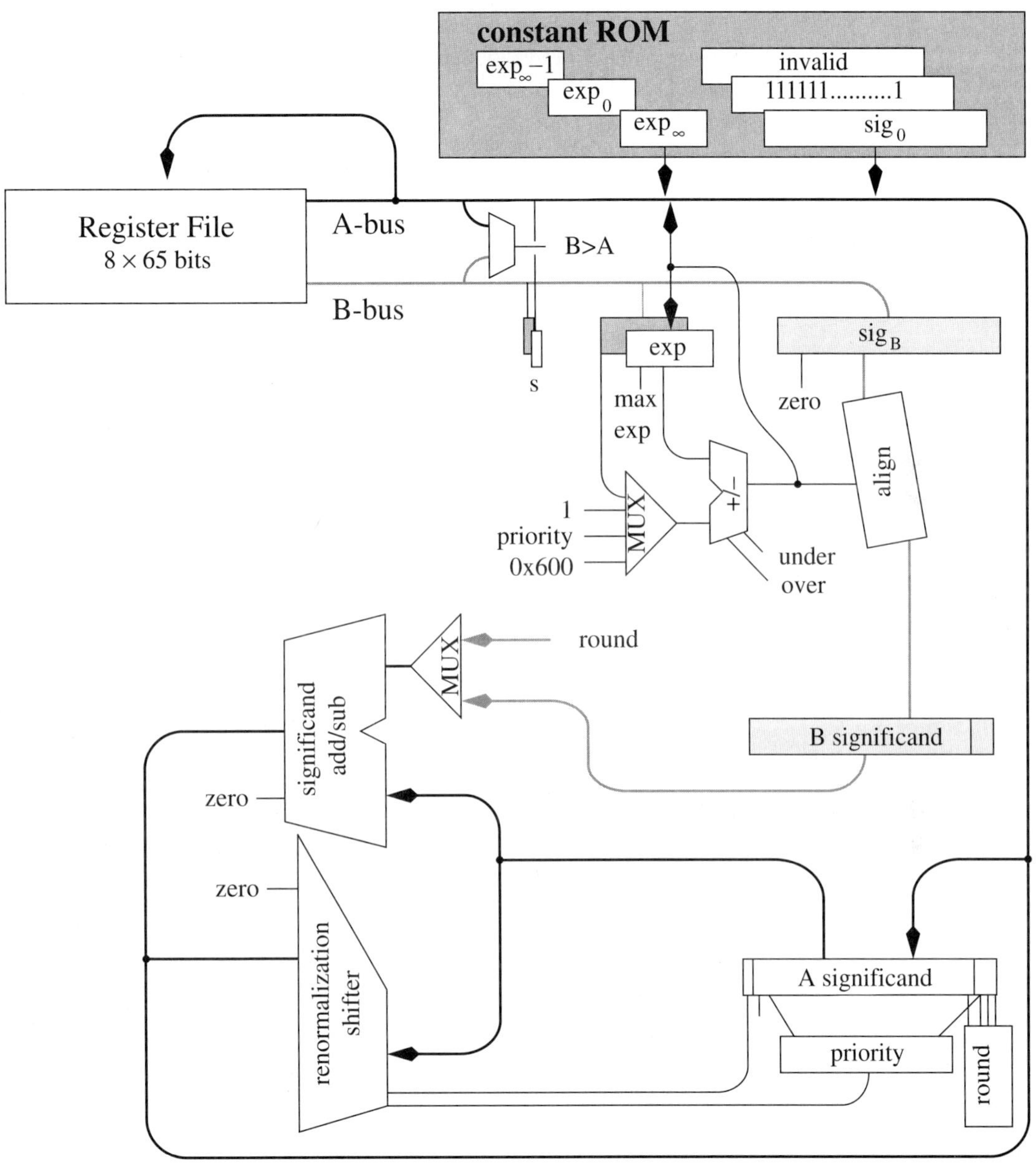

FIGURE 9.13 The hardware to do double-precision FPADD/FPSUB. The various units are controlled by the microcode, by the settings in FPUSR, and by hardware results.

the detail of the microcode follow. Notice that the normal simple FPADD or FPSUB takes 6 microinstructions, or 7 if $B > A$. (For FPADD, one SPARC FPU takes 3 clocks; the MC68882 takes 56.) Since all of this is on-chip, those microinstructions should be able to be clocked rather fast. (You might argue that the 56-bit adder/subtracter is not going to be easy to make exceptionally fast, but even that can be made reasonably quick [Mason, 87]. Within its pipeline, the 200-MHz Alpha chip accomplishes a 64-bit integer add in 2 clocks, or 10 ns [Dobberpuhl, 92].) It is not unreasonable to expect the FPU's clock to turn over at twice the CPU's clock. With that assumption, we have a floating-point add that is only three CPU instructions. The big boys playing with real money and doing it all in hardware can do it in one or two CPU instructions with overlapped execution of the CP instructions. Four is not so poor, however. Look at the program we proposed for FPADD and you cannot but agree that our FPU is going to give quite a boost to performance.

FPADD_SUB:

1. *A* is sent down the A-bus, *B* down the B-bus. The variables are split into their component parts and stored. Magnitude *A* is compared to magnitude *B*. If ($|B| > |A|$) go to 2, otherwise go to 3.
2. *B* is sent down the A-bus, *A* down the B-bus. The variables are split into their component parts and stored. Go to 3.
3. At this point we have the larger of (*A*, *B*) in the A registers. If $\exp_A$ is at MAX_exp (all 1's), go to 14. Otherwise *B* is aligned with *A* by using $\exp_A - \exp_B$ to determine the correct number of places to shift sig_B to the right. The shifter is able to shift the "1" bit fully out of the significand and into the *round*, *guard*, or *sticky* bits. Should the shift be even further, the sticky bit would retain any bit that had passed through. The result of the alignment shift is stored in B_significand. Go to 4.
4. At this point, we are ready to do the add or subtract of the significands. The operation is subtract if $(S_A \oplus S_B) \oplus FPSUB == 1$. The result goes to A_significand. If the result is 0, go to 5, otherwise go to 6.
5. S_A is appended to 64 bits of 0 and stored in the destination register, *C*. *Home*.
6. Observe that several bits derived from A_significand are available for test or control. *Priority* is the output of a priority encoder which determines which is the first nonzero digit in A_significand. *Priority* = 0 if the "one" bit of the significand is set. There is also an *overflow* bit which could be called the "two" bit. The exponent arithmetic unit (AU) is programmed to add 1 or subtract *priority* from $\exp_A$. The choice is "add 1" if the *two* bit in A_significand is set. Perform the add or subtract but do not return the result. If either *over* or *under* is asserted, go to 21, otherwise go to 7.
7. Repeat the add/subtract of exponent in step 6 but this time return the result to $\exp_A$ and also send A_significand through the renormalization shifter, which uses *two* and *priority* to properly shift A_significand from 1 to the right to fully from the *round* bit to the left. The result will be normalized and back in A_significand. Go to 8.
8. Execute round in the significand adder and store result in A_significand as well as appending S_A and $\exp_A$ and storing the result back in the destination, *C*. Round sets *inexact* bit if round took place. (If any *trap enable* matches a trapping bit, *trap* is set. "Trap" is the word used in the standard. As we have defined the words, it would be an "exception.") If *two* is asserted, then go to 9, otherwise *home*.

9. Add 1 to exp_A and append S_A and A_significand to form the answer and store in the destination, *C*. If *over* is asserted go to 10, otherwise *Home*. (If *traps* is enabled, the act of returning sets an interrupt request on the correct control lines to the MMU board, which handles interrupt requests.)

Handling_overflows:

10. Append S_A to exp_∞ and sig_0 and store in the destination, *C*. Set overflow. (Setting overflow will assert *traps* if the associated trap enable is set in the *floating-point unit status register*, FPUSR.) If no *directed_round* and no *traps* then *home*, otherwise go to 11.

11. If NOT *traps* then go to 12, otherwise do exp_A – 0x600 and append S_A and A_significand to form the answer and store in the destination, *C*. *Home*.

12. Append S_A to exp_∞ – 1 and *max_sig* (all 1's) and store in the destination, *C*. If (*round_to_zero* OR *infinity_round*) then *home*, otherwise go to 13. [*infinity_round* is a hardware variable which is $(S_A \cap round + \infty) \cup (\bar{S}_A \cap round - \infty)$. If either condition is met, the standard requires rounding to maximum.]

13. Append S_A to exp_∞ and sig_0 and store in the destination, *C*. *Home*.

Handling_infinities_and_NaNs:

14. We know that exp_A is MAX_exp. We do not know if we have ∞ or NaN. Accordingly, we must sort them out. If we do a *round* operation and get *zero*, we would know that we had an ∞. Round but do not store. If *zero* then go to 16, otherwise go to 15.

15. Append S_A, exp_A, and A_significand (the original NaN) and store in the destination, *C*. If *signaling* (we have decided that any one of the lowest 3 bits being set will indicate a signaling NaN. Those bits are ORed to produce *signaling*), then set *invalid*. *Home*.

16. This could be the sum or difference of infinities. Sum is OK and returns ±∞. Difference must return *invalid*. Do $exp_A - exp_B$. If *under* and *zero* and *subtract* (the variable which determines whether an actual significand subtraction would occur) then append S_A, exp_∞, and *invalid*, store in the destination, *C*, set the *invalid bit*, and *home*, otherwise go to 17.

17. Append S_A, exp_∞, and sig_0 and store in the destination, *C*. *Home*.

Overflow_or_underflow:

18. We get here from instruction 6, so we have an overflow or underflow on the first normalization. To separate them, we do: Perform the add or subtract on the exponents but do not return the result. If *over* is asserted go to 10, otherwise go to 19.

19. Shift significand_A left one place and store in significand_A. Subtract 1 from exp_A and store in exp_A. If NOT under then go to 19 (note we repeat the same line until *under* is asserted), otherwise go to 20.

20. Add 1 to exp_A and store in exp_A. Go to 21.

21. Round. Append exp_A and S_A and store in the destination, *C*. Set *underflow* bit. *Home*.

9.5.3 Microinstruction Components

As you scan this microprogram routine, you begin to see the components of the microinstruction. Many of the test bits can serve several masters, representing in 1 bit several events which never occur simultaneously. For example, in Figure 9.13 there are three lines labeled *zero*. These lines are ORed together to generate a single *zero* signal. It is our intention to have separate hardware for *add* and *multiply* operations. There will be many opportunities to combine signals between the two sections. One set of bits which has evolved to reasonable completion in our discussion of the FPU and the IEEE standard is the *status register*, FPUSR.The first 16 bits of this 32-bit register are shown in Figure 9.14.

The construction of the microinstruction is something of an art which we will not get far enough to practice here. It would begin with the assignment of a field in the microinstruction to each function in the machine. This will result in a very wide *horizontal* microinstruction format. Then we would try to compress that by finding a more efficient encoding. Fields are normally devoted to the sources and destinations of each bus, the functions of ALUs, the choice of register numbers, and the various features required by the microsequencer. There are several ways that compression can be accomplished. Often there are necessary relationships between different fields, so it may be possible to combine them and reduce the total number of bits required. Another possibility is to add a little logic to control some features, rather than specifying them directly in the microinstructions. The most dramatic way to reduce the size of the control store is to enumerate the microinstructions actually used, put them in a *nanomemory*, and then let each microinstruction specify the address of the appropriate nanoinstruction. This is the technique used in Motorola's MC68881/2. Much of the research that has been done on microprogramming concerns techniques of encoding control memories. See [Dasgupta, 79] for additional methods and references.

FIGURE 9.14 Layout of the lower 16 bits of the FPUSR. The upper 7 are set by loading the FPUSR register with the instruction FPLOADS. They include the 2 bits which encode the rounding mode (00 is default) and 5 bits which individually enable the five traps. The lower 9 bits are all set by the FPU. They can be read en masse using FPSTORES. They can also be transferred, 5 at a time, to the CPU's status flags using FPFLAGS. The exception bits are sticky. They are cleared by reading them. All bits are reset when the chip is reset.

rounding		trap enables				
R1	R0	inexact	overflow	underflow	÷0	invalid

exceptions					compare result			
inexact	overflow	underflow	÷0	invalid	?	>	<	=

Let us take at least a moment to look at some of the functions that we have defined. Consider, for example, the operations in lines 1 and 2. They call for sending data down two busses to working registers. There must be individual bits to enable the working registers, bits to enable the register file to write, and bits to say which of the two busses will get the *a_src* and which *b_src*. Note that there is no specification of the registers in the microinstruction. They are specified by the CP instruction in register CP (Figure 9.12). All the microinstruction is doing is choosing which datum goes to which bus. The only item that is "computed" in instruction 1 is the address choice. This is done by testing the $(B > A)$ line of the comparator which tests the lowest 64 bits of the two words. On the basis of that bit, you go to 2 or 3. At each microinstruction, you will find some function(s) being performed and generally some bits being tested. The functions require enables of line drivers, MUXs, and registers (for loads). Some of these may come from other hardware; some must be in the microinstruction. Listing all the bits needed is the first step in laying out the microinstruction format.

One of the interesting things that will be added in doing functions like square root and divide or the trig and exponential functions is a ROM of needed constants. Accessing the right ones will require an address based at least in part on the instruction in CP. An obvious way to address data is to have the ROM address in the microcode. To access data based on the instruction, we can use the opcode as the high part of the address. The low-order bits can come from the down counter (series expansions) or the data itself (square root or divide).

Since we plan to do only parts of two more instructions, we will not get the whole layout. While we suspect that you are not too disappointed in our leaving out some of the truly gruesome detail, we did want to get at least some of the flavor of this arcane art across.

9.5.4 A Look at the Multiply Hardware

Apart from a number of small but important details, floating-point multiplication comprises two acts:

- Add the exponents.
- Multiply the significands.

In doing these two operations, a SPARC 1 FPU delivers the product in five clocks, the first Alpha chip takes six 5-ns clocks, and the MC68882 consumes 76 clocks. Of the two operations, the only real problem is achieving a fast multiply of the pair of 53-bit, fixed-point binary numbers whose 106-bit product we wish to generate. Were we to use the 2-bit Booth's algorithm from Appendix I, it would need 27 passes through our single adder. Even if we did that at double the clock rate of our CPU, our customers would not be impressed with our multiplication speed. Let us reexamine *multiply* with the thought of throwing some money at the problem.

In Appendix I, we went through 1- and 2-bit versions of Booth recoding [Booth, 51]. Could we continue that to 3 or more bits? Obviously, but the results are not nearly so neat. For the 1-bit version (base-2 arithmetic), we construct all operations by looking at a pair of multiplier bits, *last* multiplier bit and *current* multiplier bit. There are four possibilities: 0 ⇒ 1 or 1 ⇒ 0, which imply a subtraction or addition respectively, and 0 ⇒ 0 and 1 ⇒ 1 which imply a pass. When we go to the base-4 case (2 bit), we must consider 3 bits at a time, but all we are trying to do is accomplish in one step what the 1-bit case would do in two steps. The only combinations one can make of the two steps are ±2×, ±1× and *pass*. If we continue this to base-8 (3 bit), considering 4 bits at a time and trying this time to do in one step what we would need three to do base-2, the combinations include ±4×, ±3×, ±2×, ±1× and *pass*. The ±4× and ±2× can be accomplished with shift-and-add, but there are only two ways to do ±3×. We need either two adders in series, or we must have 3× already computed and at hand. Since the principal wait is time through the adder, the last thing we would want to do is put two of them in series. The compute-it-and-latch-it alternative is much more viable. In fact, it is one of methods Alpha uses to achieve its remarkable 30-ns FPMUL latency [Dobberpuhl, 92]. The cost of initializing the 3× register is one clock. The gain is 18 clocks (3-bit) versus 27 clocks (2-bit). Let us assume three clocks for initialization and conclusion. If we could run this at double our clock frequency, we would be getting one FPMUL in just over 1 μs. That is to be compared first with Alpha's 30 ns latency (the direct comparison) and then completely humiliated by the fact that Alpha and many other modern FPUs are highly pipelined and can start one floating-point operation per clock. However, before you conclude that Alpha will do 200 MFLOPS, no real program ever is so exclusively floating-point that the latency is not about as important as the potential throughput. Can we improve on the latency?

Another possibility is to speed up the addition itself. Why does an add take so long? Because carries must propagate. Computing the sum and carry for a full adder takes less than a couple of nanoseconds. It is the added layers to accomplish carry propagation in the same clock that slows the adder. A rather neat way to finesse all but the last carry-propagation step is a device called the *carry-save adder* (CSA). The basic concept is to think of a *full adder* not as a circuit for adding two numbers and a carry but as a circuit for adding three numbers. With that perspective, we return to the fourth-grade view of multiplication as a sequence of additions (and shifts).

Each time that you add either the multiplicand or 0 to the partial sum, each of your adders will generate a new sum bit and a carry bit. If you are adding 54-bit numbers, your outputs will be two 54-bit numbers, *sum* and *carry*. You grab them both. No carries propagate; they just go into the carry register. Now for the critical step. The inputs to the add are:

- the multiplicand or 0
- the *sum* from the previous operation (initial value 0)
- the *carry* from the previous operation (initial value 0)

This operation is shown in Figure 9.15. Note that on each addition the partial sum is shifted one digit to the right. There is one final sum that is required at the end. This combines the partial sum and the last set of carry bits. This final sum could be done in another adder optimized for the carry propagation, or at the cost of some delay in the carry-save operation, some hardware could be added to the 53 full adders to turn them into a conventional adder.

The only problem here in utilizing this whiz-bang arrangement is providing a clock fast enough to pump this operation through its 53 steps at a rate of a step every 2 to 4 ns. Making any wide structure work in unison at 250 to 500 MHz is no small order. A great deal of care goes into accounting for clock skew. But if it were carried off, you would have the principal part of the multiply finished in 120 to 240 ns. This is two to four times faster than the best we could expect from the 3-bit Booth multiplier.

Note that the design of Figure 9.15 can deliver the full 106-bit product with no extra cost whatever. The same register which holds the multiplier ends up with the low-order 53 bits. The high-order bits are the finished partial sum. The ready availability of the full product is used to great advantage in the FPU on the IBM RS/6000. Since they provide *multiply-and-add* as a single instruction, they retain all 106 bits into the *add* and only round at the end. The added precision is particularly advantageous in accelerating the convergence of functions such as SQRT and ÷, often saving a full cycle of the routine.

9.5.5 Putting the Multiplier Pieces Together

Having chosen to do the FPU as a microprogrammed machine, the 3-bit Booth's algorithm design makes the most sense. Were we doing this chip to compete in today's market, we would not choose microcoding. Chip technology has reached the point in integration where we can get considerably faster performance without a cost penalty by doing the whole design as a *hardwired* or gate design. At this moment, a CSA design

FIGURE 9.15 Eight-bit carry-save adder. The leftmost and rightmost bits are shown fully developed. The other 6 bits replicate the leftmost. The delay around the loop is only that of a single full adder and the single AND gate. In today's technology, that would be of the order of 2 ns.

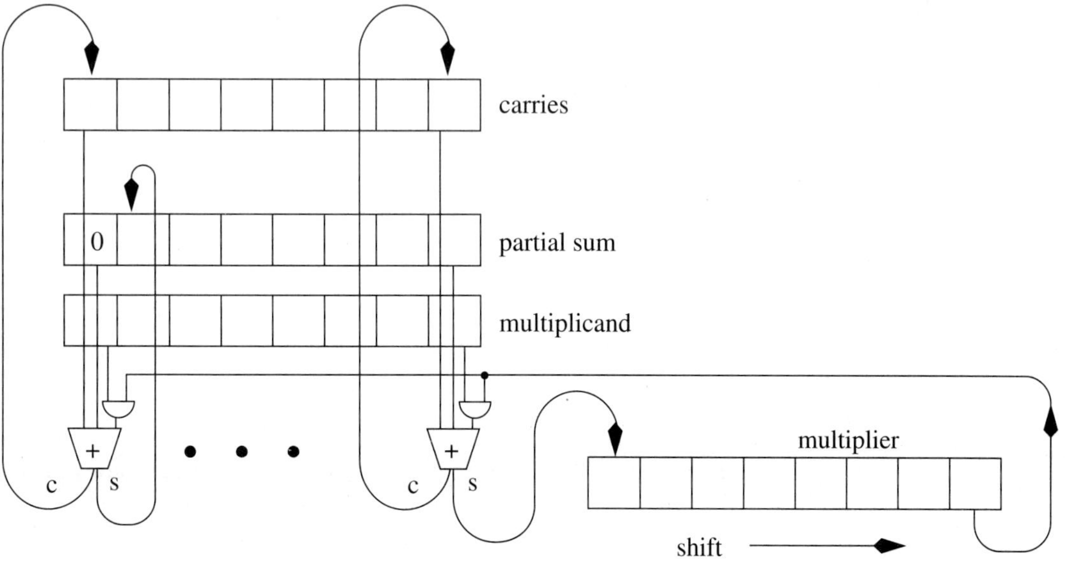

would probably be the best compromise between speed and silicon devoted to the multiplier. These can be accelerated by cascading them without intervening registers, though obviously at a cost in increased silicon area. A number of such arrangements are considered in [Goldberg, 89].

All right, we have chosen Booth's algorithm with a base-8 system. What else must be in the multiplier? We must be able to add exponents and to look for inputs of infinity and NaN and for outputs of overflow and underflow. The exceptional cases frequently make a great deal of trouble for the design. What, for example, will we do with underflow? The problem shows up in difficulties in normalization after multiplication. Instead of having that problem, we have decided to regularize normalization to right-shifting, leading to simpler rounding hardware. The idea is to do whatever left-shifting is necessary to normalize the significands, keeping track of the number of places, *count,* done in the pass through the barrel shifter. Then, when we do the sum of the exponents, we will be doing

$$\exp_A = \exp_A - bias + \exp_B - count$$

Figure 9.16 shows a first pass at the hardware. We will use the same hardware that we used in the adder to select A as the larger of $A|B$. We will never have to align A even if it is a soft zero because if $A \geq B$, then if A is a soft zero, the result underflows to a hard 0. In all other cases, having normalized sig_B to 1.xxx in a fixed-point sense, the product of the significands is always $1 \leq product < 4$, so at most one shift is required to put it between 1 and 2. However, a negative resultant $\exp_A$ could require yet more shifts to the right. Again, this could be done by the microcode, one shift at a time, or it could be done as we show in Figure 9.16 by basing the right shift on the number of places necessary to bring the exponent back to the minimum value of 1 (even though you would now return an exponent of 0 to indicate denormalization). Problem 9.15 asks you to check this hardware design for completeness and effectiveness.

Once we have dedicated hardware for multiplication and addition, could we do more than one operation at a time? There are two ways to approach this goal. One is to create an instruction which explicitly programs a multiply to be followed by an add which uses the product as one of the operands. This is what is done in the IBM RS/6000. The single instruction contains all of the operands so there is no problem of interactions or ordering of operations between instructions. The advantages of this approach include:

- This very common pair of operations runs faster because of less overhead and fewer rounding operations.
- The higher precision resulting from the fewer intermediate rounds can lead to more rapid convergence in some frequently employed algorithms.

Another approach is to try to overlap additions and multiplications so that the adder and multiplier will both be used at the same time. Keeping both units busy is accomplished by issuing commands as rapidly as the FPU hardware can handle them. To increase the rate at which the FPU can issue commands, one can pipeline the dedicated adder and multiplier units, so that several instructions of each kind may be in

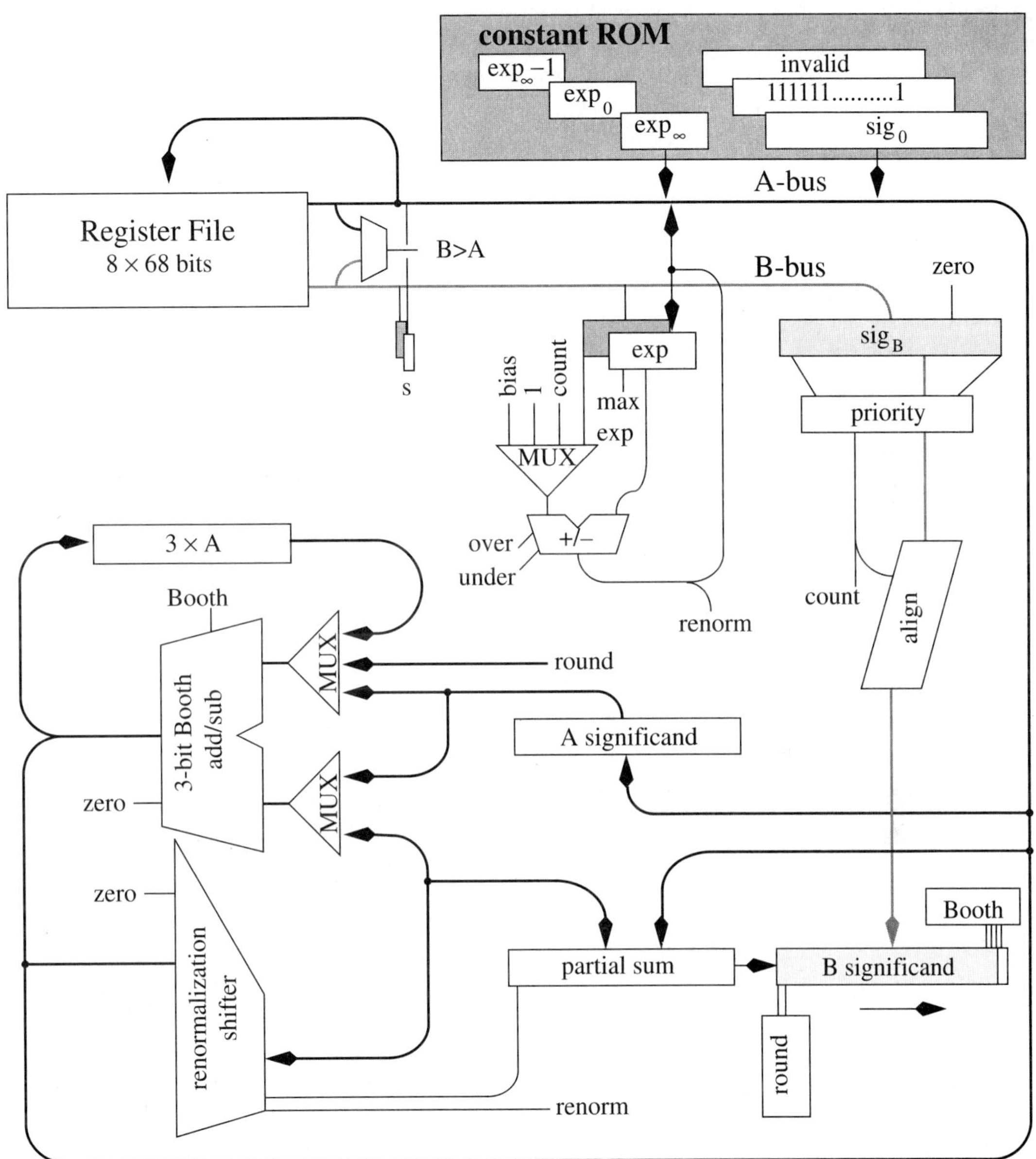

FIGURE 9.16 Hardware for the multiplier section of the FPU. Some of the hardware is shared with the adder section. *A* becomes the multiplicand and *B* the multiplier. The full product is developed in *partial sum* and *B_significand*. The second bit of *B_significand* is *sticky*. An extra low-order bit is added to *B_significand* to provide access to the last bit shifted off. Simultaneously with the passage of *partial sum* through the Booth shifter and adder/subtracter, the pair *partial sum:B_significand* is shifted right three places. Both the shift and the new partial sum are clocked in on the same clock edge. The mechanism for generating and latching the value of 3 × A is connected to the Booth adder/subtracter. Instead of the lower MUX, *A_significand* could be loaded into *partial sum* for the formation of 3 × A, with *partial sum* then being cleared to start the multiplication itself.

progress at any time. The machines designed by Seymour Cray, starting with the CDC 6600, have used both of these techniques. Most machines which do this, even single-chip machines such as the Fairchild/Intergraph Clipper and the Motorola MC88000, use a *scoreboard* mechanism to look for interactions between registers in different instructions. The scoreboard resolves conflicts in hardware usage and delays any instruction which needs the result of a previous instruction [Thornton, 70].

Clearly, our FPU is not designed for multiple instruction issue, but our system is. We have the capability for supporting four coprocessors of any type. If the identification number of the FPU is not built into the chip, then four identical FPUs could be installed in one machine. While this precludes several units working simultaneously on the same data, it does allow for concurrent issuance of instructions and an impressive number of floating-point operations per second. Consistent with the RISC philosophy, the organization and optimization of the use of multiple FPUs would be in the hands of the compiler. If the software is to run on machines with many configurations, local optimization must be done by the code itself, a not insignificant task.

At this point, with adder and multiplier more or less in hand, it seems appropriate to take a closer look at using this capability to generate one or two of the functions in our instruction set.

9.5.6 FPSIN and FPLOG

All of us have learned with varying degrees of joy that Mr. Taylor's series does indeed converge, sometimes uniformly and absolutely, sometimes conditionally. Unless you really got into numerical methods, you probably never found out whether these series expansions converged with gusto or rather like grass growing in the hot summer. Let it be said, as we are sure it was in the calculus class, that Taylor series converges rapidly in the vicinity of the origin and *nowhere else*. There are better ways and in fact you are intuitively aware of their basic principle. To demonstrate that you are better at this than you think, consider Figure 9.17, which is a plot of $\log_2(X)$ vs. X.

What you are asked to do is to draw the best *first-order* approximation (i.e., straight line) to the function shown **over the interval $1 \leq X \leq 2$**. Be careful. You must defend your choice of "best." At least one correct and defendable answer is given in Figure 9.18. Many students, when challenged by this question, select the tangent to the midpoint of the curve. That is not a bad guess, but what is the criterion on which it is best? If you made that guess, your criterion was probably that it "looked close." Not a bad rule of thumb, but if that was your reason, you must be willing to agree that there might be one that was even closer. Closer where? The tangent touches. True, but lots of lines touch. What if we ask if there is a line about which we can say: Over the interval, no other line has a smaller *maximum* error. In other words, we are looking for the line whose *maximum error is a minimum*. Now that, you must admit, sounds like a criterion. It owns the name *minimax*, which is easier to spell than its other name, *Chebyshev*. The minimax fit is shown in Figure 9.18. You can see the three extrema at 1, 2, and 1.443. They have the interesting property that all the error extrema are of equal magnitude. They strictly alternate in sign.

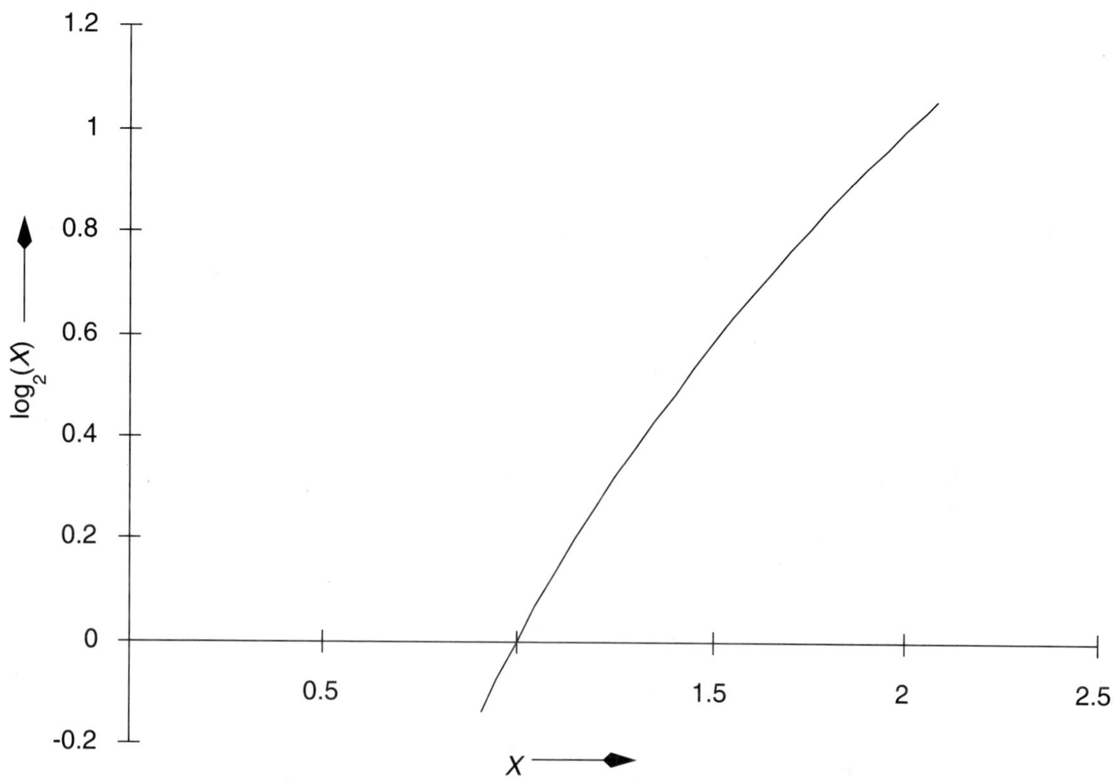

FIGURE 9.17 A plot of $\log_2(X)$ vs. X over the interval $0.9 \leq X \leq 2.1$.

Just how well does our minimax fit work? This proves rather easy to evaluate. All of the error extrema have the same magnitude: 0.0340. This should be an impressive result. We have obtained a fit to 3 percent with only one term! Try Mr. Taylor's series on that. Obviously, the Taylor series for $\log_2(x-1)$ is a perfect fit at $X = 1$ and progressively worse as you get further away, finally becoming only *conditionally stable* at $X = 2$. Problem 9.16 addresses this point.

As a criterion for function generation, the Chebyshev fit has the ideal property that one can state the worst error that will be made anywhere in the interval. If you want 10 decimal digits, fine. It will take, say, 6 terms. If you want 20, then we will need 11. Over most of the interval, you will do much better, but you know that you will never do worse. That is comforting indeed.

Looking at Figure 9.18 should make you itch to put in the second term, in essence to bend the curve a little to make the fit better. No problem, or rather yes, problem, Problem 9.17 to be exact. This is the last order for which easy algebra is possible. The second-order polynomial is decidedly better.

One last comment on the concept of *fitting over an interval*. Look at what happens in Figure 9.18 when you are outside the interval. Consider the point $x = 0$. $g(x)$ returns the pleasant value -0.9570. $f(x)$ returns $-\infty$. Now *there* is an error!

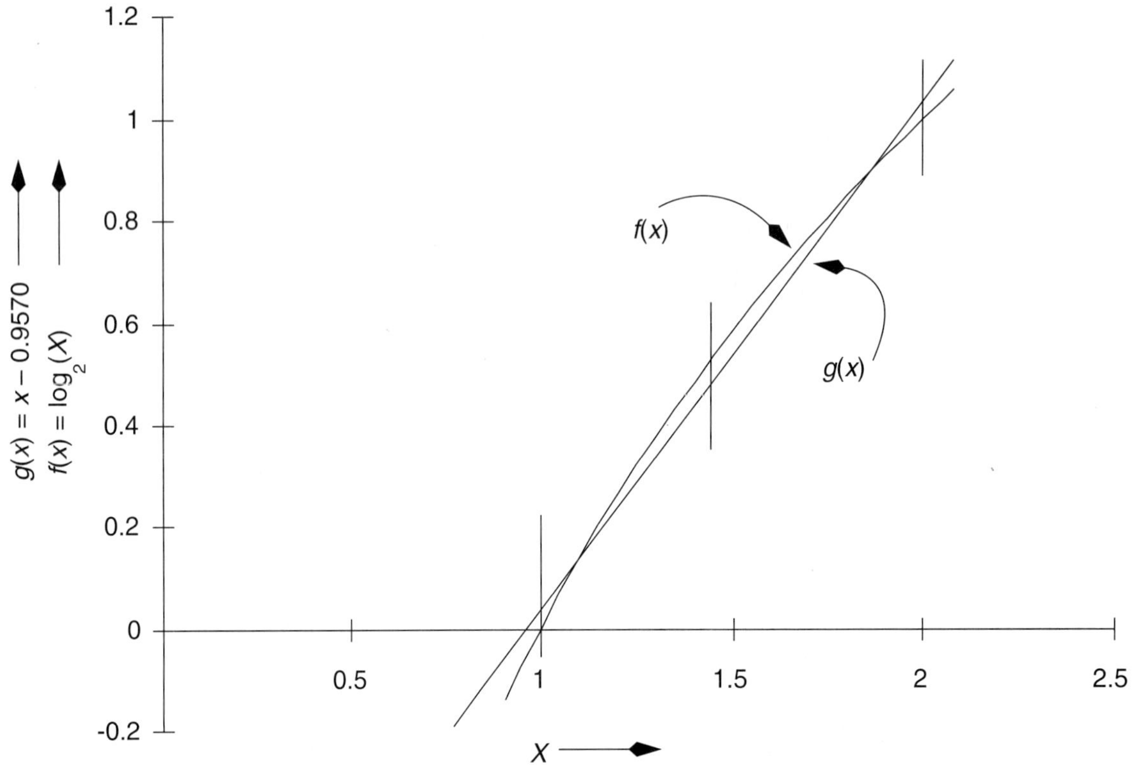

FIGURE 9.18 Approximation of the function $\log_2(X)$ over the interval $1 \leq X \leq 2$ by the straight line $X - 0.9570$, which is a minimax best-fit to the function over the interval.

So what will we do with these minimax fittings? The idea is:

- Define an appropriate interval for the function.
- Beg, borrow, steal, or, if all else fails, generate the coefficients for the approximating interval.
- Develop an efficient algorithm for getting the argument into the range of evaluation (this brings to mind the IEEE standard's REM function).
- Put the package together along with tests for special cases such as NaNs and infinities.

You can find this done in C in [Plauger, 92], who in turn obtained the coefficients from [Cody, 80] and [Hart, 78]. What you will find in the function sin(x), for example, are two sets of eight double-precision coefficients which work over the interval $-\pi/2 \leq x \leq \pi/2$. You need two sets to deal with the fact that with values in the range $\pi/4 < |x| < \pi/2$, you are actually evaluating cos(x). Once you have rolled your argument into the correct interval and chosen the correct set of coefficients, all that is required is to expand the polynomial in the form of

$$\sin(x) = \{[(A_7 x + A_6)x + A_5]x + \cdots + A_0\}$$

The operations of × and + are clearly in place. What we are missing is a method for acquiring the coefficients. Just as Plauger must include them in his C program, so we must build them into our FPU. We will need a number of these constants for each routine. Some may be sharable (π) but most will be unique to the function. Let us presume that we will use a ROM. The question is: How do we address the elements of this ROM?

We have two models, although we could fold one into the other. These are:

- an ordered sequence of coefficients such as those illustrated in sin(x)
- individual coefficients that we would like to be able to call out at will

The ordered sequence calls for some modifiable address; individual coefficients call for some form of *absolute* addressing. To have modifiable addresses, we must provide a loadable counter whose value will be added or appended to a base value which identifies that sequence. The minimum configuration would be, say, a 4-bit counter appended onto the proper number of higher order bits from the *branch address*. In other words, we will make multiple use of the branch address field. Along with that, we will need a method for loading the 4-bit counter and for decrementing it. To get absolute addressing, we could simply use the proper number of bits from the branch address field. The ROM itself must be able to feed both busses in Figure 9.13 and do the same bus-switching routine that we introduced for both adder and multiplier.

Will we need more hidden registers? Yes. While for functions such as sin( ) which are expressed as a single series, it might seem that we could use the destination address to accumulate intermediate values of the summation, what do we do with such things as argument reduction? If you need REM $(x, 2\pi)$, where will you put it? Many functions, such as log( ) and tan( ), are most efficiently expressed as the ratio of two polynomials. Here too there is a need for temporary storage. There are multiple options. We could expand our register set from the eight double-precision registers that we now have to include two or more registers available only through the microcode. Another option which is particularly appealing for function generation is a stack. Stacks are the most natural mechanism for the evaluation of algebraic expressions, as anyone who has mastered RPN calculators knows. A depth of two or four would be plenty and its presence would certainly encourage the development of instructions for *multiply-and-add* operations which do $c \Leftarrow a \times b + c$. Should our enthusiasm for this sort of thing grow, we could stack both halves of a product and achieve IBM's trick of keeping full precision until the add is completed. The microcoding would enable us to wallow around in the hardware, going slower rather than creating double-width data paths.

But enough. The methodology is reasonably clear. We have the elemental operations well developed. As Sir William Gilbert so aptly put it a century ago (*Iolanthe*, patter song "When you're lying awake"):

And the night has been long
ditto, ditto my song
and thank goodness they're both of them o-ver.

CHAPTER SUMMARY

This chapter was constructed of three principal parts:

- the IEEE binary floating-point standard
- an introduction to microprogrammed processors
- the layout of an FPU

The discussion of the floating-point standard proceeded top-down from arguments on the most efficient coding of the numbers themselves to all of the minutiae of rounding, overflow, and underflow. In dividing the fixed number of bits between *sign*, *exponent*, and *significand*, we played off dynamic range versus precision. With the gimmick of the *hidden bit*, a binary radix proved to be most efficient. The natural (by this time) selection of 32- and 64-bit formats for storing the numbers led to the complete storage specifications given in Table 9.1 and Figure 9.2.

To enable direct comparisons between the magnitudes of two IEEE standard numbers:

- The bit fields were ordered as *sign*, *exponent*, and *significand*.
- The exponent was stored in *biased* form to render it monotonic.
- The significand was stored in sign-magnitude form.

We next turned to the cases which did not fit within the bounds of these definitions: *overflow*, *underflow*, and *NaNs*. To provide space for these special cases, the maximum and minimum exponents (255 and 0 respectively for single precision) were set aside to signal something other than a normal floating-point number. Signed infinities were defined for both single and double precision as the maximum exponent and a 0 significand. All other uses of the maximum exponent were messages rather than numbers, hence NaNs. The standard requires both *signaling* and *quiet* NaNs, the former for forcing an exception if an operation is attempted on them.

While the infinities do provide a simple indication of overflow, the standard allows the user to specify that, rather than return the ∞, the FPU (or floating-point software) should trap on overflow and then deliver the wherewithal to complete the calculation without loss of precision. For overflow, this is accomplished by changing the bias by a known factor to permit the exponent to be expressed within the allotted space.

Underflow brought in the *soft zero*. The concept is that the exponent 0 is used as a flag to mean that the number is *denormalized* (*hidden bit* is 0) and that the exponent to be used is the minimum value of the exponent (1 in both formats). Since there is a zero hidden bit in the significand, what you see is what you get. Accordingly, a true zero is included as the limiting case of *soft zero*. The soft zero allows the user to trade precision for range and softens the rather abrupt floating-point transition from finite number to zero.

Once again, having defined a method for dealing with underflow, the standard allows the user to retain full precision for his or her own purposes by using a trap on underflow and then reporting the result with a rebiased exponent.

Finite precision leads to questions on how to round. The standard is replete with answers and options. The options offered include:

- round to 0 (truncation)
- round to $+\infty$
- round to $-\infty$
- round to nearest

The last is the closest to our grade-school standard of rounding up if the residue is $\geq {}^1/_2$ in the LSB. However, the case when residue = ${}^1/_2$ is made special. To remove any bias in the rounding, this special case is kept unbiased by making it depend on the essentially random LSB. The rule is that if the residue = ${}^1/_2$, then the LSB is rounded to 0. The standard specifies that the rounding shall be the same as if the *infinitely precise value* had been used for the round. After a number of examples, we concluded that an addition required only 3 extra bits to meet this requirement. The least significant of these bits had to be *sticky* in the sense that if any bit shifted through it had been 1, the *sticky bit* would be 1.

We concluded our look at the numbers themselves by asking how NaNs and infinities were and were not generated. The "not-generated" group comprised the directed roundings which carried numbers toward 0 even when they had clearly overrun the representable range. For example, truncation (round toward 0) returns the largest finite number regardless of the size of the overflow.

The NaN rules were spelled out and were quite reasonable. If the answer could not be represented as a real number (including 0 and ∞), then you get a NaN. For example, $0 \times \infty$ and $\sqrt{-5}$ both would return a NaN.

Having discussed the numbers themselves, we turned next to the operations required under the IEEE standard. These were presented in Table 9.6. Floating-point addition was presented in full detail in a C program. Multiplication came next with few surprises but some important detail. Then we turned to division and did it by what was probably a totally unexpected though rather widely used form: Newton's method. The rationale for this sudden turn was that it would probably pay to put in a superfast multiplier and that, in turn, would make Newton's method a quick way to get a fast reciprocal. From the reciprocal to division was just one more product. The method works quite well, but it has decided liabilities if the user wants the remainder. Since the IEEE standard requires that REM be available, that is an important liability. One option, of course, is to presume that REM is rarely done and then relegate it to software. Nothing in the standard requires that it be either fast or in hardware, just that it be available.

REM itself is a rather strange version of modular division. Its principal use is for argument reduction. For example, if someone requests sin(27439), the first thing that must be done is to get the remainder of $27434/2\pi$. The precise IEEE standard definition of REM is:

> x REM $y = x - y \times n$, where n is the integer nearest to the exact value x/y, and if $|n - x/y| = 1/2$, then n is chosen to be even. If y is 0 or infinite, the result is undefined; REM should return a NaN or trap. If the remainder is 0, its sign is defined to be the same as the sign of x.

Square root was the next operation considered. It is a natural for Newton's method, although problems arise with the IEEE standard on rounding.

The combination of multiplication and addition provided some interesting discussion. The FPU for the IBM RS6000 does this pair without rounding the result of the product prior to the addition. The result is increased precision with some very nice benefits not only in FPU performance but also in more rapid convergence in operations such as Newton's method. Unfortunately, it gives answers which are different from those obtained with the intervening round. Doing better than the standard is just as noncompliant as doing worse, but while conforming has its advantages, so do speed and precision.

The operation of *comparison* is complicated by the presence of infinities and NaNs. The standard defines the results of all *possible* comparisons using *four* mutually exclusive relationships:

- $<$
- $=$
- $>$
- unordered (symbolized by "?")

The issue on *possible* is that if the two operands are both numbers (including ∞), the comparison is done by subtraction. If that subtraction is not possible (e.g., $\infty - \infty$), the FPU is to signal an *invalid* operation. The *unordered* response is reserved for the case of one or both of the operands being a NaN.

The standard admits two forms of comparison. One may satisfy the standard with a single instruction, *compare*, which returns one of the four flags above (or *invalid*). Alternatively, the FPU can accept tests of the form "Is A >, ?, = B" and respond by reporting either *True/False* or *invalid*. In this second form of comparison, if an operand is a NaN and if the comparison includes either $>$ or $<$ but not ?, *invalid* must be signaled.

The IEEE standard defines limits for conversion between storage formats. While the standard defines a wide variety of formats, only three are required:

- integer
- single-precision floating point
- decimal string

Almost all FPUs and software emulations include double precision as well. The standard attempts to establish a reasonable range over which conversions between types must be supported. Two levels are defined for translations in each direction. One is an upper bound on the number of digits and the other defines the maximum range over which full precision shall be maintained. Table 9.9 gives the ranges for conversions between decimal strings and binary floating point.

The last topic included in the review of the IEEE standard was exceptions, traps, and interrupts. The IEEE standard specifies five exceptions:

- invalid operations (such as 0/0, $0 \times \infty$, and $\sqrt{-1}$)
- division by 0
- overflow
- underflow
- inexact result

The standard is concerned that programmers have the option to recover from exceptions in an informed manner and that there be *default* mode where the processor handles the exception in a known way, leaving a record that the exception occurred. When traps are disabled, one gets the default response, where the problem is indicated both by a *sticky* status bit and by the value that is returned. For example, an overflow would return a signed infinity and turn on the *overflow* status bit.

When traps are enabled (which can be done trap by trap), the values returned are, where possible, the data that is necessary to continue the calculation outside the bounds of normal formats. For example, if inexact results are unacceptable, the program could carry the result out to any precision desired.

Having completed the discussion of the design target, the IEEE binary floating-point standard, we turned to designing a microprogrammed FPU. This objective was approached in two stages. The first concerned itself with the design of *microsequencer* to control the FPU. Two rather separate parts make up the FPU. These comprise a set of hardware to store and process floating-point data and a sequencer which uses microinstructions both to control the other hardware and to select the next microinstruction. Five methods for selecting the next instruction were identified:

- *logical next*, which is typified by instruction $n + 1$ following instruction n
- *mapping*, which converts opcodes in CP to an address to start a sequence
- *branch*, which determines whether to pick an alternative to *logical next* based on a test
- *call*, which allows a *branch* while saving *logical next* for a return address
- *return*, which causes a branch to the address saved in *call*

Execution of these in crisp sequence led logically to pipelining decisions. Eventually, we arrived at almost the same point as in the CPU, using direct addressing and branch prediction instead of calculated addresses and delayed branching. The final design appeared in Figure 9.12. This finally set us up for the layout of the hardware and an overview of the microcode.

Three different FPU operations were considered. The first two were the basic operations of FPADD and FPMUL. Being the primitives of all other arithmetic operations, both were allocated a substantial amount of hardware support. The third operation or class of operation was the evaluation of functions such as sin(x) or log(x). For each of the primitives, hardware provided parallel paths for the handling of sign, exponent, and significand. Figure 9.13 shows the hardware paths for FPADD. A parallel set of paths serving FPMUL is shown in Figure 9.16. For FPADD/SUB a complete expansion was presented of the required steps to meet all of the IEEE standard's requirements. As is appropriate, normal addition/subtraction had the fewest instructions with most special cases requiring extra microcode and extra time.

For FPMUL, the central issue was how to accomplish the multiplication in very short time. We considered the possibility of cascaded *carry-save* adders (Figure 9.15), but in keeping with our modest budget and microcoded approach, we "made do" with a 3-bit (base-8) Booth's algorithm multiplier.

Finally, we considered how to generate the functions we had promised in Table 2.7. While it is easy enough to see how to expand finite series using Horner's method, the question considered very unobvious is how to arrive at a set of polynomial coefficients which would work well over a defining interval [such as $-\pi/2$ to $\pi/2$ for sin( ) or 1 to 2 for $\log_2$( )]. This brought up the minimax or Chebyshev fit. There are other generating methods, but the minimax approach certainly has the greatest clarity and appeal.

This concluded the text.

PROBLEMS

9.1. In Section 9.3.3, we presented the problem of alternately adding and subtracting 1.0B-24 from 1.0B0 rounding up when a residue of $^1/_2$ in the LSB occurs. Determine how many times you must repeat the loop before the sum reaches 2.0. What happens if we continue the loop after that time?

9.2. Design a *sticky bit* using a JK flip-flop. The bit should have synchronous $\overline{\text{reset}}$ and $\overline{\text{load}}$ controls. While the conflict should not happen, were both controls asserted at once, let $\overline{\text{reset}}$ dominate. (This borders on a trivial problem, but that is precisely the point of the exercise.)

9.3. If *x*, *y*, and *z* are defined as *float*, find $z = x + y$ for the number pairs below. Express the final result in *hex* and show all intermediate steps.

(a) x = 4EB43FFF and y = CE59A004

(b) x = 42140000 and y = C1980000

9.4. Convert the following to IEEE single-precision floating point. Express your results in *hex*.

(a) 0.71875

(b) -436.0

9.5. Write a test routine and explore the center and edges for the input domain of the single-precision FPADD routine in Section 9.4.1. Be sure to include rounding up to infinity and dealing with soft zeroes.

9.6. Write a C description of a function *sig_mul* which performs the integer multiplication for FPMUL of Section 9.4.2. The multiplier is to use the 2-bit (radix-4) Booth's algorithm of MUL, but it is to generate only a right-justified 25-bit product and the *round* and *sticky* bits as shown in the product example in Section 9.4.2. You should assume that the input numbers are always normalized so that the implied radix point is between bits 22 and 23 as shown in the product of 1×1 in that section. Store the rounding bits in a pass-by-pointer variable, *tail_bits*, and return the product itself.

9.7. Write a C description of FPMUL in Section 9.4.2 under the presumption that the function *sig_mul* defined in Problem 9.6. You may assume that the default mode of rounding is selected. Your duty is to handle all operations including normalization, rounding and dealing with NaN inputs, overflow, and underflow. Where possible, use the same constant definitions as in the FPADD program of Section 9.4.1.

9.8. Determine the inverse of the largest representable number in the IEEE single-precision format. Is this the same as the smallest number with a representable inverse? (Infinities are not *representable numbers*.)

9.9. In Section 9.4.4 we considered the problem $1 + 2^{-20}$ REM 1.5×2^{-20} but did not determine the correct result. Remedy that situation.

9.10. Write a subroutine in C to perform REM on IEEE single-precision floating-point numbers. It should be capable of handling the full range of single-precision inputs and return a proper IEEE floating-point answer. Use the NaNs defined in the FPADD routine of Section 9.4.1 to signal NaN-in and indefinite.

9.11. Using Newton's method and decimal arithmetic, compute $\sqrt{\pi}$ to eight significant figures starting with a guess of 2. How many iterations were required?

9.12. In Section 9.4.5 a direct application of Newton's method yielded an iterative solution involving division. If, instead, we seek the inverse function $y = 1/\sqrt{x}$, we will get an iterative function with only multiplications. At the end, we obtain $\sqrt{x} = x \times y_i$. Derive that iterative formula and generate a C program to compute the square root of an IEEE single-precision floating-point number. Note that the exponent must be made even before the square root of the significand is pursued. Accordingly, you must denormalize the significand if the exponent is odd. Generally, one works with 4 > significand ≥ 1.

9.13. In Section 9.4.5, Wallace's algorithm for extracting $y = 1/\sqrt{x}$ was presented. Presuming a table of guesses containing 256 equally spaced guesses (à la Section 9.4.3) in the method that you developed in Problem 9.12, determine which method converges more rapidly for finding $\sqrt{15}$.

9.14. Since the condition codes in Figure 9.12 can vary throughout the cycle, we need a Moore state machine to correctly provide the internal clock (*clk*). Design such a clock generator assuming a system clock running at twice the speed desired for *clk*. Assume that an FPU cycle begins on the rising edge of *clk*. If the branch condition is met, you wish to skip one full clock cycle of *clk*. That is, *clk* should remain low for two extra beats of the system clock.

9.15. Figure 9.16 purports to provide the hardware necessary to do floating-point multiplication. Check this assertion by writing a complete set of line-by-line commands as we did for the adder in Section 9.5.2. You can conclude one of three things: (1) the hardware is complete and workable as evidenced by a complete program for multiplication; (2) some additions or modifications are necessary, being quite explicit on what and why; (3) the hardware works but could be greatly improved by some addition or modification; or (4) there is more hardware than we need. We can take some out and lower the cost.

9.16. In Section 9.5.6, it was suggested that the Taylor series for $\log_2(x - 1)$ was very slowly convergent as you get away from $x = 1$. To test this idea, consider evaluating the Taylor series at the Chebyshev maxima which occur at 1.4427 and at 2.0. How many terms must you take in the Taylor series before you obtain a fit to better than the 3.4 percent that the minimax straight line gave? [For those to whom it did not immediately occur, $\log_2(x) = (\log(x))/\log(2)$.]

9.17. Following up the suggestion in Section 9.5.6, find the minimax polynomial of order 2 which gives a best fit to $\log_2(x)$ over the interval $1 \le x \le 2$. You will get five maxima. Determine the magnitude of the worst error over the interval.

REFERENCES

Microprogramming

[Agrawala, 74] Agrawala, A.K., and T.G. Rauscher, *Microprogramming: Perspective and Status*, **IEEE Transactions on Computers C-23:8**, 817–837 (1974).

[Agrawala, 76] Agrawala, A.K., and T.G. Rauscher, *Foundations of Microprogramming*, Academic Press (1976).

[AMD, 88] *Advanced Micro Devices, 32-Bit Microprogrammable Products* Am29C300/29300, AMD (1988). This data book includes specifications on microsequencers, and integer and floating-point arithmetic units. It also contains application notes, several of which describe floating-point algorithms.

[Andrews, 80] Andrews, M., *Principles of Firmware Engineering in Microprogram Control*, Computer Science Press (1980).

[Banerji, 82] Banerji, D.K., and J. Raymond, *Elements of Micro-Programming*, Prentice-Hall (1982).

[Dasgupta, 79] Dasgupta, S., *The Organization of Microprogram Stores*, **Computing Surveys, 11**(1), 39–65 (1979).

[Dasgupta, 89] Dasgupta, S., *Computer Architecture: A Modern Synthesis*, Wiley (1989). Chapter 5 of this textbook is on microprogramming.

[Ditzel, 87a] Ditzel, D.R., and H.R. McLellan, *Branch Folding in the CRISP Microprocessor: Reducing Branch Delay to Zero*, **Proceedings of the 14th International Symposium on Computer Architecture**, 2–9 (1987).

[Ditzel, 87b] Ditzel, D.R., H.R. McLellan, and A.D. Berenbaum, *The Hardware Architecture of the CRISP Microprocessor*, **Proceedings of the 14th International Symposium on Computer Architecture**, 309–320 (1987).

[Doran, 75] Doran, R.W., *Architecture of Stack Machines* in **High-Level Language Computer Architecture**, Y. Chu (ed.), Academic Press (1975).

[Gifford, 87] Gifford, D., and A. Spector, *Case Study: IBM's System/360-370 Architecture*, **Communications of the ACM 30**(4), 292–307 (1987). An interview with Richard Case and Andris Padegs, two of the architects of System/360-370, describing how some of the major decisions were made.

[Habib, 88] Habib, S. (ed.), *Microprogramming and Firmware Engineering*, Van Nostrand-Rheinhold (1988).

[Husson, 70] Husson, S.S., *Microprogramming: Principles and Practices*, Prentice-Hall (1970). This book has extremely detailed descriptions of microprogramming in the early IBM 360 processors.

[Koopman, 89] Koopman, P.J., *Stack Computers, the New Wave*, Halstead Press(1989). A survey of modern stack machines, many of which directly execute Forth.

[Margulis, 90] Margulis, N., *i860 Microprocessor Architecture*, Osborne McGraw-Hill (1990).

[Mick, 76] Mick, J.R., and J. Bick, *Microprogramming Handbook*, AMD (1976). This shows how to apply AMD's 2911 series microsequencers, which were very popular in small computers during the 1970s.

[Mishra, 87] Mishra, S., *The VAX 8800 Microarchitecture*, **Digital Technical Journal 1**(4), 20–33 (February 1987). Describes the Vax 8800 mechanism of converting instructions to sequences of microinstructions, which are then pipelined at the micro level.

[Multinovic, 89] Milutinovic, V., *Microprogramming and Firmware Engineering*, IEEE Computer Society Press (1989). Contains reprints of papers on optimization, emulation, VLIW machines, and software tools for microprogramming.

[Nanodata, 79] Nanodata Corporation, *QM-1 Hardware Level User's Manual*, 3rd edition (1979).

[Rauscher, 80] Rauscher, T.G., and P.N. Adams, *Microprogramming: A Tutorial and Survey of Recent Developments*, **IEEE Transactions on Computers, C-29:1**, 2–19 (1980).

[Retter, 82] Retter, C.T., *High Speed Compact Digital Computer System with Segmentally Stored Microinstructions*, U.S. Patent 4,330,823 (1982). A method for storing microinstructions in two halves, which are fetched on alternate edges of the system clock.

[Salisbury, 76] Salisbury, A.B., *Microprogrammable Computer Architectures*, Elsevier (1976).

[Wilkes, 51] Wilkes, M., *The Best Way to Design an Automatic Calculating Machine*, **Manchester University Computer Inaugural Conference**, Ferranti (1951). Wilkes introduced the idea of microprogramming at this conference.

[Wilkes, 85] Wilkes, M., *Memoirs of a Computer Pioneer*, MIT Press (1985). See pp. 178–194 for a description of the invention of microprogramming and its incorporation into EDSAC-2.

Floating-point arithmetic

[Anderson, 67] Anderson, S.F., J.G. Earle, R.E. Goldschmidt, and D.M. Powers, *The IBM System/360 Model 91: Floating-Point Execution Unit*, **IBM Journal of Research and Development**, 34–53 (January 1967).

[Booth, 51] Booth, A.D., *A Signed Binary Multiplication Technique*, **Quarterly J. of Mechanical and Applied Mathematics**, **4**, 236–240 (1951).

[Brent, 73] Brent, R.P., *On the Precision Attainable with Various Floating-Point Number Systems*, **IEEE Transactions on Computers C-22**, 601–607 (1973).

[Chen, 72] Chen, T.C., *Automatic Computation of Exponentials, Logarithms, Ratios and Square Roots*, **IBM Journal of Research and Development**, 380–388 (July 1972). A family of converging algorithms to compute the functions listed using adds, shifts, bit-counting, and a table of $\ln\ (1 + 2^{-m})$.

[Cody, 80] Cody, W.J., and W. Waite, *Software Manual for the Elementary Functions*, Prentice-Hall (1980).

[Cody, 81] Cody, W.J., Analysis *of Proposals for the Floating-point Standard*, **IEEE Computer 14**(3), 63–69 (March 1981).

[Cody, 84] Cody, W.J., D.M. Coonan, D.M. Gay, K. Hanson, D. Hough, W. Kahan, R. Karpinski, J. Palmer, F.N. Rit, D. Stevenson, *A Proposed Radix- and Word-length-independent Standard for Floating-point Arithmetic*, **IEEE Micro 4**(4), 86–100 (1984).

[Cody, 88] Cody, W.J., *Floating-point Standards: Theory and Practice*, **Reliability in Computing: the Role of Internal Methods in Scientific Computing**, R.E. Moore (ed.), 99–107, Academic Press (1988).

[Coonan, 80] Coonan, Jerome T., *An Implementation Guide to a Proposed Standard for Floating-point Arithmetic*, **IEEE Computer 13**(1), 68–79 (1980).

[Coonan, 84] Coonan, Jerome T., *Contributions to a Proposed Standard for Binary Floating-Point Arithmetic*, Ph.D. Thesis, University of California, Berkeley (1984).

[Dally, 89] Dally, W.J., *Micro-Optimization of Floating-Point Operations*, **Proceedings of the Third International Conference on Architectural Support for Programming Languages and Operating Systems (ASPLOS-III)**, 283–289 (1989). This paper applies RISC concepts to floating-point. If floating-point operations are broken into individual micro-operations, a compiler can optimize by combining redundant normalizations and overlapping some operations.

[Dewar, 90] Dewar, R.B.K, and M. Smosna, *Microprocessors, A Programmer's View*, McGraw-Hill (1990). Chapter 5 covers the IEEE floating-point standard and its implementation by various coprocessors.

[Dobberpuhl, 92] Dobberpuhl, Daniel W., et al., *A 200-MHZ 64-bit Dual-issue CMOS Microprocessor*, **Digital Technical Journal 4**(4), 35–50 (1992)

[Fowler, 89] Fowler, D.L., and J.E. Smith, *An Accurate, High-Speed Implementation of Division by Reciprocal Approximation*, **Proceedings of the Ninth Symposium on Computer Arithmetic**, IEEE Computer Society Press (1989).

[Goldberg, 89] Goldberg, D., *Computer Arithmetic*, Appendix A in [Hennessy, 89]. This appendix describes the reasons for many of the features in the IEEE floating-point standard.

[Goldberg, 91] Goldberg, D., *What Every Computer Scientist Should Know about Floating Point Arithmetic*, **ACM Computing Surveys**, **23**(1), 5–48 (1991).

[Gosling, 83] Gosling, J.B., *Some Tricks of the (Floating-Point) Trade*, **Proceedings of the Sixth Symposium on Computer Arithmetic**, IEEE Computer Society Press, 218-220 (1983).

[Hart, 78] Hart, J.F., E.W. Cheney, C.L. Lawson, H.J. Maehly, C.K. Mesztenyi, J.R. Rice, H.G. Thatcher, and C. Witzgall, *Computer Approximations*, Krieger (1978)

[Hennessy, 89] Hennessy, John and David Paterson, *Computer Architecture, A Quantitative Approach*, Morgan Kaufman (1989).

[Hwang, 79] Hwang, K., *Computer Arithmetic, Principles, Architecture, and Design*, Wiley (1979). This is a good general book on hardware mechanisms for both fixed-point and floating-point arithmetic.

[IEEE, 85] *IEEE Standard for Binary Floating-Point Arithmetic*, **ANSI/IEEE Standard 754-1985**, IEEE (1985). This document defines the IEEE floating-point standard. It specifies the required formats, operations, rounding, and exceptions. It does not explain the reasons for these choices.

[Johnstone, 89] Johnstone, P., and F.E. Petry, *Higher Radix Floating-point Representation*, **Proceedings of the Ninth Symposium on Computer Arithmetic**, IEEE Computer Society Press, 128–135 (1989). Proposes a decimal-radix system.

[Kahan, 65] Kahan, W., *Further Remarks on Reducing Truncation Errors*, **Communications of the ACM 8**, 40 (1965). Gives software methods for reducing the effects of floating-point truncation.

[Kahan, 66] Kahan, W., *7094-II System Support for Numerical Analysis*, **SHARE Secretarial Distribution SSD-159** (1966). A software package that included some of the features later incorporated into the IEEE floating-point standard.

[Knuth, 81] Knuth, D.E., *The Art of Computer Programming: Seminumerical Algorithms*, volume 2, 2nd ed., Addison-Wesley (1981). Section 4.2 is on Floating-point arithmetic. The emphasis is on software algorithms.

[Koren, 93] Koren, I., *Computer Arithmetic Algorithms*, Prentice-Hall (1993). This recent text includes four chapters on fast algorithms for addition, multiplication, and division.

[Mason, 87] Mason, R., *The Design of a Modular CMOS Adder and Adder/Subtracter to Support 25 MHz Operation for Data of Up to 32 Bits*, MSEE Thesis, Northeastern University, Boston (1987).

[MC68030, 89] Motorola, *MC68030 Enhanced 32-bit Microprocessor User's Manual*, 2nd ed., Prentice-Hall (1989). Chapter 10 is a description of the coprocessor interface, with sufficient detail for the design of a coprocessor. Actual coprocessors use only a subset of the features described in this chapter.

[MC68881, 87] Motorola, *MC68881/MC68882 Floating-Point Coprocessor User's Manual*, Prentice-Hall (1987). This manual describes two IEEE standard coprocessors designed primarily to work with the MC68020 and MC68030 processors. It includes a description of the protocol used in communicating with the CPU.

[Olsson, 90] Olsson, B., R. Montoye, P. Markstein, and M. Nguyen Phu, *RISC System/6000 Floating-Point Unit*, **IBM RISC System/6000 Technology**, 34-43, IBM, 1990.

[Plauger, 92] Plauger, P.J., *The Standard C Library*, Prentice-Hall (1992). This is a superb standard reference for anyone programming in C. It includes a wide variety of functions serving the needs of floating-point programs.

[Santoro, 89] Santoro, M.R., G. Bewick, and M.A. Horowitz, *Rounding Algorithms for IEEE Multipliers*, **Proceedings of the Ninth Symposium on Computer Arithmetic**, IEEE Computer Society Press, 176–183 (1989).

[Sterbenz, 74] Sterbenz, P.H., *Floating-Point Computation*, Prentice-Hall (1974). Although primarily about software considerations in floating-point arithmetic, this book does include a chapter on hardware. It also includes chapters on overflow and underflow, rounding, error analysis, double precision, and radix conversion.

[Swartzlander, 90] Swartzlander, E.E., *Computer Arithmetic*, 2 vols., IEEE Computer Society Press (1990). Two collections of important papers about computer arithmetic. Volume I was originally published in 1980 by Dowden, Hutchinson and Ross.

[Sweeney, 65] Sweeney, D.W., *An Analysis of Floating-Point Addition*, **IBM Systems Journal 4**(1), 31–42 (1965).

[Thornton, 70] Thornton, J.E., *Design of a Computer: The Control Data 6600*, Scott Foresman (1970).

[Ulrich, 90] Ullrich, C., ed., *Computer Arithmetic and Self-Validating Numerical Methods*, Academic Press (1990). Many of the papers in this conference were about interval arithmetic.

[Wallace, 64] Wallace, C.S., *A Suggestion for a Fast Multiplier*, **IEEE Transactions on Electronic Computers EC-13**(1), 14–17 (1964). An array multiplier built with a tree of adders. Also discusses converging algorithms for division and square root, which can take advantage of a very fast multiplier.

[Walther, 71] Walther, J.S., *A Unified Algorithm for Elementary Functions*, **Proceedings of the 1971 Spring Joint Computer Conference**, 379–385, AFIPS Press (1971). Describes CORDIC algorithms (COordinate Rotation DIgital Computer) to perform multiplication, division, square root, logarithms, exponentials, and trigonometric functions.

[Zuse, 36] Zuse, K., *Method for Automatic Execution of Calculations with the Aid of Computers*, **patent application Z 23 139 IX/42 m** (April 11, 1936). Reprinted in *The Origins of digital computers: selected papers*, Brian Randell (ed.), 3rd ed., Springer-Verlag, (1982). Describes a relay computer using floating-point arithmetic, radix-2 with a hidden bit.

APPENDIX I

DETAILS ON INTEGER MULTIPLICATION AND DIVISION

For simplicity and clarity, all of the examples worked in this appendix use 8-bit numbers and 8-bit registers. However, the methods are completely general and work identically (except for length) with the 32-bit registers that are used in the actual design.

I.1 MULTIPLICATION

Let us consider an example of 8-bit words which will illustrate the problem. Let us laboriously multiply two positive numbers, 3 × 11, in binary and then see how we can speed up the repetitive steps by taking advantage of inherent parallelism:

```
       00000011   multiplicand
       00001011   multiplier
---------------
       00000011
      00000011
     00000000
    00000011
   00000000
  00000000
 00000000
00000000
---------------
000000000100001   product
```

There are eight additions of *partial products* to form *partial sums*. While we think of the operation as adding columns of numbers, the machine would start with a 0 sum and add each partial product as it was formed. Some economies result from the fact that the multiplicand and multiplier are both positive and that the bit which hangs over on the right need not be added but just carried through. The bottom row is 0 and can be ignored. The leftmost two bits of the product must be 0. Since seven passes through the adder is rather slow, the sums could be done with an obvious appeal to maximum parallelism by grouping the pairs and adding them as three parallel additions (plus the seventh line), then summing the four in two parallel adders, and finally summing the last output. We cannot "reuse" the adders if we want the process to go as fast as possible. In the first place, we do not want to latch the answers in the middle. In the second, the width of adders increases as we progress through the layers. Accordingly, the speed of the first layer of four is faster than the speed of the second layer of two, which in turn is faster than the lowest layer. We would need six adders to do this operation. How much have we saved over a single adder? A single adder would have to be cycled seven times and have the same speed as the top layer in our proposed array. On ripple adders, the speed is inversely proportional to width. The delay in carry-skip adders so popular in CMOS VLSI increases as $\sqrt{32n} - 4$ [Koren, 93]. The delay is not really a smooth function of n, but it is an approximation which will serve well enough. Using the 8-bit adder as unity, the first stage of 8-bit adders will take 1 unit of time; the next layer of 10-bit adders will require 1.30 times as much; and the last stage of a 15-bit adder will take 1.49 times as long. The sum total is 3.87 unit adds. The single-stage adder will require latching between adds. That adds a modest amount of settle and propagate time, perhaps 10 percent of an 8-bit add time. The array of adders need not be latched except at the end. Thus, we must add eight latch times to the single-stage adder and one to the three-stage version. The ratio of times will be 7.7/3.50 = 2.2. Thus, for what is obviously a considerable expenditure in gates, we have achieved a substantial if not overwhelming speedup.

For 32 bits, we go from 3 to 5 layers and from 6 to 30 adders. The speedup is roughly 6 times, and the size/cost of the unit by 31 times. This is getting a little absurd. First, let it be said that there are better algorithms for multiplying nonnegative numbers. One of them is addressed in Section 9.5.4. It uses a *carry-save* adder which is extremely fast and which can be cascaded very effectively. While array multipliers enjoy some popularity where fast multiplication is a critical necessity, our point here is to show that it can be done if you really want to spend your money that way. Our first question should be: Do we want to devote so much chip area to integer multiplication in our slim, trim machine? The answer is, as usual, a definite maybe. Integer multiplication per se is rather uncommon. That would suggest that we should look at the best multiplier that we can make—hardware or software—using the basic integer ALU that we have. On the other hand, multiplication is as common as addition in floating-point arithmetic. Where floating point is dominant, exceptional measures may be well justified. The MUL instruction is not used enough to make it worthwhile for us to put that much of our resources into this instruction. For FPMUL, we have a different answer.

Once we have pulled back from going for broke, we have two other levels that we can consider. One is the pure software approach, with shift and add repeated enough times to finish the task. This approach is slow—slow enough to make a noticeable impact on some program speeds even with the relative infrequency of MUL. What we can do is provide an inexpensive hardware boost to the software that will make it fast enough. Without spending a great deal, we can provide a combination of shift and add that will accomplish one, two, or, stretching somewhat harder, three lines above in our single clock cycle. The additional hardware required includes:

- A single multiplier/quotient register—MQ—which can shift its contents (rightward in this case) and bring in from the left the rightmost bit of the sum. This special register will be one of our regular set of 32, capable of doing all normal operations. Only on MUL (and DIV) will it do something special.
- A 33rd and possibly a 34th bit on the adder and shifter.
- A small addition to the gate array which accomplishes instruction interpretation.
- Possibly some extra shift layers (if the main barrel shifter is not in line with the adder).

From fourth grade on you have shifted left on each partial product to account for the place value of the multiplier's digit. Recognizing the inherent difficulty in opening up space to the left in a register of fixed length, we will replace the left shifts of the partial products above with a right shift of the partial sum (PS) after each addition. To avoid having to provide an extra register to pick up the low-order bits carried out of PS to the right, we can take advantage of the fact that the multiplier gets used up at just the rate that we are shifting those low-order bits to the right. With that observation, the multiplication operation for 16 bits with *nonnegative numbers* is essentially this little C program (note that the answer returned is 32 bits wide):

```
unsigned long mul(unsigned short x, unsigned short y) {
    unsigned short mq, cand, ps, n;
    unsigned long product;

    mq = x;                              /* multiplier into MQ */
    cand = y;                            /* multiplicand entered */
    ps = 0;                              /* clear partial sum */
    for (n = 0; n<16; n++) {
        if (mq & 1) ps = ps + cand;      /* add if LO multiplier bit is 1 */
        mq = mq >> 1;                    /* unsigned right shift brings in 0 */
        mq = mq | ((ps & 1) <<15);       /* bring over rightmost bit of PS in HO bit of MQ */
        ps = ps >> 1;                    /* now shift the partial sum */
        ps = ps & 0x8000;                /* if shift brought in a 1, clear it. */
        }
    product = ps;
    return((product << 16) | mq);
    }
```

Hardware can speed up this short section of code by providing the combined operations of testing the rightmost bit of *mq* and providing an *add-and-shift* or *shift* operation based on the outcome of that test. Such an arrangement is shown in Figure I.1.

The problem with both the hand and hardware methods is that they do not work directly with negative numbers. To do negative numbers with these methods, you must do what you do on paper: make the routine generate all positive numbers, do multiplication as in Figure I.1, and then correctly include the sign.

Booth suggested a better way almost as soon as there were real computers to multiply on [Booth, 51]. What he observed was that any binary number can be represented as an *alternating* sequence of powers of 2. Since this is crucial to seeing how this rather neat method works, consider a few simple examples of this Booth recoding shown in Table I.1. The rule in general is:

> Proceeding from right to left and starting with an initial state of 0, shift and count until you find a number of the opposite state. If the transition is from $0 \Rightarrow 1$, then subtract 2 to the power of the count; if the transition is $1 \Rightarrow 0$, then add 2 to the power of the count. Note that this operation must leave a positive number if the leftmost digit is 0 and a negative number if it is 1.

Now what has this to do with multiplication? Simply this: Multiplying by 2^n in a binary-based system is a shift of n places. If we admit both addition and subtraction operations, then any sequence such as those above will represent a series of shifts (the

FIGURE I.1 The single-stage multiplier doing the first line of the accompanying 8-bit multiplication 3×11. Recall that the ALU can, among other things, add its inputs or pass one of them through unchanged. If the partial sum is not 0 at the end, or if the sign bit of MQ is set, the multiplication overflowed (in the sense of not fitting in MQ), but the two registers will together contain the correct product. This example works only for positive numbers.

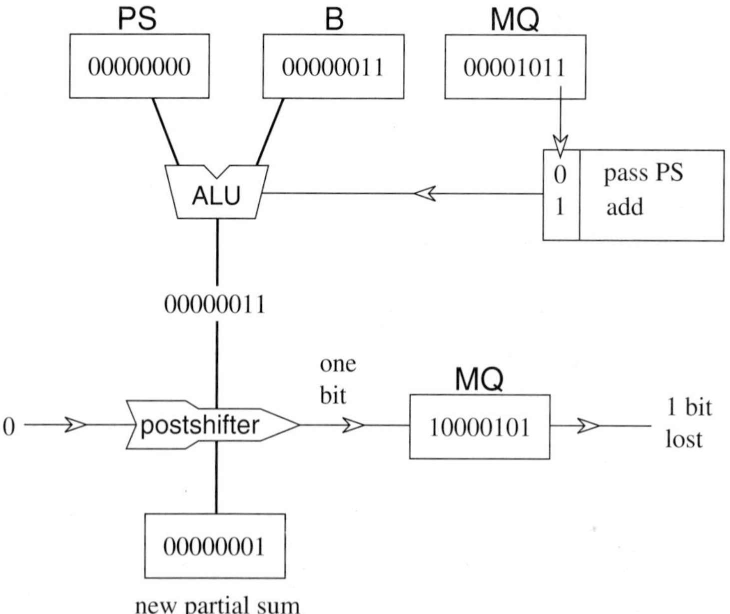

TABLE I.1 Booth recoding of five twos complement numbers

Value	Binary	Sequence
2	0010	$-2^1 + 2^2$
-2	1110	-2^1
4	0100	$-2^2 + 2^3$
6	0110	$+2^3 - 2^1$
-6	1010	$-2^3 + 2^2 - 2^1$

power of 2) followed by either an addition or subtraction of the multiplicand to or from the partial sum. In essence, multiplication by 6 involves subtracting 2 × *multiplicand* and adding 8 × *multiplicand*. It is hard to argue with the fact that that gives 6 × *multiplicand*. Similarly, to multiply by -6, one would subtract 2 × *multiplicand*, add 4 × *multiplicand*, and finally subtract 8 × *multiplicand*. Again, it is hard to argue with the fact that that leaves you with (-6) × *multiplicand*. What is not obvious at this point is how easy it is to achieve this (and even speed it up) in hardware. To this we now turn.

I.1.1 Booth's Algorithm 1 Bit at a Time

To carry out the multiplication using Booth's algorithm, we can use the same basic apparatus as in Figure I.1. All that we must change is the control logic to allow the processor to decide whether it has a transition ($0 \Rightarrow 1$ or $1 \Rightarrow 0$) or not ($0 \Rightarrow 0$ or $1 \Rightarrow 1$) and make the ALU operation appropriate to what it finds. In all cases, it will shift after the arithmetic operation. The whole system is shown in Figure I.2.

The control logic needs to retain the last bit shifted out of MQ. To hang on to that bit, we pass it to the carry bit (rather than any carry which might arise from the addition or subtraction itself).

The control logic has three different outputs. They correspond to the four possible combinations which could be found in traversing the multiplier. For the example of Figure I.2, in multiplying 3 × 11 with 11 as the multiplier, we would subtract in the 0th place, pass in the 1st, add in the 2nd, subtract in the 3rd, and add in the 4th. All of the remaining places are just passes. $(16 - 8 + 4 - 1) = 11$ as advertised. Similarly, multiplying by -6 = 1111 1010, the same logic would result in a pass in the 0th place, a subtraction in the 1st, an add in the 2nd, and a subtraction in the 3rd, followed finally by four passes, yielding $(-8 + 4 - 2) = -6$.

There is a special case if B just happens to have the most negative number possible, 1000 0000 in the 8-bit case above. The problem with that number is that it has no legitimate complement in a register of the same size. In effect, the subtraction overflows.

The cure is simple. Add an extra bit in the ALU. The input bits to that extra line are simply the sign-extensions of the normal inputs. The extra bit on the output becomes the sign bit of the new PS.

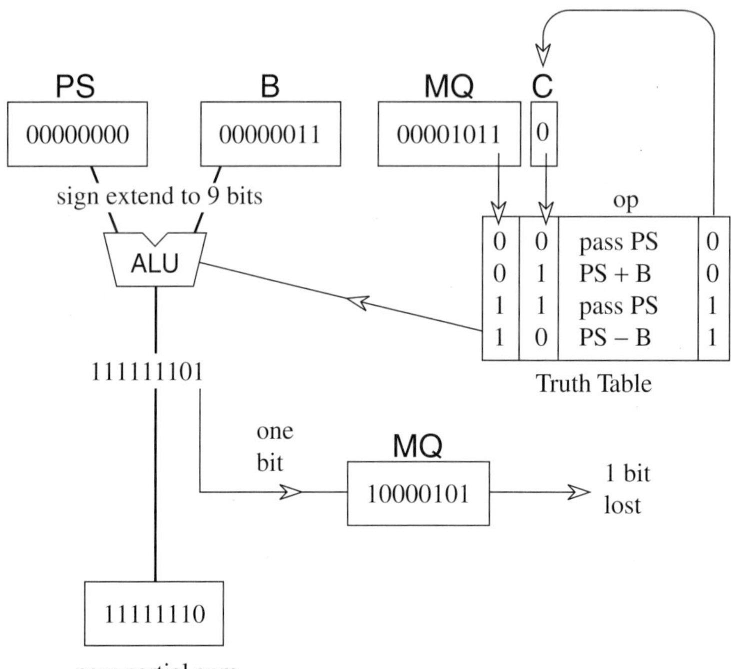

FIGURE I.2 The single-stage Booth's multiplier doing the first line of the 8-bit multiplication 3 × 11. Compare this figure with Figure I.1. The additions include sign-extended operands, a 9-bit ALU, and setting C (the carry) bit according to the truth table (or, more simply, shifting the carry-out of MQ into C). The leftmost eight bits of the ALU's output go back to PS as the new partial sum. The rightmost bit goes into MQ as its most significant bit. Where long strings of 1 or 0 occur, this method saves add/subtract steps, though in our system of a combined adder-shifter above, this would save steps only if we were able to observe long strings of 1's or 0's and do multiple shifts at once.

Note that to set up the multiplication, you must load rB and MQ and then clear PS and C. The clearing can be done in one step by simply executing SUBc PS, PS, PS (n.b., PS is *not* a special register). That done, MUL away.

I.1.2 Booth's Algorithm 2 Bits at a Time

Now for a little speedup on the cheap. If you examine the algorithm above doing 2 bits at a time rather than 1, you have eight combinations of carry and the two end-bits in MQ. It is easy to develop the algorithm. All that you must do is consider going through the 1-bit algorithm twice. For example, a sequence 010 would become 10 followed by 01. From the truth table in Figure I.2, that would correspond to subtract-shift-add or (2×) – (1×), which nets out to be 1×. That, in fact, is what you will find in the truth table at 010 in Figure I.3.

There is one other piece of hardware that we need. When using 2 bits, we have to allow for pass, add/sub once, or add/sub twice. With a base of 2, multiplying by 2 is simply a shift of one place left, so we must install a preshifter in our diagram. This is shown in Figure I.3. The preshifter shifts left by 1 or 0 according to the operation from

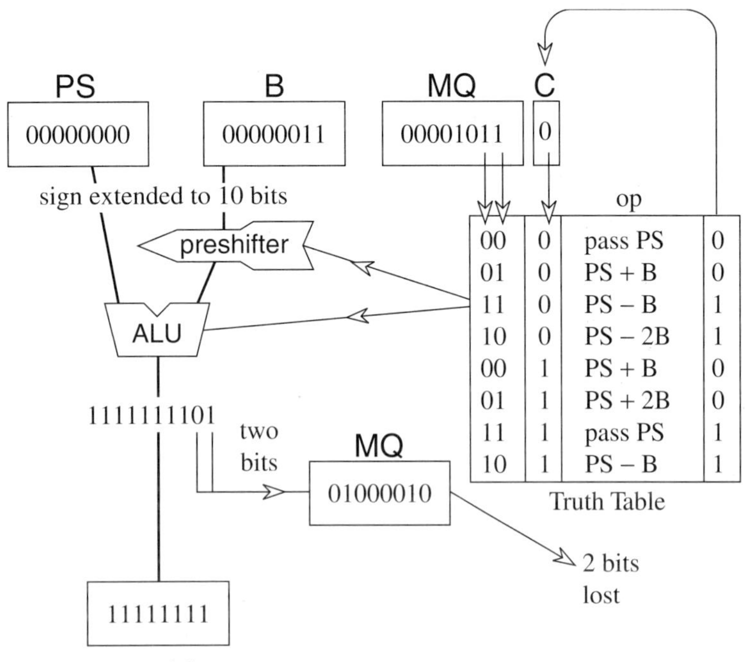

FIGURE I.3 The 2-bit Booth's algorithm as it will be realized in our machine. The last two bits of MQ and the bit stored in the C flag determine the next operation. To do the 8-bit multiplication indicated, MUL would have to be called only four times. The ALU for this case would be 9 bits wide in order to accommodate the multiplicand shifted one place left by the preshifter and then 10 bits wide to accommodate the complement of the most negative number 2 × (-8). Compare this figure in detail to Figure I.2. The numerical result differs only in the result of the 2-bit shift since both operations were PS-B.

the truth table. In going to the 2-bit algorithm, we must add yet one more bit to the ALU (now to 10 bits) and peal two bits off the right side of the result to become the high-order pair of MQ, but that is a small price to pay for a 2× speedup in multiplication. Remember always that our objective is a streamlined design, not a minimalist one.

Exercises for this algorithm are found in the problem set at the end of Chapter 2. Sections 9.5.4 and 9.5.5 discuss the 3-bit Booth's algorithm. Figure I.3 finally is the MUL we will use. What it gives us is a reasonably fast multiplication with very little addition of logic. To do the whole 32-bit multiplication in the shortest possible time, one would encode it by writing 16 successive MULs with no intervening loop. Apart from setup—which depends on where things are at the start—the actual multiplication would take 16 clock pulses, roughly 1.6 μs on our 10 MIPS machine. That is not blazingly fast, but it is not awkwardly slow either. It is at least as fast as the weight of the instruction in normal usage would call for. At that point, we can rest our case.

I.2 DIVISION

DIV is considerably more obdurate than MUL, as your experience in fourth grade undoubtedly revealed to you. The essential problem in division is that you have to guess the next step in the quotient and then correct what you just did if the guessed digit is either too small or too large. With binary numbers, the range of possible guesses reaches rock bottom—1 or 0—which presents an opportunity for simplification, but nothing nearly so neat as Booth's algorithm has emerged. While algorithms for doing signed, twos-complement division do exist, they do not save steps or hardware over separating sign determination from the division itself. As a consequence, they are not much used, and we choose to ignore them entirely.

What we will do instead is consider the division of positive numbers only and leave it up to the program to determine the sign of the result and to feed the DIV instruction with purely positive numbers.

This still leaves us with a choice that is unique to radix-2 numbers. In other bases, you try a test value for the next digit, go through the subtraction, look at the remainder, and decide whether to raise, lower, or stick with the guess. If you are writing with pencil or chalk, you simply erase any rejected intermediate steps, thus restoring the previous state.

In a radix-2 system, we begin with 1 as the "guess"; we can judge if we are wrong by whether the sign of the remainder is negative. If it is, we have subtracted too much. Now two choices are in front of us:

1. We could simply add back what we just subtracted (an extra step or, alternatively, an extra path to preserve the original dividend), guess 0 for that digit (no guess at all!), and go on to the next digit. Such a method is called *restoring* division.
2. Alternatively, we could recognize that we overdid it, put a 0 into the quotient, and go on to the next digit, keeping in mind that we have overdrawn on our account. To repay the overdraft, we proceed by adding the divisor to the remainder and continue doing so in each successive step until the sign of the remainder turns positive again. We have continued adding zeros to the right side of the quotient until the sign of the remainder finally swings positive. At that point, we have paid back our excess on the first subtraction, so we put a 1 into the quotient. Note that we never paused to restore the dividend. Hence this method is called *nonrestoring* division.

There is one finishing touch that comes up in nonrestoring division—the remainder. Remainder is an essential part of integer division. The operator MOD in Pascal or "%" in C delivers the integer remainder. In restoring integer division, the remainder is what is left after you have subtracted the last full divisor. It is of the same sign as the dividend, so in our case, it will be + until we account for the original signs. In nonrestoring division, we might end up with a little surplus or a little deficit; both signs of remainder are possible. When a negative remainder occurs, it really means that we still have (1-*rem*) to repay. Accordingly, *if the remainder is negative*, the true remainder is found simply by adding the divisor to the negative apparent remainder.

Let us see an explicit pair of 8-bit examples. Let us divide 19 by 5 and 4. The mechanics of the operation comprise:

1. B $\Leftarrow$ | dividend |, REM $\Leftarrow$ 0
2. Think of REM:B as a 16-bit dividend. Each step will involve

a. shifting the dividend *left*
b. adding or subtracting the divisor (add if dividend < 0)
c. replacing the last bit of MQ with the complement of the sign bit

In our 8-bit example, the first subtraction determines the 128ths place of the quotient. Since we are admitting only positive numbers into our divider and since the largest 8-bit positive number is 127, we have guaranteed that the first bit (which is the sign bit of the quotient) will be 0. After that, anything can happen. The steps are shown in Table I.2 for the two examples. One yields a negative remainder, the other a positive one. The integral symbol ∫ separates the rightmost digit of the dividend from the leftmost digit of the quotient. Once again, we are shifting in the opposite direction to which you were indoctrinated in fourth grade. The bit shifted out to the left is inevitably simply a redundant sign bit.

An important restriction crept in without much notice. What we have done is limited the dividend to 8 bits. Having done so, there are no restrictions on the divisor (other than the usual proscription on *dividing by zero*, although even that "works" in the sense of terminating at the end of eight cycles with a known answer). While it is true that one can divide a 16-bit dividend by an 8-bit divisor to get an 8-bit quotient and remainder, you must be able to guarantee that the divisor is larger than twice the upper 8 bits of the dividend. If the user will guarantee that condition, the hardware will work just as we have shown in Table I.2. No other restrictions apply. To include a check on the user's adherence to this rule (we will not do it in hardware), one must check that the first subtraction yields a negative result, thus fixing the leftmost digit of the quotient as a 0. If that digit is a 1, the divide *overflows*.

Control is as easy as with Booth's algorithm. A negative REM implies *add*; a positive REM implies *subtract*. We never look back. This makes it particularly easy to work in hardware. Without much ado, we can make the hardware of Figure I.3 do a nonrestoring division step. The principal additions to the MUL hardware are another preshifter (now on the A side of the ALU) and the requirement that MQ be able to shift left as well as right. These are shown in Figure I.4.

The setup for the DIV is the same as in MUL except for the requirement that flag N at the start be 0. The setup is accomplished by loading a (positive) divisor into rB, a (positive) dividend into MQ, and then clearing rREM by subtraction, SUBc rREM, rREM, rREM. This clears not only rREM but N as well. Follow that with eight DIVs (or 32 in the real machine) and you have your quotient in the MQ and the integer remainder in rREM. If rREM is negative, the correct remainder is obtained by doing ADDx rREM, rB, rREM. (Of course, if the original signs of divisor and dividend were not the same, then the positive quotient must then be negated. The remainder should be given the sign of the dividend.)

As in MUL, rREM is both source and destination and MQ (r28) is implied in the instruction. The format for the instruction is

```
DIV rREM, rB, rREM
```

TABLE I.2 Nonrestoring division for $\frac{19}{5}$ and $\frac{19}{4}$

19/5	REM	MQ	19/4	REM	MQ
start	0000 0000	0001 0011	start	0000 0000	0001 0011
⇐	0000 0000	0010 011ʃx	⇐	0000 0000	0010 011ʃx
−	0000 0101		−	0000 0100	
x = 0	1111 1011	0010 011ʃ0	x = 0	1111 1100	0010 011ʃ0
⇐	1111 0110	0100 11ʃ0x	⇐	1111 1000	0100 11ʃ0x
+	0000 0101		+	0000 0100	
x = 0	1111 1011	0100 11ʃ00	x = 0	1111 1100	0100 11ʃ00
⇐	1111 0110	1001 1ʃ00x	⇐	1111 1000	1001 1ʃ00x
+	0000 0101		+	0000 0100	
x = 0	1111 1011	1001 1ʃ000	x = 0	1111 1100	1001 1ʃ000
⇐	1111 0111	0011 ʃ000x	⇐	1111 1001	0011 ʃ000x
+	0000 0101		+	0000 0100	
x = 0	1111 1100	0011 ʃ0000	x = 0	1111 1101	0011 ʃ0000
⇐	1111 1000	011ʃ0 000x	⇐	1111 1010	011ʃ0 000x
+	0000 0101		+	0000 0100	
x = 0	1111 1101	011ʃ0 0000	x = 0	1111 1110	011ʃ0 0000
⇐	1111 1010	11ʃ00 000x	⇐	1111 1100	11ʃ00 000x
+	0000 0101		+	0000 0100	
x = 0	1111 1111	11ʃ00 0000	x = 1	0000 0000	11ʃ00 0001
⇐	1111 1111	1ʃ000 000x	⇐	0000 0001	1ʃ000 001x
+	0000 0101		−	0000 0100	
x = 1	0000 0100	1ʃ000 0001	x = 0	1111 1101	1ʃ000 0010
⇐	0000 1001	ʃ0000 001x	⇐	1111 1011	ʃ0000 010x
−	0000 0101		+	0000 0100	
x = 1	0000 0100	ʃ0000 0011	x = 0	1111 1111	ʃ0000 0100

The issue of overflow arises not only if the user chooses to put something $\geq 2 \times$ *divisor* into REM but also if the divisor is the most negative of integers. Since we allow only positive numbers in the actual DIV steps, the routine must convert initially negative values to their positive equivalent. In the conversion itself, an overflow will result for the most negative number (1 followed by all 0's) which has no positive equivalent.

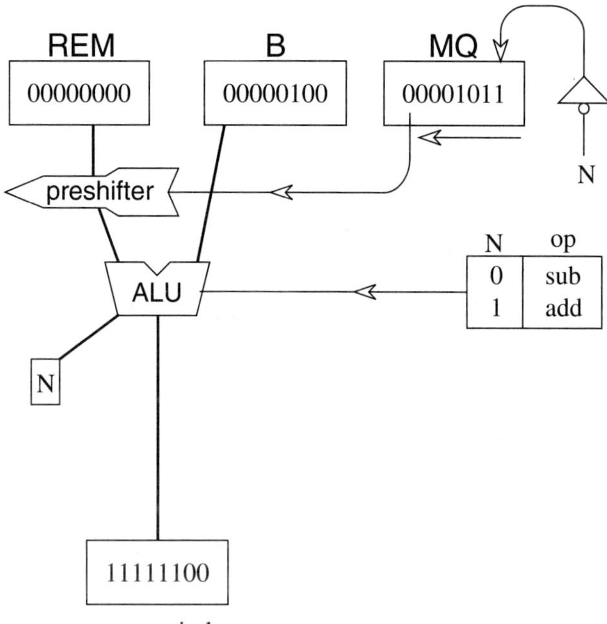

FIGURE I.4 The DIV operation, using much of the same apparatus that was used for MUL. The preshifter operates on the eight bits of the remainder. It shifts one place left, bringing in the leftmost bit of the MQ register and simply ignoring the bit shifted out. The ALU performs an ADD or SUB according to N (negative flag) from the last step. The operation generates a new N bit. The MQ is shifted left by 1 bit, bringing in the complement of the (new) N flag. At the end of eight DIVs, the apparent remainder is in REM and the quotient in MQ. If REM < 0, then the true remainder is B + REM; otherwise, it is REM.

Note, however, that the overflow occurs when the negative number is subtracted from 0 to form the positive version, not when the division itself is conducted. The following C function performs the full task of 64-bit integer division, calling on a routine called *trap* to handle overflow problems. Note the overhead of dealing with the possibility of 64-bit dividends.

```
#include <stdio.h>
#include <stdlib.h>

#define bigneg     0x80000000
void trap(int x) {
    exit(x);                                /* something more would be called for */
}

int divide(int *rem, int dvdnd, int divisor){
    unsigned int n, ps, div, mq;
    int temp, sign, cx;
```

```
if (divisor == bigneg) trap(33);          /* unworkable in 32-bit registers */
                                          /* make all working numbers positive */
if (dvdnd == 0){
    sign = (*rem & bigneg) ^ (divisor & bigneg);
    if (*rem < 0) mq = -*rem;
    else mq = *rem;
    ps = 0;
    }
else {
    sign = (dvdnd & bigneg) ^ (divisor & bigneg);
    if (dvdnd < 0){                       /* 64-bit sign change ... careful! */
        ps = ps ^ -1;                     /* 1's complement */
        mq = (*rem ^ -1) + 1;             /* 2's complement */
        if (!mq) ps + = 1;                 /* complete carry */
        }
    else {
        ps = dvdnd;
        mq = *rem;
        }
    }
if (divisor < 0) div = -divisor;
else div = divisor;

if ((ps<<1)((mq & bigneg)>>31) >= div) trap(32);     /* check for overflow */
n = ps & bigneg;                                     /* initialize n bit */

for (cx=0; cx<32; cx++){
    ps = (ps << 1) + ((mq & bigneg) >> 31);          /* 64-bit shift */
    mq = mq<<1;
    if (n) ps += div;
    else ps -= div;
    n = ps & bigneg;                      /* grab sign bit */
    mq += (n==0);                         /* complement of n to rightmost bit in mq */
    }
if (ps > bigneg) ps += div;               /* correct for deficit in remainder*/
if (divisor < 0) *rem = -ps;
else *rem = ps;
temp = mq;                                /* convert to signed integer */
return (sign ? -temp, temp)
}
```

The actual division is not an overwhelmingly significant part of the program, especially if you think of the loop being unrolled into 32 DIV instructions. Since the rest of the code is necessary to handle all possibilities, the only way to greatly accelerate DIV would be to put all of the steps surrounding the DIV part into a hardware divider. A good exercise at this point is convert this C program into assembly language. For speed, use 32 DIVs and no loop. Then compare the weight of DIV to the rest of the overhead, giving some reasonable probability for each branch operation. If the weights roughly match, we have a reasonable balance.

REFERENCES

[Booth, 51] Booth, A.D., *A Signed Binary Multiplication Technique*, **Quarterly Journal of Mechanical and Applied Mathematics 4**, 236–240 (1951).

[Koren, 93] Koren, Israel, *Computer Arithmetic Algorithms*, Prentice-Hall, 1993.

APPENDIX II

SPREADSHEET SOLUTION OF THE BUS TRANSIENT

II.1 THE BASIC CONCEPT

Describing how to solve bus transients on a spreadsheet without the spreadsheet would be equivalent to describing how to ride a bicycle without the bicycle—useless. This appendix presumes that you have available the software which accompanies the text. In the later sections, which get quite specific about the spreadsheet, as you read the text, you should bring the spreadsheet up on a processor and examine the formulas and the evaluation of the formulas right on the spreadsheet. The example will be in EXCEL for the Macintosh.

The classical solution to the traveling wave problem is in the form shown in Equation (8.2). It has a time-and-position relationship of the form

$$e^{j(\omega t - kx)}$$

We can represent this time-and-position relationship on a spreadsheet by having distance represented by column number and time by row number. In other words, distance along the line increases from left to right while time increases from top to bottom. Each row should be thought of as a photograph showing the distribution of some waves at a particular moment of time; each column can be thought of as a strip chart or oscillogram showing the voltage at a particular point as a function of time. Easy concepts, but since these are waves, values travel diagonally downward across the spreadsheet; adjacent columns are coupled.

If all you want to do is let waves travel back and forth, reflecting at several points on resistive terminations, as in Figure 8.3 on page 413, the "photos" and "strip charts" are simple to lay out. The value at some place and time is simply the sum of values at some other points and previous times. Spreadsheets are superb at doing such calculations. The problem (and the interest) arises, at least for us, if the terminations or *loads* on the line are capacitive. Capacitive loads are the norm in computer applications. It is not that the designers want capacitive loads; they just get them. These loads are the input capacities of receivers or the output capacities of drivers. When working with loaded lines as depicted in Figure 8.6 on page 416, we must represent the capacitive loads by differential equations. On an incremental basis, a capacitor is a *voltage source*—another way of saying that the voltage across a capacitor cannot change instantaneously. At such a termination, one can say that the incoming wave sees a *short circuit* and thus reflects in its entirety. Thus, the capacitive loading effectively isolates the different segments of the line. The only "communication" between segments is through the charging of the capacitance. The wave itself never travels past the capacitance on either side of a segment. It is trapped. Since the incoming wave sees a "short," the reflected wave has equal magnitude and opposite sign. This means that if the incoming wave carries current V_{in}/Z_0, the outgoing reflected wave will, because it is going in the opposite direction, also carry current V_{in}/Z_0, leading to a charging current of

$$\frac{2V_{\text{in}}}{Z_0} \tag{II.1}$$

This charging of the capacitor changes the voltage wave generated by the capacitor, thus allowing the wave in one segment to eventually influence the wave in the adjacent segment.

The capacitor's voltage is given by

$$V_C = \left(\frac{1}{C}\right)\int i_C dt \tag{II.2}$$

The only problem with this is that we must approximate the integral by numerical methods. While there are neat methods for this, such as Runga-Kutta quadrature, we will use a particularly simple approximation due originally to Euler. We will say that

$$\Delta V = \left(\frac{i}{C}\right)\Delta t \tag{II.3}$$

This will yield results that are accurate only to the extent that i is sensibly constant during Δt. To meet that standard, we must make the time difference between rows, Δt, small. "Small" means that the change in i during the interval is of the order of a few percent or less.

Just as there is an essential equivalence between time and position in the propagation expression, so in the spreadsheet, if you want to increase the time resolution, you must also increase the spatial resolution. While this sounds as if we would be dealing with spreadsheets which grow as $1/\Delta t^2$, it is not necessary to represent all of the intermediate points in the line, only those representing transitions. This is a fixed, small number. Accordingly, the spreadsheet grows only as $1/\Delta t$.

We begin by dividing the length of the line into n sections of equal length; each section is one unit delay time from its neighbor. At the speed of light, with a line 0.5 m long, that makes each unit

$$\Delta t = \frac{0.5}{0.3 \times n} \text{ ns} \tag{II.4}$$

from its nearest neighbors. In practice, we have used n's of 40 or greater, so we can deal well with problems where the Δt must be less than 0.04 ns. How will we know if Δt is short enough? One can be very analytic and look at the rates of change of the capacitor voltages, but by experience, we have found that there is a rather sharp break between the "reasonable" waveforms one obtains when the integration is accurate enough and essentially unstable performance when it is not.

In bus definitions, as illustrated in Figure 8.5 on page 416, the slots are uniformly spaced. We will want a fine subdivision which is commensurate with this gross division. For our 0.5-m line, we chose to break up the line into eight equal segments, 0 … 7 with the slot in the middle of the section. We let each section be N units long, where N is any even number. If we make the whole line 128 steps long, slot 0 is at 8, slot 1 is at 24, and so forth. Terminations are at 0 and 128. We chose arbitrarily to fill four slots—0, 3, 4, and 6, as shown in Figure II.2 on page 563.

We need not represent each step or even every section in the spreadsheet. It is certainly true that, in the absence of discontinuities in the line, what is at the point x now was at points $x \pm m \times \Delta t / c$ m units of time ago. If every point were on the spreadsheet, that would simply be m steps sideways and m steps up. Or, if we leave out the *uninteresting* columns, it might be 1 step sideways and m steps up. By leaving out the uninteresting columns, we can drastically reduce the dimensions of the spreadsheet. All that we must represent on the spreadsheet are the filled slots and the terminations, places where there are impedance changes causing reflections and sources causing wave generation.

What we now must do is "handle the details." We will use the Futurebus as our illustration.

II.2 DEVELOPING THE CELL FORMULAS

In Equation (8.7), we got expressions for transmission and reflection coefficients. In Figure II.1 we show the two components from which we will construct the model of the transmission line. Combinations of these two components would be joined by simple pieces of transmission line, but since these sections of line represent only a delay, we will not devote columns to represent them. What we wish to do is to develop appropriate cell formulas for these two configurations. It is really rather direct.

Let us start with the end termination. The constant supply voltage will provide a constant outgoing wave of

$$V_{CC} \times \frac{Z_0}{Z_0 + Z_t} \equiv V_{CC} \times div \tag{II.5}$$

where the expression on the right shows the variables defined on the spreadsheet. To the outgoing wave from the voltage supply must be added the reflection of the incident wave

$$V_{\text{in}} \times \frac{Z_t - Z_0}{Z_t + Z_0} \equiv V_{\text{in}} \times ref \tag{II.6}$$

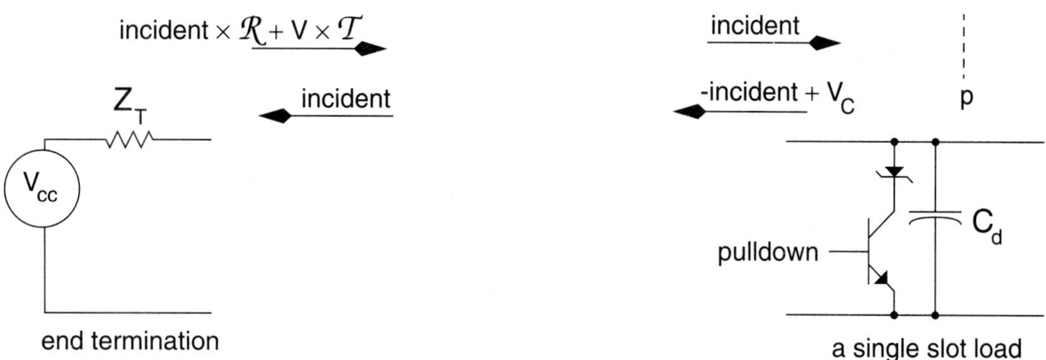

FIGURE II.1 The two different types of termination points for the loaded bus. On the left is an end termination comprising a pullup resistor and a voltage source. On the right is a slot load comprising a capacitor and a pulldown transistor represented by current, i_d., when asserted (Figure 8.7 with V_d displaced right 0.25 V for the Schottky diode) and by an open circuit when deasserted.

There is only one variable in this pair of equations, V_{in}, a variable which is just a cell in an adjacent column and some rows up. Just as in HLL programming, you calculate the constants outside of the cells to avoid repetition of the calculation. (Remember that there is no compiler to remove constant subexpressions!) The only thing conspicuously not present in Equations (II.5) and (II.6) is the rule for specifying the appropriate cell. That is not difficult in principle but we delay for a moment getting started and look first at times beyond $t = 0$.

Let us take a first look at how one can express Equations (II.5) and (II.6) directly on the spreadsheet. If you have the software available, open the file *futurebus sim* which will bring up both files needed for the simulation. To begin with, one *names* the coefficients. This is best done using two cells, the defining expression itself in one and the name of the variable directly above it. You then click on the lower of the cells and select *define name* and you can use the name in the upper cell to mean the contents of the lower cell. With the coefficients named, the two equations on the left side get set into the spreadsheet as shown in Table II.1. The three columns there represent the waves on the line at the left termination.

TABLE II.1 Formulas in the first three columns of the spreadsheet

	A	B	C
8	L	R	SUM
82	=IF(ROW(A73)>=delay_1,OFFSET(D$9,ROW(F73)-delay_1,0),D$9)	=VCC*Div+A82*ref	=A82+B82
83	=IF(ROW(A74)>=delay_1,OFFSET(D$9,ROW(F74)-delay_1,0),D$9)	=VCC*Div+A83*ref	=A83+B83
84	=IF(ROW(A75)>=delay_1,OFFSET(D$9,ROW(F75)-delay_1,0),D$9)	=VCC*Div+A84*ref	=A84+B84

The labels on the outside are column and row labels. Row 8 contains column titles. The simulation itself begins in row 9. We have chosen three rows in the middle. Column A, which is the wave going to the left at the left termination, shows explicitly how one simulates the transmission delay function; column B expresses the sum of Equations (II.5) and (II.6) which is the wave going to the right. Finally, column C presents the voltage at this point in space and time, being the sum of the two cells to the left. In Excel notation, the leading "=" should be read, "This cell equals ..." Let us begin with column B. The term **A83** is V_{in}, the wave coming from the left at time represented by the 83rd row. The other terms are as named in the equations. These named variables are, of course, defined in other cells not shown. Notice that as you step down the column, the value of **An** tracks the row number. You do not have to write all of these in (or no one would use spreadsheets.) Cells copied down automatically increment the row number; cells copied right automatically increment the column number. If you do not want a cell specifier to change, you precede it with a "$" as in column A.

The transmission delay function of column A is initially a bit more formidable, but it really says exactly what we should expect. The function **ROW(A83)** returns 83. **Delay_1** is the time (in cell steps) that it takes a wave to propagate from the first occupied slot to the left termination. In this simulation, **Delay_1** = 8. The function **OFFSET(***base cell, row displacement, column displacement***)** is the spreadsheet version of base-displacement addressing. The function **IF(test, if true, if false)** simply accounts for the fact that the events of interest begin at t = 0 (row 9) but the waves arriving before t = 8 steps all were on the way before t = 0. The **if false** value is always the value from row 9. Once the **test** is true, **OFFSET()** delivers successive cells in the column. This is the desired delayed action-at-a-distance that we wanted.

What one normally wants to see in a spreadsheet is the values, not the formulas. These are provided for rows 82 through 85 in Table II.2. We deliberately used the rows where the termination first finds out about the pullup. Thus, rows 82 and 83 show no change, and then, in 84 and 85 the voltage begins to rise. This, by the way, is the spreadsheet that was used to generate the Futurebus pullup of Figure 8.10 on page 423 and you are looking at the pullup resistor beyond C_0, which is the last to discover the pullup. The time associated with row 84 is 0.98 ns.

The capacitively loaded slot with or without pulldown is only slightly more elaborate. Let us consider it first without the pulldown (i.e., the transistor is off). We will have incident waves coming from both sides. Each will be inverted and reflected. To

TABLE II.2 Evaluation of the cells in Table II.1

	A	B	C
82	-0.4518034	1.36856436	0.91676096
83	-0.4518034	1.36856436	0.91676096
84	-0.4516546	1.36853278	0.91687823
85	-0.4512274	1.36844218	0.91721476

that, we must add, as part of the outgoing wave, the capacitor voltage. (Note that since the incident wave's voltage is precisely canceled by the reflected wave, the incoming and outgoing waves add up to the voltage on the capacitor. How convenient!)

We are assuming that the capacitor voltage is sensibly constant over the time interval represented by a row. Accordingly, we take as that voltage the V_C of the row above. Then we determine the new V_C by the formula

$$V_C(n+1) = V_C(n) - \frac{\Delta t}{C_d}\Sigma i(n) = V_C - \frac{2dt}{Z_0 C_d} \times (V_C - V_{\text{incident left}} - V_{\text{incident right}}) \qquad \text{(II.7)}$$

where collecting terms gives

$$V_C(n+1) = \alpha(V_{\text{incident left}} - V_{\text{incident right}}) + \beta V_C \qquad \text{(II.8)}$$

To add the pulldown transistor, all one has to do is to add the extra current term $I_d(\text{pulldown type}, V_d)$ to (II.8). The set of cell formulas which result is shown in Table II.3 and evaluated in Table II.4.

The first two columns are similar to those in Table II.1, with a delayed wave traveling to the right and being reflected to the left with the addition of the wave generated by the capacitance. A mirror image of these formulas would be found in columns S and T. However, the two mirrored delay functions would have different delay constants, allowing quite different waves to build up. Column R is the combination of pulldown transistor and capacitance shown in the right on Figure II.1. It has only one term that is different from column C in Table II.1, the drop in voltage due to the pulldown current, I_d. The transistor is described by the IF( ) statement as either *on* with current I_d or *off* with current 0. The Boolean variable in the cell labeled **pulldown** determines which state is used. The function which generates the correct current for I_d is on a *macro sheet* called *Ipull* which is connected to the main worksheet through the "workbook," the file named *Futurebus sim*. Accordingly, if you look on the actual spreadsheet $I_d()$ bears the awesome handle

```
'[Futurebus sim]Ipull'!Id(1,R81)
```

TABLE II.3 Formulas from three columns at slot 4, the drive slot

	P	Q	R
8	**L**	**R**	**drive**
82	=R82-Q82	=IF(ROW(W73)>=delay_3,OFFSET(N$9,ROW (W73)-delay_3,0),N$9)	=R81*beta-IF(Pulldown, dt*Id(1,R81)/Cd,0)+(Q81+S81)*alpha
83	=R83-Q83	=IF(ROW(W74)>=delay_3,OFFSET(N$9,ROW (W74)-delay_3,0),N$9)	=R81*beta-IF(Pulldown, dt*Id(1,R81)/Cd,0)+(Q81+S81)*alpha
84	=R84-Q84	=IF(ROW(W75)>=delay_3,OFFSET(N$9,ROW (W75)-delay_3,0),N$9)	=R81*beta-IF(Pulldown, dt*Id(1,R81)/Cd,0)+(Q81+S81)*alpha

TABLE II.4 Evaluation of the cells in the drive slot

	P	Q	R	S	T
8	L	R	drive	L	R
82	1.35683	0.5736	1.9304	0.7082	1.2267
83	1.3404	0.5619	1.9022	0.6997	1.2116
84	1.3173	0.5571	1.8744	0.6932	1.1941
85	1.2889	0.5585	1.8474	0.6885	1.1748

We shortened it in Table II.3 for better readability. The function contains several lines which define what the inputs and outputs should be, but all of the work is contained in one compound IF( ) statement

```
=IF(type,IF(Vd<0.45,0,IF(Vd<0.95,(Vd-0.45)/7.69,0.065)),IF(Vd<0.2,0,IF(Vd<0.7,(Vd-
0.2)/7.69,0.065)))
```

Type is a Boolean which selects one of the two functions, the first for Futurebus BTL drivers and the second for a VME TTL driver. These are each versions of the three line segments in Figure 8.7. The value returned is a current between 0 . . . 65 mA.

There is, of course, earlier activity in the drive slot in rows 82 . . . 85 than in the termination columns of Table II.2. You can see that all of the cells are changing and also that the right and left sides are not identical. Equally important, however, is the fact that the difference between vertically adjacent cells is small. Were it not, we would have to doubt the accuracy of our integration approximation, (II.2). The cure if the changes become too large is to increase N.

II.3 THE COEFFICIENTS AND THE INITIALIZATION

Our setup, shown in Figure II.2, comprises two terminations and four filled slots at various places on a 0.5 m Futurebus. The circuit and most of the parameters used in the simulation are shown in Figure II.2. We begin by setting up all of the constants and coefficients that the simulation requires. These are provided in Table II.5, which corresponds to columns A . . . K and rows 1 . . . 4. Most of the coefficients have already been defined or are taken directly from Figure II.2, but units and the few new entries should be explained.

Basic units include Ohms, Volts, Amperes, nF, nS, and meters. For example, the speed of light, used in determining dt, is entered as 0.3 m/ns. Two coefficients tie the whole simulation together. These are N and dt. N is the number of subdivisions of length between slots. It defines the unit of length for a step of one column which in turn determines the size of the time step between rows. Their relationship is given by

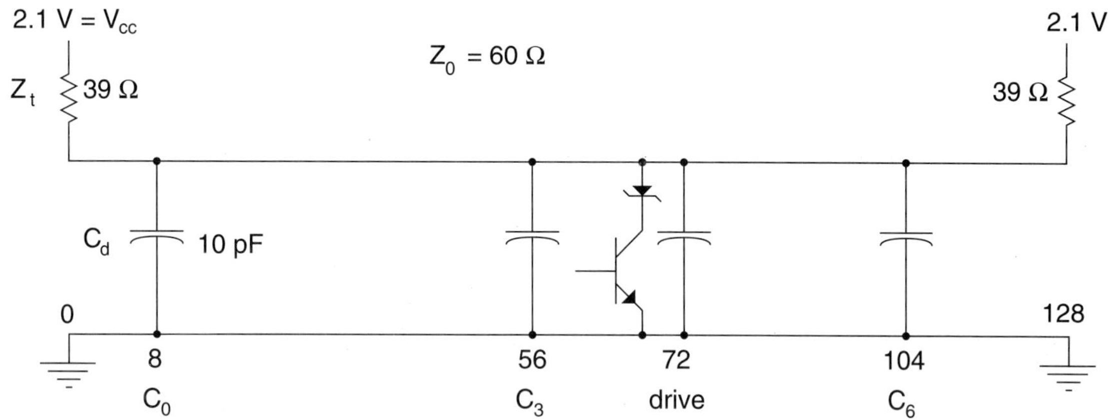

FIGURE II.2 The example configuration. The four loaded slots have identical capacitance. One is prepared to pull down. Terminations at the end are pullup resistors. Distances are relative to the left side. The line's length is 0.5 m. The slot names along the bottom correspond to column labels in row 8 on the spreadsheet.

$$dt = \text{length} / (c \times 8 \text{ sections} \times N \text{ sections/block}) = x/0.3 \times 8 \times N$$

The other new terms in Table II.5 include **one**, **zero**, **Zd** and **Ipull**. The first two are simply the threshold values for the two states. Z_d is the slope in Figure 8.7. I_{pull} is the solution for the DC current flowing in steady-state pulldown (=(VCC-0.45)/(0.5×Zt+Zd)).

Since dt depends on N, the delay function for each section of the line must be made dependent on N. In each of the **offset()** functions that you find in Table II.1 or II.3 is a variable of form **delay_n**, where n runs from 1 to 5. The "distance" numbers below the capacitors in Figure II.2 are functions of N and found in row 7 of the spreadsheet. Since steps sideways correspond to steps down, the *delays* are simply the differences between these two numbers. For example, the delay between C_0 and C_3 is 48 cells.

To initialize the line, you want to create an initial row—row 9 in our spreadsheet—which simply defines what the line is doing in the steady state. If you look at Figure II.2, with the transistor off the voltage on all of the capacitors and the line is the source voltage, 2.1 V. If we choose to start with the line pulled down, we want to select our starting point which might better be represented by a saturation voltage such as $V_C = 0.81$ V. In this second case, there will be a net current I_d flowing into the line,

TABLE II.5 Constants and coefficients for the futurebus simulation

ref	Zt	Z0	dt	VCC	N	Cd	VL_L	VL_R		one
-0.2121	39	60	0.013	2.1	16	.010	-0.45180	1.36856		1.55
x	**Div**		**alpha**	**beta**		**Pulldown**	**Ipull**		**Zd**	**zero**
0.5	0.6061		0.0434	0.9566		0	0.06068		7.69	1.55

half from each side. What we want to do in this initialization row is to establish the steady-state waves in each of the appropriate cells which could be extended indefinitely and always represent this initial state. It may not be obvious that there are waves on this line which is everywhere at the same voltage. While one can paint other models, the only one that is consistent with how you get into the steady state from the transient state has waves traveling on those lines *forever and forever.*

The model with steady state waves is different from the transient model only in the fact that the solution is independent of time. That, however, is a pretty big difference. Each capacitor isolates what is on the right side from what is on the left, but somehow, a net current must be able to flow. View the line as being two lines which feed into the *drive* slot. Let us take the line on the left and solve for case where the line is fully pulled down. Let us specify the net DC current that would be flowing as the pulldown current, I_{pull}

$$I_d = I_{\text{pull}} = (V_{CC} - 0.45) / (0.5Z_t + Z_d) \tag{II.9}$$

Half of that current is flowing from each end. From the traveling wave perspective, we may write the net current at the first slot on the left as twice the current coming from right—the incoming current plus its reflection—less the wave started to the left by the voltage on capacitor

$$(2V_R - V_C) / Z_0 = I_d/2 \tag{II.10}$$

From which we obtain

$$V_R = \frac{Z_0 I_d}{4} + \frac{V_C}{2} = \frac{Z_0 I_d}{4} + \frac{V_R + V_L}{2} = \frac{Z_0 I_d}{2} + V_L \tag{II.11}$$

At the left pullup, we may write this same wave as

$$V_R = \mathcal{R} V_L + \mathcal{T} V_{CC} \tag{II.12}$$

Solving (II.11) and (II.12) for V_L, we obtain

$$V_L = \frac{V_{CC}\mathcal{T} - (Z_0 I_d/2)}{1 - \mathcal{R}} \tag{II.13}$$

Remember that on the spreadsheet, $\mathcal{T} \equiv \text{div}$ and $\mathcal{R} \equiv \text{ref}$. Substituting (II.13) back in (II.11) will give V_R. Since the initial I_d in our model can take on only one of two values, I_{pull} or 0, (II.11) and (II.13) give us our initial waves for pullup and pulldown. In the coefficient section of the spreadsheet, these two waves are represented as VL_L and VL_R for "voltage on the left going left" and "voltage on the left going right." The waves on the right side of the pulldown transistor would be mirror images. Note that for pulldown, where we want an initial condition for $t = 0^-$ of $I_d = 0$, the two waves have the same amplitude, $V_{CC}/2$. The values shown in Table II.4 are correct for the pullup, where you start with the line fully pulled down. If you apply the two values in Table II.5 to (II.10), you get the correct value of $I_d = I_{\text{pull}}$.

The final piece of spreadsheet lore is dealing with the excess of data that you obtain. A graph such as Figure 8.10 took 384 lines to cover the 5 ns. That is far too many points to plot. The points get in each other's way. To make a reasonable figure, every fifth point is plenty. That final operation of extracting every fifth point is nicely automated in the spreadsheet. You must set up three things:

1. A *database*, the set of data—a rectangular area—from which the extraction will be made, must be defined. This database should include the title line by which the columns are to be identified. For our spreadsheet of 384 lines of simulation, this area was A8:AG392. The line with the column labels is A8. In Excel, one defines the database by selecting the area and then clicking the mouse on *Set Database*, which is on the pulldown menu under *Data*.
2. The *criteria* to be used for the selection must be defined. In our case, we will have a single criterion: **=MOD(ROW(A9)-9,5)=0**. The criteria must form a single Boolean expression by which the extractor can decide whether to include the data or not. One must put a name in a cell above the criterion. We used **crit**. One defines the criteria by selecting the two cells and then clicking the mouse on *Set Criteria* on the pulldown menu under *Data*.
3. The final item to set up is the set of fields to extract. You do this by simply listing the names of the columns from the database that you want to extract. The names must match but the order is unimportant. In our case, we wanted **time** on the left, since the first column is the default column for the abscissa. Our *extract* row is shown in Table II.6. As in the previous two cases, you set *extract* by highlighting the names and clicking on *Set extract* under *Data*.

The final operation is to do the extraction by clicking on *Extract*. A dialog box appears asking if you want unique records only. Simply click on the OK button and the extraction will happen. Then you can plot that extracted data in normal fashion. One last cautionary note. If you recompute the original data, the spreadsheet replots the data. However, the data in the extracted fields is the old data. You must still do *Extract* to move the new data into the extract fields. Excel does not replot after the extract operation, so you must force a replot. One way to do this is to have saved the original plot and simply reopen it. When Excel stores a plot, it stores the data used with the plot. However, upon opening the plot, if it finds open the original data block from which the plot was done, it uses the new data instead of the old. Since it does this very rapidly, it is a quick way to get replots on demand.

TABLE II.6 The data extract row

	AG	AH	AI	AJ	AK
8	time	C0	C3	drive	C6

APPENDIX III

MECHANICS OF THE HARD DISK

III.1 OVERVIEW OF THE PROCESS

Disk drives are ubiquitous, taken for granted, and seldom explained in any of the detail which a curious engineer would enjoy. While disk drives are not a central theme in a text on computer architecture, we felt that we would be somewhat remiss if we did not present at least an introduction to these products, whose high technology has made practical much of what we do computationally and whose not infrequent failures represent one of the banes of computer users both large and small. What we present is but an overview. A general review of magnetic recording can be found in [Wood, 86]. The bible of magnetic recording is the three-volume work of Mee and Daniel [Mee, 87]. A set of articles describing the design of DEC's RA90 appears in the February 1989 issue of *Digital Technical Journal*.

Figure III.1 shows the general layout of one surface of a single platter. The platter is clamped to a central shaft which rotates at 3600 to 5400 rpm. The read/write head is shown attached to an arm clamped to another shaft. This shaft provides position control by rotation. All of the arms on all of the platters connect to this single shaft and rotate in unison. Good photographs of the components of a modern disk drive will be found in [Crane, 89]. The dimensions of the large components shown are not grossly out of scale with real disks and arms, but real tracks are so narrow that they could not be represented on a drawing of such large scale. In the best of today's disk drives, track density is of the order of 130 tracks/mm and a single bit is but 0.3 μm long and 7 μm wide.

We begin with the rather obvious question: How can the mechanical components in the high-density disk systems common today keep in registration with the bit pattern written on the platter? There are three coordinates to the mechanical equivalent of an address. The height (Z) is equivalent to platter surface selection; the radius (R) is

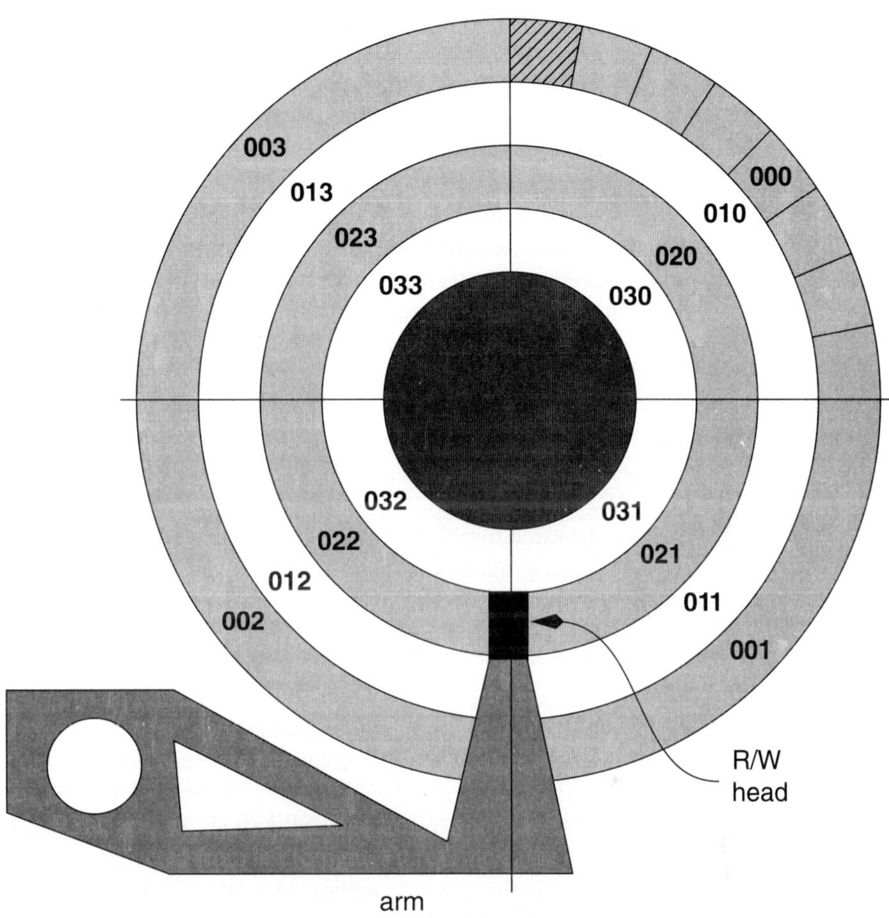

FIGURE III.1 Layout of a single platter on a disk drive. The platter comprises a thin aluminum substrate coated on both sides with a very thin film of ferromagnetic recording material. The space in the center contains the hole and space for clamping to the drive shaft. Space for parking the head on startup and shutdown is often provided in this area as well. The platter is shown to have 4 cylinders, each containing 4 sectors, although reality would be something closer to 4000 cylinders per surface on a 3.5" disk with about 100 half KB (net) sectors per cylinder per side. Other platters on the same spindle would have the same layout, but the addresses of their sectors would be numerically higher. The address format, shown as three digits, is *platter surface*, *cylinder*, *sector*. Sector 000 is special, containing the root directory, which is shown as having seven fixed-length entries though many more would be found in a real root directory. The beginning of each sector contains the sector ID and a burst signal to aid tracking in the radial direction. An ID would be found at the beginning of each sector on the disk (shown as hatched on sector 000). In most cases, both sides of the platter are used. Each arm will carry two heads or two head pairs, one for the platter surface on either side of the arm. See also Figure III.9.

equivalent to cylinder; and the angle (θ) is equivalent both to sector and to bit position within the sector. In general, gross coordinate selection is no problem; it is the differentials, ΔZ, ΔR, and $\Delta\theta$, which will provide the control problem.

To a first order, Z is simply the selection of the correct head, and R is the arm position controlled by the angle of rotation of a shaft common to all of the arms. The last item, θ, is established by time. This last perhaps is the hardest to imagine being controlled to the precision necessary, since you must know where bits begin and end to know whether you have a 1 or 0. However, keeping the moving head centered over a narrow strip of bits which follow a not quite circular path is equally difficult and necessary. The only coordinate that is easy to control is Z because it depends on a physical law, not feedback control.

The competitive economics of disk-system design clearly favor packing as many bits onto a disk as can be reliably written, stored, and read. A single bit on a modern platter occupies about 2×10^{-8} cm^2. Working against the urge to cram yet more bits on the platter are limits imposed by the mechanical positioning system, head dimensions and sensitivity, magnetic domain size, and error recovery, all of which interact to establish the probability that an undetected or uncorrectable error will be made in the round loop of storing and reading a file. That probability must not rise above what is considered to be an acceptable level.

Consider now what the problem is: In all cases, position and bit frequency have been determined by writes which may have occurred weeks ago and not necessarily even on the same machine. Any scheme which is to have any hope of achieving a high packing density must be able to lock onto and correctly track and interpret the data *where is* and *as is*. To do that, tracking information must come from the disks themselves and not from the outside.

It is perfectly legal for the program to write less than a whole segment. Some types of computer service, such as transaction processing, are predicated on writing back onto permanent storage, essentially on a real-time basis, small parts of records whose size in part or whole has nothing whatever to do with the computer's page size. Equally obviously, this patch cannot be inserted into a sector without destroying the error-correcting codes. What must be done by whichever processor is serving as the disk controller is to read off the data from the sector to be rewritten, replace the selected data, recompute the *error-correcting code* (ECC) bits, and then rewrite the whole sector. As discussed in Chapter 3, an arbitrary insertion of 1 byte could require not only the rewriting of a whole file but also substantial revision of its directory. Such complex processing can make disk performance look quite poor even when the read and write operations are performed with remarkable dispatch. Much more is going on than meets the eye.

III.2 POSITIONING THE ARM

Most disk drives employ multiple platters, with each surface of a platter having its own arm bearing a planar integrated read/write head. (See Figure III.1.) All of the arms are controlled in unison by a single shaft, so that at any instance, they all hover over the same cylinder (track) on their respective platters. In the high-end products, which have multiple disks and large capacities even in their minimum configuration, one of the platter surfaces is devoted entirely to tracking information and the rest carry principally data. Each data platter would be rather like Figure III.1. Each sector would begin with a sector ID, followed by the data itself. Along each track, the data is arranged in serial fashion, with the data that came from memory immersed in an error-correcting pattern.

The platter surface containing the tracking information, called the *servo disk*, is prerecorded (by the disk manufacturer or the company selling the disk unit) and defines "forever" the position of the tracks on all disks. (Damage either to the tracking head or the surface of the platter can reduce "forever" to a much shorter time.)

Runout on the platter shaft, thermal gradients, variations from one drive unit to another, and mechanical disturbances such as air turbulence and vibration from oafs stomping about the computer room all contribute to errors in radial tracking from platter to platter. Keep in mind that we are talking about a track that is 7 μm wide. That is not much runout in a system that is spinning 3.5" disks at 5400 rpm. To get local information on the platter in question, the sectors on the data platter are separated by short blocks of tracking signal. These tracks are prerecorded just as with the servo platter. Low-end disk drives may have only this on-platter servo signal. Since the on-platter servo signals are relatively sparse, the low-end products will have noticeably poorer tracking, which translates to longer settling times. With both the dedicated servo platter surface and the on-platter servo signals, tracking to a few micrometers is routinely reproducible in normal operation.

The elements of the tracking scheme are shown in Figure III.2. The motor which drives the arms can place the head approximately on the desired track. The two adjacent

FIGURE III.2 Tracking cylinder for generating the servo signal for arm extension. Track separation is typical of state-of-the-art production units today—4000 tracks per inch.

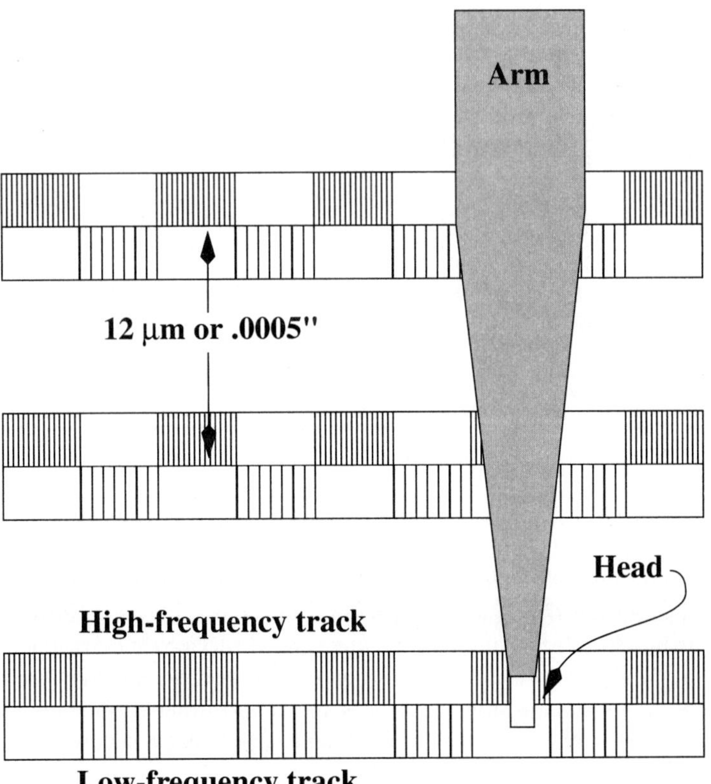

halves of the track have prerecorded signals of different frequency. If the head is off-center, one of the signals will be of greater amplitude than the other. One simply drives the head in the direction to increase the lower signal. Since the tracks which generate these signals predate any data recording, they define the cylinders. With disk drives which allow a disk pack to migrate from one drive to another, you can see that having these definitions travel with the platters is essential.

Given the minuscule spacing between tracks, you might wonder how the system would discriminate against a lock onto a cylinder adjacent to the one desired. The answer is that each sector on a given track has an ID. The intelligent system managing the mechanical components reads these IDs as part of its determination that lock has been achieved. If the ID from an adjacent track is observed, the head must be moved again. In this way, the loop is closed and the system can guarantee proper tracking.

Any process of locking onto a prerecorded track will have acquisition and settling delays. These are mechanical systems with finite energy and stiffness, so the delays in settling onto a track will be of millisecond order. Along with the delay in settling, there will be delays in getting the head from one track to another as well as waiting for the sector of choice to come around. That last item, one-half of a revolution on the average, on a 3600-rpm unit will amount to 8.3 ms. On IBM and Imprimis 5400-rpm units—a major increase in drive power and all that goes with it—it is still 5.6 ms. With head accelerations of 22 g or more, the mean time for acquiring a random track is about one-third the time to span the whole active area—another 4 or 5 ms. The settling time adds another 1 ms or so. The sum of these gives seek times of the order of 8 to 10 ms for modern designs. As long as disk drives remain mechanically roughly the same, great improvements in average seek times are not expected.

III.3 SYNCHRONIZING THE READ/WRITE CLOCK

Once we have the heads tracking properly on the cylinders, the next item must be adjusting the read/write clock to synchronism with the data rate on the platters. Once again, it is the platter that defines the standard to which the read/write mechanism must conform. In this case, however, there is no mechanical servo; the operations are all performed electronically.

The *write* head is generally a remarkably small magnetic yoke with a very narrow gap in it; the *write* head may be used as the *read* head or the *read* head may be a separate *magnetoresistive* thin-film transducer. As described below, the head(s) rides but a few hundredths of a micrometer above the ferromagnetic surface on the platter. Figure III.3 shows the essence of the construction with the heads shown on opposite surfaces of a platter. To write, one puts a current of sufficient amplitude through the coil to raise the field in the gap well above the transition threshold for the magnetic medium underneath. If one uses the *write* head for reading as well, to read, one detects the induced voltage caused by the magnetized surface running under the gap. Since Faraday's law limits us to seeing changes in the flux, the scheme that has been adopted is to write 1's as transitions and 0's as the lack of transitions. Note that this means that a sequence of 1's has alternating magnetic polarity; a sequence of 0's has all the same

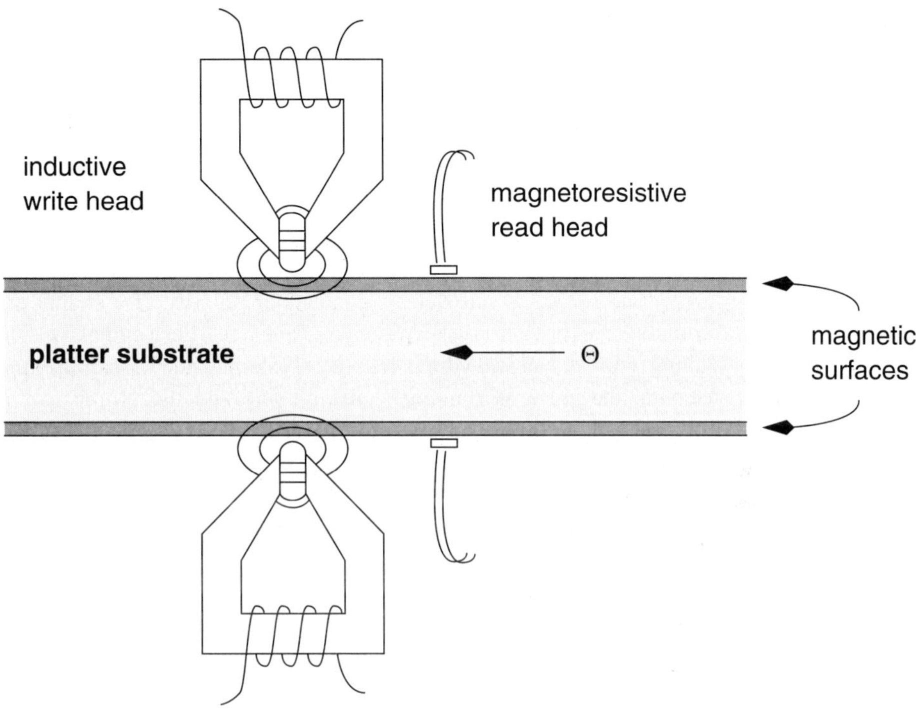

FIGURE III.3 Figurative layout of the *read* and *write* heads on both sides of a platter. Both are created with thin films and planar technology. Note that the magnetization has components in both the Z and θ directions. The magnetic medium's thickness is of the order of 0.1 μm and the gap between heads and platter surface of the order of 0.01 μm.

polarity. If one uses a magnetoresistive *read* head, the gradient in magnetic polarity causes a detectable change in the resistance of the thin magnetic film of the transducer. While far more complex thin films with higher outputs are in the offing, a simple film of permalloy will give a reasonable change in resistance (2 percent). The advantage of the magnetoresistive *read* head is that it gives a good signal without having to have many turns—it has one. To have an equivalent response from the inductive head requires many turns and that means larger L and C and poorer rise and fall times.

Since far more power is available for writing than can be coupled through the gap for reading,[1] one can use fewer turns for writing and make the write circuit fast enough. Since the inductance goes as n^2, a small decrease in n means a large improvement in rise time.

The scheme shown in Figure III.3 polarizes the magnetic film dominantly in the θ direction. By adjusting the gap shape and by using magnetic materials with a pre-

[1] There is plenty of power for a good read signal, since it comes from the rotational drive of the disks themselves, but it is coupled through the air gap between disk and head. This is rather like a trailer truck passing a telephone pole 4 m away. Plenty of power but no coupling.

ferred vertical polarization, it is possible to make the dominant polarization normal to the surface (*Z*-axis). The vertical polarization seems to hold the promise of greater recording density, but to date, the two schemes are competitive. The dominant technology is horizontal recording.

Now let us ponder the question of synchronizing our clock with that of the bit stream. Consider first a sequence of 0's. Since nothing changes—there are no "edges" to detect—how does one know how many bits have passed by? The answer is direct enough: by time. In concept, there is a sampled data system which figuratively tests the magnetic polarity of the surface underneath the head. In reality, of course, one detects $d\phi/dt$ and not ϕ, so one detects changes of polarity. If a change takes place in the bit window, you have a 1; otherwise, you have a 0. These signals are shown in Figure III.4, along with the clock which tells the system when to sample $d\phi/dt$. In the example shown, the clock is running at the bit rate and the proper sampling time is on the upstroke of the clock. Essentially what the system does is to see if the *magnitude* of the voltage is greater than some threshold when the clock makes its upstroke. If it is above the threshold, the value is a 1. By having a threshold, one obtains a noise margin against the inevitable noise from adjacent channels, surface, and electronics. Look carefully at the figure and you will see that the signal is 1001 0100 0101 0001 0100 0001 0010 0001.

Figure III.4 shows the clock correctly synchronized with the bit stream. The question that we must answer here is how did it get that way? One could, of course, do the same thing that one does with radial control—prerecord the timing pattern. This is not done for two reasons: first, because it is unnecessary, and second, because timing channels would consume very valuable disk turf. Instead, one generates the clock signal with a *voltage-controlled oscillator* (VCO) which uses the bit stream itself as a comparison signal in what has become a standard electronic servo, the *phase-locked loop* (PLL).

What the servo action of the PLL does is to compare the time difference, Δt, between the upstroke of the clock and the peak of the induced voltage and then drive the VCO in the direction to reduce this difference. If the VCO were ticking a little too fast, its positive going edge would get ahead of the bit transition. As this error signal increased, negative feedback would lessen the voltage controlling the VCO and the frequency would decrease. By employing integral control, the error in both phase and frequency can be made quite small.

While we said that there is no prerecorded timing pattern, that is not precisely true. In fact, the PLL will not stay in synchronism without reasonably frequent edges to synchronize with. A grainy pattern must be established and maintained. A very simple way to do that is to have two bits recorded for every bit written. 1-0 and 1-1 would be used respectively for 0 and 1. In the worst case, you would never have more than one bit-window pass by without a transition. Such a code consumes surface area by writing twice as many transitions as there are data bits, but it guarantees more than sufficient density of edges for synchronization. Since a stream of 1's would appear as a signal at twice the frequency as a stream of 0's, the code that we just described is called *frequency modulation* (FM). It is inefficient in that only half the transitions are data. (For that reason, it is called a *data rate* $^1/_2$ code.) Another way to look at the evil of low data rate is the high

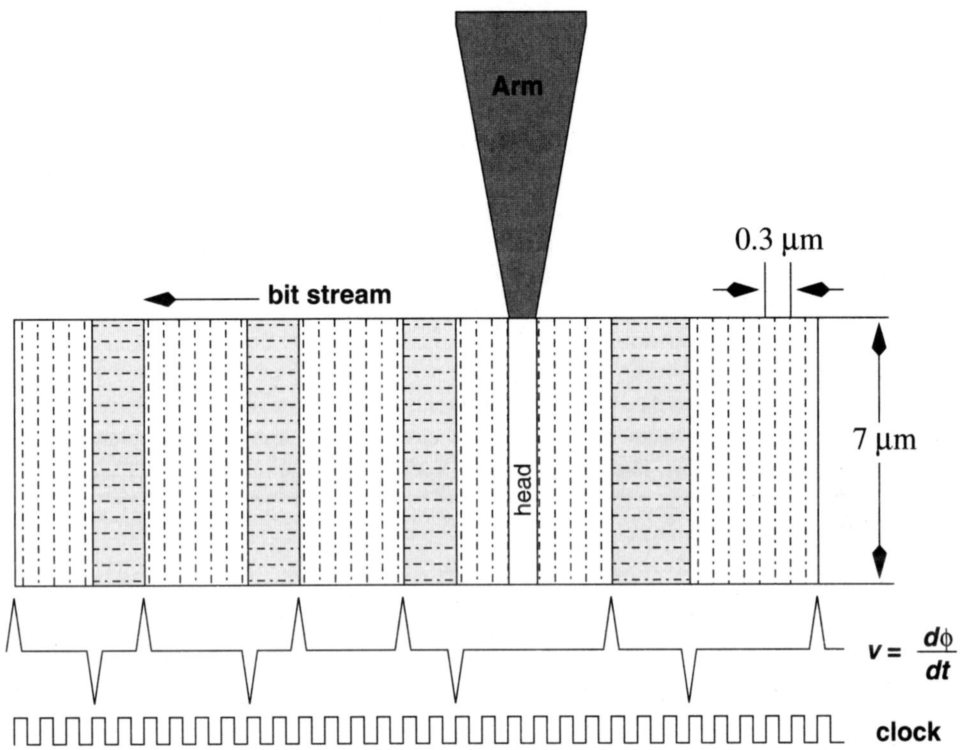

FIGURE III.4 The data pattern traveling from right to left under the head and two related signals. *v* is the detected voltage. The clock is reconstructed locally from the bit stream. Transitions of either polarity mark the 1's. The bit dimension shown (0.3 μm long by 7 μm wide) is found in state-of-the-art production units today. The intertrack width is about 2 μm, which gives the 130 tracks/mm quoted in Figure III.1.

transition rate. The system must be able to read and write bits at twice the actual data rate. Both theorists and practitioners quickly tried to find codes which would sustain synchronism while keeping the read/write rate as close to the data rate as possible and also putting more data per centimeter of track. Since synchronism requires a certain number of 1's per unit of time, the codes could be defined by the minimum number of zeroes, *d*, and maximum, *k*, between 1's. This earned them the name (d, k) codes. Because the run of 0's is always limited, the codes are often called *run-length limited* (RLL) codes. FM is a (0,1) code. A good review article on these codes is found in [Siegel, 85].

Consider the rate at which these bits are arriving. On the 3.5" platters in the 5400-rpm IBM drives, the 0.3-μm bits will be passing under the head at approximately 23.4×10^6/s. The window in which a bit must "appear" to be counted is the reciprocal of that number, or 43 ns. To keep the window accurately centered, the system wants 1's as often as possible. On the other hand, a glance at Figure III.4 will convince you that with even a modicum of noise and a little jitter in the window, it would not be hard for a 1 going up to cancel an adjacent 1 going down. This is the *intersymbol interference* issue. To reduce intersymbol interference, you want a code with nice long strings of 0's between 1's. In this sense, in a (d,k) code, d is a measure of the intersymbol interference and k is a measure of the clock or window control.

One of the first popular digital recording codes was *modified FM* (MFM), which is a (1,3) code. Note that the signal in Figure III.4 does not satisfy this coding rule, for there is one substring of four and another of five 0's in the string. What the MFM code did was to require at least one 0 after every 1 but allow no more than three 0's. A good way to look at this MFM code is to consider always inserting an extra bit just as in FM but making it a 1 only if the previous and current data bits are 0. This makes the interpretation of a pair of bits depend on the previous bit. Figure III.5 formalizes the transitions as a Moore machine. Note that the only data sequence which gives three 0's is 101, which becomes encoded as 01 00 01. Thought of that way, you can see that MFM is still a data-rate 1/2 code, but the read/write rate is now equal to the data rate rather than twice the data rate. While the read/write rate, which is closely related to the power that must be used in the write process and the intersymbol interference rate for both read and write, has been reduced in MFM, the timing precision has not been relaxed. The system must still be able to read or write a bit in a length on the track representing twice the data rate.

To do better than MFM, somewhat more elaborate (d, k) codes have been developed. Two are particularly popular. These are from the (2,7) and (1,7) codes. If you look at the bit stream in Figure III.4, you will see that it satisfies a (1,7) sequence but not a (2,7) sequence, since there are 1's separated by a single 0. Both of these improve on the MFM as long as the PLL stays in lock. The (2,7) code, which was used in the IBM 3370-3380 drives, gives a required read/write rate only 2/3 of MFM but no improvement in the detection window (length along the track). The (1,7) code is a data-rate 2/3 code to begin with, so it gives a 33 percent larger window as well as a read/write rate of 75 percent of MFM. While encoding and decoding logic for these extended codes is more elaborate, that has not proven to be a problem.

Figure III.6 shows the stages through which the original data passes enroute to and from the disk. In real life, transient read errors are not that uncommon. There are both long-span (Reed Solomon) and short-span ECC in the recorded data. If an error is detected on a read and if simple, local, ECC cannot correct the error on the fly, a number of attempts are made to reread the data to see if an error-free read is possible (the

FIGURE III.5 State transition diagram for MFM coding. A datum of 1 always gives an output of 01 and puts the system in state B. A datum of 0 always puts the system in state A but the output is 10 or 00 depending on whether the current state is A or B.

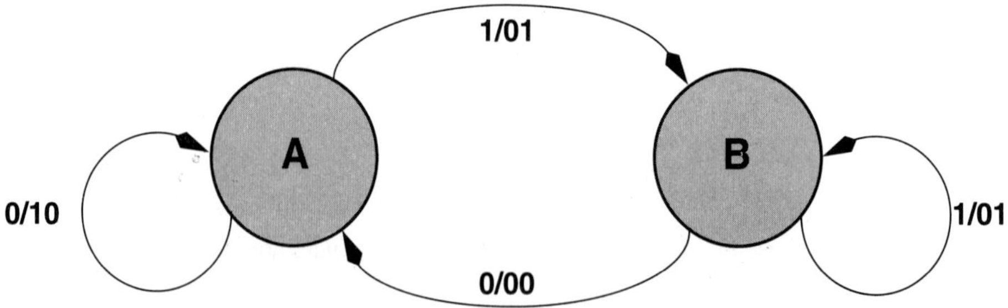

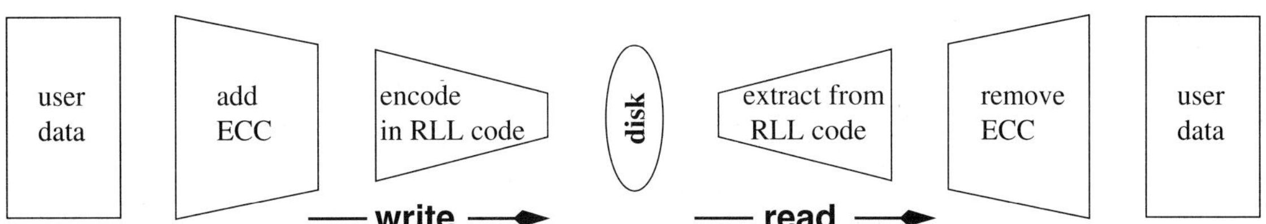

FIGURE III.6 The encoding and decoding of the data as it is moved to and from the disk storage unit. Horizontal width of the trapezoids is indicative of length of signal at each stage. After [Siegel, 85].

usual outcome). If rereading fails to eliminate the errors, the longer-span ECC is used to try to repair the error. In high-reliability systems, a write will be followed immediately by a read to see if the data read is equal to that written. If rereads fail in that case, the errant record is rewritten. Only when read data equals written data is a successful transfer reported. Such care does indeed result in reliable data transfers, but only at the cost of much controller sophistication and a transfer rate much slower than the raw capability of the disk hardware.

III.4 DETECTING THE BITS

The determination of whether there is a bit in the window calls for some sophisticated electronics. The signal will contain noise from the channel itself, from adjacent channels, and from the electronics themselves. To give some noise immunity and a reasonably unambiguous decision on where a 1 belongs, the raw input signal is filtered, peak-detected, and finally differentiated. If a peak of sufficient amplitude is not detected, that implies a 0. If a peak is above the threshold, then the zero crossing of the differentiated signal is detected and compared with the sequence of windows. The window in which the zero crossing is detected gets the 1.

The basic signal treatment is shown in Figures III.7 and III.8. A flux transition, shown without added noise, comes directly from the read head. It is passed through a low-pass filter which removes much of the noise but also widens the pulse. The pulse is full-wave rectified to render both positive and negative transitions as positive. If the resulting pulse exceeds the detection threshold, a 1 has been detected. The filtered pulse

FIGURE III.7 Development of the several signals used in detecting whether a 1 has been read and when. The original signal, $d\phi/dt$, is shown without noise, but in the real world it would be impacted by noise from a variety of sources.

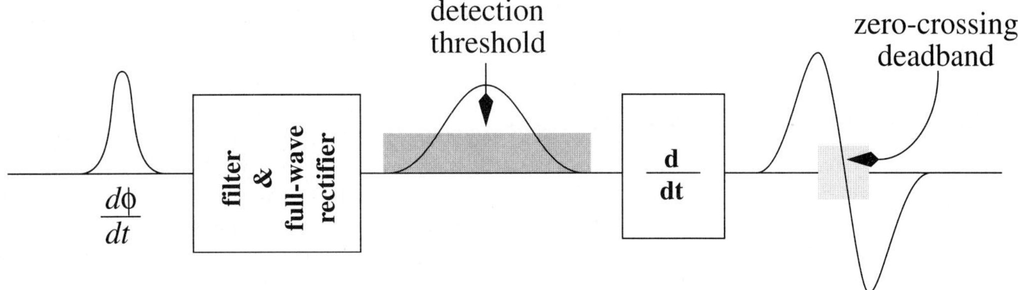

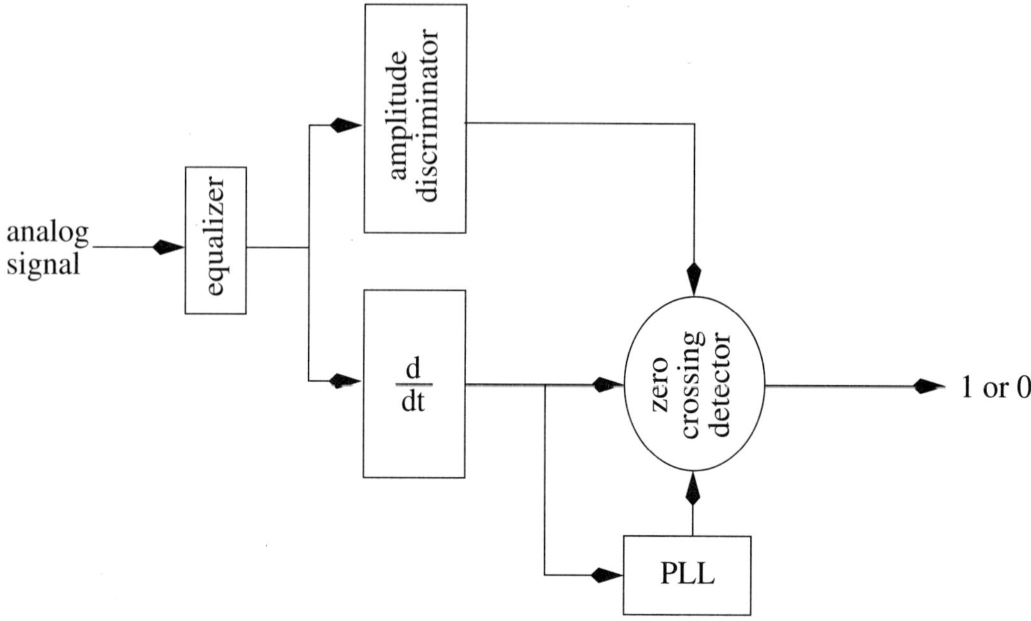

FIGURE III.8 A simplified diagram of the signal processing involved in translating the noisy $d\phi/dt$ signal into a string of 1's and 0's.

is then differentiated and the resulting zero crossing is used to determine when the pulse occurred. There is some imprecision in determining the zero crossing, just as there will be some imprecision in locking the window to the bit positions. Accordingly, there is still some likelihood of attributing a 1 or 0 to the wrong position. Care must be taken in the construction of the RLL code to be sure that such an error will not propagate very far. The propagation arises because the interpretation of the successor bit will depend in part on the interpretation of its predecessor. If the error propagation is small, the ECC will permit reconstruction of the improperly determined bits. If ECC cannot span the stretch of ill-determined bits—whether the noise arises from propagation of a single bad bit or an error in tracking the cylinder or locking with the bit rate—all that one can hope is that rereading the sector will remove the error. When a tracking error occurs on a write, you have a much more serious problem. You might be writing on an adjacent track, making data on another sector and track unreadable. For random errors, successive rereads can achieve success. Unfortunately, tracking errors can result from damage to platter surfaces or the heads or from dirt. In that case, all you have going for you is the long-span ECC. If that fails, the data is essentially lost, at least from that disk.

III.5 A BRIEF LESSON IN GLIDING

This leaves us with microcontrol in the last dimension, *Z*. At rest, the head is held against the platter surface by static spring tension. In that way, head position is independent of the orientation of the platter with respect to gravity. Given the bit dimensions shown in Figure III.4 (0.3×7 μm), how is it possible to hold the head close enough to the surface to pick up and write perturbations of so small a size? A typical hard disk drive operates between 3600 and 5400 rpm.[2] A hard drive spinning at that rate cannot permit the head to drag on the surface, while at the same time it cannot permit the head to get more than a small fraction of a micrometer away from the bits it is reading or writing. Such spacing is less than the wavelength of visible light. How can such spacing be held with any precision? The answer is that the head hovers over the surface on *ground effect*, a phenomenon you can feel directly in flying a small plane. Anyone who has attempted to land a low-winged plane, particularly one that sits very close to the ground, such as a glider, knows that if you get the plane flying horizontally near the ground at moderate to high speed it is almost impossible to push it down onto the ground. You have to slow down to land. It feels as if there is an elastic ball trapped under the plane. In fact, there is. The ball is made of air. The phenomenon of ground effect is not unlike the image charge induced in a ground plane (except that the ball is repulsive). The normal smooth flow of air under the wing is reflected by the ground, increasing the pressure under the wing. Since the increase in pressure grows as the ground gets closer, the air close to the ground feels stiffly elastic.

The height above the ground is determined by speed and by the shape of the airfoil. The airfoil will hover above the ground at the level where the lift is precisely equal to the weight supported. In the disk drive, the airfoils are the heads and the lift works against the spring tension which holds the head against the platter. Even if the surface is not perfectly flat, the head will follow gradual contours without any problem. Typical heights off the surface today are about 0.2 μm—about half the wavelength of the bluest light you can see. You might wonder about surface imperfections and particles. Platters must be remarkably clean when assembled, and they must stay that way. At a clearance of 0.2 μm, a cigarette smoke particle would look like a 2-ft boulder in the road. Drive over it and you will leave an impressive imprint in the car. Although disk packs are assembled under conditions of extraordinary cleanliness and isolated through highly filtered breathing ports while still in that pristine atmosphere, perfection is not only hard to achieve but even harder to sustain. One of the most common causes of disk failure is a surface damaged beyond readability by dirt collecting on a head. If the failure occurs in the directory, recovery of any data may be impossible. A correct and sobering aphorism is that it is not *if* a disk unit will fail but *when*. Backups of data are crucial both to recover from unintended erasure as well as to protect data against a total disk failure. The sealed Winchester drives[3] generally have methods for continually filtering the air. Smokers are unwelcome near disk packs even in North Carolina.

Along with dirt, the other obvious problem for head and platter is preventing damage when the disk is not spinning at full RPM. A typical drive takes times of the

---

[2] A typical floppy, by contrast, operates at 360 rpm. At these slow speeds, the head can stay in direct contact with the surface. To prevent excessive wear, the drive spins only when a read or write is in progress and for a brief period afterward. Slow rotation and a startup delay imply very low data rates.

[3] The name Winchester for sealed disk drives appears to have been a nickname for the first such design, an IBM disk drive which had been called the 3030 during development. The number reminded people of the famous Winchester 30-30 rifle, hence the name.

order of a fraction of a minute to accelerate. During that long transient and while the platters are at rest, it is best to prevent head contact with the data area on the platter. Keeping the head away from the data is referred to as *parking the head.* All disk controllers must be designed to properly park the head whenever the power is removed, whether the removal is of the orderly shutdown sort or simply an unexpected power failure. Most accomplish this by allowing contact but keeping the parking area away from the areas where data is recorded. Other systems go through a complete head extraction before the disk is shut off. Upon restart, the heads are kept in the parking area until the platters have come up to speed. Even with the best of designs, heads will occasionally hit the surface even at full speed. To protect both head and surface, the surface is coated with films that provide both lubrication and good wear. One of the more popular materials for wear is amorphous carbon. The amorphous carbon is purported to have a hardness approaching diamond, although research at IBM Almaden Laboratories has indicated that surface damage shows up not so much as a scrape than as an event which triggers local crystallization of the carbon, building up dangerous little hillocks. Keep in mind the dimensions of the gap between head and surface. Only thin films are acceptable. The magnetic layer itself is less than 0.1 μm in thickness—about 2000 atoms high … or less. There is a crystal orientation film under the magnetic layer and the carbon layer on top—both about 0.03 μm thick.

Finally there is the lubricating layer itself. That material is some slippery fluorocarbon averaging less than a monomolecular thickness. Less than a monomolecular layer? Indeed. It is really an imperfect layer, one that is a single molecule thick where it exists, but with holes where there is nothing. It is essential that the layer be there and equally essential that it not get thick. Given that such organic films have finite vapor pressures, you might well despair of getting anything that thin to stay down for the requisite 5 to 20 years of disk life. The film is maintained by having a reservoir which sustains an equilibrium vapor pressure. This ensures that the film remains intact, balancing evaporation with redeposition. Nowhere is it written that disk drives are or should be easy to make.

Figure III.9 shows the inside of the IBM 0662 one-GB drive, which has the highest bit density available of any drive at the time of the writing of this text. The three 3.5" platters deliver 1052 MB of storage along with a dedicated servo surface. The platters spin at 5400 rpm; track density is 160 tracks/mm and the maximum linear bit rate is 3,421 bits/mm. That comes to 54.9 Mb/cm^2. The pivot point for the arm assemblies is in the back. You can see a single head protruding from under the protective shroud, parked on the data-free inner area of the disk. Using a magnetoresistive read head, the maximum disc data rate is 6 MB/s. With a 0.5 MB buffer, external data transfers on *fast* and *wide* SCSI II can be as high as 20 MB/s. It would be amusing to look instead on the platters for the original disk drive, IBM's RAMAC (1956) [Bashe, 86]. The magnetic surface was quite literally painted on. The whole disk drive, which was the size of a washing machine, provided 5 MB of storage on 60 disks with 600 ms average seek! It was certainly the certified wonder of its day, but today, you can get nearly that much storage on a single 3.5" floppy.

What is particularly fascinating about the numbers which are strewn about this appendix is that they in no way represent the "end of the line" in magnetic disk storage.

FIGURE III.9 The IBM 0662 Drive (photograph courtesy of International Business Machines Corporation). The top head (of six) is parked on the surface of the disk near the hub, an area not used for recording. In use, the unit is enclosed by a shroud, the right half of which is visible in the photo. Rather than a hermetic seal, the unit is allowed to breath slowly to equilibrate with the atmosphere around it. The SCSI II connector is shown on the front-left. The power connection is on the front-right.

IBM, which has certainly been one of the world's leaders in magnetic storage since developing the RAMAC in the late 1950s, has already developed and demonstrated technologies which will permit an order of magnitude increase in bit density over the next few years. As prices fall and densities increase, it looks as if magnetic storage techniques will continue to be the secondary storage of choice beyond the next decade. It will not be replaced until some other system can surpass both its low cost for mass storage and its high speed for retrieval.

REFERENCES

[Bashe, 86] Bashe, Charles J., Lyle R. Johnson, John H. Palmer, and Emerson W. Pugh, *IBM's Early Computers*, MIT Press (1986). Chapter 8 covers the development of RAMAC.

[Crane, 89] Crane, Barbara, *Disk Drive Technology Improvements in the RA90*, **Digital Technical Journal 8**, 46-60, (February 1989).

[Mee, 87] Mee, C. Dennis and Eric Daniel (eds.), *Magnetic Recording*, McGraw-Hill (1987).

[Siegel, 85] Siegel, Paul H., *Recording Codes for Digital Magnetic Storage*, **IEEE Trans actions on Magnetics, MAG-21**, 1344-1349, (1985).

[Thompson, 89] Thompson, David, *Science and Technology for Storage in the Nineties*, **International Conference on Computer Design: VLSI in Computers & Processors**, IEEE (1989).

[Wood, 86] Wood, Roger W., *Magnetic Recorder Systems*, **Proceedings of the IEEE, 74**, 1558-1569 (1986).

APPENDIX IV

PROCESS-CREATION, QUEUING, TERMINATION

IV.1 SPAWNING NEW PROCESSES AND PIPING DATA BETWEEN PROCESSES

When an operating system using virtual memory management creates a process, the operating system may initialize it with a generous helping of its minimum daily requirements or the system may be completely minimalist and provide nothing but the requisite pump priming. Consider what a program looks like on disk. Generally, a program will comprise *at least* the segments that we show in Figure 4.12 on page 191: *abs*, *text*, *data*, and *stack*. Only some of these exist prior to running—generally, *abs* and *text*. The program name is an index into the disk directory which the operating system knows how to use. The index gets the system the list of sectors containing the program. Up front, the program must have a header which will tell the operating system how many pages each of the program's sections should be. To conserve disk space, most sophisticated compilers will not store blocks of uninitialized data on disk. The system will supply these pages from its freelist, on demand, nicely initialized to zero, hence the name *demand-zero pages*. Along with this information, the header specifies the protection for each segment. For those pages which are extant on disk, the directory provides a path for the driver. A typical header list might decode as shown in Table IV.1.

Now comes the question about what the system should do to start this child of some other process on its way. Child of some other process? Well, you typed the equivalent of **RUN**, or you logged in (child of the *login* process) or you submitted a batch process (child of a process which launches batch jobs). Jobs, unlike Topsy, don't just grow. They get launched by another process. You might ask where the first process came from, and in this case—finite automata being so nicely closed—there is an answer. The boot program is not a process; it runs all by itself and not under the operating system. It sets

TABLE IV.1 Header data in the first page of a typical program. We have used the four segments that are appropriate to our system but other systems may have more or less. The header will contain sundry other necessary tidbits including the virtual address at which to start each segment and the address of the first instruction—the entry point.

Header Loading Data

Segment	**Protection**		**Loading** data on disk	**Loading** demand zero
abs	read only write	shareable private	7 pages 4 pages	0 pages 0 pages
text	read only	shareable	467 pages	0 pages
data	write	private	0 pages	24 pages
stack	write	private	0 pages	1 pages

up the operating system, launches *init*, and then gracefully vanishes. *Init* launches *getty*, which looks for startup activity from terminals, and *login*, which launches user processes, which in turn can launch other processes. Okay. We now have the begats. We still must answer the question of how this baby grows. The operating system designer has many choices here. One thing that has to be there at the start is the process control block. The PCB is what gets queued; that is, it is joined to linked lists such as the run queue or the waiting-for-I/O queue. It has to be there to switch the context into the run state. After that, the options begin. One option is to build pagetables for all the pages initially specified. For this modest but not tiny program—467 KB of text—you can see that it isn't really such a big deal. There would be only four pages at the pagetable level and the one midtable in Figure 4.12. That isn't a big effort. You might even want to bring in the starting page from disk and allocate one demand-zero page to stack as a place to put any arguments from the launching process (i.e., those items written after the program name on the command line). But with demand paging, only the stack page is essential. It is only necessary to have enough information in the pagetable and PCB to allow the first fetch of an instruction. With our memory management mechanism (described in Section 4.6 on page 179), that may simply be a midtable with all descriptors marked invalid. If this minimalist approach is your choice, then each memory reference to a new area will cause page faults, possibly for missing pagetable pages in addition to missing pages. The page-fault handler can then build the pagetables as they are needed. Naturally this requires information about the legal addresses in each segment of the program, which would be taken from the header loading information and kept in the PCB.

A reasonably simple but particularly interesting and informative example of process generation occurs in UNIX. It contains one of UNIX's most useful concepts: the *pipe*. A pipe is literally a buffer between two concurrent processes in which the output of one is the input of another. Let us say that you had a long document—an example which comes to mind is a textbook. For one reason or another, you would like to determine how many times you reference a particular text. If the document was written in $\TeX$, a reference to a book by Kenah takes the form **\cite{Kenah}**. Let us say that there were three chapters. Then to get the count of references to Kenah, you must get the chapters, find every line with a **\cite{Kenah}** in it, and then count the number of lines. (Let us ignore the unlikely possibility that someone would put two citations to the same work in the same line.) UNIX provides a program to do each of these tasks:

Command	Action
cat file1 file2 file3	feeds the three files in order to its standard output
grep "**cite{Kenah}**"	copies lines with **\cite{Kenah}** from the standard input file to the standard output file
wc -l	counts the number of lines in standard input and writes that number to standard output

Let us begin by building this sequence of tasks in a way that is explicit and obvious. Then we will see how UNIX's *pipes* improve the interaction between processes. In general, standard input (*stdin*) is initialized to be the keyboard and standard output (*stdout*) is initialized to be the screen, but redirection of either is easy. If one wanted the number of citations written to the screen, one could merge the three files with *cat* and search for the quoted expression with *grep*. In each case, an intermediate file would be created. In the third step, the lines in the second file would be counted and the count written to the screen. Finally, the intermediate files would be discarded. The command sequence would be

```
cat chap1 chap2 chap3 >temp1             # output redirected to file temp1
grep "\\cite{Kenah}" <temp1 >temp2       # input redirected to temp1; output to file temp2
wc -l <temp2                             # input redirected to temp2
rm temp1 temp2                           # removes the two temporaries
```

What this sequence of instructions does is to *spawn-and-wait* three times, creating files on disk for the next process to consume and then throwing them away. UNIX has a more efficient paradigm for accomplishing the same sequence of transactions:

```
cat chap1 chap2 chap3 | grep "\\cite{Kenah}" | wc -l
```

The vertical bars tell the UNIX command interpreter (the *shell*) to *pipe* the output of one process to the input of the next. This is a *streaming* operation. As soon as *process_1* has generated some output, *process_2* can consume it. As soon as the data generated by

1 has been consumed by *2*, it can be dispensed with. The transferred data is inexpensively buffered in memory, with *1* trying to fill the buffer and *2* trying to empty it. Since one task may be much lengthier than the other, one of the two may succeed in its ambition. If *1* fills the buffer, it stops until there is more room for data; if *2* empties the buffer, it stops until there is more data in the buffer. How would it know—"it" being either one? The buffer is a circular list of bytes—no other inherent structure—with two pointers: *read* and *write*. The rule is that *read* must wait if it equals *write*; *write* must stop if it now equals *read*. The circular buffer with a *read* and *write* pointer is not the same as a normal file; both the circularity and the sharing are different. Since `read()` and `write()` calls go through the kernel, the system must keep track of the fact that it is using a pipe and use appropriate routines for reading or writing. The process itself is blissfully unaware that it is reading from or writing to a pipe. A simplified example of two such routines which maintain circularity and prevent overrunning of the pointers is presented below.

```
#define null 0
#define TRUE 1
#define FALSE 0

struct pipe {char *read,*write,*start;};

int ReadPipe(struct pipe *pipename, char *x)
    /* pipe is 1024 bytes long */
    /* return value is boolean indicating successful read*/
    {
        if (pipename->read != pipename->write)
        {
            *x = *pipename->read++;
            if (pipename->read == pipename->start+1024)
                pipename->read = pipename->start;
            return(TRUE);
        }
        return(FALSE);
    }

int WritePipe(char y, struct pipe *pipename)
    /* pipe is 1024 bytes long */
    /* return value is boolean indicating successful write*/
    {
        if (pipename->write != pipename->read)
        {
            *pipename->write++ = y;
            if (pipename->write == pipename->start+1024)
                pipename->write = pipename->start;
            return(TRUE);
        }
```

```
        else return(FALSE);
    }
```

The actions that the shell takes to deal with the command above are worth looking at in a little detail, to provide a sense of completion and closure in the creation and interaction of subprocesses[1]. In conventional UNIX systems, processes are created in two steps: a *fork* system call duplicates the current process, and then the child process does an *exec* system call, which replaces its inherited program and data with a new program from the disk. It may seem startling to start a process by duplicating the entirety of the previous process, but if you think of a process as a command interpreter executing commands, rather than a general program doing almost anything at all, the idea will make sense. What is needed is to see how the new process gets sent off in a different direction than its parent will go. If *fork* really copies the entirety of the parent process into the child, then both child and parent—since both are now independent processes—will next look at the number which fork returns. Think of *fork()* as a regular C routine which:

- Obtains a new and unique *process ID number from the system.*
- Copies the entirety of the parent process—data, text, stack—except for the return value of the *fork* function itself and the process ID in the child's PCB.
- Returns the child's process ID to the parent and 0 to the child. It is this single difference which makes it possible for the two processes to diverge.

Now, when each of these processes next executes (immediately for the child process, which is the active process as we build the pagetables), they are both at the same point in interpretation of the current command line. All that differs is the return value of *fork()*. Obviously, to get different results from parent and child, both must be executing a statement like

```
if (fork() == 0) { ... }
```

The child will do what is in the brackets; the parent will not. What is in the brackets will cause the child process to execute the program specified in the very same command line that the parent was looking at when it *fork*ed. After all, if you copied the entirety of the parent process to the child, the child gets the command line too.

Think of the command line above, which appears in process **X**, which is in the form of:

```
A | B | C
```

where **A**, **B**, and **C** each comprises a program name and a list of input parameters for the called program. The absence of "&" at the end tells process **X** to await the conclusion of

[1] A complete but simple shell can be found in Chapter 6 of [Rochkind, 85].

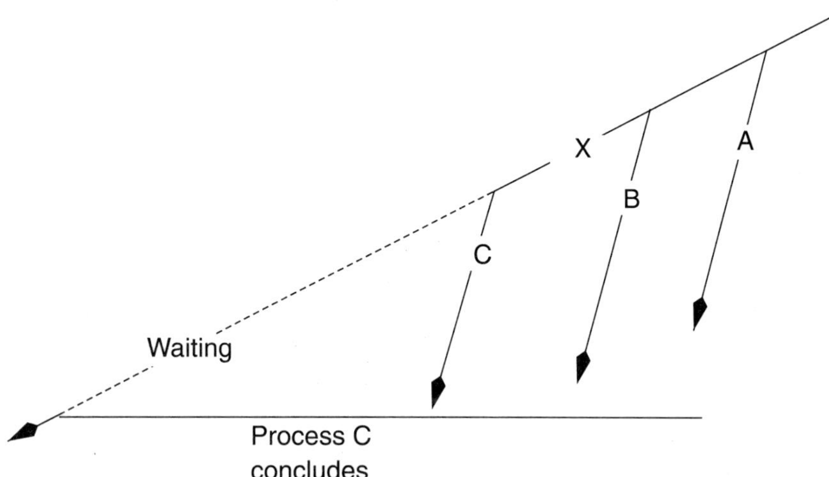

FIGURE IV.1 Process generation through forking and process concurrency.

C before proceeding. The command will require not only that the three processes come spilling out of **X** but that **A** and **B** and **B** and **C** be connected by pipes. Finally, it requires that each process execute the program intended for it, which presumably (but not necessarily) would be three different programs. It sounds much worse than it is, particularly in the simple structure that UNIX imposes on a process. Figure IV.1 shows the order of generation and the process concurrency resulting from this statement. Figure IV.2 shows the data connectivity among the several processes. Process **X** will retain its connections to **stdin** and **stdout**, which it had passed on to all its children. **C** retains its connection to **stdout** but redirects its input to the output of the first pipe, and so on.

Just because the spawning is identical for every subprocess, the shell need only recognize that a spawning operation is called for, not which kind of process it will become. The parent process will

- Set **rightpipe** to *null* and enter its spawning loop.
- Set **leftpipe = rightpipe**.
- Cut the command line up to the first separator and paste it into a line we have named **ProgCall**. Should that first separator be a pipe, the parent process will create a pipe

FIGURE IV.2 Connectivity of the four concurrent processes. Process **C** begins with the connectivity of **X**, **B** with **C**'s, and **A** with **B**'s. Each redirects as specified by the pipes. **A** returns to **stdin** as the default when no input is specified in the line.

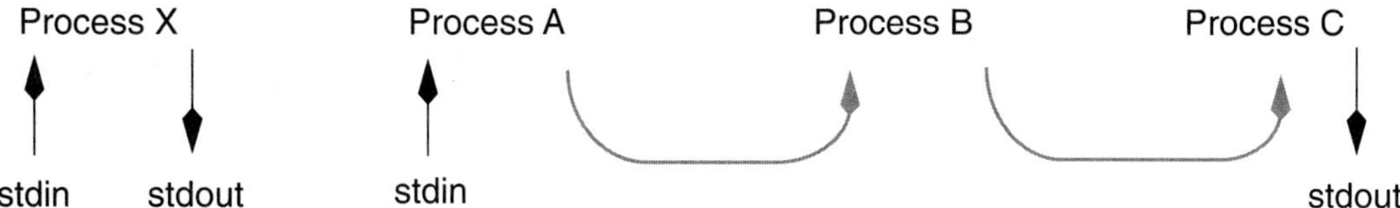

and set its pointer equal to **rightpipe**. Should the last character be &, that character is not included in the cut and paste.

- The parent does *if (fork()){...}*. If the command line is not yet finished, the spawning loop is repeated.
- If the last character is not &, the parent goes into a wait state until all processes from the command line finish.

The child process is initially identical in all respects but for the value returned from **fork**(), for its own pagetables and for the process ID. Now the child starts scanning the **ProgCall** line that it was handed, reading from the left. If it finds the *pipe* symbol, "|" on the left, it will close **stdin** and connect its input to the output of **leftpipe**. If it finds a *pipe* on the right, it closes **stdout** and connects its output to **rightpipe**. If it does not find the pipe symbol, it will get the parent's **stdin** and **stdout**. It removes the pipe symbols from **ProgCall** and does

```
exec(ProgCall);
```

That command sends it off on its unique task. Upon successful completion of the task, it returns a *happy number* to the operating system and the whole process (though not what is in the output pipe) vanishes from the scene. An error denouement is decidedly more complicated, since there are so many loose ends to tie up, so we will not treat that here.

A programmatic version of the creation process is given in Figure IV.3. Figure IV.3 is an awful figure, but the repetitiveness is by design. All four of those columns are essentially the same. Only a few of the comments are different. There is supposed to be comfort in regularity and predictability. If that is truly true in the absolute, then there is comfort in Figure IV.3, but we doubt it.

One might well ask whether all this copying was worthwhile, particularly since the child process is presumably not going to be doing the same thing that the parent is. Simplicity has much to recommend it, so having one transaction that fits all may be worthwhile in reducing the complexity of the operating system, but doesn't all this copying generally waste a lot of time? The answer is the answer you must now expect: "That depends." The first thing that it depends on is how much baggage a process carries along with it. In the VAX/VMS system, processes are remarkably complex affairs. Doing a **fork** there (called *spawning*) produces a remarkably long pause from the system. UNIX, on the other hand, right from its inception had as an important objective the idea of pipes. This required that the overhead in creating a process had to be small. Generally, what the processor must copy is the parent's shell. That is a program of some size—a command interpreter—but unless the child decides to invoke a new shell, the shell of choice is *already* up and running. The parent has it active and has just used it to do the fork. This means that if the shell is shareable—it almost always is—only a private data area, pagetables, and stack area need be created. What if you specified running a program other than the shell? Well, if you want to run a program, it follows that you must have it loaded. That hasn't changed by doing the fork. Thus, when the child does *exec()*, it is going to replace the shell with another program. But there is little loss in the initial copy because there was little to copy.

Process X

Determine if the first word is a shell command. It isn't. Therefore, we do:

```
rightpipe = null;
do {
  leftpipe = rightpipe;
  ProCpy(Comlin,ProgCall);
  if (*ProgCall[0] == ' | ')
    rightpipe = CreatePipe();
  else rightpipe = null;
  if (fork() == 0) {
```

Parent process gets back the process number of the child process so it fails the test and goes to the end of the bracket.

```
    }
}
while (strlen(ComLin) != 0 &&
    (strlen(ComLin) != 1 ||
       *Comlin[0] != ' & '))
if (*ComLin[0] != ' & ')
          wait(status);
```

If the last character is **&**, the parent simply goes on its way after creating the child. With any other character, it awaits the completion of the child process.

Process A

fork() will equal 0 so this process goes inside the brackets. The child has the same variables as the parent (X).

```
{
  if (*ProgCall[0]  == ' | ')
  {
    close(stdin);
    pipein(leftpipe);
    *ProgCall[0] = '  ';
  }
n = strlen(ProgCall) -1;
  if (*ProgCall[n]  == ' | ')
   {
     pipeout(rightpipe);
     *ProgCall[n] = ' \0 ';
   }
  exec(ProgCall);
}
```

The process is changed to the program specified in *ProgCall and so ceases to execute the instructions inherited from its parent. Upon the completion of the program specified, the process will be terminated. Only permanent records on disk and files shared with other still extant processes will be left.

Process B

This process is essentially identical to its brother (A) except for process number and page tables. It will, of course, receive *variables* different from A for *ProcCall, rightpipe and leftpipe since these were changed prior to its creation.

Process C

This process is essentially identical to its brothers (A and B) except for process number and page tables. It will, of course, receive *variables* different from B for *ProcCall, rightpipe and leftpipe since these were changed prior to its creation.

FIGURE IV.3 Development of the three subprocesses that are derivative from the process X for the command line **A | B | C**.

To further reduce the amount of copying, since, in many cases, almost no use will be made of the inherited data, some systems make the PTEs in both processes point to the same pages, and mark both PTEs as *read-only* and *shared*. When one of the processes tries to write to a page of data, a page fault will occur, and the page-fault handler will discover that it must create distinct pages for the two processes. At that time it copies the data and creates new PTEs for each process, allowing write access. This mechanism is called *copy-on-write*.

Having talked about the creation of processes and declared that UNIX made it a point to make process creation particularly easy and efficient, it is worthwhile to think about the downside of having all of these processes competing for memory resources. To keep all of these processes working well, each must get a worthy helping of memory. There is only so much memory left for processes, so it is not too hard for the system to have more demand than product. To pick up more memory, virtual memory management must resort to swapping. If the total memory required for the working sets of all processes exceeds the available physical memory, some of the processes should be swapped to disk. Even though it may be possible to run a huge number of process concurrently by having only a few pages in memory for each one, running a process without enough of its pages in memory causes it to waste too much time reading and writing the blocks between disk and memory—*thrashing*. Virtual memory management systems have two "daemon" processes: a *page-out* daemon which looks for infrequently used pages to page out to disk, and a *swap-out* daemon which looks for low-priority processes to swap out to disk. The page-out daemon will run only if there are too few pages free, and the swap-out daemon will run only if the combined working set sizes of the processes in memory is too large. To avoid sending any process off to the deep freeze forever, the operating system inevitably has a system for promoting longsuffering disk dwellers to a high enough priority so that they get some time in the ready-to-run queue.

IV.2 BUILDING THE PAGETABLES FOR A NEW PROCESS

While each process in UNIX begins life as the image of its parent, transfer of control to a new application simply dumps most of the inherited pagetable structure along with its associated pages. These pages are returned to the freelist, and the building starts anew with a clean slate. The first step is to determine how much memory the new process requires to start, including the space for its pagetables. The data about the program itself is stored on disk in a header for the program file. If there is not enough free memory available, we block the process until there is. In a multiprocessing environment, space will become available sooner or later. Once we have room, we may build the process pagetables. This begins by taking a physical page off of the freelist, zeroing it to render all entries void, and assigning it to this process as process midtable. Nothing is in it yet, but we have its PA in hand. We insert that PA into four locations: the three *current process* pointers shown in Figure 4.12 and into the *inherited process control block* as a permanent record of where this process begins. Next, we take four more pages from the freelist and assign them to the process pagetables. Their PAs are loaded into the just-designated process midtable and the TLB flushed. Note that our loader now can use the logical address for the PTEs in the process midtable since we updated the one-and-only PTE in the kernel data pagetable which points at the current process midtable. Once we have loaded the process pagetable PTEs into the process midtable, we may begin loading the program into the process pages. We will pull pages off the freelist, insert PTEs into the appropriate process pagetables, and queue requests for a read from disk. All of the PTEs referenced strictly by the kernel—process pagetables and the midtable—will be marked as *valid*, *kernel write*, *process none*, *unmodified*, *unused*, and *cacheable*. In numeric terms, the protection byte becomes 1000 0101. For the process root and process midtables, we must add *process read* since the machine will most often be in process mode when accessing these tables. For the process pagetables, correct privileges must be given according to function. For example, bin 0 will be *process read*, bin 1 and entries in the data and stack pagetables should be *process write*, and entries in the text pagetable should be *process execute* or *process read*.

To load pages (in contrast to pagetables), we would be invoking kernel I/O services. Most disk reads would be done using *direct memory access* and PAs. Smaller systems use the host CPU to handle the overhead (setting up each page transfer and doing any buffer-to-process-space copying which might be necessary) using an interrupt from the DMA device to trigger each necessary intercession on the CPU's part. Many modern systems, particularly very large ones, use separate I/O processors to handle the overhead. A few even deal with virtual addresses, but most systems have the CPU deliver the PA of each page involved in a transfer. To do that, we will want to access the process pagetables. The route for that, from Figure 4.12, is the one proceeding through the process root table (used as a midtable). After obtaining the desired PTE, the PA for the page can be generated just by clearing the lower 8 bits. One way or another, all of the necessary pages from the process get loaded in. While that slow procedure is progressing—loading 1000 pages may take 10 s or more—other already loaded programs will be running. Whenever the loading is complete, the process can be added to the *ready-to-run* queue.

Let us build a function in C which creates a new process in the sense that it builds the pagetables and loads the pages. Rather than use demand paging, we will load the whole image at once. To simplify further, we will assume that the kernel is non-preemptable and runs on a uniprocessor, so we can ignore the synchronization problems described in Chapter 3. The following is simplified to show only the principal memory management issues. We will assume the existence of three system routines:

mem_alloc(n)	returns a pointer to a linked list of **n** free, zero-filled memory pages. If fewer than **n** free pages are available, the function returns the NULL pointer.
read_block(a)	reads the next block of the program file into the physical address **a**, using and updating the disk and file data obtained by the loader. If the page transfers properly, the function returns 0. Otherwise, it returns an error code which tells why the transfer failed (e.g., end of file = 1).

sleep(&x)	the system puts the process which calls this function in a *waiting for event* queue. The parameter **x** identifies a resource which is needed to continue (e.g., some free memory). When it becomes available, the system will put *all* processes waiting for that resource back in the *ready-to-run* queue. If the first process grabs it all, the others may have to go back to sleep.

The function that we are about to write would be called by the system during `exec().Exec()` receives the file name of the program to be run and uses it to obtain the program's header file from disk. The program's disk *image* is a single file that begins with a header and then follows with a file of four bins (see Table IV.1). The length of each bin is given in words, but the last page of each bin is filled as necessary with 0's so that each bin is an integral number of pages. The loader checks all lengths to be sure that they are proper values, sets a global pointer to the beginning of the first page of bin 0 on disk, and then calls our function, *proc_create*. *Proc_create* will return 0 if everything works, but should it get some sort of error in transferring a page—the world is not perfect—it will return the error message that it receives from *read_block*.

Empty pages may be "loaded" in the *data* and *stack* areas in the sense that unfilled pages are listed in the process data and stack areas. In general, uninitialized structures are not stored on disk. Why store a bunch of meaningless zeros? Stack begins with only the parameters passed by the shell and heap always starts the day empty. If the request for pages exceeds the length of the file on disk, that is not an error. It simply means that the program is getting some initial space for structures to be created at run time. At the end of the program, where we are reading in the program's pages, we check for success after every page. If we get an EOF (error = 1), then we just break out of the read loop and leave with the empty pages in place. Of course, if we get some other error message such as a bad read or what have you, we also abort the loop but under these circumstances, we report an error. Now to the function. Keep Figures 4.11 and 4.10 in mind as you read it.

```
 struct mlink { struct mlink *link; /* link to next page, 0=end */
    int paddr;                      /* address of the memory page */
    };
struct mlink *mem_alloc(int)

struct pcb {struct mlink *memory;   /* memory is pointer to list of assigned pages */
    int pmid;};                     /* pmid is PTE for process midtable */
 int freemem;
```

```
#define KWPN         0x05          /* kernel write, process none, valid */
#define KWPR         0x07          /* kernel write, process read, valid */
#define KWPW         0x0D          /* kernel write, process write, valid */
#define KWPE         0x0F          /* kernel write, process execute, valid */
#define KAPA         0x17          /* modified, kernel all, process all, valid */

#define k_pmid       0x11000300    /* (constant) SVA of current process midtable */
#define kData_pmid   0x11000003    /* constant location where PA of pmid is put*/
#define kData_proot  0x11000200    /* (constant) SVA of process root table */
#define kData_Kroot  0x11000110    /* (constant) SVA of kernel root table entry */
                                   /* for current process midtable */
#define ppageAbs     0x20000000    /* (constant) SVA of first entry in current */
                                   /* process's ABS pagetables */
#define ppageStack   0x2000FFFF    /* (constant) SVA of first entry in current */
                                   /* process's stack pagetables */
#define wtop(x)((x+0xFF)>>8)       /* convert words to integral number of pages */
```

```
int proc_create(pcb, bin0size,bin1size, tsize, dsize, ssize)
    struct pcb *pcb;                               /* pointer to process control block */
    int bin0size, bin1size, tsize, dsize, ssize;   /* segment sizes in words */
{      int b0s, b1s, ts, ds, ss;                   /* segment sizes in pages */
       int b0t, b1t, tt, dt, st;                   /* table sizes in pages */
       int i, total, *pp, error;
       struct mlink *p, *memp;

    b0s = wtop(bin0size); b0t = wtop(b0s);
    b1s = wtop(bin1size); b1t = wtop(b1s);
    ts = wtop(tsize);      tt = wtop(ts);
    ds = wtop(dsize);      dt = wtop(ds);
    ss = wtop(ssize);      st = wtop(ss);

                                                   /* calc total pages for memory, */
                                                   /* pagetables, and midtable */
    total = b0s + b0t + b1s + b1t + ts + tt + ds + dt + ss + st + 1;
    while (freemem < total) sleep(&freemem); /* wait until enough memory is available */
    p = mem_alloc(total);                          /* get the memory pages */
    pcb->memory = p;                               /* remember where they are in PCB */
    pcb->pmid = (p->paddr | KAPA);                 /* and PTE used in context switch */
    pp = (int *) kData_pmid;
    *pp = pcb->pmid;                     /* give kernel access to process midtable */
    pp = (int *) kData_proot;
    *pp = pcb->pmid;                     /* give kernel access to process pagetables */
```

```
    pp = (int *) kData_Kroot;
    *pp = pcb->pmid;                    /* give kernel access to process process pages */
    flush_TLB();                        /* flush ald transactions */

    p = p->link;
    for (i=b0t, pp = (int *) k_pmid; i>0; i--)
        { *pp++ = p->paddr | KAPA; p = p->link; }
    for (i=b1t; i>0; i--)
        { *pp++ = p->paddr | KAPA; p = p->link; }
    for (i=tt; i>0; i--)
        { *pp++ = p->paddr | KAPA; p = p->link; }
    for (i=dt; i>0; i--)
        { *pp++ = p->paddr | KAPA; p = p->link; }
    for (i=st, pp= (int *) (kData_pmid+255); i>0; i--)
        { *pp-- = p->paddr | KAPA; p = p->link;}/* starts at top of table, grows down */
    memp = p;                                   /* remember start of memory pages */
                                                /* Now insert the PTEs into the */
                                                /* process pagetables */
    for (i=b0s, pp=(int *) ppageAbs; i>0; i--)
        { *pp++ = p->paddr | KWPR; p = p->link; }
    for (i=b1s; i>0; i--)
        { *pp++ = p->paddr | KWPW; p = p->link; }
    for (i=ts; i>0; i--)
        { *pp++ = p->paddr | KWPE; p = p->link; }
    for (i=ds; i>0; i--)
        { *pp++ = p->paddr | KWPW; p = p->link; }
    for (i=ss, pp=(int *) ppageStack; i>0; i--)
        { *pp-- = p->paddr | KWPW; p = p->link; } /* grows down */
                                                /* read in the data and text segments */
                                                /* from disk */
                                                /* this assumes that they are stored: */
                                                /* absolute data, text, struct data */
                                        /* Note: process will be blocked during reads */
    for (i=b0s+b1s+ts+ds, p=memp; i>0; i--)
        {   error= read_page(p->paddr);
            if (error) break;               /* end of file, the rest is uninitialized */
            p = p->link;
        }
    if (error == 0 || error == 1) return(0);    /* an EOF is OK but not necessary */
        else return(error);
}
```

Note how we set up and then use the three PTEs which point to the process mid-table in Figure 4.12. A detailed development of the addresses is shown in Figure IV.4. The three locations in which that PTE is inserted are fixed. Those three are where the

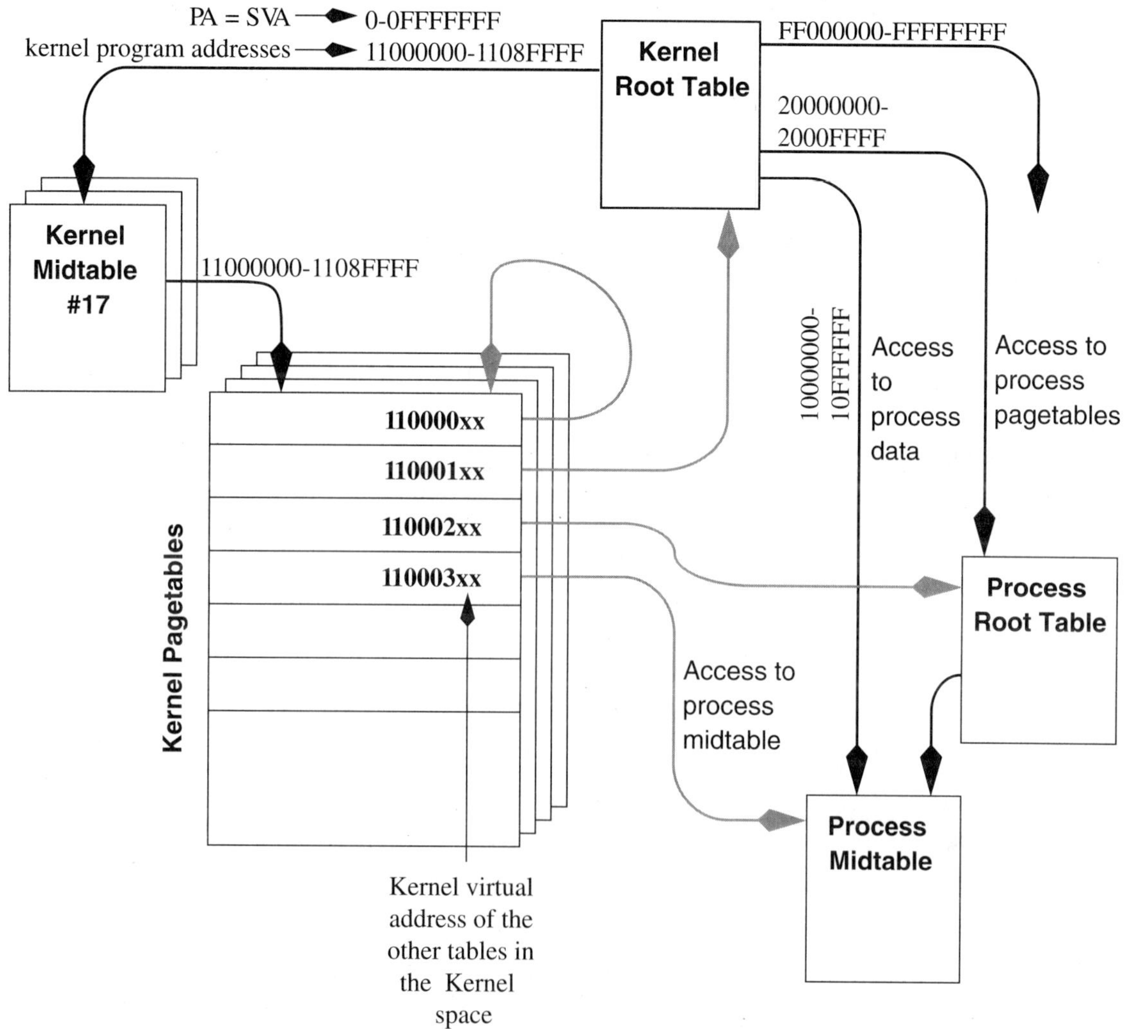

FIGURE IV.4 Expansion of the center of Figure 4.12 to show how the appropriate kernel virtual addresses select the desired physical page and datum in that page. The assumptions in coming up with these numbers are:

Physical memory comprises 256 MW. To make PA = SVA, this requires 16 pages of kernel midtable.

The kernel requires a total of 500 KW. That span is easily contained in one more midtable. In fact, it requires only eight pagetables plus one for the stack.

We have chosen to make the first *absolute* page of the kernel be the pagetable with references to itself and to the other basic tables of Figure 4.12. This placement is arbitrary but functional. The order of the entries is equally arbitrary. With these choices, the kernel would, on a context switch, install the physical page number of the new context's process midtable at SVA at the three addresses:

11000003 (access to process midtable at 110003xx)
11000110 (goes into kernel root table to provide access to process data at 10xxxxxx)
11000200 (goes into process root table to provide access to process pagetables at 2000xxxx)

current process PTE always goes. The first four addresses which are defined in the box of "higher level" definitions above the program are kernel VAs which get translated through the route:

kernel root ⇒ kernel mid ⇒ kernel pagetable ⇒ kernel page.

Notice that one address of the four is in *kernel absolute*, so one of the PTEs in *kernel absolute* points at kernel data. In fact, in some sense, it points at itself. That is not strange at all. It just means that in the course of getting the three PTEs that must be extracted to obtain a datum in memory, for this case the same physical page address occurs twice—once in the midtable and again in the pagetable. As the French like to say: "No problem!"

Once those three addresses are in place, we can load the three levels of process tables and pages by using the correct kernel virtual address, to wit:

loading the process midtable	kernel root ⇒ kernel mid ⇒ kernel data ⇒ process mid
loading the process pagetables	kernel root ⇒ process root ⇒ process mid ⇒ process pagetables
loading the process pages	kernel root ⇒ process mid ⇒ process pagetables ⇒ process pages

The program sets the *modified* bit in the PTEs which reference other tables, but not the *referenced* bit or the *modified* bit in the PTEs in the pagetables. In this simple *whole program* form of management, these bits serve no purpose, but if this were a full *virtual memory* management system, these bits would be used to determine what data should be kept in memory and which pages must be copied out to disk to preserve the data in them. The pages of program exist unchanged on disk, but the pagetables have just been created. If we wanted to reuse some of the physical pages occupied by pagetables while the process was still running, we would have to copy their contents out to disk to save the data. Only then could we free up the pages. In virtual memory management, we will want to keep in memory only the active pages and spend as little time copying things back and forth as we can. These two bits are a major help in determining how to do just that.

Reading code being what it is, we have kept this program as lean and simple as we could make it, at the cost of leaving out some essential side issues. In particular, some of the memory management issues have been ignored. For example, before loading, we would check system tables to determine if a shared text segment is already in memory, in which case we could just copy its PTEs into the new pagetables. Additional memory space should be allocated to give the new process a kernel stack and space for various process context information.

REFERENCES

[Rochkind, 85] Rochkind, Marc J., *Advanced Unix Programming*, Prentice-Hall (1985).

APPENDIX V

ALTERNATIVE ARCHITECTURES

V.1 RISC VERSUS CISC

While most of this book is devoted to the design of a RISC processor, it seems appropriate to devote a little space to alternative and historically important architectures. "Good architecture" has never been a static target. The fact that most of the computers made by most computer companies are CISCs suggests that CISCs must have provided good and cost-effective performance. While we have discussed CISCs at some length, much of that discussion was to point out and critique choices that were made in important CISC architectures. Many of the instruction set improvements which emerged in Chapter 1 might seem to be exclusively RISC-oriented. While the instruction set improvements were genuine and were the result of some excellent insights, often by RISC architects, we would be remiss if we did not say that most if not all can be (and have been) applied with success to CISC architectures. Things such as *load-store* architectures, branch prediction and delayed branching, and, most particularly, pipeline optimization for the most critical instructions have appeared on a wide variety of machines. If one central concept can be said to characterize the CISC design philosophy, it is that the instruction set itself—the user architecture—should be quite independent of the underlying hardware structure. The idea was to preserve binary code compatibility across a family of machines which spanned not only a wide price-performance scale but also an era or two of marketing success. CISCs have done this by implementing the instruction set architecture in microcode, allowing them to define a different microarchitecture for each new processor.

Some architects still find these reasons compelling. See [Gifford, 87] for such opinions from two of the IBM 370 architects. The CISC side of the RISC/CISC debate has been presented in the literature from the very beginning of the debate [Clark, 80] [Colwell, 85] [Flynn, 87]. As RISC processors have moved into the mainstream, such fundamental concerns as binary compatibility and upward migration of customer applications to newer, more powerful computers have become critical elements in their architectures. The best ideas of RISC were quickly incorporated in other machines whose designers did not see themselves as RISC proponents and are found even in architectures which were designed before the debate began. For example, the most central single RISC element, *Load/Store* architecture, was a central design element in all Cray machines and in the Data General machines of the '70s and '80s. What made RISC so very compelling to its early advocates was the ability to get the whole design on a single chip and to bring it to market in a very short design cycle. There was no doubt that being *on-chip* was inherently faster than being *off-chip*. The lower level of complexity seemed equally important, but now that VLSI has permitted us to figuratively put the whole workshop on a single chip, pipelines are again getting more complex even as speeds are surging ahead. The following paragraph from [Hester, 90] is a good summary of the current prospect:

> Much has been written lately about what RISC is and is not, and how it differs from a Complex Instruction Set Computer (CISC). Much of this confuses the basic issue that many variations in instruction set functionality and cycles per instruction are possible. Recent CISC microprocessor designs (such as the Intel 80486 and Motorola MC68040 designs) have shown that CISC designs can in fact be implemented using many concepts that were previously only associated with RISC designs. Further, there has traditionally been a view that RISC designs should have an inherently faster clock cycle (for a given technology) than a corresponding CISC design. Much of this is attributed to the *simplified* control structure of the RISC design. This is not necessarily true, as the typically higher degree of pipelining and parallelism in the current RISC designs gives rise to as much complexity (and corresponding logic stages and circuit loading) as conventional designs. This leads to the belief that the second generation RISC designs and traditional CISC microprocessors will have essentially equal cycle times, with the underlying technology contributing more to the cycle time capability than the choice of RISC or CISC. Therefore, the real performance leverage will be in optimized definition of the instruction set, machine organization, and logic design.

Both RISC and CISC architecture definitions can burden successive designers with structures which do not scale well to new and better computer hardware. Examples abound:

- VAX did not make the setting of flags a programming option, ruling out once and for all the ability to have the compiler optimize the machine code for the known ordering and delays in the pipeline.
- MIPS and SPARC both use delayed branching. This scales very poorly in superscalar architectures (and was specifically avoided in favor of branch prediction in the Alpha architecture).

The point is that it is always possible to do it better with 20/20 hindsight. Good architectures are those which extend the market's appetite when they arrive and then grow along with the market for many years. Probably the record for such an architecture is the IBM 360/370 series, which has prevailed in the mainframe market for three decades. It is most decidedly a CISC. DEC's RISC, the Alpha, has been designed with a 20-year lifetime in mind. We hope to survive to see if it makes it. In the meanwhile, let us consider two quite different organizations.

V.2 VERY LONG INSTRUCTION WORD COMPUTERS

The same compiler developments of the '70s and '80s, which inspired the RISC philosophy that substantially improved performance could be obtained by opening the inner workings of the processor to compiler optimization, spawned some other architectures with even grander ideas. One of these was the *very long instruction word* (VLIW) machine, whose central idea was to provide multiple parallel hardware paths which a very clever compiler could employ both for improved performance and for improved reliability.

The VLIW concept is an extension of the *horizontal microinstruction*, which was discussed in Chapter 9. The advantage of the horizontal microinstruction's wide microinstruction format is that it allows many of the hardware functions to be controlled in parallel. Since a microprogram is relatively small, one can afford to make the microinstructions very wide. Such width seemed much less acceptable for regular programming, but in the early '80s, compiler technology emerged which could identify significant amounts of instruction-level parallelism [Colwell, 88] [Fisher, 83] [Ellis, 86] [Cohn, 89] [Sohi, 89]. VLIW machines grew, naturally enough, out of Josh Fisher's work on compiling horizontal microinstructions, which led to the ELI project at Yale (a marvelous pun from *enormously long instructions*), and later to the founding of Multiflow Computers, Inc., to produce commercial VLIW machines. The startup was founded in 1984 and foundered in the worldwide computer market slump of 1990. Over that interval, Multiflow constructed more than 100 machines. The initial machine performed 6 MFlops in a double-precision LINPACK 100×100 benchmark. Financial failure should not be equated with either a poor concept or a poorly constructed product. It is an unfortunate truism that cash flow is more important than MFlops. A fascinating tale of the technical problems in getting this startup's new product up and out the door is found in [Colwell, 92]. The 100+ machines were delivered and worked well. Some of the largest had 28 parallel processors. Let us see what they were trying to do and what problems arose.

The idea behind the VLIW architecture is to create a machine with many parallel units, each controlled by its own field in the wide instruction. In effect, it resembles a wide microprogrammed machine in which the microinstructions are produced directly by the compiler. Obviously, this produces some of the advantages of both RISC and CISC architectures, but it also produces some of the disadvantages of each. It is the mix that is different. Like a RISC, it has fixed-size, easily pipelined instructions, but this makes its programs even larger than RISC programs, increasing the cache miss and page-fault problems. Like a CISC, it can take advantage of parallelism in the processor, and since the parallelism is scheduled by a compiler, it is optimized for the particular application program, rather than being optimized for an instruction set architecture that may not have been ideal for this particular program. However, VLIW instruction sets are closely tied to the processor design, which makes it difficult to retain binary compatibility when improving the processor.

While the parallelism in microcoded machines is often achieved by hand optimizations of both the microprogram and the underlying hardware, in a VLIW even greater parallelism must be exploited by the compiler. How much parallelism can be used depends on the program. If we are doing a long sequence of calculations, and each calculation depends on the result of the previous one, it may be difficult to exploit any parallelism in our hardware. In contrast, if we want to add two vectors together, we can probably use as many adders as the hardware contains. Earlier attempts at compiling programs for machines with multiple functional units had produced only limited improvements within basic blocks of the program, essentially the sections between branches. Basic blocks are relatively short, so the amount of parallelism would not be sufficient to justify a VLIW machine, which would have much of its hardware idle most of the time. The proponents of VLIW believe that there is much greater parallelism available in typical scientific programs, if the compiler ignores basic blocks and schedules longer paths or traces through a routine. See [Ellis, 86] and [Colwell, 88] for a detailed discussion of trace scheduling.

Much of the parallelism that is implemented automatically in a RISC pipeline is done by the compiler in a VLIW machine. For example, the instruction DSTORE R3, 8(R5) on our RISC machine requires an addition (8+R5) in the second stage of the pipeline, followed by a store from R3 to the memory in the next stage. In a VLIW machine, the addition and the store would be scheduled by the compiler, and they might be moved much farther apart, if that would help to execute them in parallel with something else. The address calculation is just another integer arithmetic operation, and it can be done whenever the integer arithmetic unit is available. In a VLIW machine, any dependencies involving when the address is available in R5, when the data is in R3, and when those registers are needed for other instructions are handled by the compiler.

Branches are handled in ways that are similar to microsequencer branches. They typically are executed in parallel with other operations. For example, the iWarp processor [Cohn, 89] can encode the following loop into a single 96-bit instruction, overlapping the address calculations, two floating-point arithmetic operations, incrementing the counter, testing, and the branch:

```
for (i=0; i<n; i++) {
    a[2*i] = c + d * b[i];
    }
```

In more complicated programs several branches may be combined into a single multiway branch, as would be done for important cases in a microprogram. The most common way to do this is to evaluate the conditions in parallel and use each of them to specify one of the least significant bits in the destination address. The ELI architecture [Ellis, 86] contains a multiway branch that is more like a lisp COND statement—it consists of a list of (*condition, destination*) pairs. The conditions can all be evaluated by a priority encoder to find the first one which is true. Then the program branches to the destination paired with that condition.

Integrated circuit technology continues to allow ever more gates to be placed on a single chip. The extra gates provide all sorts of opportunities. The most conventional approach is to surround the processor with caches, an FPU, and an MMU. But where do you go from there? A different approach, and one that is greatly expandable, is to put multiple processors on one chip. The individual processors can be used in lockstep parallelism (*single-instruction multiple-data*, or SIMD), as would be appropriate to vector operations, or they may be used quite individually (*multiple-instruction multiple-data*, or MIMD). The art and science of developing effective programs for architectures comprising large numbers of simple processors have been brought quite well along by work at Thinking Machines, Multiflow, and other workers in this field. The VLIW approach is to use multiple functional units, all controlled by a single long instruction. Where the compiler can use the extra parallelism, VLIW organization may be an effective way to use much larger chips than we have now.

V.3 STACK MACHINES

A *stack* machine is a computer which performs its basic operations on elements stored in one or more pushdown stacks. Since ALU operations like ADD or AND always combine the top two elements on the stack and return the result to the top of the stack, there is no need for any operand specifiers in most instructions. For that reason, stack machines are sometimes called *0-operand* machines. Stack processing of algebraic expressions is remarkably natural once you get the hang of it [Bruno, 75]. Anyone who has mastered *reverse Polish notation* (RPN)[1] on the HP calculators knows how much easier it is to do elaborate arithmetic in RPN than in either algebraic or the older fashioned "four-function" style calculators. The RPN calculators are stack machines with a stack depth of 4. Compilers normally parse input lines into RPN, regardless of the destination machine.

In RPN, you expand expressions from right to left, eliminating the parentheses, which are constructed from left to right. For example, the expression

$$A = B \times (C + (-A/D))$$

becomes the following sequence of operations:

```
push A      ;original A to TOS (top of stack)
CHS         ;change sign on TOS
push D      ;D to TOS
÷           ;A and D are popped off stack and TOS now contains -A/D
push C
+           ;TOS now contains C + (-A/D)
push B
*           ;TOS now contains the desired result
pop A       ;if desired, the result can be returned to memory
```

[1] "Polish" in honor of its inventor, Jan Lukasiewicz (Wu-ka-sha-vich), noted Polish mathematician (1878–1956). Apparently despairing of getting listeners to relate "Wu-ka-sha-vich" with Lukasiewicz, promoters of the notation have named it for his country.

Note that the only data specifiers are those that move a datum to or from the stack. There are no parentheses or register specifiers. So what? These are special-niche machines. "So what?" cannot be answered until we see where they came from and where they now are used.

Stack machines first became popular in the early 1960s, after the language Algol-60 was introduced. Algol-60 was a block-structured language which attempted to rectify what was wrong with the first HLLs (Fortran, in particular). Among its many innovations, Algol permitted recursion. (Fortran did not!) Accordingly, it needed a mechanism to separate the variables and parameters from different activations of subroutines. While recursion is easy to accomplish with a stack in memory, this is not what we mean by a *stack machine*. Note that in the coding snatch above the top elements on the stack are the working registers. It is this explicit coupling of all ALU operations to a hardware stack which sets these machines apart.

First generation stack machines, such as the Burroughs B5000, B5500, B6700, B7700, Hewlett-Packard HP3000, and ICL2900, were designed to execute languages like Algol-60 [Doran, 75]. Most of these had a single stack which was used for holding temporary data, passing subroutine parameters, and saving subroutine return addresses. These machines enjoyed some commercial success but faded with the rising sun of general-register machines. They had not yet found their special niche.

In 1969 Charles Moore invented a simple extensible programming language called Forth, which he used to control radio telescopes at the National Radio Astronomy Observatory. In 1972, he left NRAO and formed Forth, Inc. The language was available during the 1970s from Forth, Inc., and in public-domain versions, but it didn't become popular until 1978, when the Forth Interest Group (FIG) was founded. FIG created its own version of Forth, and wrote simple, public-domain interpreters for most microprocessors. Forth has been most successful in applications where very small program size is important. For example, it is used in PROMs in Sun workstations to boot the operating system. Postscript, another stack language derived from Forth, is built into many printers.

In 1981, after leaving Forth, Inc., Moore began designing a processor capable of executing the most important Forth operations in hardware. In 1985 the processor was fabricated by Mostek in a 4000-gate CMOS gate array; it was sold as the Novix NC4016. Later Harris Semiconductor designed a standard-cell version of this processor, the RTX2000, which includes two large on-chip stacks and a single-cycle hardware multiplier. Note the dates. This is roughly concurrent with the emergence of RISC as a design philosophy. A number of other Forth chips have been built, such as the Johns Hopkins/APL FRISC3, which is available commercially as the Silicon Composers SC32 [Koopman, 89]. Unlike most earlier stack machines, these Forth processors have two stacks, one to hold temporary data and pass subroutine parameters, and the other to save subroutine return addresses and loop counters. Rather than simply providing an instruction for each Forth primitive operation, most of these machines have instruction formats similar to microcode, where each field controls a part of the machine. As a result, a keyhole optimizer can combine as many as seven Forth primitives into a single instruction (RTX2000). This overstates the amount of parallelism that can be expected, but the ability to access two stacks and the memory simultaneously allows a significant amount of parallelism. To see how easy this is, combine operations in the little program above. All but the first and last can be doubled up.

Now for the niche. Stack machines have several inherent advantages over typical RISC and CISC processors:

- Very compact program size
- Very fast execution of arithmetic operations and subroutine calls
- Very fast and predictable interrupt latency

We will get to the weak points in a moment, but these characteristics make stack machines ideally suited to embedded real-time control applications. The newer Forth chips are designed for that market. The FRISC3, for example, is intended to be used in spacecraft.

Programs written in Forth have always been known for their compactness. There are several reasons for this:

- Most obvious is the fact that stack machines do not use any space in the program to specify most operands.
- Parameters passed to subroutines are usually on the stack already, so usually no extra push instructions are required.
- No instructions are required to save or restore registers when subroutines are called.
- A less obvious but very important reason is that good Forth programmers use many more subroutines than programmers in any other common language. The overhead for a subroutine call is so low that sequences consisting of only two or three instructions can profitably be converted to subroutines in Forth. Even if you tried to do that in a normal HLL like C or Fortran, a good compiler would turn any such call into in-line code.

Programs are very small, but the call and return mechanisms must and can be very fast. Koopman [Koopman, 89] claims that stack machine programs can be 2.5 to 8 times smaller than CISC programs. That result presumes that the stack operations are encoded particularly compactly. In practice, many stack machines choose a simple, uniform instruction format to increase hardware speed and reduce complexity. Even then, Forth programs are decidedly smaller than the typical CISC equivalent and even more impressive when compared with RISC machine code. In a simple embedded control application, the processor chip may be able to hold both stacks and the program memory, greatly reducing system cost and cycle time. Even in a larger system, the cost of the memory tends to be reduced by the small program sizes and the fact that fewer memory accesses are required than on RISCs or CISCs. Most data, parameter, and return address accesses go to the stacks, so they do not use memory bandwidth, and they can occur in parallel with other memory accesses.

Arithmetic operations tend to run fast on stack machines because access to operands is so direct. Consider some mechanisms used to hold temporary data in various processors.

- The most general place to keep data is in the **memory**. That avoids the allocation problem for the compiler and makes it possible to refer to the data with pointers. Unfortunately, fast access to memory calls for a data cache on the CPU chip. Data caches are fairly complex devices. Even a direct-mapped cache requires a tag store and comparator, in addition to the random access data array. Cache misses make the execution speed somewhat unpredictable, an important issue in real-time systems. There can be cache consistency problems if anything else can write into the addresses which are represented in the cache. Finally, because they are addressed, data caches are seldom multiported. One can access only one operand at a time.
- The most common place to keep the most active data is in a file of **general-purpose registers**. New machines typically have 32 general-purpose registers in an array which is simple enough to multiport. That allows simultaneous read access to two source operands for one operation and a simultaneous write access to a third register. Registers have none of the addressing and validation obligations of a data cache, so they are substantially faster. The downside of no addressing is the burden on the compiler to allocate registers efficiently. Simple allocation techniques within each subroutine require saving and restoring registers each time a call is done. Better compilers try to do global register allocation, so that they can avoid much of the saving and restoring. That does help but dynamic linking of library routines is becoming common, and the library routines already have their registers allocated. Even though register files are not addressed in the sense that the cache is, they are random access arrays which are large enough to entail significant access delays. To accommodate these delays, RISC processors often devote one pipeline stage to reading the source operands and another pipeline stage to writing back the result. We certainly did.
- In a stack machine, temporary data is kept on a hardware **data stack** in the order it will be used. A typical ALU operation on a stack machine combines the top two numbers on the stack, moves the stack up one place, and returns the result into the top location. If all operations work like that, the stack does not have to be a random access memory. Instead, it can be a bidirectional shift register, with the top two stages connected directly to the ALU. The significance of that is that no time is required to read or write large random access arrays. Stack machines do not require pipelined execution units. The fetch of the next instruction may be pipelined, but a two-stage pipeline is much simpler to manage than the typical three or four stages in a RISC machine or the even more complex designs typical of CISCs.

Allocation of stack space is much simpler than register allocation, although some effort may be involved in machines which use small on-chip stacks. The machines listed above have very different stack sizes. The Novix NC4016 was built with a small gate array, so it has no on-chip stacks, only the top-of-stack registers. The commercial version, the Harris RTX2000, on the other hand, has a 256-word data stack and a 256-word return stack on chip. The FRISC3 has only 16-word stacks, but it includes automatic logic to handle overflows into a standard memory stack. The FRISC3 also provides direct access to the top four words on each stack, since some common Forth operations access words below the top two.

A fast subroutine calling mechanism is essential to Forth programs. Newer stack machines try very hard to make calls and returns fast. Having parameters on the stack and not having to save registers helps, but the actual call and return must be fast too. Having a second stack for the return address significantly improves the return speed. Most Forth machines specify a return using one bit in the instruction, so a return can be folded into any other instruction and requires no extra time. This is possible because the return address comes from a dedicated stack, which is not used by instructions doing arithmetic. Since an address has to be specified in a call, it is much more difficult to fold calls into other instructions. Doing so requires an instruction wide enough to contain the address in addition to other operations. That approach is often taken in microsequencers. Some Forth machines, such as the Harris RTX32P, use wide instruction formats and can fold calls, returns, and branches into other instructions. That trade-off improves execution speed, but because sequentiality makes instruction packing imperfect, the added speed comes at the cost of somewhat larger program size. Most Forth machines emphasize small program size, so they require a separate instruction for each call and fold only returns.

The effort to compact the code leads to something like this. The instructions are divided into two classes. CALLs and other things. That takes one bit. If the CALL bit is set, the rest of the instruction is the new address, with the current PC being pushed onto the return stack. The other commands are all tiny. Several can be packed in one instruction. One field of the instruction can be used to load a literal from the instruction stream onto the data stack. That literal can be used as an address by the next instruction to push or pop an item on or off the stack. Coupled with such a command can be the command RETURN.

In a machine with a fast subroutine calling mechanism, it isn't necessary to have conditional branches. Conditional branches need to specify both a condition and an address in the same instruction. Since many Forth machines have instructions just 1 bit larger than their address size (and we have already used that bit for CALL), there is no room for a conditional branch. A common solution is to use PC-relative addressing for branches, with limits on the displacement. Another solution is to provide only a conditional return instruction. An IF...THEN pair is converted into a subroutine which evaluates the condition and either returns or continues into the THEN clause. This is essentially the way the original version of the language LISP did conditional operations.

Another strange use for the fast subroutine calling mechanism is present in the Harris RTX32P. In Forth, variables which cannot be kept on the data stack are stored in the program memory (which is called a *dictionary*). Since reading a variable from the program memory is so much like fetching an instruction, the RTX32P uses a subroutine call to do it. The only difference is that the data coming back from the dictionary is placed on the data stack, rather than the instruction register, and an immediate return takes place, which just continues executing the next instruction.

One of the strongest features of stack machines is their interrupt performance. An interrupt is essentially an unexpected subroutine call. Like RISC machines, stack machines generally execute each instruction in a single clock cycle, so there is very little delay between the interrupt signal and the response to it. However, while most other computers have to save some state when an interrupt occurs, a stack machine has to save only the return address, just as it would with a subroutine call. Since nothing is pipelined, except possibly a fetch, there is no pipeline to save. Since any temporary data is kept on the stack, there are no registers to save. Whether condition codes are pushed onto the stack or kept in dedicated flag bits depends on the machine. A machine which pushes them onto the stack as a result of a compare instruction can avoid the problem of saving them during an interrupt. Interrupts are so direct on stack machines that the interrupt latency is extremely short. Furthermore, Forth machines generally do not use caches of any kind, since their programs tend to be small enough to fit in fast static RAM. That means that there is nothing unpredictable about their timing, which is very desirable in the embedded real-time control applications where they are most often used.

Switching to another lightweight task, or *thread*, is also simple. If the task switching is allowed only at places where the stacks are empty, the tasks won't interfere with each other. Naturally a complete context switch to another process, as the result of a clock interrupt, is more difficult. Saving all of the information on the stacks can obviously take a long time. But other machines have essentially the same problem. Registers have to be saved, and data in caches gets saved and restored automatically but still uses up memory bandwidth and delays the new process with cache misses. Naturally the stacks can be duplicated if fast context switching is required, just as register window machines like the AMD 29000 or SPARC can switch windows for that purpose.

In summary, the newer stack machines are extremely efficient in embedded real-time control applications. They tend to require less hardware than conventional RISC or CISC processors, and they may run faster. In addition, they offer extremely fast and predictable interrupt latency, which is important in real-time control. In other types of applications, they may not perform so well. If programs are written in languages other than Forth, they will tend to make less use of the fast subroutine calling mechanisms on stack machines and use large numbers of local variables and pointers, which are difficult to handle. Access to structured data types or arrays of data are also less efficient on stack machines. Forth provides very versatile mechanisms to define data types (or to add any new feature to the language), but making array and structure accesses as efficient as they are in CISCs would require adding hardware. Some stack machines provide other addressing modes for data in the main memory to improve their performance when running programs written in languages that are not stack-oriented. However, when using such features, they are not functioning as stack machines.

Being a niche occupier can be very profitable. When you step out of your niche, however, you tend to be trampled by the big guys. We are not suggesting that the stack machines are competitive players in the general computing market. They are not. But it is interesting to see how so different a computing format can succeed by satisfying at bargain price a particular market's thirst for speed and predictability.

REFERENCES

CISC architectures

[Case, 78] Case, R.P. and A. Padegs, *Architecture of the IBM System/370*, **Communications of the ACM 21**(1), 73–96 (1978). Describes the extensions made to System/360.

[Clark, 80] Clark, D.W., and W.D. Strecker, *Comments on 'The Case for the Reduced Instruction Set Computer'*, **Computer Architecture News 8:6**, 34–38 (1980). This is the CISC reply to the original RISC paper by Patterson and Ditzel.

[Colwell, 85] Colwell, R.P., C.Y. Hitchcock, E.D. Jensen, H.M.B. Sprunt, and C.P. Kollar, *Computers, Complexity, and Controversy*, **IEEE Computer 18**(9), 8–19 (1985).

[Flynn, 87] Flynn, M.J., C.L. Mitchell, and J.M. Mulder, *And Now a Case for More Complex Instruction Sets*, **IEEE Computer 20**(9), 71–83 (1987). A careful comparison of a variety of architectures. Concludes that instruction density is important.

[Gifford, 87] Gifford, D., and A. Spector, *Case Study: IBM's System/360-370 Architecture*, **Communications of the ACM 30**(4), 292–307 (1987). An interview with Richard Case and Andris Padegs, two of the architects of System/360-370, describing how some of the major decisions were made.

[Hester, 90] Hester, P.D., *RISC System/6000 Hardware Background and Philosophies*, **IBM RISC System/6000 Technology**, 2–7, publication SA23-2619, IBM (1990).

[Husson, 70] Husson, S.S., *Microprogramming: Principles and Practices*, Prentice-Hall (1970). This book has extremely detailed descriptions of microprogramming in the early IBM 360 processors.

[IBM370] *IBM System/370 Principles of Operation*, **IBM GA22-7000-9**. This manual defines the instruction set architecture for the IBM 370 family. It is not easy to read, but it does include examples showing the use of some complex instructions.

[Prasad, 89] Prasad, N.S., *IBM Mainframes*, McGraw-Hill (1989). This book includes an overview of IBM's 360 architecture and its newer extensions, plus more detailed chapters on four specific processors.

VLIW machines

[Cohn, 89] Cohn, R., T. Gross, M. Lam, and P.S. Tseng, *Architecture and Compiler Tradeoffs for a Long Instruction Word Microprocessor*, **Proceedings of the Third International Conference on Architectural Support for Programming Languages and Operating Systems (ASPLOS-III)**, 2–14, Boston (1989).

[Colwell, 88] Colwell, R.P., R.P. Nix, J.J. O'Donnell, D.B. Papworth, and P.K. Rodman, *A VLIW Architecture for a Trace Scheduling Compiler*, **IEEE Trans. on Computers 37**(8), 967–979 (1988).

[Colwell, 92] Colwell, R.P., *Latent Design Faults in the Development of Multiflow's Trace/200*, **Proceedings of the 22nd Annual International Symposium on Fault Tolerant Computing**, 468–474, (July 1992).

[Ellis, 86] Ellis, J.R., *Bulldog: A Compiler for VLIW Architectures*, MIT Press (1986).

[Fisher, 83] Fisher, J., *Very Long Instruction Word Architectures and the ELI-512*, **Proceedings of the 10th Annual Symposium on Computer Architecture**, 140–150, (1983).

[Milutinovic, 89] Milutinovic, V., *Microprogramming and Firmware Engineering*, IEEE Computer Society Press (1989). Contains reprints of papers on optimization, emulation, VLIW machines, software tools for microprogramming.

[Sohi, 89] Sohi, G.S., and S. Vahapeyam, *Tradeoffs in Instruction Format Design for Horizontal Architectures*, **Proceedings of the Third International Conference on Architectural Support for Programming Languages and Operating Systems (ASPLOS-III)**, 2–14, (1989).

Stack machines

[Brodie, 84] Brodie, Leo, *Starting Forth* and *Thinking Forth*, Prentice-Hall (1981, 1984). Describe the Forth programming language and how to develop programs in Forth. Forth makes much more use of efficient subroutine calls than other high-level languages, and it allows the programmer to extend or modify virtually anything about the language. As a result, programming in Forth often involves creating a new language suited to the problem being solved.

[Bruno, 75] Bruno, J., and T. Lassagne, *The Generation of Optimal Code for Stack Machines*, **Journal of the ACM 22**(3), 382–396 (1975).

[Doran, 75] Doran, Robert W., *Architecture of Stack Machines*, in *High Level Language Computer Architecture*, Yoahan Chu (ed.), Academic Press (1975). Discusses stacks in general and their relation to compilers. Describes the basic features of the first-generation stack machines: B5500, B6700, B7700, KDF-9, HP3000, ICL2900.

[Koopman, 89] Koopman, Philip J., *Stack Computers, the New Wave*, Halstead Press (1989). Includes short descriptions of many stack machines, or machines capable of being used as stack machines. Concentrates on the new Forth machines, which have separate data and return stacks. Includes block diagrams and instruction sets of the Novix NC4016, Harris RTX2000 and RTX32P, Johns Hopkins/APL FRISC3, and several machines designed by the author. Also contains detailed comparisons of stack machines with RISCs and CISCs, and Forth instruction frequency data.

[Keedy, 78a] Keedy, J.L., *On the Use of Stacks in the Evaluation of Expressions*, **Computer Architecture News 6**(6), 22–28 (1978).

[Keedy, 78b] Keedy, J.L., *On the Evaluation of Expressions using Accumulators, Stacks, and Store-to-Store Instructions*, **Computer Architecture News 7**(4), 24–27 (1978).

[Keedy, 79] Keedy, J.L., *More on the Use of Stacks in the Evaluation of Expressions*, **Computer Architecture News 7**(8), 18–22 (1979).

INDEX